AMATEUR BUILDER'S HANDBOOK

AMATEUR BUILDER'S HANDBOOK

Over 1001 picturized new ideas show how to save hundreds of dollars in home building and repair

Edited by

HUBBARD COBB

1954

WM. H. WISE & CO., INC.

NEW YORK

2549

Printed in the United States of America

ACKNOWLEDGMENTS

Acknowledgment is gratefully made to the following manufacturing companies and industrial institutes for permission to print material concerning their particular fields, as indicated in each case: The American Society of Heating and Ventilating Engineers, temperature chart; American Structural Products Company, glass blocks; American Zinc Institute, galvanized roofing and siding; Anthracite Institute, coal bins; Armstrong Cork Company, insulation, wallboard, resilient tile, linoleum; Chimney Sales Company, metal chimneys; Condensation Engineering Corporation, chimney flues; Copper & Brass Research Association, brass pipe, flashing; David E. Kennedy, Inc., resilient tile; Douglas Fir Plywood Association, plywood, insulation; Edison Electric Institute, electrical installations; The Emerson Electric Mfg. Co., manufacturers of Emerson Electric Fans, ventilation, fan installation; Homasote Company, building board; Hunter Fan and Ventilating Company, fans, ventilation; Industry Committee on Interior Wiring Design, wiring; Insulation Board Institute, insulating board; Johns-Manville, asbestos board, asphalt tile, insulating board, ceiling panels; Kaiser Aluminum & Chemical Sales, Inc., screening; National Electrical Manufacturers Association, Electric Fan Section, fans; National Lumber Manufacturers Association, from their publications *Exposing the Termite, House Framing Details, Wood Walls*; National Mineral Wool Association, insulation; National Oak Flooring Manufacturers' Association, hardwood flooring; National Woodwork Manufacturers Association, Inc., glazing; Paint, Varnish and Lacquer Association; Pittsburgh Plate Glass Company, plate glass; Portland Cement Association, cement, concrete, masonry blocks, stucco, cement plaster, cement paints; Red Cedar Shingle Bureau, shingles, roofing, siding; Southern Pine Association, softwood flooring; Square D Company, electrical equipment and systems; Structural Clay Products Institute, efflorescence, flashing; Surface Combustion Corporation, makers of Janitrol heating equipment; The Tile Manufacturers' Association, Inc., tile; The Upson Company, wall and ceiling tile, wallboard, ceiling panels; Zonolite Company, insulation.

Acknowledgment is also gladly made to: The National Board of Fire Underwriters, for material on chimney construction; National Fire Protection Association, for material on fire stopping, chimney construction; Oregon State College, for material on shingles; John Wiley & Sons, Inc., publishers of *Kidder-Parker Architects' and Builders' Handbook*; Popular Science Publishing Company, for various material concerning tools, installation methods, time-savers, and other miscellaneous subjects; and to the following U. S. Government departments and agencies: Federal Security Agency, U. S. Office of Education; Housing and Home Finance Agency; The National Bureau of Standards; U. S. Department of Agriculture; U. S. Department of Commerce; U. S. Department of the Interior; U. S. Public Health Service; and the War Department.

We wish to make grateful acknowledgment also to The Black & Decker Manufacturing Company for the text and illustrations covering portable electric tools, and to the Kimberly-Clark Corporation for text and illustrations on insulation.

CONTENTS

SECTION I: Concrete, Masonry Blocks, Bricks and Glass 1

Testing Aggregates—Concrete Proportions—Concrete Aggregate—Cement Coloring Materials—Aggregate in Cold Weather—A Small Cellar—Extending Foundations and Footings—Concrete Support for Garage Wall—Concrete Floors on Ground—Proper Insulation Adds Comfort—Finishes for Concrete Floors—Covered Concrete Floors—Roughened Concrete Floors—Maintaining and Cleaning Concrete Floors—Roofing Paper Seal—Concrete Tamper—Widths for Drives—Staking Out Drives—Turning Areas and Street Entrances—Drainage for Drives—Concrete Posts—Lawn Roller—Tooled Joints—Precast Joist Concrete Floors—Building Interior Walls—Building Around Door and Window Frames—Placing Sills and Lintels—Masonry Block Patterns—Masonry Block Shower Stall—Suction—Bottle Caps in Stucco Work—Refinishing Old Stucco Jobs—Fireplace Construction—Basic Installation of Mortar-Set Glass Blocks—Minimum Openings for Glass Block Panels—Glass Block Partitions—Using Flexible Glass in Your Home—Lighting Stairways—Damp Basements—Membrane Waterproofing—Layers of Felt—Plaster Coats—Retaining Walls for Steep Driveways—Grading.

SECTION II: Rough Carpentry 63

Suitability of Woods for Various Uses—Standard Widths and Thicknesses of Rough and Surfaced Yard Lumber—Standard Thicknesses and Widths for Softwood Yard Lumber—Standard Hardwood Grades of Lumber—Standard Widths and Thicknesses of Lumber—Contents of Lumber—Cutting Down Waste—Methods of Seasoning Wood Posts—Inexpensive Incinerator—Fire Stopping—Installing an Extra Post—Plumbing Corner Posts—Method of Plumbing and Straightening Wall—Nailing Studding—Siding Sizes and Estimating Quantities—Figure in Wood—Bridging of Walls—Roof Trusses—Advantages of Roof Trusses Joining Roofs to Walls—Methods of Laying Out Rafters—Estimating Shingle Requirements—Application of Red Cedar Shingles—Mark Location of Studding—Spaces Let Sub-flooring Expand—Fitting Warped Boards.

SECTION III: Millwork, Flooring, Windows, Doors and Closets 143

Old Mortise Built Up with Shims—Rabbeting and Grooving by Hand—Standard Oak Flooring Grades—Beech, Birch, Hard Maple Flooring Grades—Pecan Flooring Grades—Standard Sizes, Counts and Weights—Standard Grades of Softwood Flooring—Nail Schedule for Flooring—New Strip Flooring over an Existing Finish Floor—Installation of Plank and Parquet Flooring—How to Estimate Amount of Hardwood Flooring Required—Edge Grain and Flat Grain Flooring—Hiding Cracks Between Flooring and Baseboard—Compression Set—Sub-floor Construction—Laying and Nailing Oak Floors—Finishing Oak Floors—Refinishing Hardwood Floors—Puttying Window Panes—Block Holds Glazier's Points—What's Wrong?—Hinge Locks Sliding Window—Combination Screen and Storm Door—A Quickly Built Door—Making a Door Stay Shut—Awnings for Casement Windows—Bedroom Closets—Shoe Racks—Business Closet—Dining-Room Storage—Easy-To-Build Kitchen Cabinets—Food Storage Room—Shelves and Cabinet Transform Extra Closet—Folding Table Seats Eight—Building Outdoor Stairs—How to Carpet Stairs—Jig Assures Square Corners When Assembling Picture Frames—Usual Dimensions and Spacings for Picket and Stretcher Fences.

SECTION IV: Roofing, Flashing, Insulation and Ventilation 209

Shingle Quantities—Preventing Drip From Gables—Shingle Estimating—The Proper Nails—Shingle Nailing—Never Soak Wood Shingles before Laying—Shingle Exposure—Red Cedar Shingle Grades—Shingling Hips and Ridges—Overroofing with Red Cedar Shingles—Overwalling with Red Cedar Shingles—Staining and Painting Shingles—Moss on Roofs—Roll Roofing—New or Replacement Roll Roofing—Canvas Roofing—How to Paper a Roof—Galvanized Sheets—Precautions with Galvanized Sheets—Zinc Paint—Protect Against Lightning—Stop Leaks in Old Roofs—New Roofs over Old—Roofing Nails—Gutters and Downspouts—Snow Guards—Slate Roof Repair—Repairing Roofs—What's Wrong?—Flashings—Removing Efflorescence—More Flashing Tips—Attic Insulation—Tools for Insulating Attic Floor—Insulating Your Present Home—Where to Place Insulation—Cutting and Measuring—Insulating Walls—Insulating Ceilings—Insulating Attics—Insulating Floors—Ventilation—Attic Ventilation—Exhaust Fan Installation—Safety Control for Exhaust Fans—Estimating Required Fan Capacity—Exchanging Inside and Outside Air for Comfort.

SECTION V: Electrical Systems and Equipment and Lighting 279

Summary of Required Light Fixtures—Things to Remember in Wiring—Measure Your Lighting—Light Reflection—Outlet Requirements—Space Heating by Electricity—Special Outlets—Service Requirements—Circuit Requirements—Summary of Required Outlets—Additional Lighting—Electrical Wiring Tips—Low-Voltage Wiring—Low Voltage Controls Lights—Low-Voltage Control—Switch Control.

SECTION VI: Plumbing, Heating, Fireplaces and Chimneys 307

Selecting Pipes—Copper and Brass—Cast Iron—Wrought—Cast-Iron Soil Pipe—Water Pipe Sizes—Drainage and Vent Pipes—Fittings—Corrosion and Life of Pipe—Comparison of Pipe Material—Cutting, Threading and Installation of Brass Pipe—Threading Brass Pipe—Threading Nipples and Pipe of Large Diameter—Reaming Brass Pipe—Making Up Joints—Dope—Upside Down Joints—Inserting Fitting in an Existing Line—Deciding Sewer Grade—Jointing Sewer Pipe—Joints and Connections—Opening Joints in Soil Pipe—Simple One-Pipe System—A Two-Pipe System—Insulating Pipe—Recommended Construction Details for Drainage and Vent Systems—Hot Water Tanks—Adjusting Flush Valves for Toilet Tanks—Connecting Range Boilers and Water Backs—Cleaning Clogged Pipes—Thawing Pipes—Stopping Leaks in Pipes and Tanks—Repairing Cracked Laundry Tubs and Garden Hose—Removing Scale from Water Backs and Coils—Saving Hot Water—Garage Drain Trap—Collar Fits Corner Shower—Bathroom Plans—Facts on Bathroom Fixtures—Storage and Accessories—House and Equipment Inspection—Radiators and Convectors—Floor Furnaces—Coal Bin Construction Details—Hand Furnace Operating Hints—Heating and Fireplaces—Metal Chimneys—Avoiding Condensation.

SECTION VII: Interior Wall Materials and Finishes 383

Planning the Linoleum Floor Job—Measuring, Cutting, and Packing Linoleum—Installing Linoleum in Single Rooms—Installing 12-foot Linoleum through Doors in Double Rooms—How to Do Pattern Scribing on Linoleum—Linoleum Scribing around Radiators—Linoleum Cove Base—Linoleum on Counter Tops—Turn-Down Sink Rims—Repairing Counter Tops—Stair Treads,

SECTION VII

Runners, Edgings—Installing Asphalt Tile—Installation Instructions for Resilient Tile—Protection of Asphalt Tile—Dampness Test for Concrete Subfloors—Tile on Wood Floors—Ceramic Tile, Terrazzo, and Marble Subfloors—Metal Subfloors—Fitting Tile to Straight Walls—Installation of Resilient Tile Stair Treads—Plaster—Plaster Proportions—Peeling of Paint—Wrinkling of Paper—Pencil as Expansion Plug—Asbestos Board—Tileboard—Replacing Ceiling Tile—Applying Ceiling Panels—Patching Wallboard—Waterproofing Tileboard—Glass Panels.

SECTION VIII: Paints, Painting and Finishes 443

Brushes—Keep Brush Clean—Used Brushes—Reclaiming Brushes—Deep-Dipping Spoils Brush—Power Paint Equipment—Spraying Machines—Paint Preparation—Color Blending—Painting Masonry—Home-Mixed Cement Paint—Paint Precautions—Paint Dipping—Clean Before Painting—Smooth the Surface—Dust First—Putty Practices—Spray Painting—Tinting Paints—Painting Interior Wood—Transparent Finishes for Wood—Painting Screens and Frames—Painting near Seashore—Estimating Painting Needs.

SECTION IX: Tools, Nails, Screws and Hardware 463

Finding Angles with a Framing Square—Saw Blade Used for Draw Knife—Bench Planes—Holder Aids in Sawing Curves—Broken Blade Makes Small Saw—Nail Head Used as Nail Set—Filing to a Line—Wedge Screwdriver Grips Screw—Lag Screws Driven with Brace–Don't Fall for These–Hold Tight–Portable Electric Tools–What Nail?–Know Your Hinges–Screw Sizes–Special Plywood Fastenings–Rescreening Tip–Another Screening Tip.

INDEX 497

SECTION I

CONCRETE, MASONRY BLOCKS, BRICK AND GLASS

Testing Aggregates—Concrete Proportions—Concrete Aggregate—Cement Coloring Materials—Aggregate in Cold Weather—A Small Cellar—Extending Foundations and Footings—Concrete Support for Garage Wall—Concrete Floors on Ground—Proper Insulation Adds Comfort—Finishes for Concrete Floors—Covered Concrete Floors—Roughened Concrete Floors—Maintaining and Cleaning Concrete Floors—Roofing Paper Seal—Concrete Tamper—Widths for Drives—Staking Out Drives—Turning Areas and Street Entrances—Drainage for Drives—Concrete Posts—Lawn Roller—Tooled Joints—Precast Joist Concrete Floors—Building Interior Walls—Building Around Door and Window Frames—Placing Sills and Lintels—Masonry Block Patterns—Masonry Block Shower Stall—Suction—Bottle Caps in Stucco Work—Refinishing Old Stucco Jobs—Fireplace Construction—Basic Installation of Mortar-Set Glass Blocks—Minimum Openings for Glass Block Panels—Glass Block Partitions—Using Flexible Glass in Your Home—Lighting Stairways—Damp Basements—Membrane Waterproofing—Layers of Felt—Plaster Coats—Retaining Walls for Steep Driveways—Grading.

CONCRETE, MASONRY BLOCKS, BRICK AND GLASS

TESTING AGGREGATES

The silt test is used to detect the presence of too much extremely fine material. The colorimetric test is used to detect the presence of harmful amounts of vegetable matter.

In making the silt test, an ordinary quart milk bottle or quart fruit jar is used (fig. 2). Fill the container to a depth of 2 inches with a representative sample of dry sand to be tested. Add water until the bottle or jar is about three-fourths full. Shake vigorously for 1 minute—the last few shakes being in a sidewise direction to level off the sand. Allow the jar to stand for an hour, during which time any silt present will be deposited in a layer above the sand. If this layer is more than ⅛ inch thick, the sand from which the sample is taken is not satisfactory for concrete work unless the excess silt is removed. This may be done by washing.

In making the colorimetric test, an ordinary 12-ounce prescription bottle, such as druggists or physicians use, is filled to the 4½-ounce mark with a sample of the sand (fig. 3). To this is added a 3-percent solution of caustic soda which is made by dissolving 1 ounce of sodium hydroxide (household lye) in a quart of water, preferably distilled. The solution should be kept in a glass bottle tightly closed with a rubber stopper.

Handling sodium hydroxide with moist hands may result in serious burns. Care should be taken not to spill the solution, as it is highly injurious to clothing, leather, and most other materials.

As soon as the solution of sodium hydroxide is added to the sand, shake the contents of the bottle thoroughly and then allow it to stand for 24 hours. The color of the liquid will indicate whether the sand contains too great an amount of vegetable matter. A colorless liquid indicates a clean sand free from vegetable matter. A straw-colored solution indicates some vegetable matter but not enough to be seriously objectionable. Darker colors mean that the sand contains injurious amounts and should not be used unless it is washed and tested again.

CONCRETE PROPORTIONS

Specifications for concrete mixtures always give the proportions by volume, such as 1:2:4, which means 1 part cement, 2 parts sand, and 4 parts pebbles or crushed stone. A sack of cement is equal to 1 cu. ft.

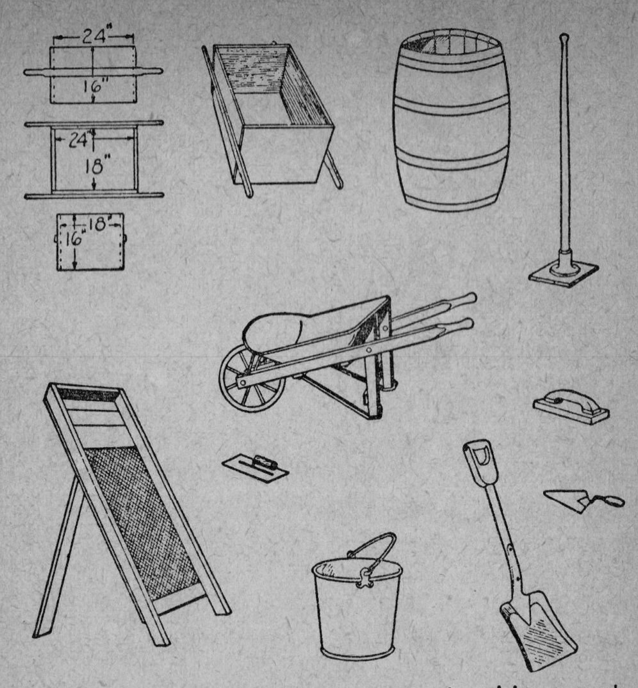

Fig. 1. Typical equipment required for screening aggregate, mixing concrete, and laying concrete by hand.

If one sack of cement, 2 cu. ft. of sand, and 4 cu. ft. of gravel are used, a total of approximately 4.5 cu. ft. of concrete can be expected, not 7 cu. ft., since most of the sand and cement fills the voids between the larger particles. Waste and the size of the coarse aggregate cause some variation in the amount of finished concrete.

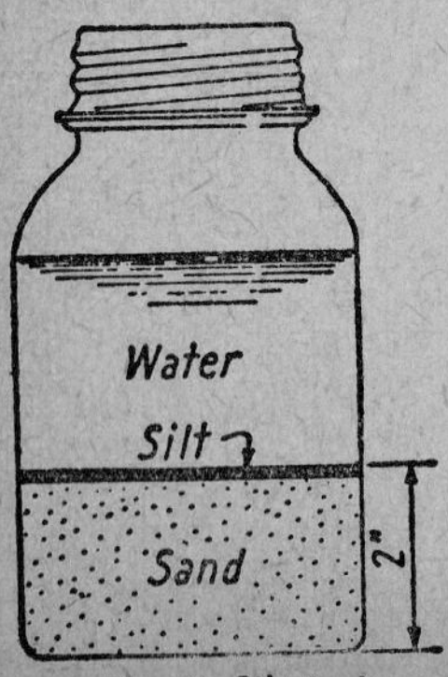

Fig. 2. Silt test.

Following are proportions used for various concrete jobs:

1:1½:3 or 1:2:3—one-course roadways, walks, and floors; pavements; such watertight work as tanks, reservoirs, swimming pools, and cisterns; and such cast work as sewer pipe, drain tile, and fence posts.

1:2:4—general reinforced-concrete work, beams, columns, floors, and walls; work subjected to a moderate amount of water and dampness; bridges, engine foundations, and other work subjected to vibration; and, in addition, silos, elevators, and coal bins.

Fig. 3. Colorimetric test.

1:2½:5—base courses for sidewalks, floors, and pavements; basement walls not required to be waterproof; foundations; mass dams; and retaining and wing walls of bridges and culverts.

1:3:6—mass construction, large footings, and large foundations.

CONCRETE AGGREGATE

Both coarse and fine aggregate are required in strong cement. The coarse aggregate consists of crushed stone or pebbles graded in sizes from ¼″ to 1½″ or up to 3″ for mass concrete work. It should be clean and hard. Fine aggregate is sand, graded from very fine to ¼″, and should also be clean and hard. By graded is meant that the aggregate should contain many sizes from small to large. In the mixture, the small particles fill the voids between the large, while the cement fills the voids between the small particles.

Bank-run gravel, that is, the natural deposit of combined sand and pebbles, may be used for aggregate if it is clean, but for best results it should be screened, the sand separated from the pebbles, and reproportioned. As it comes from the bank, gravel usually contains a greater amount of sand than required.

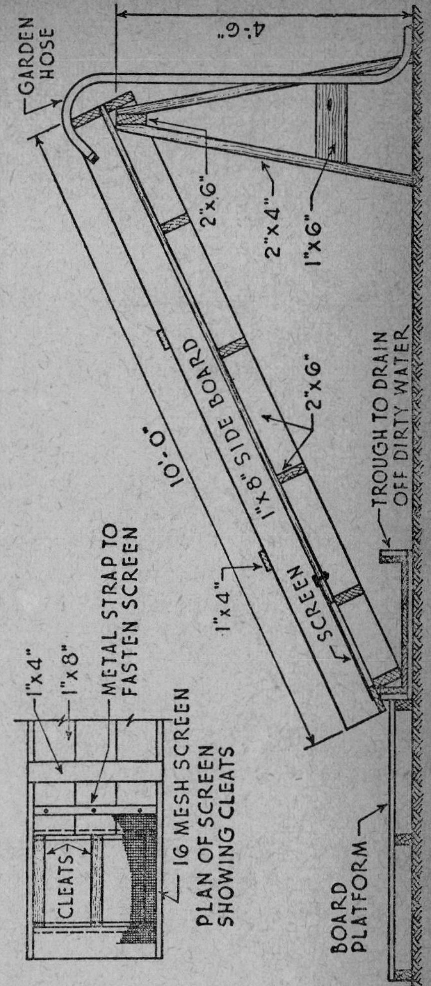

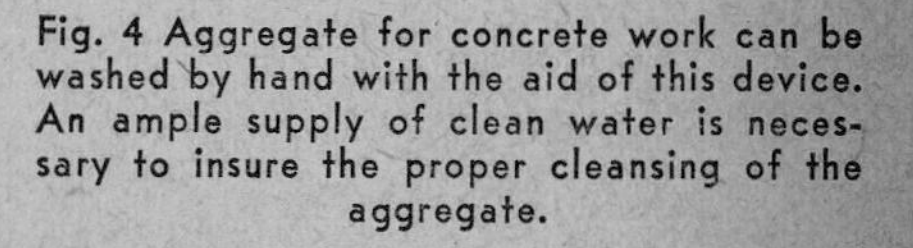

Fig. 4 Aggregate for concrete work can be washed by hand with the aid of this device. An ample supply of clean water is necessary to insure the proper cleansing of the aggregate.

Dirty sand may be made suitable for use by washing with a hose on an inclined shallow trough fitted with cleats and having a screen at the lower end to separate sand from pebbles. A trough should be provided to drain off water from the receptacle under the screen. The unwashed sand is, of course, put on at the top of the incline and washed down. Two or three washings may be required, for if silt, clay, and loam are mixed in the concrete, they will coat the aggregate and prevent bonding by the cement.

What is known as "cinder concrete" can be made of cement mixed with cinders for aggregate. It is cheap and light in weight and is used chiefly for floors that will not carry heavy loads and in some fireproof structural-steel work. The cinders should be hard-burned boiler cinders free from fine ash. They should be wetted 24 hours before use to slack out free lime and neutralize sulphur. The proportion is ordinarily 1 part cement to 5 parts cinders. Don't attempt to use household cinders; they are too fine.

CEMENT COLORING MATERIALS

A general guide for the selection of coloring materials follows:

For maximum brightness and clearness of color and for light shades, use white portland cement.

For *white,* use white portland cement.

For *brown,* use burnt umber or brown oxide of iron. Yellow oxide of iron may be added to obtain modification of this color.

For *buff,* use yellow ochre or yellow oxide of iron. Red oxide of iron may be added in limited quantities.

For *gray,* use small quantities of black iron oxide, manganese black or Germantown lampblack.

For *green,* use chromium oxide. Yellow oxide of iron may be added.

For *pink,* use small quantity of red oxide of iron.

For *rose,* use red oxide of iron.

For *cream,* use yellow oxide of iron in small quantities.

AGGREGATE IN COLD WEATHER

A section of metal pipe with a fire inside it makes a suitable means of heating sand or gravel for concrete work during freezing weather (fig. 5). Aggregate should be sufficiently hot to prevent the fresh concrete from freezing until after it is poured. When the concrete is in place, use coverings to prevent the concrete from freezing until it has cured.

A SMALL CELLAR

Unless a building is of sound construction and in good condition it is poor economy to build a large cellar. However, sufficient space for a heating plant can be provided without great cost or labor, if the chimney is accessible, by locating a cellar 8 to 10 feet wide near one outside wall. The farther the cellar is under the house the greater the amount of work involved. One or more rows of piers are generally used to support interior girders. An opportunity is thus afforded for digging trenches midway between rows of piers and for building the walls without the need of elaborate temporary braces. If headroom permits make the side walls (fig. 6, *ae*, and *bf*) parallel to the girders because it is relatively easy to span a cellar only 8 to 14 feet wide with steel I beams or heavy wood girders (*cd*) so that their ends will rest securely in slots in the walls. Such girders can be used to support the interior girders instead of the piers which are to be removed. If the two side walls are perpendicular to the girders, steel beams can be slipped directly under the house girders. An existing foundation wall must be carried down below the cellar floor.

After these operations have been completed the earth in the cellar between the new walls can be removed through an opening which may later be used for a door in the outside wall. The rear wall of the cellar can be built after the excavation has been completed. When the foundation is entirely of piers, four masonry walls are needed.

EXTENDING FOUNDATIONS AND FOOTINGS

When unit masonry is used for extending walls to a lower level, the top tier of blocks immediately under the old footing may have to be omitted and the space filled with stiff concrete because of the unevenness of the bottom of the concrete footing. Ordinarily too much labor is required to chisel off the projections

Fig. 5.

or variations from a true level to permit fitting the last tier of blocks in place; however, all adhering earth must be removed to secure a good bond. A boxlike form can be used to keep the concrete in place.

Figure 7 suggests a convenient arrangement of forms where the extension is to be of poured concrete. The projection of the footing may be chiseled off plumb with the wall or only small sections, 12 to 18 inches long, chiseled out to facilitate placing the last few inches of concrete.

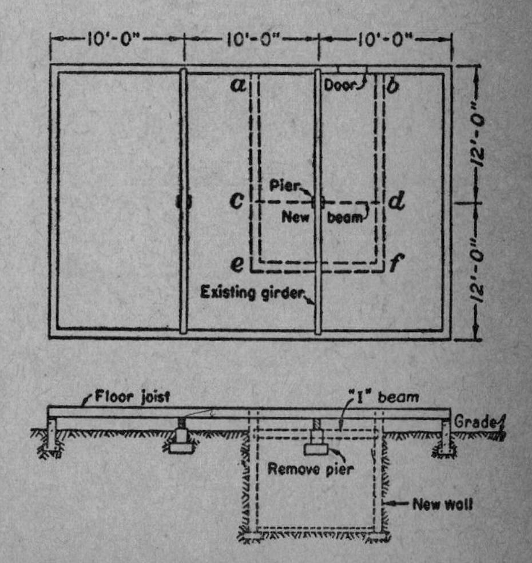

Fig. 6. In locating a small cellar care must be taken not to let sliding sandy soil undermine nearby piers or walls.

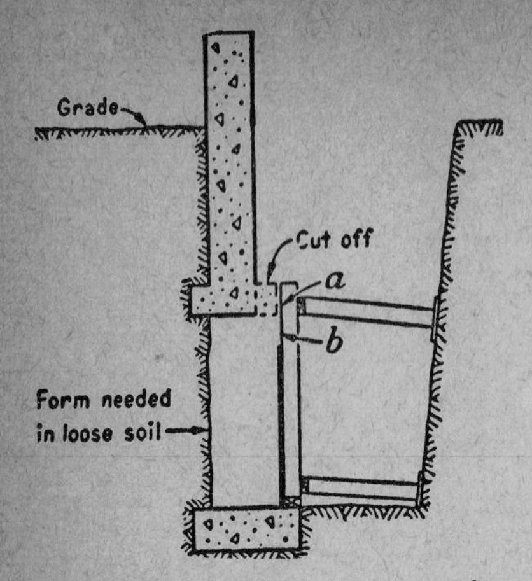

Fig. 7. The top boards of the form at b are omitted until the concrete reaches the top of the highest board in place; they are then slipped in behind the studs and the balance of the concrete poured, as a soft mortar if necessary through the openings, a, provided in the old footing.

While it is feasible to build a retaining wall within the area of a proposed cellar rather than to excavate and extend the masonry down directly under the foundation, this is not good practice except under special supervision. Unless such a wall is so placed that it is not subject to pressure from the old wall, it must be built strong enough to resist the pressure or be reinforced. The safe distance that must be allowed between the two walls to avoid lateral pressure depends upon the angle of repose of the earth and the vertical height between the old and new footings. In loose, sandy soils do not put the new cellar wall closer to any foundation than 1.5 feet for each vertical foot between the two footings. If the new footing is 4 feet lower than the old footing, 6 feet must be allowed between the walls. The horizontal distance to be allowed for each vertical foot varies for different soils, as follows: Damp plastic clay, 2 feet; various mixtures of sand, dry clay, gravel and ordinary soil, 1½ feet; rotten rock, cinders, ashes, 1 foot. If the soil becomes very wet, greater distances must be used. Where such a condition is likely, special consideration is required.

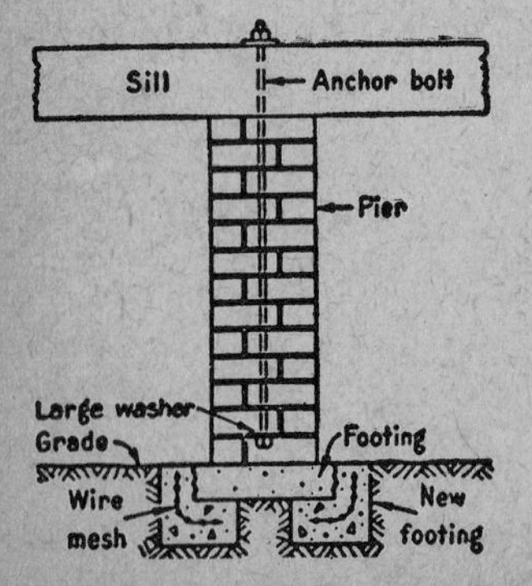

Fig. 8. A method of increasing the width of a footing. The load on the pier must be relieved until the new footing has hardened.

Repairing defects. Foundations that have settled indicate they are not deep enough to withstand erosion or frost action, or that the piers or walls have too little bearing area for the type of soil and the load carried. Settlement may also be due to rotted wood posts and sills or defective masonry.

The building can be jacked up level and supported while the foundations are being repaired or replaced. A good method of increasing the width of a footing is shown in figure 8.

Where a wall has been slightly undermined and the masonry is not damaged, it is often feasible to ram

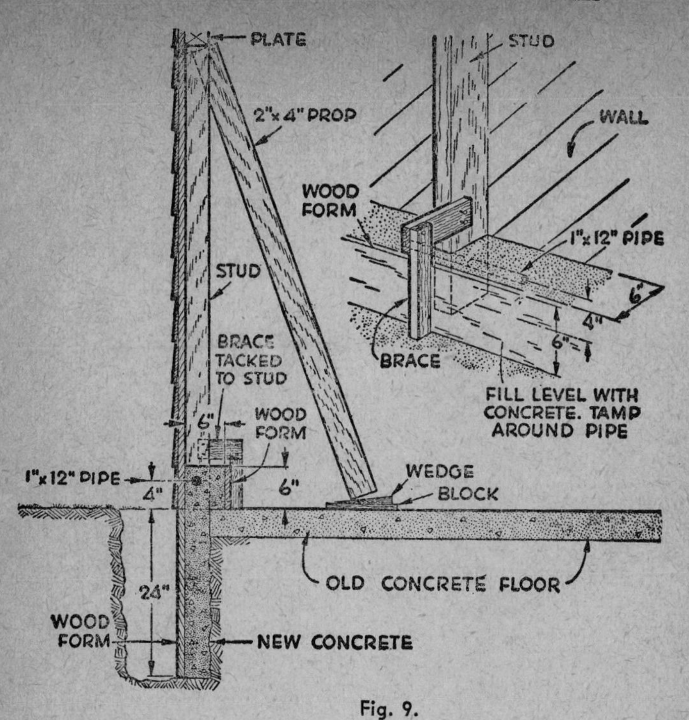

Fig. 9.

damp (not wet) sandy clay earth under the footing so as to secure a firm bearing; 5 to 8 percent portland cement, by volume, mixed with the earth will produce a harder and more enduring packing. Earth is then banked against the wall high enough for frost protection and the surface sloped to divert surface and roof drainage. Heavy sod or shrubbery afford protection from wind erosion.

It is frequently more economical to relieve overloaded foundations by installing extra piers than to increase the width of existing footings. Care must be taken to make sills and girders actually rest on new and old work. New footings may settle a little when the superstructure is lowered onto the piers so that shims or wedges of durable material like slate or flat pieces of hard tile must be used to secure a tight fit and a level girder. Occasionally a pier is made one-half inch higher than its final grade to allow for settlement.

CONCRETE SUPPORT FOR GARAGE WALL

Sag in a garage wall traced to a rotten mudsill can be permanently repaired by replacing the old sill with a concrete foundation. At several points along the wall, jack the sinking studs with a hydraulic or heavy screw jack. Wedge two-by-fours under the plate at each of the jacked-up points until the wall is level.

Next dig a 2′ deep, 8″ wide trench flush with the inside of the studs and running the length of the wall. Remove the sills and any old foundation posts; then build a form flush with the outside of the studs. For the inside form use 6″ boards braced 2″ from the studs. About 4″ from the bottom of each stud, bore a hole for a short length of reinforcing 1″ pipe.

Pour concrete level with the inside form. Tamp the concrete around the pipe inserts.

When the concrete has set remove the forms and braces from around the work. (Fig. 9.)

CONCRETE FLOORS ON GROUND

In recent years there has been a large increase in the number of concrete floors placed on ground. They have become increasingly popular for use in that part of the house under which there is no basement, and they are suitable without other floor covering for washrooms, utility rooms and recreation rooms. In areas where it is customary to build houses without basements, a concrete first floor placed on ground provides a satisfactory, economical, long-life

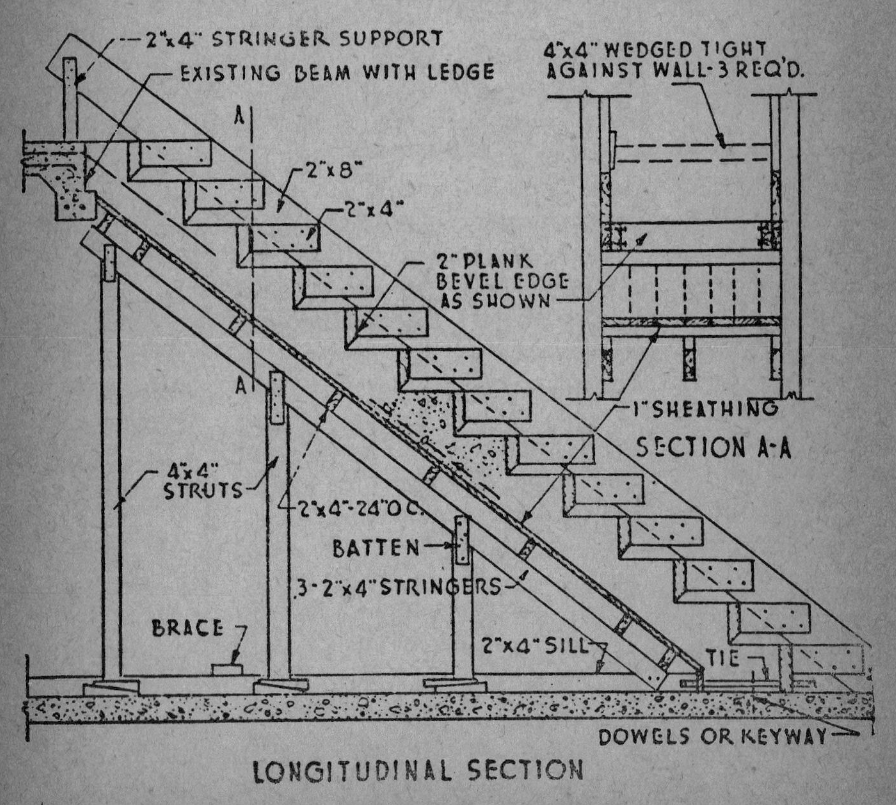

Fig. 10. Poured concrete stairs.

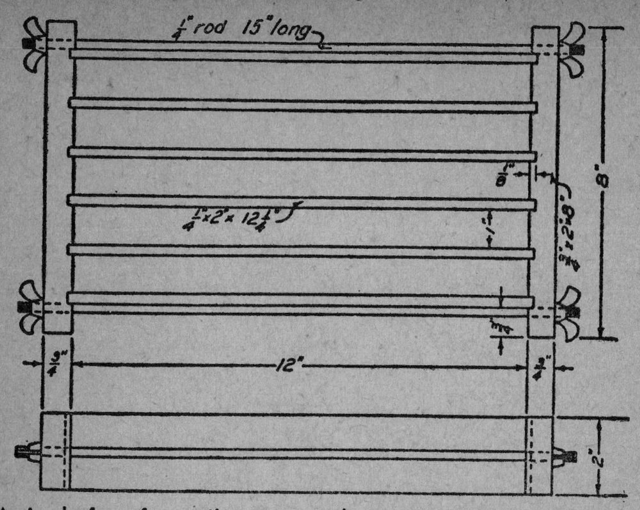

Fig. 11. A simple form for casting concrete beams. The beams should be at least 1 inch wide by 2 inches deep by 12 inches long.

type of construction. Properly built, such floors will be dry and warm. Any desired type of floor covering—hardwood, carpet, tile, linoleum, etc.—can be applied over such floors, in which case they serve as concrete subfloors.

It is recommended that the following steps be taken in constructing concrete floors on ground:

A first requirement is that there be a fill placed under the floor. This fill should be of coarse gravel, crushed stone or screened cinders at least 6 in. thick over the entire area to be floored. Ordinary gravel and cinders are run over a screen to take out material smaller than ½ in. in size. This fine material is not good for dry fill. The fill is leveled off and tamped until firm; it should bring the finished concrete floor well above the surrounding grade. If the building site does not have good natural drainage, tile lines are put in to assure drainage.

Over the fill are placed two layers of 15-lb. roofing felt or other waterproof fabric. Strips of this material are lapped and sealed with asphalt. The strips are turned up 4 in. against the wall to make a watertight seal between floor and wall. When the first layer of strips is laid, it is mopped thoroughly with hot asphalt. The second layer of strips, also sealed with asphalt, is laid at right angles to the first layer; ends are turned up 4 in. against the wall. When laid, the second layer of waterproofing felt is mopped all over with asphalt. Care is taken not to break or puncture the felt in working over it. Some builders place a thin layer of cement grout over the fill a few days before putting down the waterproof felt to provide a smooth puncture-proof surface.

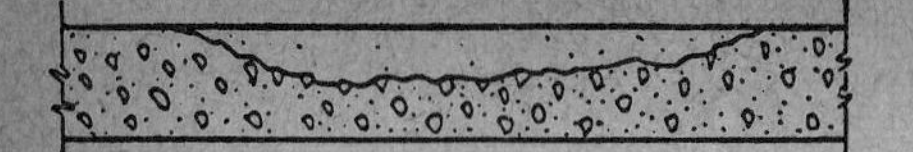

Fig. 12. Incorrectly installed patch. Patches installed with feathered edges will soon break down under trucking.

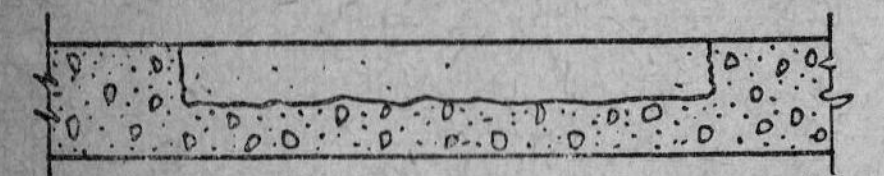

Fig. 13. Correctly installed floor patch. The chipped-out area should be at least 1 in. in depth with the edges perpendicular.

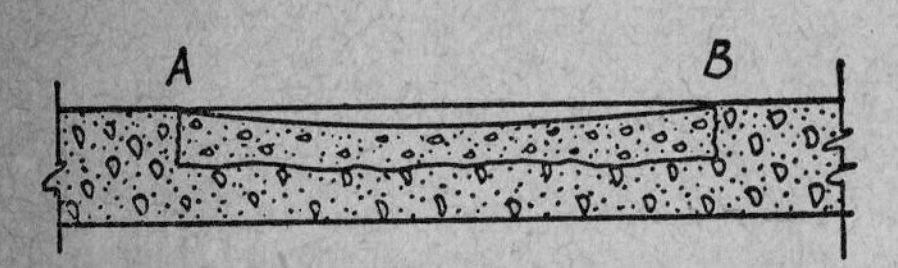

Fig. 14. Results of incorrect screeding of patch. When a patch is originally struck off to the level of the floor, the concrete will sag in the center, due to the fact that the straightedge has a tendency to cut off slightly below its lower edge and to the fact that the concrete shrinks during hardening. Additional concrete placed in the concave area will soon chip out under traffic.

Around the edge of the floor where it abutts against exterior walls a strip of vaporproof insulation about 1 in. thick and 4 in. wide is placed. This insulation prevents heat loss around the edge of the floor and is very important in constructing warm, dry floors.

The concrete slab is usually made 4 in. thick.

The entire floor is placed in one continuous operation, and the same mixture is used throughout. It is leveled off, wood floated and cured the same as flat slab concrete floors.

Metal reinforcement weighing not less than 40 lb. per 100 sq. ft. with cross-sectional area of the reinforcement equal in both directions is placed in the concrete slab 1½ in. from the top surface.

PROPER INSULATION ADDS COMFORT

Often you have heard someone describe one house as being "warm and cozy" and another as being "cold as a barn." The houses referred to may have been much alike in size and appearance. The difference lay in the way they were built. Any house, whether constructed of wood, brick, metal, stone or concrete, can be warm and cozy if it is properly insulated. Houses easily kept warm at low fuel cost are constructed so that heat lost through walls and roof will be kept to a minimum. Such houses will usually be comfortably cool in hot weather, because proper insulation is just as effective in keeping heat out of the house in summer as in retaining heat in winter.

In a normally constructed residence without special provision for insulation, the heat loss will be distributed approximately as follows:

35 per cent through doors and windows
30 per cent through the roof
20 per cent through exterior walls
15 per cent through infiltration around doors and windows

To have an easily heated house, provisions must be made to cut down loss of heat through and around doors and windows and through roof and walls.

Heat losses around and through doors and windows can be reduced materially by use of storm windows, storm doors, weatherstripping, double glazing of glassed areas, and so on.

Heat losses through the roof are commonly reduced by placing insulation between the attic ceiling joists or in the roof structure. Various forms of loose fill, reflective, rigid and blanket types of insulation are used for this purpose. For example, in an average house with a pitched roof and unventilated attic the use of a 1-in. thickness of rigid insulation over the ceiling joists will reduce heat losses through the ceiling by at least 50 per cent. Local builders are usually familiar with the kinds and amounts of insulation materials used in your community.

Flat slab concrete roofs are insulated by laying insulation material, usually of the rigid-board type, over the concrete slab. This insulation is then covered with a watertight roofing which is applied in accordance with the manufacturer's directions.

Heat losses through walls are also reduced through the use of some suitable insulating material applied to or incorporated in wall construction.

Methods of insulating concrete walls. Granular fill insulation—such as granulated cork, vermiculite and similar material—is frequently placed in the cores of concrete masonry walls and in the air spaces of hollow double walls.

Blanket insulation is placed between the furring strips on exterior walls. Rigid insulation board is normally placed over furring strips and

Fig. 15. Correct method of screeding of patch. The strike-off board is held slightly above the level of the floor by strips or shims laid the length of the patch on two sides. For large patches the thickness of these strips will be greater than for small patches. The concrete is allowed to rest for 1 to 2 hours. This allows the concrete to attain some of its initial shrinkage before being troweled to its final plane and will result in a uniformly level surface, plane with the rest of the floor.

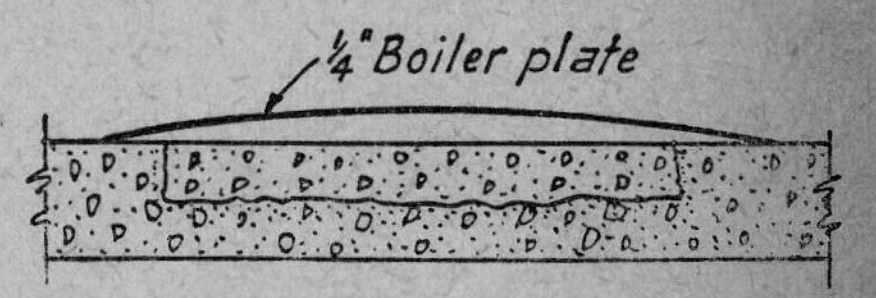

Fig. 16. Protection of patches. Patches should be kept continuously wet and protected from traffic during the curing period. An economical method of protection consists in using a piece of ¼-in. steel sheeting bent as shown and placed over the patch to take traffic during the curing and hardening period.

serves as a plaster base or as an interior finish without plaster. Reflective insulation must have an air space to be effective and therefore is used with furring strips.

Many manufacturers of insulation furnish instructions on proper application of their materials. They also can give you data on the insulating value of their products.

FINISHES FOR CONCRETE FLOORS

Concrete tile, ceramic tile, slate, flagstone, etc. A concrete subfloor is required for the proper setting of tile, slate, flagstone and other finishes of this kind. The concrete subfloor is given a rough finish or a coarse, broomed texture to provide a good bond for the mortar used in setting these floor materials. Just before setting, a slush coat of neat cement grout is broomed into the surface of the hardened concrete base slab. Before the grout hardens, the base is covered with a mortar setting bed about ¾ in. thick. This consists of 1 volume of portland cement and 3 or 4 volumes of sand mixed with sufficient water to obtain a plastic working consistency. Only as much mortar is spread at one time as can be covered with the flooring material before the mortar begins to harden. The floor covering units are placed upon and tapped into the setting mortar until true and even. Then joints between are filled with mortar composed of 1 volume of portland cement, not more than 1 volume of sand and the required mixing water. Mortar is forced into joints until they are well filled. All surplus mortar is removed before it hardens and the faces of the floor materials are cleaned.

Plain troweled finish. Floors in recreation rooms, utility rooms and other rooms that serve similar purposes are often given a plain troweled cement finish. A plain concrete topping not less than 1 in. thick is placed over the concrete subfloor, the surface of which has been roughened by a broom or other means to insure proper bond between base and topping. The surface of the concrete subfloor is cleaned and dampened, and a neat cement grout is broomed on just before the topping is placed. Concrete topping mix consists of 1 volume of portland cement, 1½ to 2 volumes of sand and 1½ to 2 volumes of aggregate up to ⅜ in. in size. Only sufficient mixing water should be added to produce a stiff mushy consistency. The topping is brought to the required level by screeding and is compacted by wood floating. After the surface has become quite stiff and the water sheen has completely disappeared, the surface is given final finish with a steel trowel, the less troweling the better. As soon as the topping has hardened sufficiently, it is covered with 1 in. of wet sand or other material. This is kept wet constantly for 7 days when normal portland cement is used, or for at least 3 days when high early-strength portland cement is used. Curing is very important in building durable, dust-free concrete finish floors.

Other concrete floor finishes. Concrete floor finishes can be colored by incorporating mineral pigments in the topping mixture. Colored finishes are also obtained by applying inorganic acid stains which have been developed for this purpose and which are used in accordance with manufacturer's directions.

COVERED CONCRETE FLOORS

Where concrete floors are to be covered with linoleum, composition tile, prefinished wood tile or planking, carpeting or similar materials, it is not necessary to provide a heavy-duty wearing surface on the concrete. The dust coat method of finishing may then be used.

Fig. 17. Ordinary metal bottle caps nailed to a block of wood make a very suitable tool for removing bits of concrete from wood used for concrete forms.

The structural slab is struck off reasonably true at the required floor level and excess water or laitance removed. A mixture of dry materials consisting of 1 part of portland cement and 2 parts of coarse, clean sand is dusted on the unhardened concrete in a uniform layer not over ⅛ in. thick. When the dry materials have absorbed moisture from the slab and the concrete has hardened enough to allow finishing, it is floated and troweled to unite the dust coat with the base and give an even surface free from air holes, depressions and other blemishes. The floor should be protected and cured as recommended for other types. This dust coat method of finishing should not be used for uncovered floors where the finish would be directly subjected to traffic.

When wood, linoleum, rubber or cork tile is to be used, the concrete must be thoroughly dry before cementing the surface material into place. Moisture, even in very small quantities, will eventually lead to the decomposition of the adhesive. A simple test to determine whether or not the concrete is dry may be made by laying pieces of linoleum at several places on the floor, weighting them down so they will have uniform contact with the surface. If after 24 hours moisture appears on the underside of the linoleum, it will be necessary to let the concrete dry further before cementing the covering to it. The directions of the manufacturer of the materials being used should be followed.

Floors to be covered with carpet require wood nailing strips, usually around the border of the area. These should be well seasoned lumber, dressed to 1 x 2 in. and embedded in the unhardened concrete. Special snap inserts are sometimes embedded in the concrete instead of nailing strips. In this case fastening devices are attached to the underside of the carpet.

The surface of the concrete floor should be screeded and troweled flush with the tops of the wood strips and should present a smooth, even surface. It should be cured and allowed to dry before placing the carpet. Pads or cushions under the carpet prolong the life of the carpet and assist in producing soundproofness.

ROUGHENED CONCRETE FLOORS

Floors that have been improperly constructed may become roughened under service, or pitting may occur due to heavy impacts. Often such floors may be put into satisfactory condition by grinding off the roughened surface and will give good service for many years. On the other hand, if the concrete is of such poor quality that the surface will soon become roughened or pitted again, it

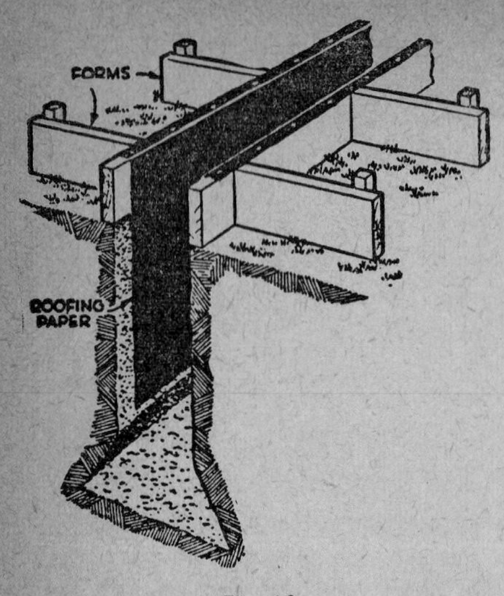

Fig. 18.

would be more economical to resurface it with the proper quality of concrete.

MAINTAINING AND CLEANING CONCRETE FLOORS

Properly constructed concrete floors will require little maintenance other than cleaning. Periodic cleaning is essential to durability, as grit on floors subjected to considerable traffic will be ground into the finish and accelerate the rate of wear.

Floors subjected to spilled milk, syrups, fruit juices, brines, fats and oils should be thoroughly scrubbed. Warm, soapy water and stiff brushes should be used, after which the floor should be mopped clean. Electric scrubbing machines are widely used for cleaning large floor areas.

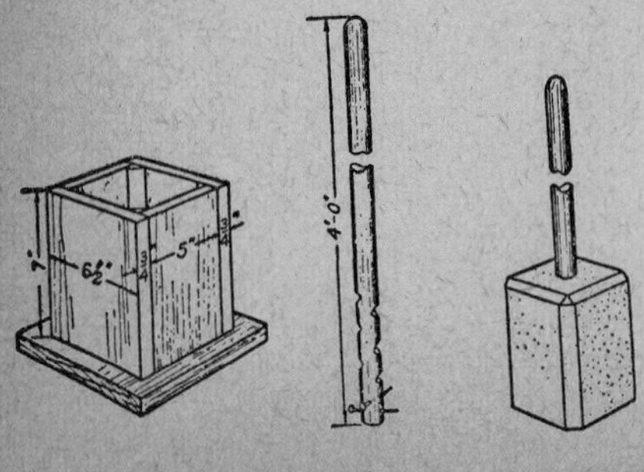

Fig. 19.

ROOFING PAPER SEAL

Foundations for small buildings frequently are made by pouring the concrete directly in a trench usually 12″ wide and 3′ or 4′ deep. A form is needed, however, to retain the portion above ground, and at this point difficulty may arise if the ground is uneven, for the concrete leaks between the earth and the bottom edge of the form.

Roofing or building paper nailed to the top of the forms and allowed to hang down the sides of the trench makes an excellent seal during the pouring. It also permits easy removal of the forms and greatly improves the finished work. Only that portion of the paper above ground is removed. (Fig. 18.)

CONCRETE TAMPER

A concrete hand tamper (Fig. 19) is a practical tool to have in the home; it may be used to compact the base and subgrade for sidewalk, a driveway, backfill or similar work. The handle of the tamper should be held in the center of the form and about 1 inch above the pallet while the concrete is placed around it. Note how the handle is notched at the lower end and that nails are driven through it to prevent the handle from pulling out or turning. The top edges of the tamper may be beveled with a trowel.

Materials and equipment. One quart of cement; 1 1/3 pt water; 2 qt sand; 3 qt gravel; oil; trowel; quart measure; wood pallet; 4 strips triangular mold; handle from discarded broom, hoe or rake; lumber as required by the drawing. Approximately 4½ gallons of water are added per sack of cement, using average damp sand.

WIDTHS FOR DRIVES

Most drives are designed to be used in the following manner: The car leaves the street or alley, goes forward over the drive and into the garage. On leaving, the car is backed out of the garage, backed over the drive and into the street or alley. Drivers are more adept at handling a car when driving forward than when backing, and drives that are to be used in backing should have greater width than those used for forward driving only.

The following discussion of drive widths presumes that the drives will be used by backing vehicles. For short drives that are to be used only by vehicles moving forward, the recommended widths might be reduced by 4 inches.

Passenger cars are fairly well standardized with regard to several of the dimensions that influence the design of drives. The range of dimensions for a large majority of the passenger cars on our highways is as follows: Gage of front wheels, 55 to 61 inches; gage of rear wheels, 56 to 63 inches; turning radius (radius of the smallest circle that the outside front wheel will trace in turning), 18 to 25 feet; over-all length, 15 to 20 feet; and over-all width, 69 to 78 inches. The length of wheel base, a very important dimension affecting the design of curved drives, ranges from 112 to 154 inches.

Another dimension that must sometimes be considered is the distance from the front axle to the front extremity of the car. As shown in figure 20, this overhang requires a clearance, *d,* beyond the outside front wheel when the car is on a curve. For most cars this overhang ranges from 26 to 33 inches. On a 30-foot radius curve, a car having a front overhang of 29 inches and a wheel base of 112 inches requires an additional clearance, *d,* of 14 inches on the outside of the curve. Most cars require a clearance of about 8 inches on the inside of a curve (*e,* fig. 20), and a clearance of at least 8 inches should be allowed for on each side of a straight drive.

The added width of drive required for these clearances need not be surfaced like the rest of the drive, but allowance should be made for clearances on both sides of drives constructed near such obstructions as buildings, trees, or retaining walls.

In going around a curve, the rear wheels of a car do not follow in the paths traced by the front wheels, but trace paths slightly nearer the center of the curve. The distance between

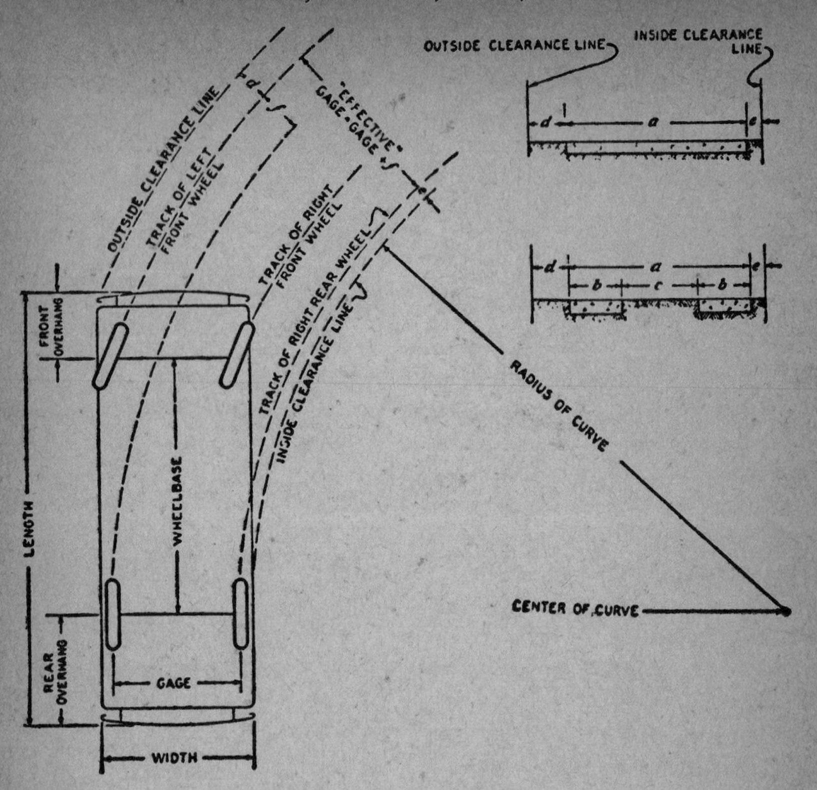

Fig. 20. Illustration of wheel offset f and clearances d and e, distances that must be considered on curved drives.

the paths traversed by the outside front and rear wheels when going around a curve is dependent upon the radius of the curve and also upon the length of wheel base. Thus, for a car with a 112-inch wheel base traveling on a 30-foot radius curve, this distance, *f*, is approximately 15 inches, and for a car with a 144-inch wheel base traveling this same curve, *f* is approximately 24 inches.

Another consideration with regard to widths of curved drives is the direction of the curve. When driving forward, drives curving to the left and those curving to the right can be driven over with nearly the same ease. However, it is definitely easier to back around a drive when the driver is on the inside of the curve than when he is on the outside. In backing around a curved drive the driver, when on the inside, can easily judge the position of the car because a large portion of the drive can be seen. By keeping the left rear wheel near to the inner edge of the drive, the curve can be negotiated with comparative ease. In backing around a drive when the driver is on the outside of the curve, the left rear wheel must be kept away from the outside edge of the drive, but the driver has difficulty in determining his position because the back of the car blocks his view of the drive.

The gage of the average car is 58 inches. When the car is driven straight forward, the two tire tracks are 58 inches apart. However, when

RECOMMENDED WIDTHS OF CURVED AND STRAIGHT DRIVES OF BOTH RIBBON AND SLAB TYPES

For Drives Curving Left[1]

Wheel base	Probable front overhang	Radius of curve	Minimum outside clearance (d)	Offset distance (f)	Ample			Adequate			Minimum		
					Ribbon width[2] (b)	Ribbon spacing (c)	Over-all width of surface (a)	Ribbon width[2] (b)	Ribbon spacing (c)	Over-all width of surface (a)	Ribbon width[2] (b)	Ribbon spacing (c)	Over-all width of surface (a)
Inches	Inches	Feet	Inches	Inches	Inches	Inches	Inches	Inches	Inches	Inches	Inches	Inches	Inches
		20	17	20	....	....	114	....	....	108	44	14	102
		30	14	15	....	....	109	45	13	103	39	19	97
112	29	40	12	12	....	....	106	42	16	100	36	22	94
		50	11	9	45	13	103	39	19	97	33	25	91
		60	11	8	44	14	102	38	20	96	32	26	90
		20	17	23	....	....	117	....	....	111	....	....	105
		30	15	17	....	....	111	....	....	105	41	17	99
120	29	40	13	13	....	....	107	43	15	101	37	21	95
		50	12	11	....	....	105	41	17	99	35	23	93
		60	11	9	45	13	103	39	19	97	33	25	91
		20	18	28	....	....	122	....	....	116	....	....	110
		30	15	20	....	....	114	....	....	108	44	14	102
132	29	40	13	16	....	....	110	46	12	104	40	18	98
		50	12	13	....	....	107	43	15	101	37	21	95
		60	11	11	....	....	105	41	17	99	35	23	93
		20	20	33	....	....	127	....	....	121	....	....	115
		30	17	24	....	....	118	....	....	112	....	....	106
144	32	40	15	19	....	....	113	....	....	107	43	15	101
		50	13	16	....	....	110	46	12	104	40	18	98
		60	12	13	....	....	107	43	15	101	37	21	95
		20	21	37	....	....	131	....	....	125	....	....	119
		30	18	28	....	....	122	....	....	116	....	....	110
154	33	40	16	22	....	....	116	....	....	110	....	....	104
		50	14	18	....	....	112	....	....	106	42	16	100
		60	13	15	....	....	109	45	13	103	39	19	97

For Straight Drives[3]

Wheel base	Probable front overhang	Radius of curve	Minimum outside clearance (d)	Offset distance (f)	Ample (b)	Ample (c)	Ample (a)	Adequate (b)	Adequate (c)	Adequate (a)	Minimum (b)	Minimum (c)	Minimum (a)
....	....	....	6	....	30	28	88	24	34	82	18	40	76

[1] For drives curving right, add 6 inches to ribbon widths and over-all surface widths shown for drives curving left.

[2] Ribbon widths of 46 inches are considered to be the maximum that it is practical to build; therefore, values are not shown for ribbons wider than 46 inches.

[3] Dimensions of straight drives are the same for all lengths of wheel base.

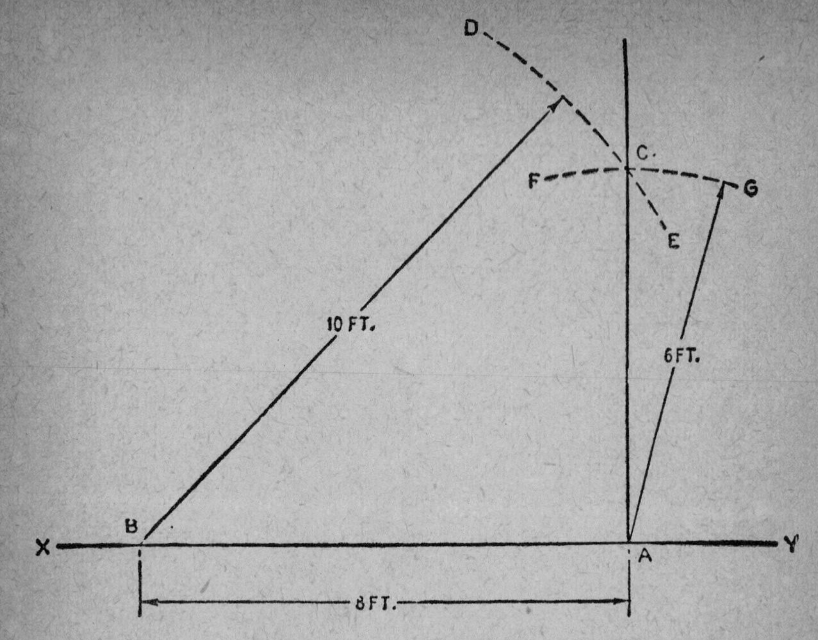

Fig. 21. Method of erecting perpendicular to given line **XY** at point **A.**

driving around a curve the two outside tire tracks are 58 inches apart (the gage) plus *f*, and this total distance may be called the "effective gage" (fig. 20).

Because of construction difficulties, it is not practical to construct concrete or some of the bituminous-mix drives with ribbons more than 46 inches wide, and it is doubtful whether ribbons of this width are desirable. The space between 46-inch ribbons is only 12 inches, and the full width of drive can be surfaced with only a small increase in the amount of materials.

A drive designed for a long car will easily accommodate the shorter cars. Conversely, curved drives of the widths for short cars can be used by longer cars, though more care would have to be exercised to keep the car on the drive. It may not be advisable to design a curved drive for a short car, as the home owner may in the future own a longer car, or the drive may occasionally be used by longer cars owned by friends. On the other hand, the home owner may feel that the expense of building the additional width will not be justified because use by longer cars will be infrequent.

STAKING OUT DRIVES

The staking out of a straight drive is fairly simple and can be done with a tape measure, a few stakes, and some string. Stakes can be set along the drive's center line, along its actual outline, or they can be offset 1

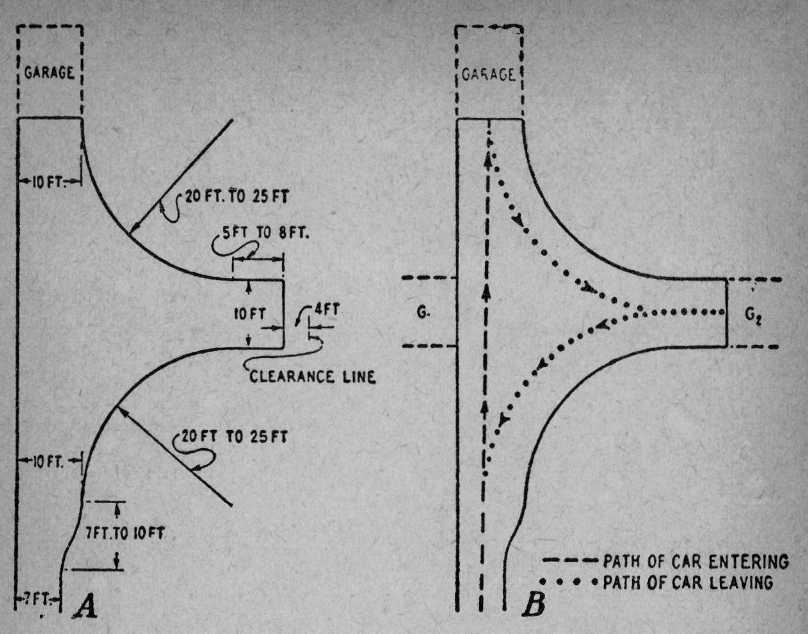

Fig. 22. Design of turning Y suitable for alternate garage locations: **A**, ranges in dimensions for short and long cars; **B**, paths of car entering and leaving garage. G_1 and G_2 indicate alternate garage locations.

or 2 feet from the drive's outer edges. Setting offset stakes is recommended, as they need not be disturbed during construction and thus are constantly available as reference points. The end stakes are first set, and at measured intervals intermediate stakes are set, true alignment being obtained either by eye or by means of a string stretched between the end stakes. An engineer's transit can be used for this purpose if available, though sufficient accuracy can be obtained by the other methods.

After one line of stakes has been set, stakes should be set in the other line directly opposite those already placed. This is best done by locating the end stakes directly opposite those in the first line, and then placing intermediate stakes at the interval used in the first line.

End stakes for the second line are placed the required distance from those already set and on lines through the end stakes and perpendicular to the drive. A handy method of locating this perpendicular line is to construct a right triangle with sides of 6 feet, 8 feet, and 10 feet, as shown in figure 21. In constructing a perpendicular to line XY at point A, point B is located 8 feet from A. Using point B as a center and with a 10-foot radius, arc DE is scratched on the ground. Using point A as a center and with a 6-foot radius, arc FG is scratched on the ground. The line connecting point

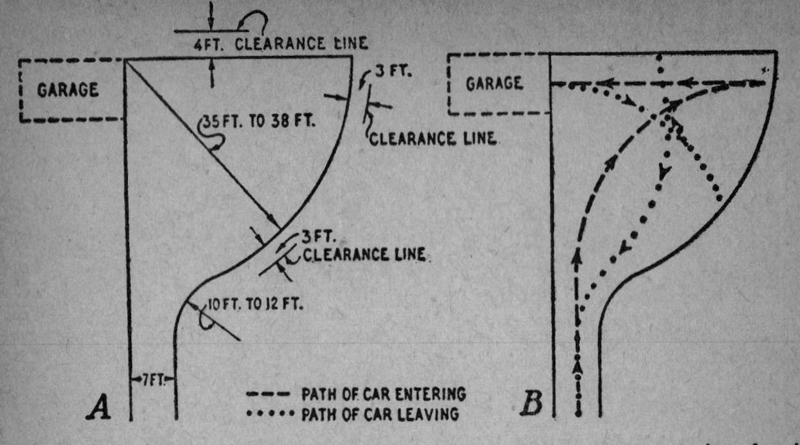

Fig. 23. Design of turning area: **A**, ranges in dimensions indicate minimum values for short and long cars; **B**, paths of car entering and leaving garage.

C, the point where these arcs cross, with point A is the desired perpendicular. A smaller right triangle may be constructed by using the dimensions 3, 4, and 5 feet.

For a larger triangle use 12, 16, and 20 feet.

Curved drives are staked out by locating the center of the curve, swinging arcs of the desired radii, and setting stakes at intervals along these arcs. The center of the curve must be on a perpendicular line at the beginning of the curve.

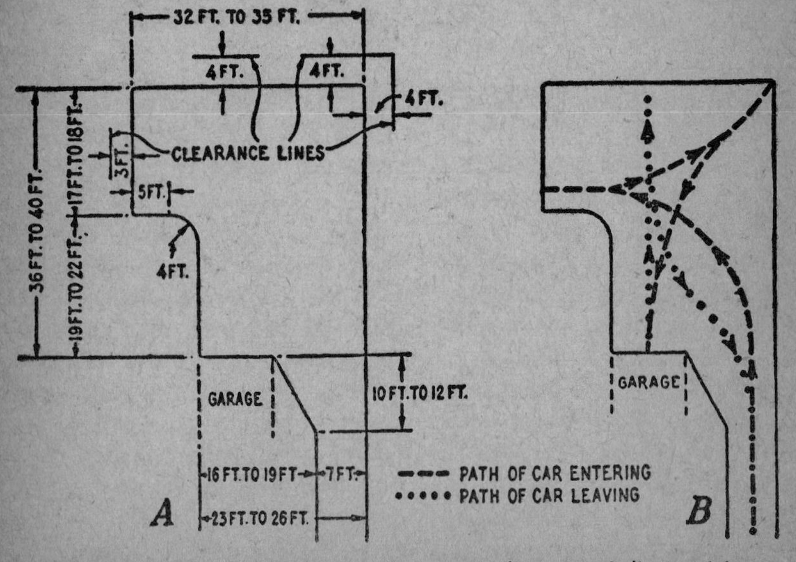

Fig. 24. Alternate design of turning area: **A**, ranges in dimensions indicate minimum values for short and long cars; **B**, paths of car entering and leaving garage.

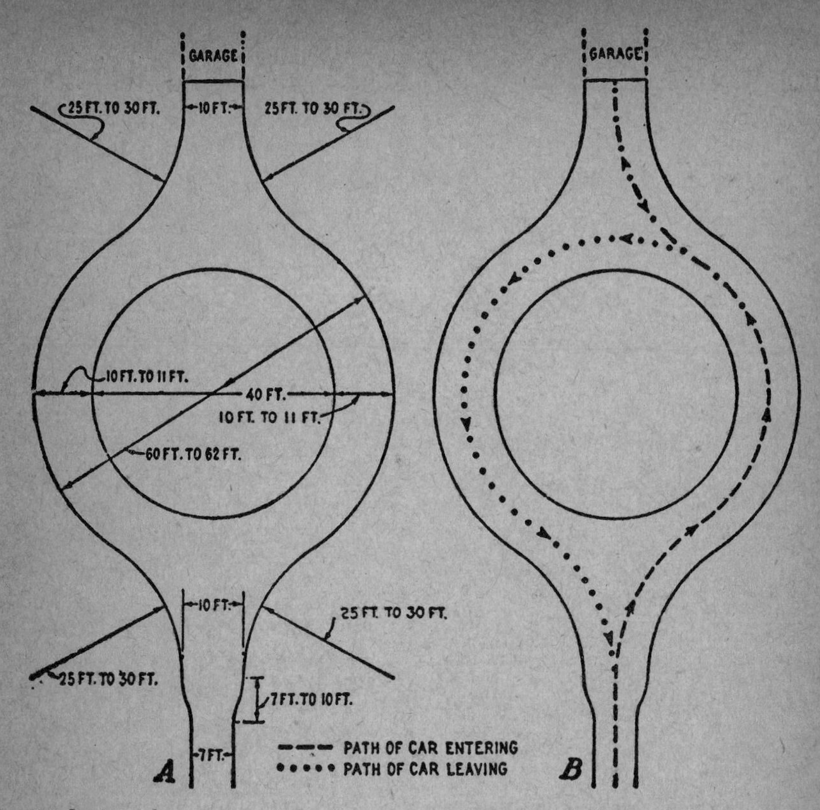

Fig. 25. Design of a turning circle: **A**, ranges in dimensions indicate minimum values for short and long cars; **B**, paths of car entering and leaving garage.

Drives that are straight for a distance and then curve need to be wider on the curve than on the straightaway because the effective gage is greater. At the point where the curve begins the drive needs to be a certain width on the one side for the straight part and a greater width on the other side for the curve. Rather than having an abrupt increase in width at this point, the drive should flare outward from a point on the straight section about 7 to 10 feet from the point of curvature (fig. 22). This flare will add to the appearance of the drive and will enable drivers to negotiate the curve more easily. The appearance of the drive will also be improved by rounding all corners, as shown.

It is suggested that before any drive is constructed it first be staked out, cleared of obstructions, and driven over a few times to determine whether it is satisfactory. The outline of the drive can easily be marked by setting small stakes at intervals and connecting them with white string. A curved drive might even be located by first driving the car over the path where it is desired to build the drive. Stakes could then be set

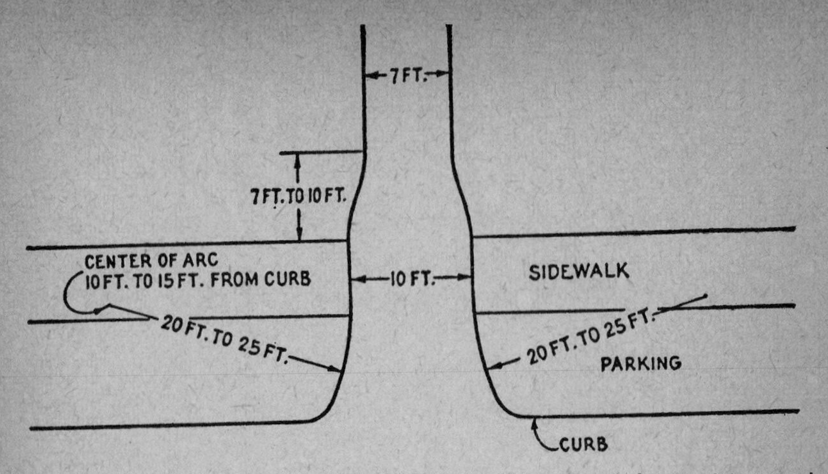

Fig. 26. Design of street entrance for drive. Ranges in dimensions indicate minimum values for short and long cars.

to outline the path traversed, allowing sufficient width so that the proposed drive can be driven over repeatedly without running over any of the outlining stakes.

TURNING AREAS AND STREET ENTRANCES

Home owners sometimes desire that turning areas be built on their drives, particularly if the drive is long or leads from a busy street. Such conditions make backing over the drive difficult or backing into the street dangerous. Drives are sometimes so located that a turning area must be provided in order to enable both entrance to and exit from the garage.

A few designs of turning areas are shown in figures 22 to 25. Any of the materials described for use in drive construction are also adaptable for use in surfacing turning areas. Contraction joints should be provided at 10-foot intervals in each direction in concrete turning areas.

The paths traced by a car when entering and leaving the garage are also shown in these figures. The clearance lines indicated are needed because of front and rear overhang of the car. For most cars the front overhang ranges from 26 to 33 inches; rear overhang ranges from 43 to 57 inches. The ground adjacent to the turning area at these clearance lines should be free from obstructions so that the full turning area can be used, as indicated by the dotted and dashed lines.

The turning areas shown are designed to be easily used with a minimum of turning and backing. Some home owners may be faced with space restrictions that do not permit use of the designs or dimensions shown. In such cases more backing and turning may be required to maneuver the car in to and out of the garage.

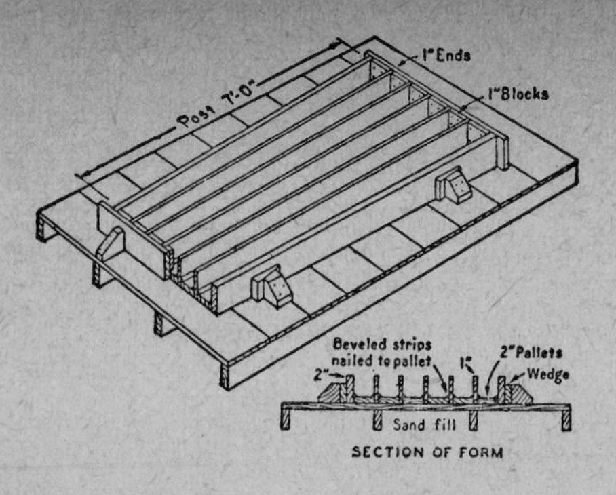

Fig. 27. Form for making concrete posts.

Ranges in dimensions are shown in figures 22 to 25. The smallest values are considered suitable for short cars; the largest values are considered suitable for long cars.

DRAINAGE FOR DRIVES

Drainage is not often a serious problem in drive construction, as most drives are not over 100 feet in length and drain but a small area. However, care should be taken to insure the prompt disposal of water that may collect and run onto the drive. This can usually be accomplished by constructing the drive on a slight grade and by diverting surface water that might run onto the drive. Surface drainage will adequately dispose of rain water in almost every instance. If underground drainage must be used, a line of 4-inch tile placed about 1 foot below the surface will usually suffice. Care should be taken to place sandy soil, gravel, or other porous material over the tile, as clay or impervious covering will prevent percolation and the proper functioning of the drain.

Drives that slope downward to the garage can be drained by installing a drainage inlet in the center of the drive about 4 feet in front of the garage doors, and connecting this inlet with the sewer outlet serving the house. The garage floor can be sloped so that it also drains to this inlet. City regulations sometimes prohibit carrying outside surface water to a sewer or limit the area that may be so drained. Local authorities or a plumber should be consulted on this point, also as to fees and permits for sewer connections.

CONCRETE POSTS

When metal concrete post forms are not available, the posts can be cast with the aid of the wood form shown in figure 27. This home-made form will produce posts 7′ long, 4″ x 3″ at the top, and 4″ x 5″ at the bottom. Each post should be reinforced with four ¼-inch rods accurately located, one in each corner, so as to have at least a ¾-inch covering of concrete. Square rods are better than round rods, which are more

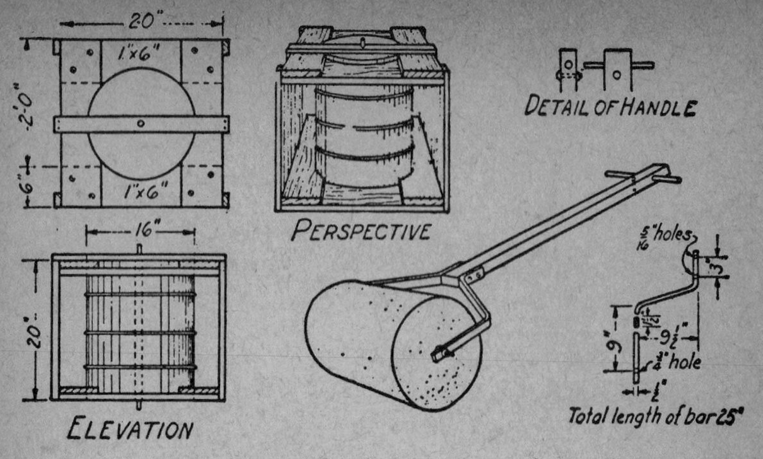

Fig. 28. Construction details for a concrete lawn roller.

often used. The rods should be 3 inches longer than the post to permit bending hooks on the ends to prevent the reinforcement from slipping when stressed. A good plan sometimes followed is to bend long rods into hairpins, with hooks on the ends, and use two hairpins instead of four separate rods. As a post can be seriously weakened by misplaced reinforcement, use spacers made of baling wire to hold rods in position.

The concrete should be mixed in the proportions of 1:2:2, and it should be just sufficiently plastic to place around the steel.

In placing the concrete, about 1 inch should be put on the bottom of the form, then two rods, or one hairpin, fastened together with five wire spacers, should be pressed into the concrete so as to be three-fourths of an inch from the bottom and sides. Concrete should be placed on these

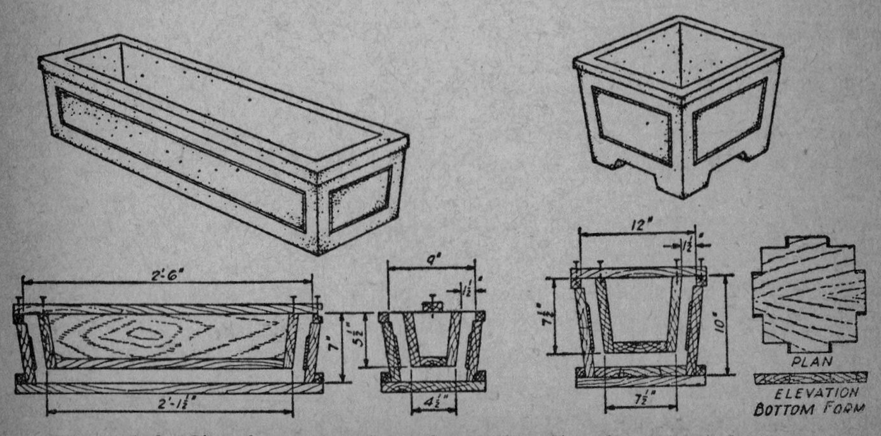

Fig. 29. **Left**—Plans for concrete flower box. **Right**—Plans for concrete flower pot.

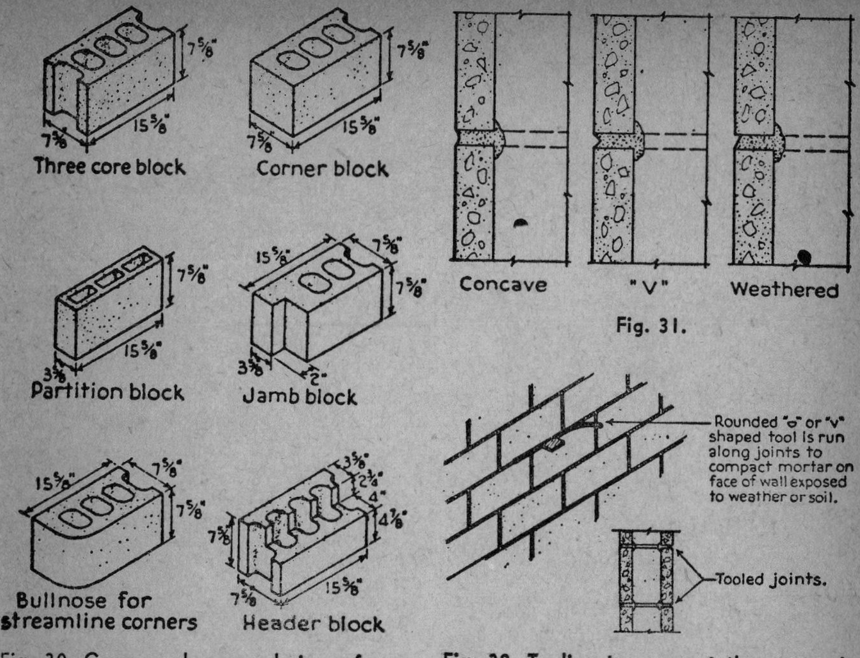

Fig. 31.

Fig. 30. Common shapes and sizes of concrete masonry units.

Fig. 32. Tooling to compact the mortar in the joint.

to three-fourths fill the form, then two more rods with spacers should be placed similarly to the first pair, and the form filled. As the forms are filled they should be jarred or tapped to compact the concrete, and the aggregate should be pushed back from the sides by spading, but care must be taken not to displace the reinforcement. The exposed surface can be smoothed with a float. Because posts of small cross section are easily broken when new, care must be exercised to properly cure them and guard against jolts that may cause damage. The posts should be left in the forms until the concrete hardens—24 hours in summer—after which they can be carried on the pallet to the curing site. A bed of sand or soft moist earth is desirable, as the posts can be turned and slid carefully from the pallet and then covered with moist sand where they should be left 28 days protected from heat and drying winds. Posts should not be set in the fence row until 28 days after casting, and it is better to let them cure 2 to 3 months.

A post of the cross section mentioned above weighs about 109 pounds and has a volume of three-fourths of a cubic foot. Approximately 36 posts can be made from 1 cubic yard of concrete. One man should be able to make 5 posts an hour. Reinforcement is sold by the pound, and 6 feet of ¼-inch round steel or 4.71 feet of ¼-inch square steel weighs about 1 pound.

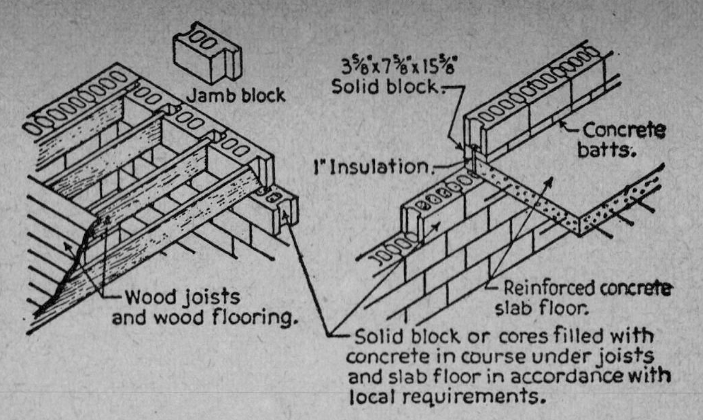

Fig. 33. **Left**—Detail showing building of wood floor joists in walls. **Right**—Reinforced concrete flat slab floor on wall.

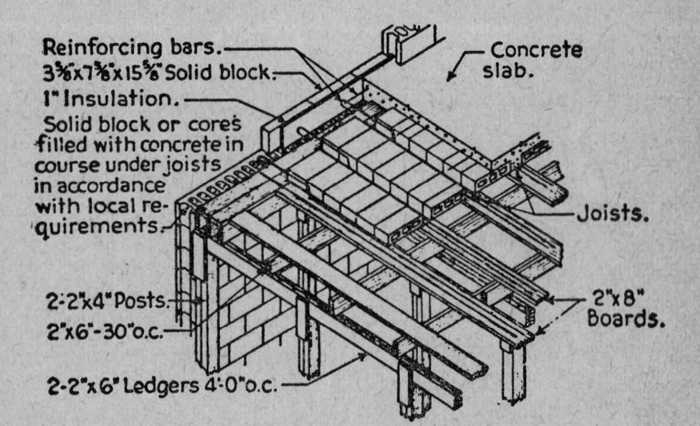

Fig. 34. Framing concrete block joist floors in walls.

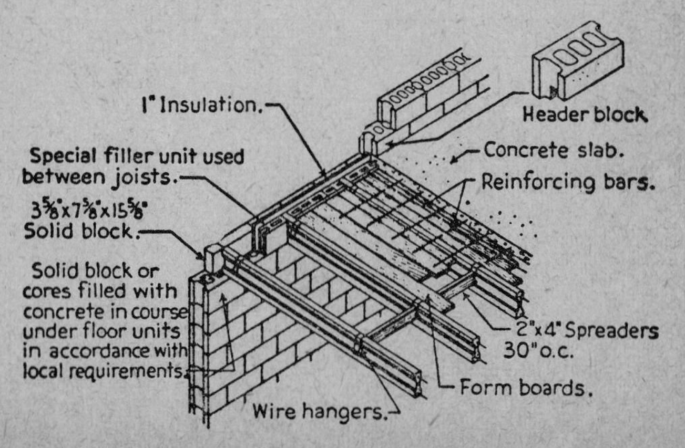

Fig. 35. Framing of precast concrete floor joists in walls.

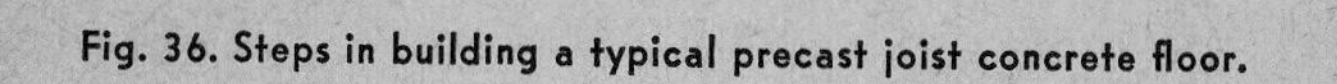

Fig. 36. Steps in building a typical precast joist concrete floor.

LAWN ROLLER

Plans for making a practical, long-lasting concrete lawn roller are shown in figure 28. The forms are assembled as indicated, fitting the clamps around the galvanized iron sheet which is bent to circular form with its ends overlapping. If necessary the metal may be tacked to the clamps. An iron pipe is set in the exact center of the form, using wood strips with accurately bored holes to fit the pipe.

TOOLED JOINTS

Tooling is essential in producing tight mortar joints. Mortar has a tendency to shrink slightly and may pull away from the edges of the masonry units, causing fine, almost invisible cracks at the junction of mortar and masonry units. Tooling compacts the mortar and presses it firmly against the units, increasing the water-resistance of the joint. It should be done after the mortar has partially set. Figure 31 shows three types of approved tooled mortar joints. Figure 32 shows detail of making tooled joint.

PRECAST JOIST CONCRETE FLOORS

Precast joist concrete floors consist of precast concrete joists covered with cast-in-place concrete slab. The joists are usually made in a concrete products plant (fig. 36).

Usual spacing of joists is from 27 to 33 in., depending upon the span and the load. The cast-in-place concrete slab is usually 2 or 2½ in. thick and extends down over the heads of the joists about ½ in.

Precast concrete joists are usually made in 8, 10 and 12-inch depths. The 8-in. joists are used for spans

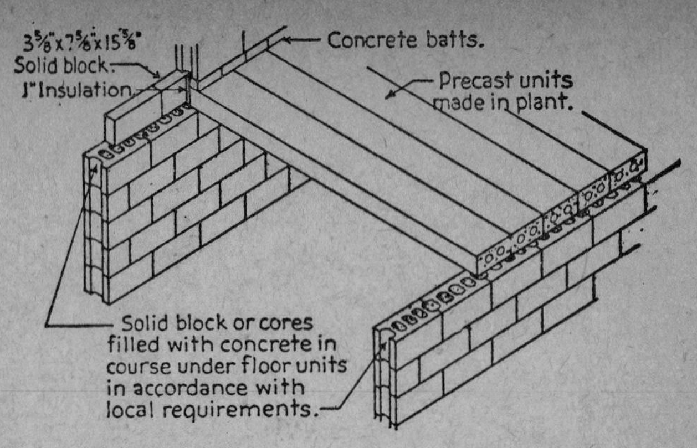

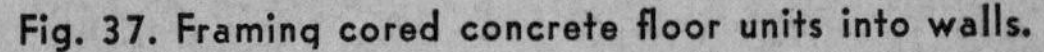
Fig. 37. Framing cored concrete floor units into walls.

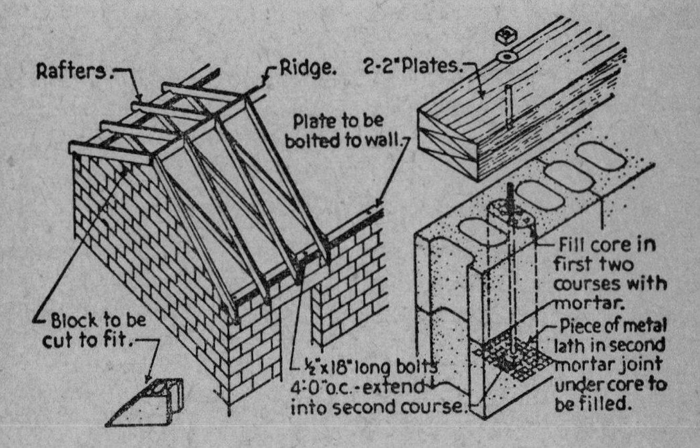

Fig. 38. Anchoring sills and plates to concrete masonry walls by bolts.

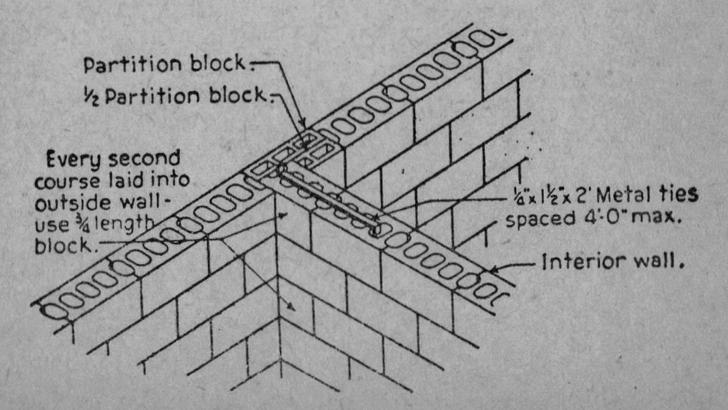

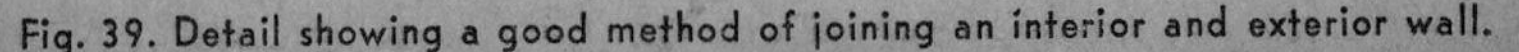
Fig. 39. Detail showing a good method of joining an interior and exterior wall.

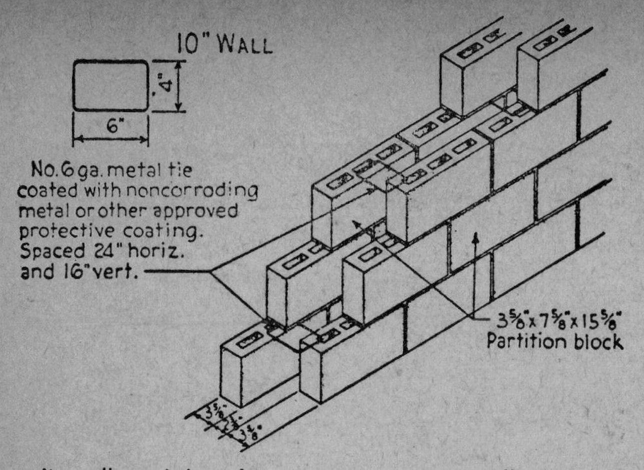

Fig. 40. A cavity wall consisting of two concrete masonry walls. Metal ties are laid in mortar joints.

up to 16 ft.; the 10-in. joists for spans between 16 and 20 ft.; and the 12-in. joists for spans from 20 to 24 ft.

Where non-load-bearing masonry partitions are placed parallel to the joists it is customary to double the joists under the partition. If the partition runs at right angles to the joists, usual practice is to design the floor to carry an additional load of 20 lb. per sq. ft.

Precast concrete joists may be left exposed on the underside and painted,

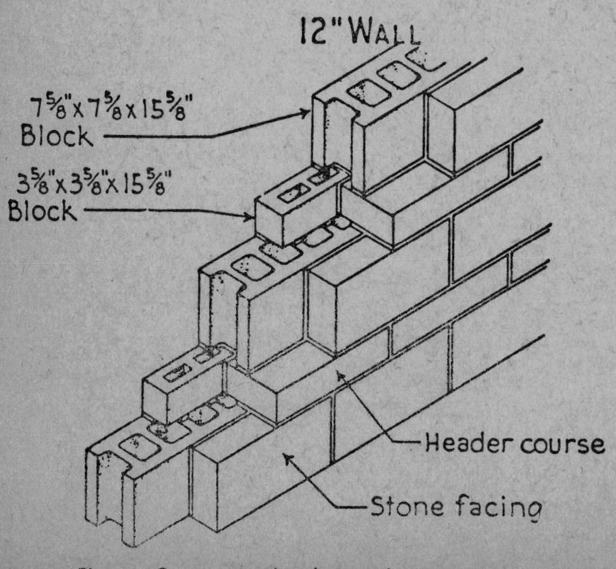

Fig. 41. One way to bond stone facing to masonry.

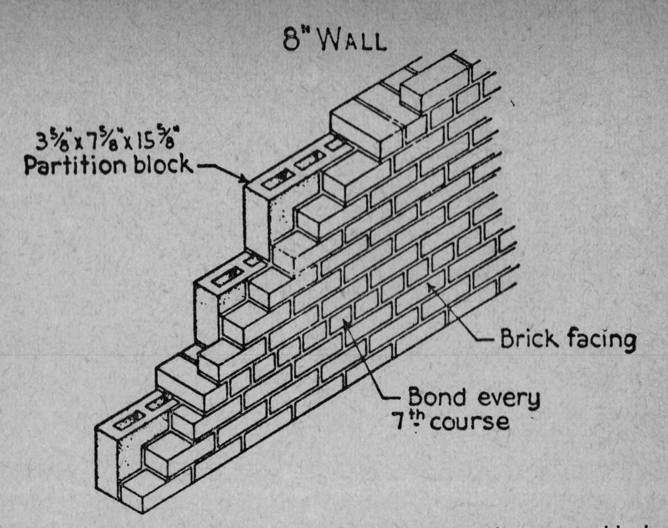

Fig. 42. A wall with 4-inch brick facing and 4-inch concrete blocks.

or a suspended ceiling may be used. An attractive variation in exposed joist treatment is to double the joists and increase the spacing. Where this is done the concrete slab is made 2½ in. thick for spacings up to 48 in. and 3 in. thick for spacings from 48 in. up to 60 in.

Joists may be doubled by setting them close together or by leaving a space between them and filling the space with concrete.

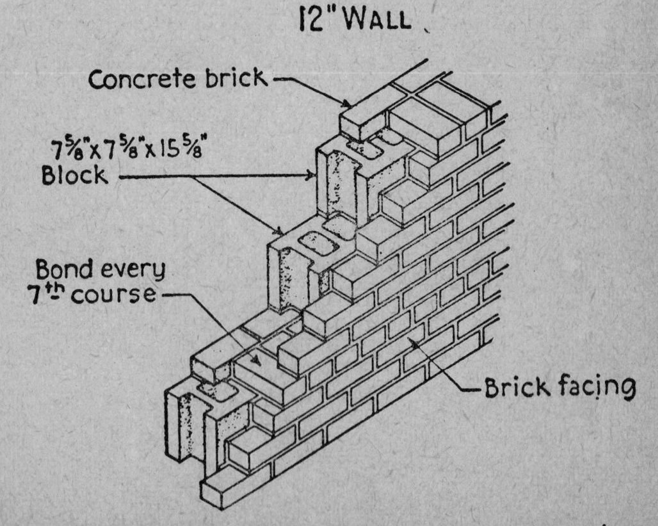

Fig. 43. Bonding brick facing to concrete masonry by making every seventh course of brick a header course.

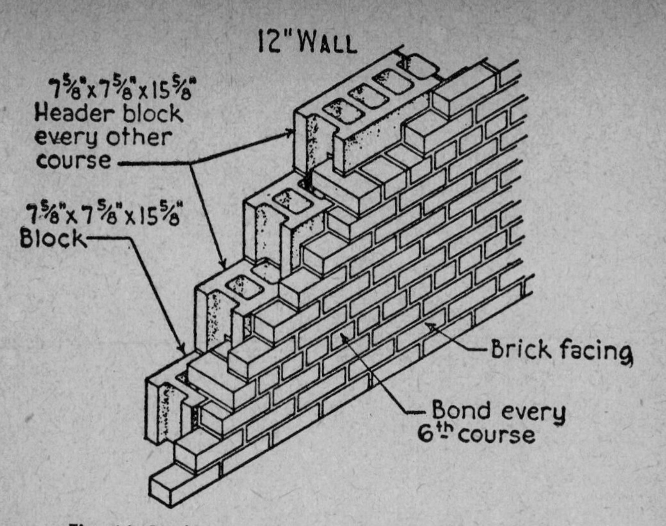

Fig. 44. Brick facing bonded to special header blocks.

BUILDING INTERIOR WALLS

Interior walls are built in the same way as exterior walls. Load-bearing interior walls are usually made 8 inches thick; non-load-bearing partition walls are usually 4 inches thick. The recommended method of joining interior load-bearing walls to exterior walls is shown in figure 39.

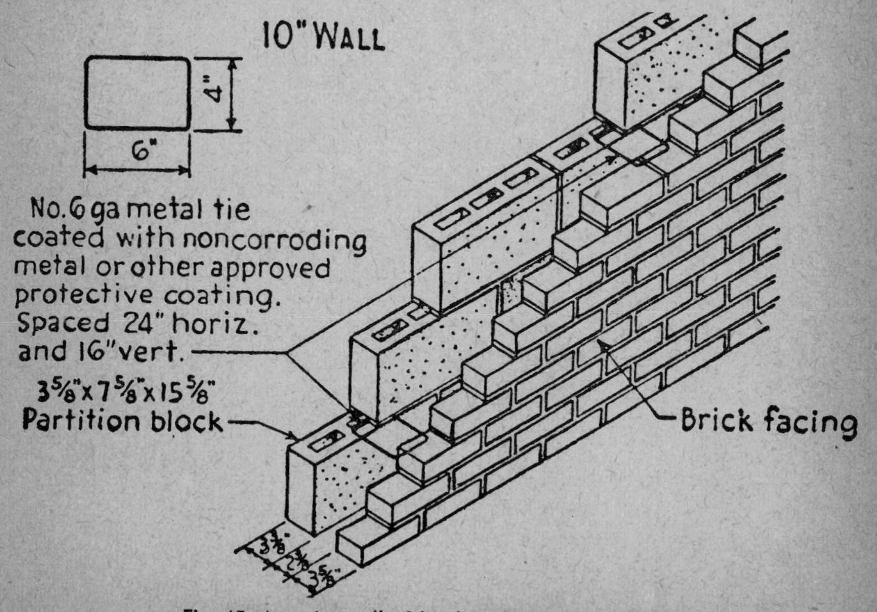

Fig. 45. A cavity wall of brick and concrete masonry.

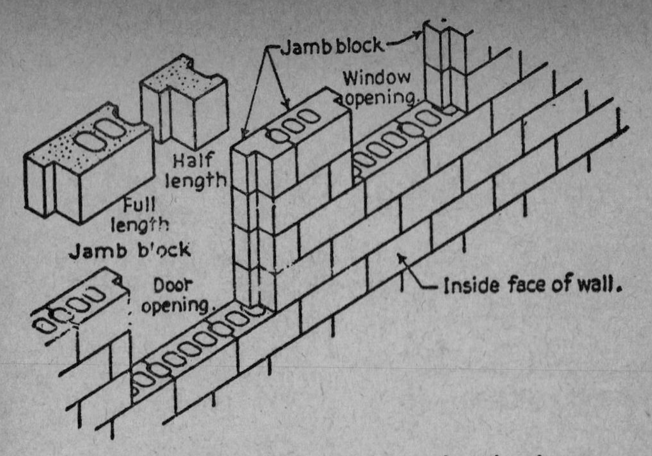

Fig. 46. Openings to receive door and window frames.

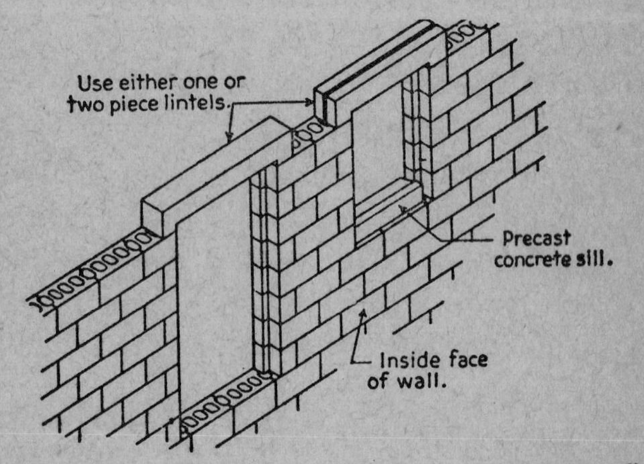

Fig. 47. Precast concrete sills and lintels in concrete masonry walls.

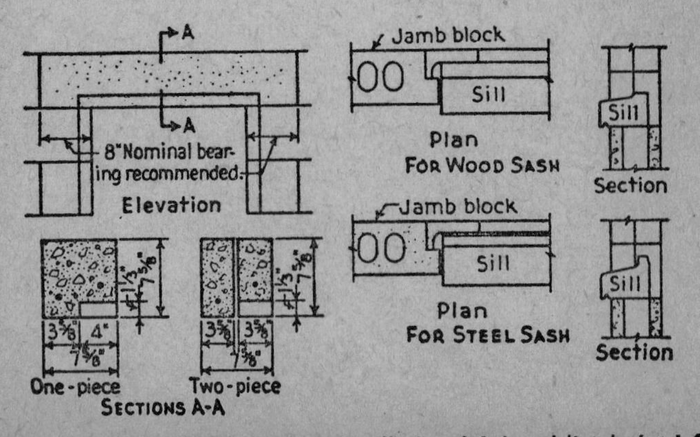

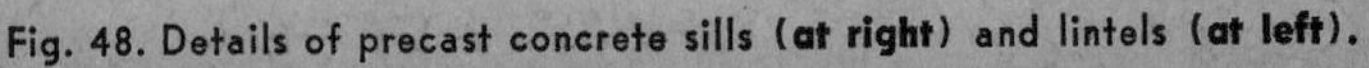

Fig. 48. Details of precast concrete sills (**at right**) and lintels (**at left**).

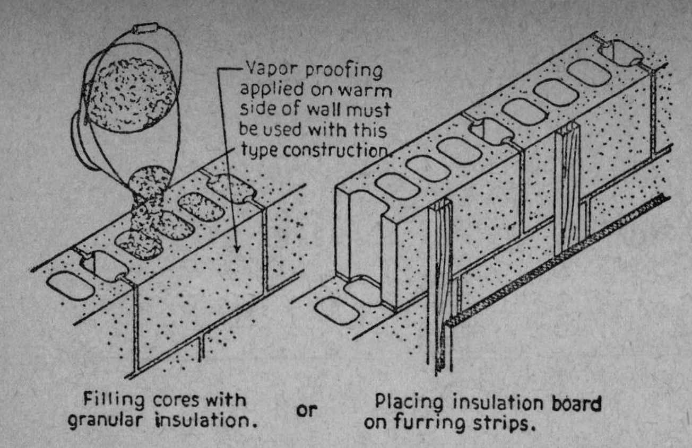
Vapor proofing applied on warm side of wall must be used with this type construction
Filling cores with granular insulation.
or
Placing insulation board on furring strips.

Fig. 49. For increased insulation, fill cores with granular material or place rigid insulation over furring strips attached to the inside wall face.

BUILDING AROUND DOOR AND WINDOW FRAMES

There are several acceptable methods of building door and window frames in concrete masonry walls. One method, much used in the past, is to set the frames in the proper position in the wall. The frames are then plumbed and carefully braced after which the walls are built up against them on both sides. The frames are often fastened to the walls with anchor bolts passing through the frames and embedded in the mortar joints. A more recent method

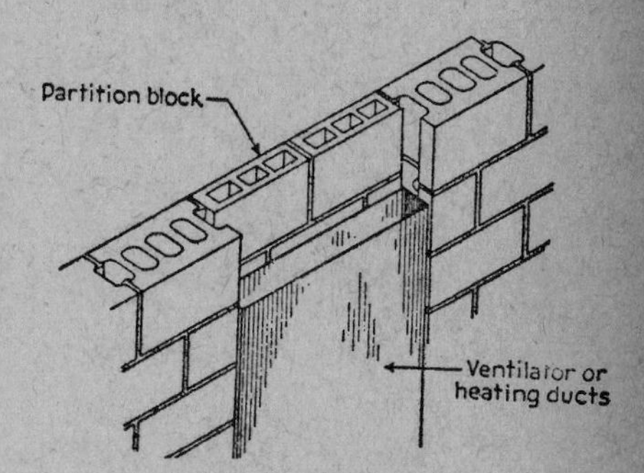
Partition block
Ventilator or heating ducts

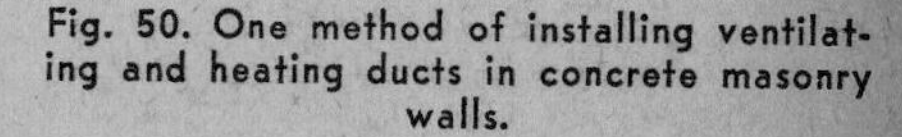
Fig. 50. One method of installing ventilating and heating ducts in concrete masonry walls.

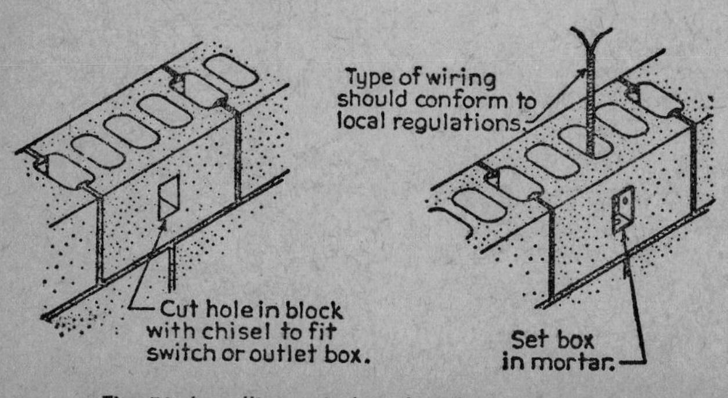
Type of wiring should conform to local regulations.
Cut hole in block with chisel to fit switch or outlet box.
Set box in mortar.

Fig. 51. Installing switch and outlet boxes in walls.

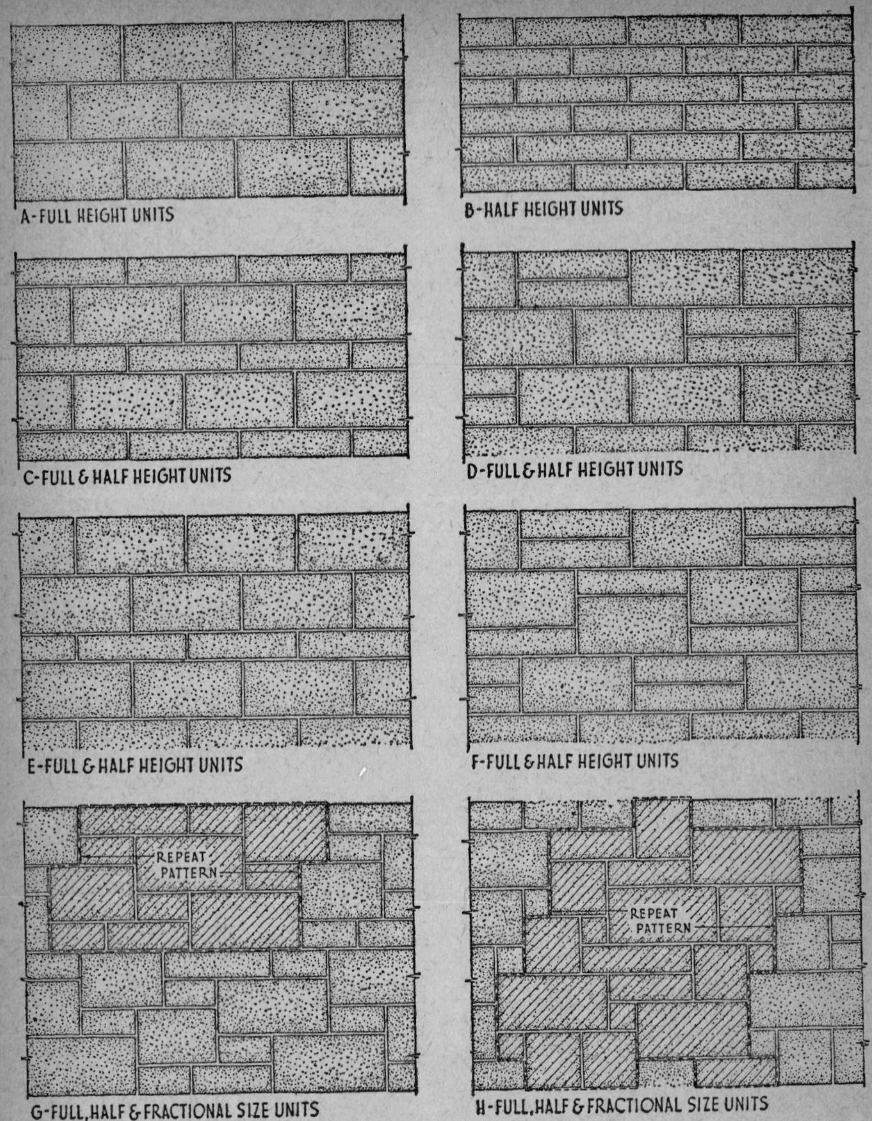

Fig. 52. Several of the attractive patterns possible with concrete masonry construction.

of building frames in concrete masonry walls is to build openings for them using special jamb blocks (fig. 46). The frames are inserted after the wall is built. The advantage of this method is that the frames can be

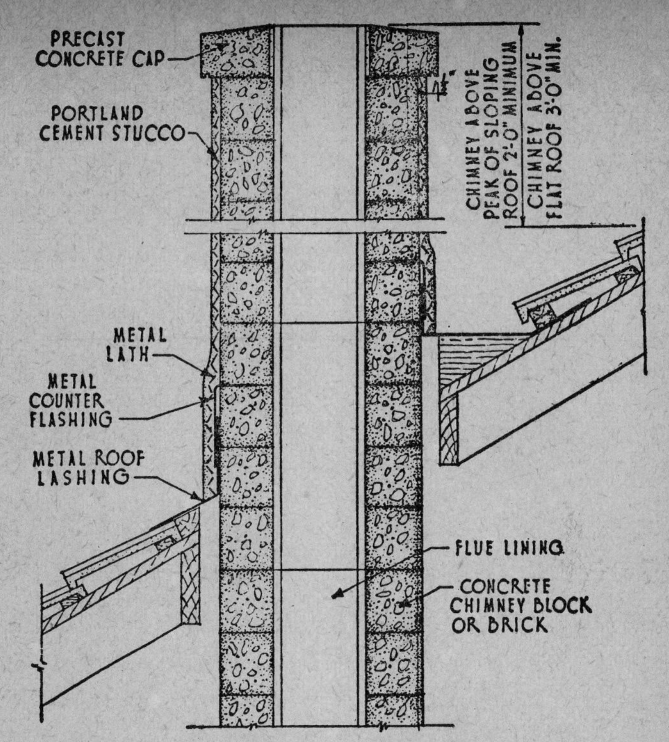

Fig. 53. Detail of concrete masonry block chimney. Note that the flashing between chimney and roof is set under the coat of stucco which is attached, not directly to the masonry blocks, but to metal lath.

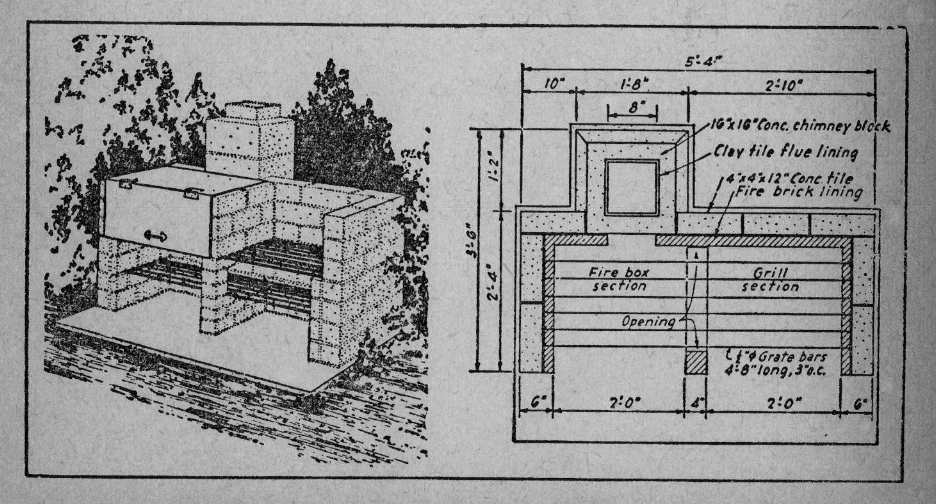

Fig. 54. Details of construction for a concrete masonry barbecue pit or stove.

Fig. 55.

taken out readily without damaging the wall.

PLACING SILLS AND LINTELS

Openings over doors and windows are bridged by reinforced concrete beams called lintels (fig. 47). These are usually precast in a plant but can be cast on the job. Lintels are reinforced with steel bars about 1½ inches from the lower side. The number and size of reinforcing rods depend upon the width of the opening and the weight of the load to be carried. Sills may also be either precast in a products plant or cast in place on the wall (figs. 47 and 48). Sills are made to project about 1 inch beyond the face of the wall and are provided with a drip so that rain water running down the sill will fall free and not flow down the wall, possibly streaking and staining it.

MASONRY BLOCK PATTERNS

Figure 52 shows several of the many attractive patterns possible with concrete masonry block construction. The patterns can be produced with standard units of 8″ x 16″ face, 5″ x 12″ face and 3¾″ x 12″ face.

MASONRY BLOCK SHOWER STALL

An inexpensive shower stall can be made out of standard size concrete masonry blocks (fig. 55). The base for the stall is made out of poured concrete approximately 2½ inches thick, with a drain fitting at the center. The bottom of the stall should slope on all four sides down to the center for good drainage. Standard shower-stall drain fittings are used and installed before the concrete base is poured. Pipes are run through the voids in the concrete blocks. The inside can be plastered with cement plaster and finished with a cement-base paint.

SUCTION

Suction is absolutely necessary in order to get the proper bond of stucco on masonry or cast-in-place concrete. It is also necessary in first and second coats so that succeeding coats will bond properly.

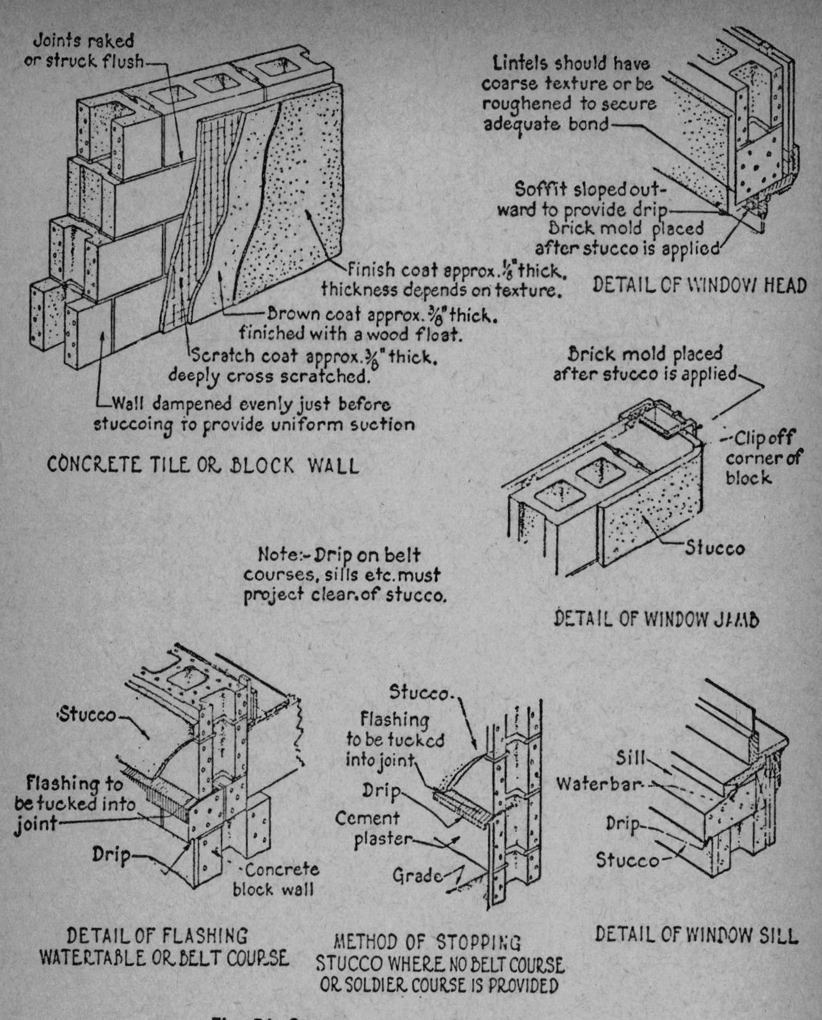

Fig. 56. Stucco on concrete masonry.

Uniform suction helps to obtain uniform color. If one part of the wall draws more moisture from the stucco than another, the finish coat may be spotty.

Obtain uniform suction by dampening, but not soaking, the wall evenly before applying the stucco. If the surface becomes dry in spots, dampen these areas again to restore uniform suction. A fog spray is recommended for this work. Work on the shady side of buildings when possible, for it is hard to keep walls damp when they are exposed to the sun. If waterproofing is used in base coat mortar, dampening the first and second coats to obtain uniform suction may not be required except in hot, dry weather.

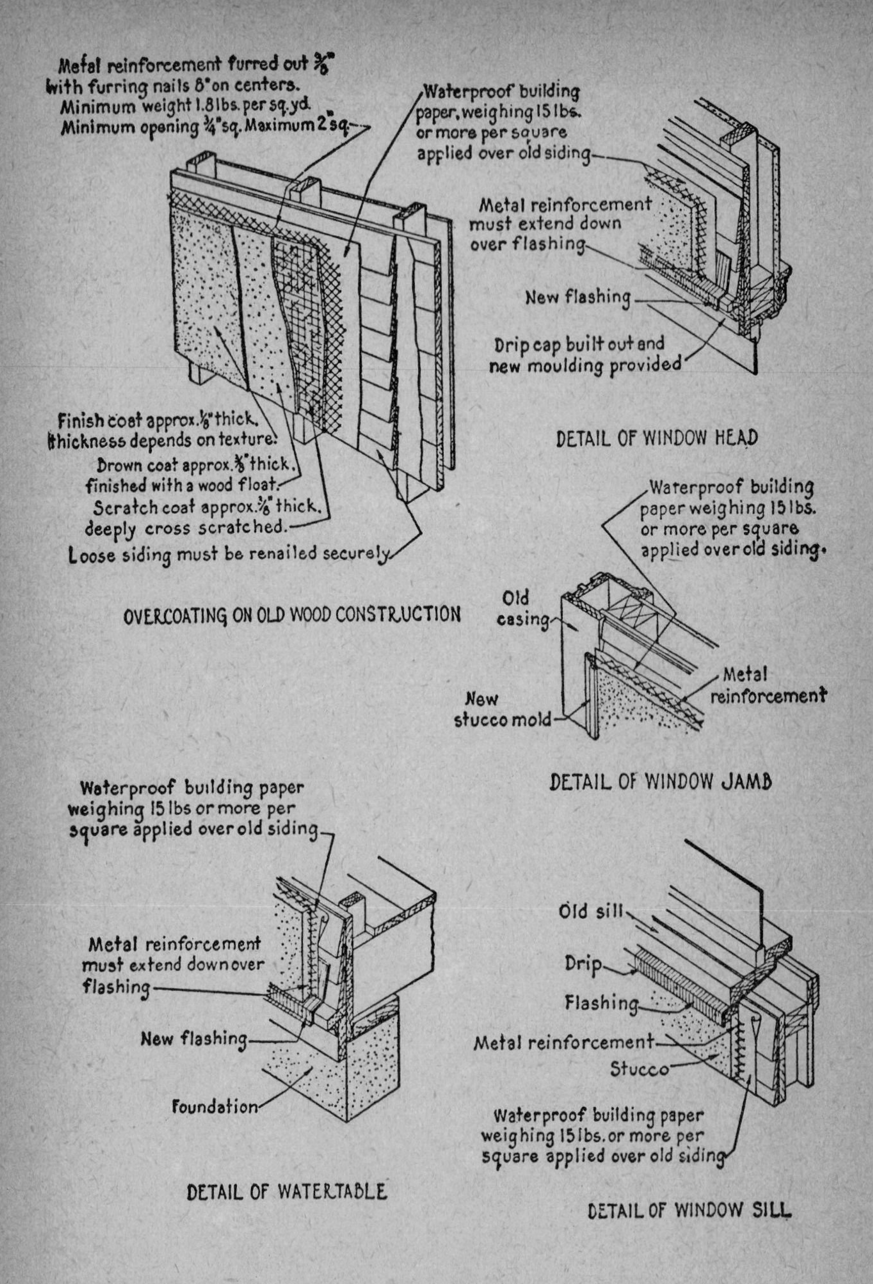
Metal reinforcement furred out 3/8"
with furring nails 8" on centers.
Minimum weight 1.8 lbs. per sq. yd.
Minimum opening 3/4" sq. Maximum 2" sq.
Waterproof building
paper, weighing 15 lbs.
or more per square
applied over old siding
Metal reinforcement
must extend down
over flashing
New flashing
Drip cap built out and
new moulding provided
Finish coat approx. 1/8" thick.
thickness depends on texture.
Drown coat approx. 3/8" thick.
finished with a wood float.
Scratch coat approx. 3/8" thick.
deeply cross scratched.
Loose siding must be renailed securely
DETAIL OF WINDOW HEAD
Waterproof building
paper weighing 15 lbs.
or more per square
applied over old siding.
OVERCOATING ON OLD WOOD CONSTRUCTION
Old
casing
Metal
reinforcement
New
stucco mold
DETAIL OF WINDOW JAMB
Waterproof building paper
weighing 15 lbs or more per
square applied over old siding
Metal reinforcement
must extend down over
flashing
New flashing
Foundation
Old sill
Drip
Flashing
Metal reinforcement
Stucco
Waterproof building paper
weighing 15 lbs. or more per
square applied over old siding
DETAIL OF WATERTABLE
DETAIL OF WINDOW SILL

Fig. 57. Stucco overcoating on wood frame.

BOTTLE CAPS IN STUCCO WORK

If furring nails aren't available, stucco wire stretched over asphalt felt can be held with old bottle caps and 1¾″ nails having large heads. Slip a cap under a mesh joint to hold it away from the wall as it is stretched, and nail as illustrated in figure 58.

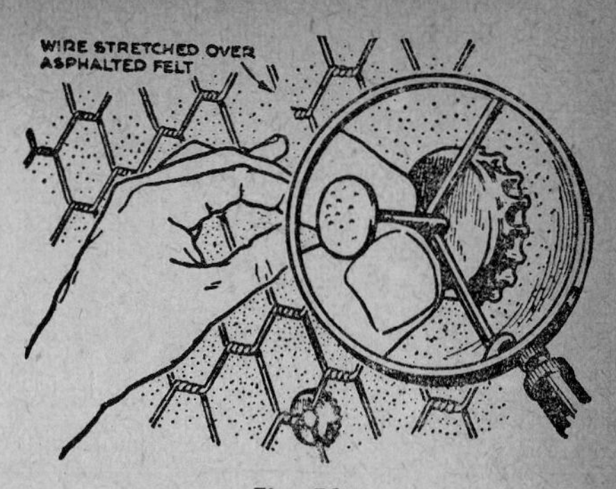

Fig. 58.

COMMON BOND

ENGLISH BOND

FLEMISH BOND

ENGLISH CROSS OR DUTCH BOND

FLEMISH CROSS BOND

RUNNING HEADER BOND

DOUBLE STRETCHER FLEMISH BOND

PATTERNS

GARDEN WALL BOND

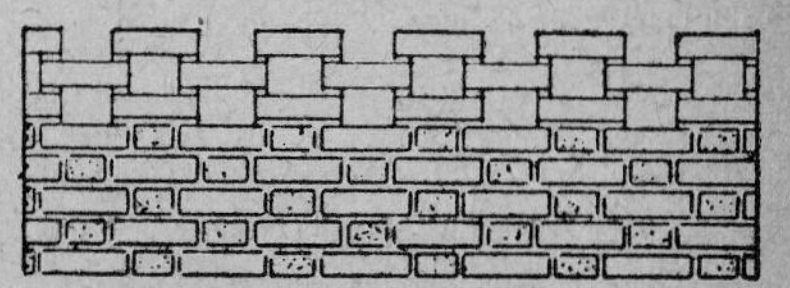

PATTERNS

Fig. 59. Various pattern bonds used in brickwork.

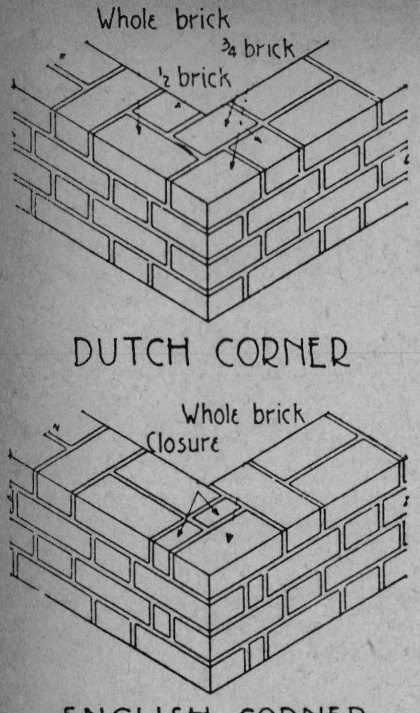

Fig. 60. Corners of 8-inch brick walls laid up in Dutch and English pattern bonds. The Dutch pattern bond corner illustrated at the top uses a three-quarter brick on the face of alternate courses. The English pattern bond illustrated at the bottom uses a quarter-closure brick on alternate courses.

REFINISHING OLD STUCCO JOBS

Old stucco jobs may be resurfaced to renew finish and change color or texture, or both. The new stucco may be applied direct provided the old stucco is sound. If original stucco is unsound, it is necessary to remove the old material entirely and apply a new three-coat job.

Where old stucco is not removable, it is necessary to cover the old surface with paper and metal reinforcement and then apply the standard three coats.

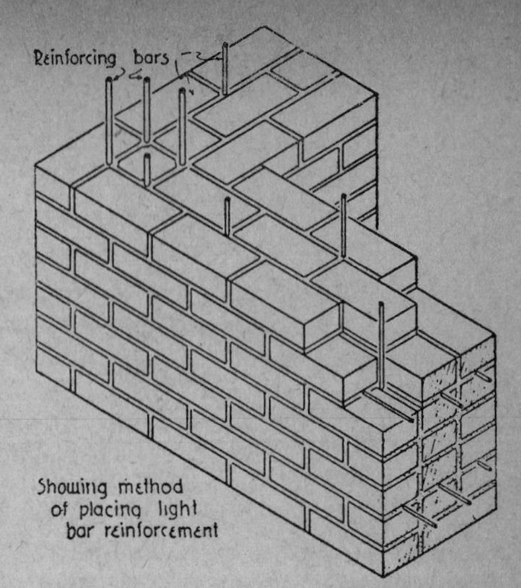

Fig. 61. Reinforced brick masonry wall. Reinforcing rods are placed in bed and vertical joints. Where rods over ⅜-inch in diameter are used as uprights, it is necessary to clip the corners of the brick so the width of the mortar joints will not be increased.

How to prepare surface. Prepare sound stucco surfaces for refinishing as follows:

Wet the entire area; then clean it with a solution of 1 part muriatic acid and 6 parts water. (Handle this acid with extreme care.) After acid-treatment, wash it thoroughly with water to remove all traces of the acid. Allow wall to dry thoroughly; then moisten it just prior to applying the new coat. On surfaces of coarse or rough texture, the new finish may be a single coat applied with the trowel. If the old surface lacks roughness, apply two coats, dashing on the first in order to establish bond.

After the dash coat is properly cured, trowel on the finish coat.

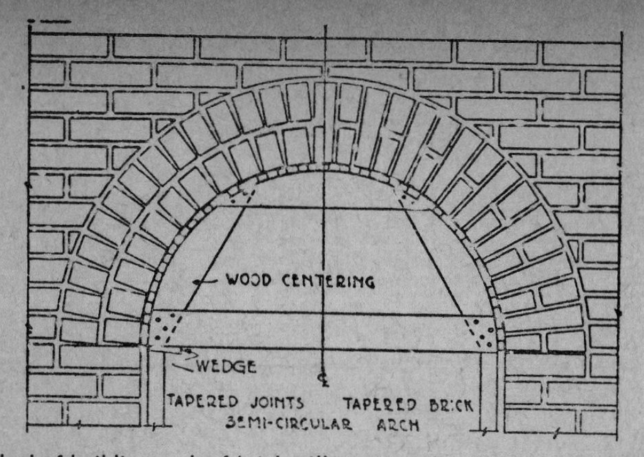

Fig. 62. Method of building arch of bricks. Illustration shows two types of arch and method of installing wood centering in position.

Never apply portland cement stucco directly over lime, gypsum or magnesite stucco. These materials either should be removed entirely or they should be covered first with waterproof paper and metal reinforcement.

In either case, apply the standard three coats of portland cement stucco.

FIREPLACE CONSTRUCTION

Figure 64 shows the plan view of a fireplace with two flues built out of hollow tile. Figure 65 shows the method of staggering the tile at each course in chimney construction. Figure 66 indicates the method of firestopping required for this type of construction.

BASIC INSTALLATION OF MORTAR-SET GLASS BLOCKS

Glass block panels may be installed in either masonry or frame houses. They are erected with standard tools and masonry mortar. Not load-bearing, glass blocks require openings framed as for windows. Rough opening dimensions are shown in table below. Procedure for installing panels is as follows (fig. 72).

1. Apply a coat of asphalt emulsion to the sill.

2. Install expansion strips at jambs and heads of openings.

3. Lay glass block, using full mortar joints. Mortar mix: 1 part port-

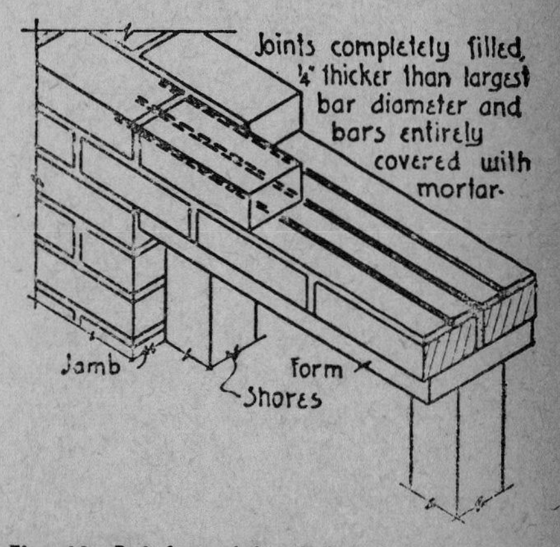

Fig. 63. Reinforced brick lintel. Illustration shows the position of steel reinforcing rods in bed of an 8-inch brick wall.

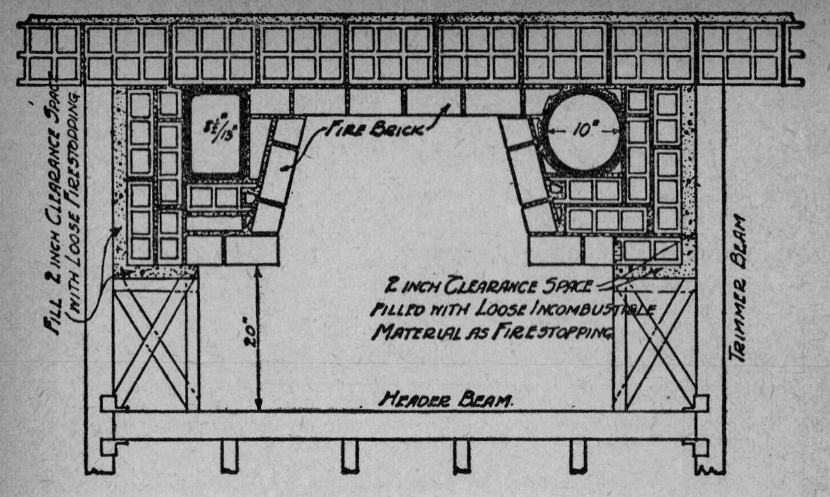

Fig. 64.

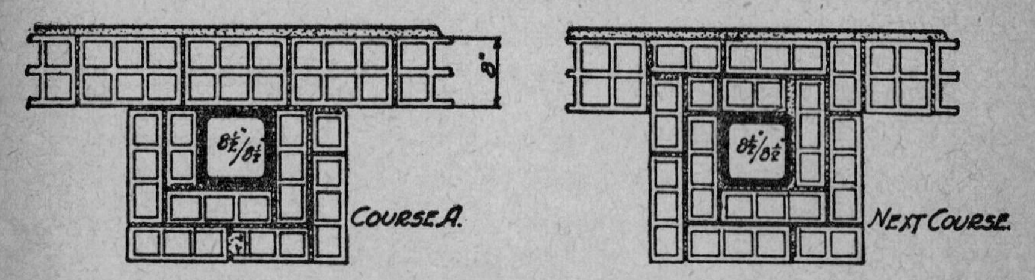

APPROVED HOLLOW TILE CONSTRUCTION FOR FIREPLACE AND CHIMNEY.

Fig. 65.

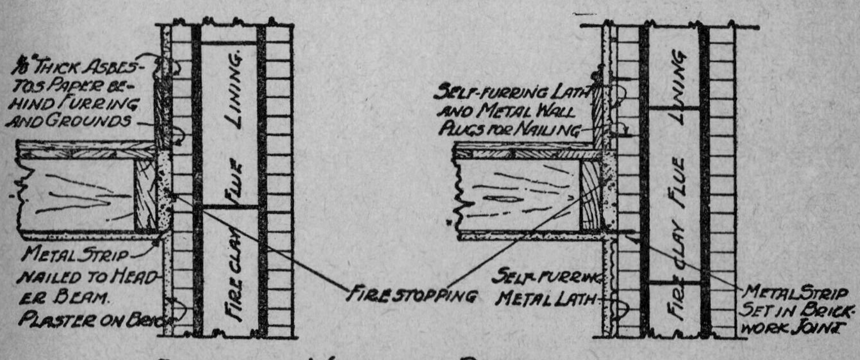

APPROVED WOODWORK PROTECTION.

Fig. 66.

land cement, 1 part hydrated lime and 4 parts sand. Use stiff consistency.

4. Install wall tiles in horizontal joints as follows: 6″ block, every 4th course; 8″ block, every 3rd course; 12″ block, every course.

5. Anchor panels at jambs by setting into rebates formed by casing, or use anchors on 2′ centers.

6. Tool joints and give blocks preliminary cleaning before mortar reaches final set.

7. Calk perimeter of panel with calking compound. Where wood sills are used, sill joint should be raked and calked. Head should be flashed wherever head joint is exposed.

8. Give panel final cleaning.

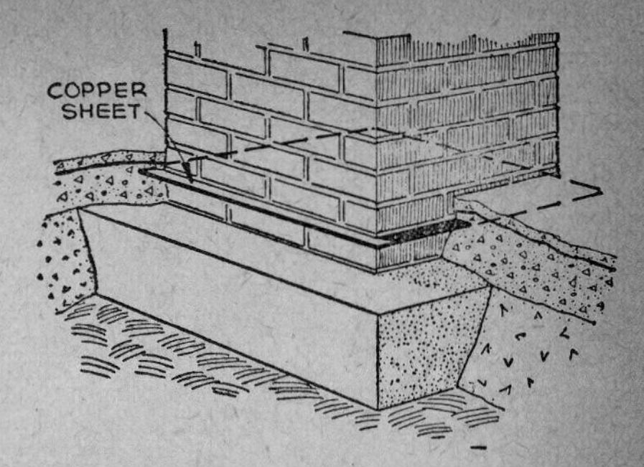

Fig. 67. The possibility of a chimney's becoming damp through capillary action of the masonry can be eliminated by installing a sheet of copper between the brick about one foot above the grade level.

MINIMUM OPENINGS FOR GLASS BLOCK PANELS

The table below shows the minimum size openings needed for panels

Number of Blocks	Block Size 5¾″ x 5¾″ Height	Width	Block Size 7¾″ x 7¾″ Height	Width	Block Size 11¾″ x 11¾″ Height	Width
1	6⅝″	6½″	8⅝″	8½″	1′–0⅝″	1′–0½″
2	1′–0⅝″	1′–0½″	1′–4⅝″	1′–4½″	2′–0⅝″	2′–0½″
3	1′–6⅝″	1′–6½″	2′–0⅝″	2′–0½″	3′–0⅝″	3′–0½″
4	2′–0⅝″	2′–0½″	2′–8⅝″	2′–8½″	4′–0⅝″	4′–0½″
5	2′–6⅝″	2′–6½″	3′–4⅝″	3′–4½″	5′–0⅝″	5′–0½″
6	3′–0⅝″	3′–0½″	4′–0⅝″	4′–0½″	6′–0⅝″	6′–0½″
7	3′–6⅝″	3′–6½″	4′–8⅝″	4′–8½″	7′–0⅝″	7′–0½″
8	4′–0⅝″	4′–0½″	5′–4⅝″	5′–4½″	8′–0⅝″	8′–0½″
9	4′–6⅝″	4′–6½″	6′–0⅝″	6′–0½″	9′–0⅝″	9′–0½″
10	5′–0⅝″	5′–0½″	6′–8⅝″	6′–8½″	10′–0⅝″	10′–0½″

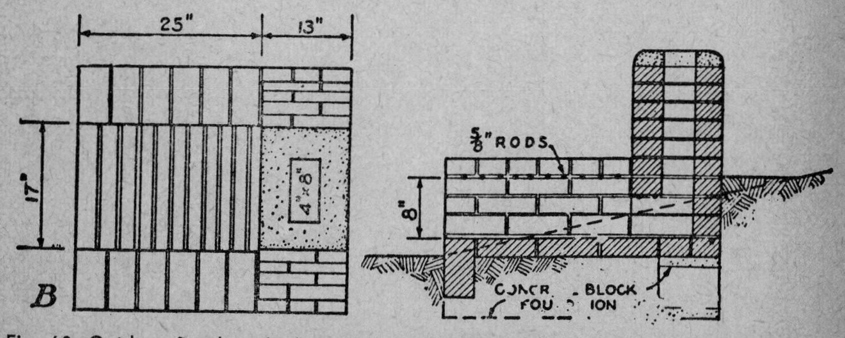

Fig. 68. Outdoor fireplace built out of one hundred and twenty bricks and six concrete blocks. This type of fireplace is easily constructed and the cost of materials comes to only a few dollars. In place of brick and cement blocks, field stone can be used.

Fig. 69. A satisfactory incinerator for household use.

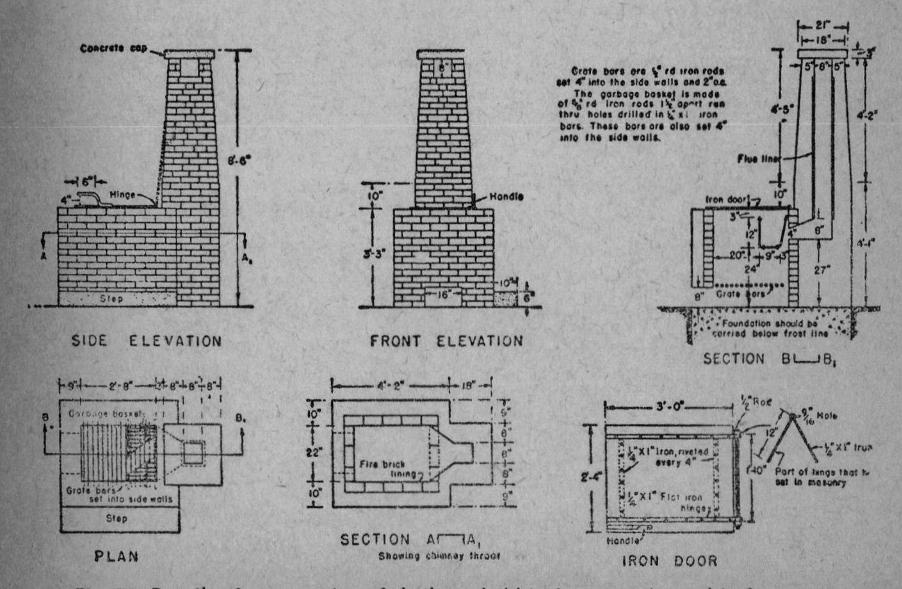

Fig. 70. Details of construction of the household incinerator pictured in figure 69.

of various numbers of glass blocks, allowing for ¼″ mortar joints. Example: a panel of 7¾″ x 7¾″ blocks, 5 blocks high and 7 blocks wide requires an opening 3′ 4⅜″ by 4′ 8½″.

GLASS BLOCK PARTITIONS

Panels of glass block which are not exposed to weather may be built by a simple method using prefabricated wood strips instead of mortar. Building a set-in-wood partition is not much harder than building with toy blocks, yet the result gives lasting satisfaction.

There are many advantages to set-in-wood partitions. They may be dismantled and used again in another location without loss of material. Joints are always of even thickness, and for unusual decorative effects, the wood strips may be painted in whatever colors suit your tastes. They do not have the high sound reduction or the fire resistance of mortar-set panels, however.

Step by step instructions

Preparing the Opening. Determine dimensions of opening from table below. Build frame, strong and true, using double 2 x 4's. *Then* (fig. 75):

1. Nail grooveless wedges at top and sides of frame with 2 two-penny nails each. Locate wedges in center of each row of block on either 8″ or 12″ centers. Thin edge of wedge should be up.

2. Plane off beads on one side of a horizontal joint strip; cut to full width of opening and lay on base with remaining beads up.

3. Nail bottom strip to the base.

4. Lay course of block, inserting vertical strips between blocks and end of block and wedges.

5. Insert grooved half of wedges at ends of course. Be sure that grooves in wedges are on beads of vertical strips. Drive wedges snug, applying the same pressure from both ends.

6. When wedges are tight, tap top of each vertical joint strip—so that notches fit over beads of horizontal strip below.

7. Place next horizontal strip. Thereafter, repeat steps 4, 5, 6 and 7 for each course. Be sure vertical joints are plumb and true. Wedge panel evenly from each end all the way up.

After last horizontal strip is in place, wedge panel at top, just tight enough for a rigid wall.

Last, nail on trim as shown on details. Lap trim over half the end joints. Strips and trim may be finished as desired.

REQUIRED FRAME OPENING DIMENSIONS

12″ Block	W	H	8″ Block	W	H
1	1′–1¾″	1′–1 3/16″	1	9¾″	9 3/16″
2	2′–1¾″	2′–1 3/16″	2	1′–5¾″	1′–5 3/16″
3	3′–1 13/16″	3′–1¼″	3	2′–1¾″	2′–1 3/16″
4	4′–1 13/16″	4′–1¼″	4	2′–9¾″	2′–9 3/16″
5	5′–1 13/16″	5′–1¼″	5	3′–5¾″	3′–5 3/16″
6	6′–1⅞″	6′–1 5/16″	6	4′–1¾″	4′–1 3/16″
7	7′–1⅞″	7′–1 5/16″	7	4′–9¾″	4′–9 3/16″
8	8′–1⅞″	8′–1 5/16″	8	5′–5¾″	5′–5 3/16″
9	9′–1 15/16″	9′–1⅜″	9	6′–1¾″	6′–1 3/16″
10	10′–2″	10′–1⅜″	10	6′–9¾″	6′–9 3/16″
			11	7′–5¾″	7′–5 3/16″
Maximum Panel			12	8′–1¾″	8′–1 3/16″
Area 75 Sq. Ft.			13	8′–9¾″	8′–9 3/16″
Max. Width, 10′			14	9′–5¾″	9′–5 3/16″
			15	10′–1¾″	10′–1 3/16″

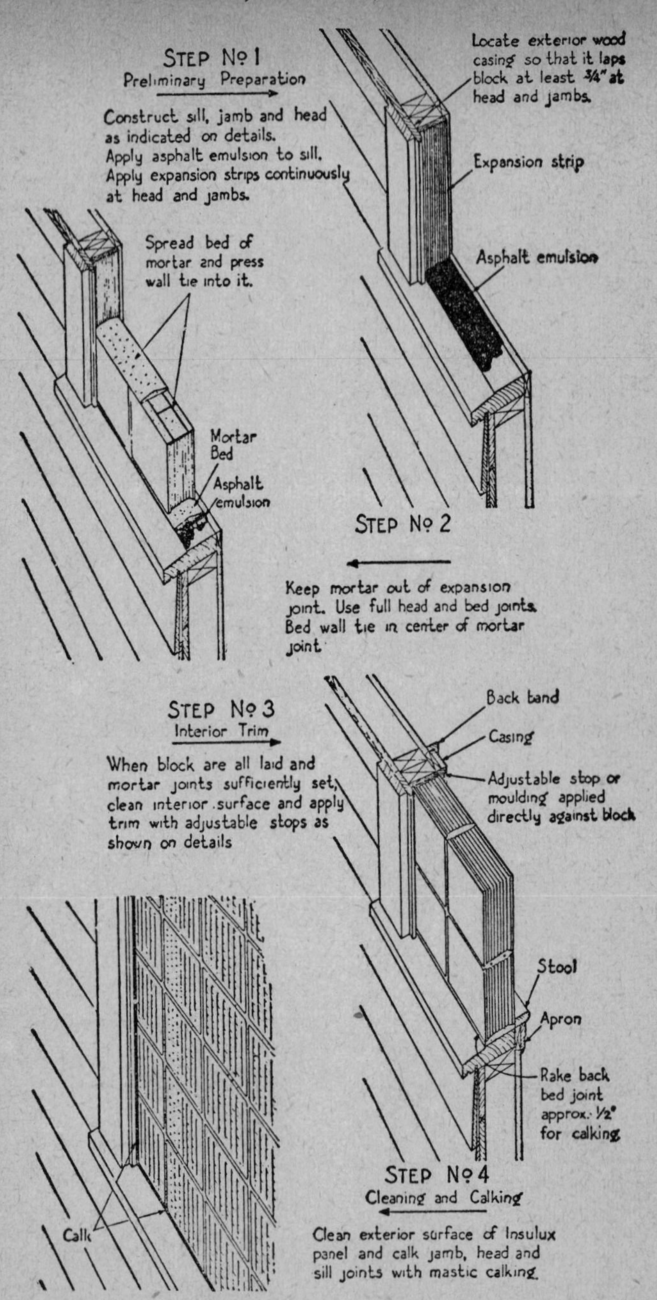

STEP No 1
Preliminary Preparation
Construct sill, jamb and head as indicated on details. Apply asphalt emulsion to sill. Apply expansion strips continuously at head and jambs.
Spread bed of mortar and press wall tie into it.
Mortar Bed
Asphalt emulsion
Locate exterior wood casing so that it laps block at least 3/4" at head and jambs.
Expansion strip
Asphalt emulsion
STEP No 2
Keep mortar out of expansion joint. Use full head and bed joints. Bed wall tie in center of mortar joint.
STEP No 3
Interior Trim
When block are all laid and mortar joints sufficiently set, clean interior surface and apply trim with adjustable stops as shown on details
Back band
Casing
Adjustable stop or moulding applied directly against block
Stool
Apron
Rake back bed joint approx. 1/2" for calking
Calk
STEP No 4
Cleaning and Calking
Clean exterior surface of Insulux panel and calk jamb, head and sill joints with mastic calking.

Fig. 71. Typical steps for laying glass blocks.

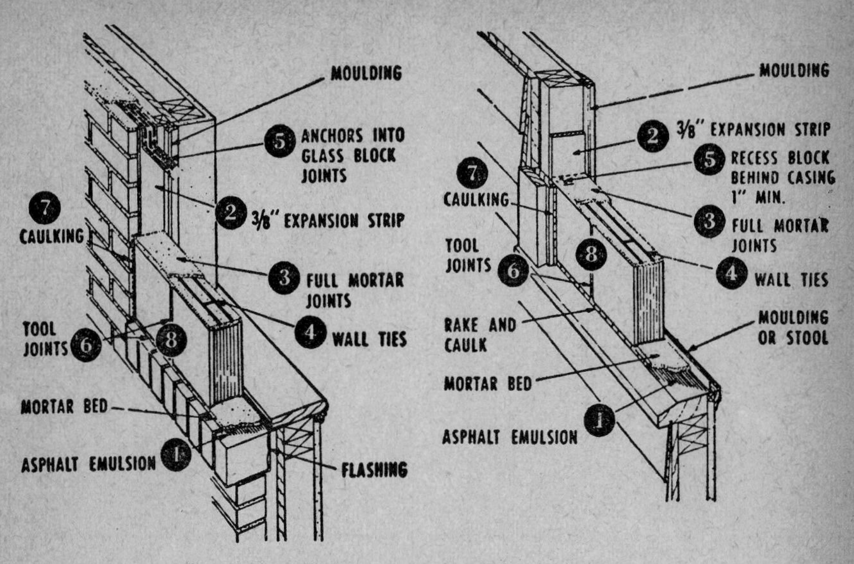

Fig. 72. Installing mortar set panels of glass blocks.

USING FLEXIBLE GLASS IN YOUR HOME

One of the newest structural materials to hit the market looks like colored corrugated glass, and yet it is light, flexible, and transmits light and air but blocks vision. It has dozens of uses around the house. With it you can build partitions, design radiator covers or light fixtures, or face old desks or cabinets to give them a bright, new look.

The porous, translucent material is formed into 8′ sheets that weigh about 7 lb. per 1/16″ panel. It is available in more than a dozen colors and three corrugations: 5/16″, ⅝″, and 1½″. The smallest is recommended for lampshades, wastebaskets, screens, door panels, and radiator enclosures. Depending on the depth of the corrugation, the panels come in three widths: 24″, 30″, and 32″.

Because of its lightness and tensile strength (23,000 lb. per sq. in.) this material needs no heavy supporting framework, and construction is consequently fast. It can be nailed, drilled, punched, and cemented. Sheets can be cut to size with ordinary tin snips. Although it is rigid in

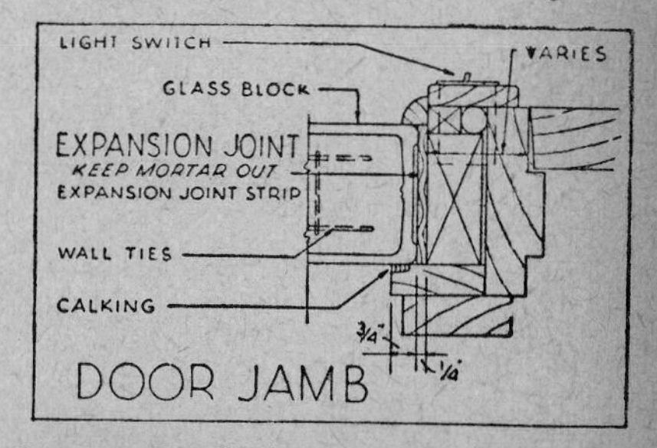

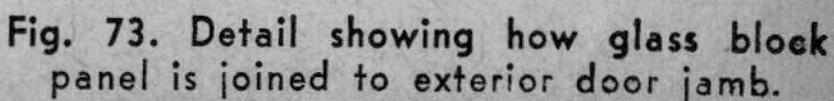
Fig. 73. Detail showing how glass block panel is joined to exterior door jamb.

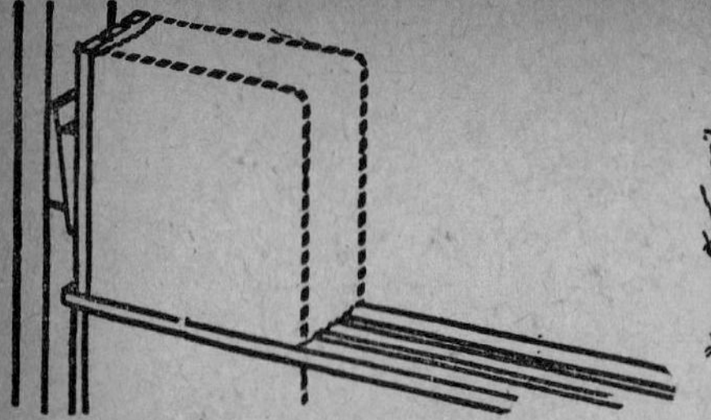

Fig. 74. Vertical and horizontal strips and wedges make a simple prefabricated system for erecting glass block interior partitions. Ordinary trimming can be used. Doors, windows and other standard openings can be set into these panels of glass block.

the direction of the corrugations, it is flexible across the panels. It can readily be formed into columns or shaped to fit curved surfaces. Released from a curve, it springs back to its original shape.

Colors do not change or lose brilliance even after prolonged exposure to sunlight, salt water, or high temperatures. It will not soften or change up to 350 deg. F. and is rated in fire tests as a self-extinguishing material. The glass has a high resistance to moisture and will not shrink or warp.

A few suggested uses are sketched in figure 78. An obvious one, of course, is using it to panel the walls and ceiling of a room, or using it as a wall of an outdoor dining room. Since it is weather resistant, it may be used either indoors or out.

LIGHTING STAIRWAYS

There are many ways that glass blocks can be used to make stairways lighter, more comfortable and

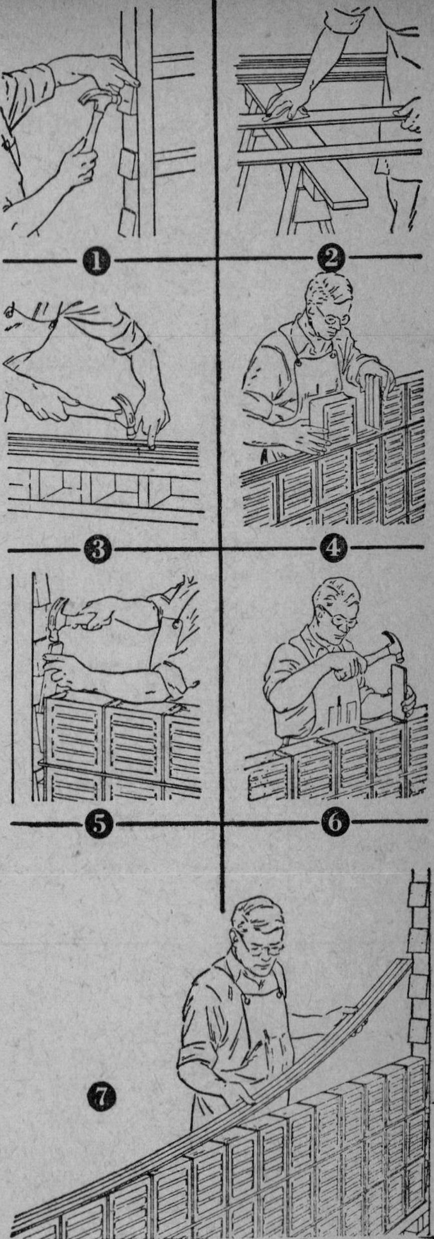

Fig. 75.

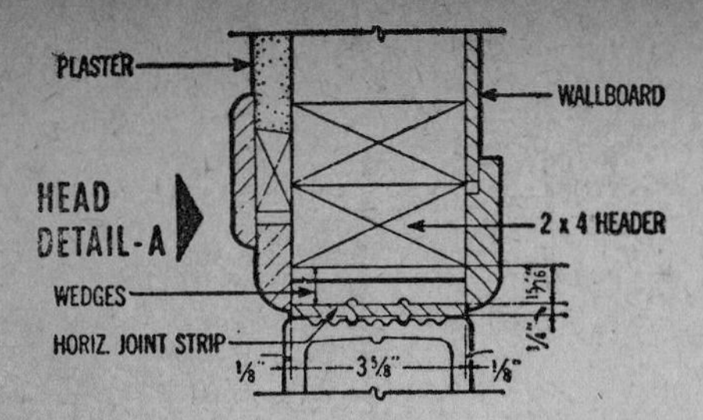

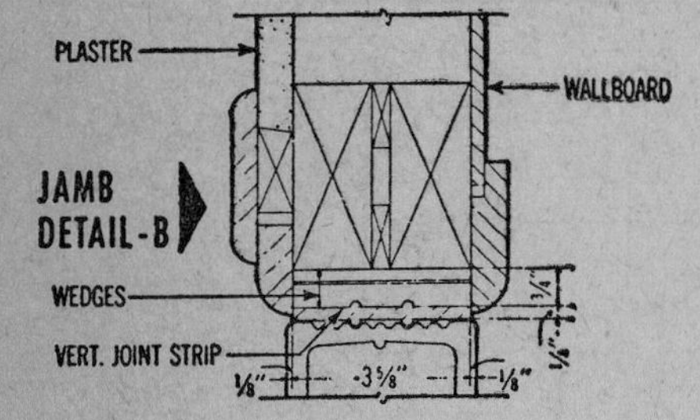

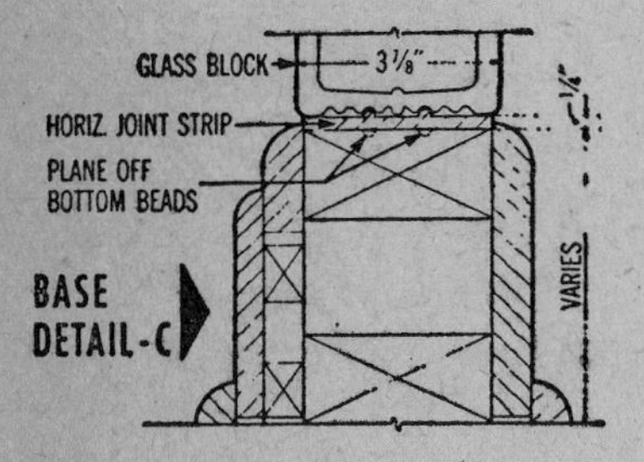

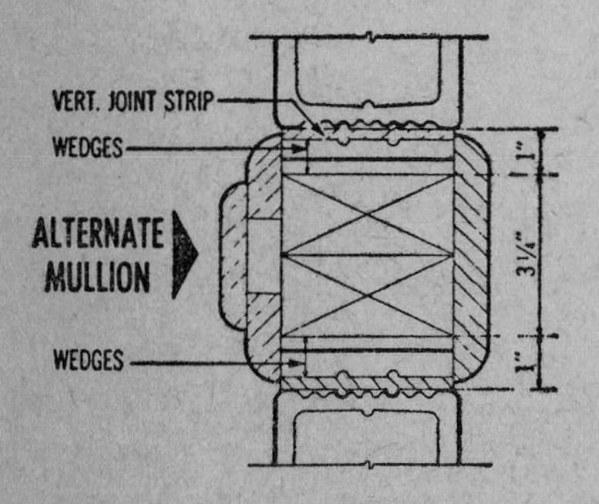

Fig. 76. Details of installing glass block panels. Wedges and joint strips are same width as 2 x 4 framing and line up with it.

more attractive. A few suggestions are shown in figure 79. In the bottom sketch, light is "borrowed" from an adjoining room, yet because the blocks are not transparent, stairs remain hidden.

DAMP BASEMENTS

The first floor of homes without basements often tends to be damp. One solution is shown in figure 82. The ground under the first floor is covered with strips of roll roofing. Each seam is lapped 4 inches and the joints between foundation wall and roofing are sealed with hot tar. Another method of damp-proofing is to cover the earth under the house with ½ inch of dry Portland cement.

MEMBRANE WATERPROOFING

The membrane method of waterproofing and damp-proofing concrete, brick, tile, or stone work consists of laying overlapping layers of a prepared waterproofing fabric and thoroughly coating and bonding every lap with hot asphalt or hot coal-tar pitch. The masonry itself may be leaky, but water-tightness is obtained by the coated fabric or membrane; which is laid through and around the masonry and virtually constitutes a turned-up mat or box outside of the main walls and floor. The method is reliable when the work is done by experienced men, and the ordinary individual by closely following instructions can do a reasonably good job. Sketches, specifications, and explicit directions

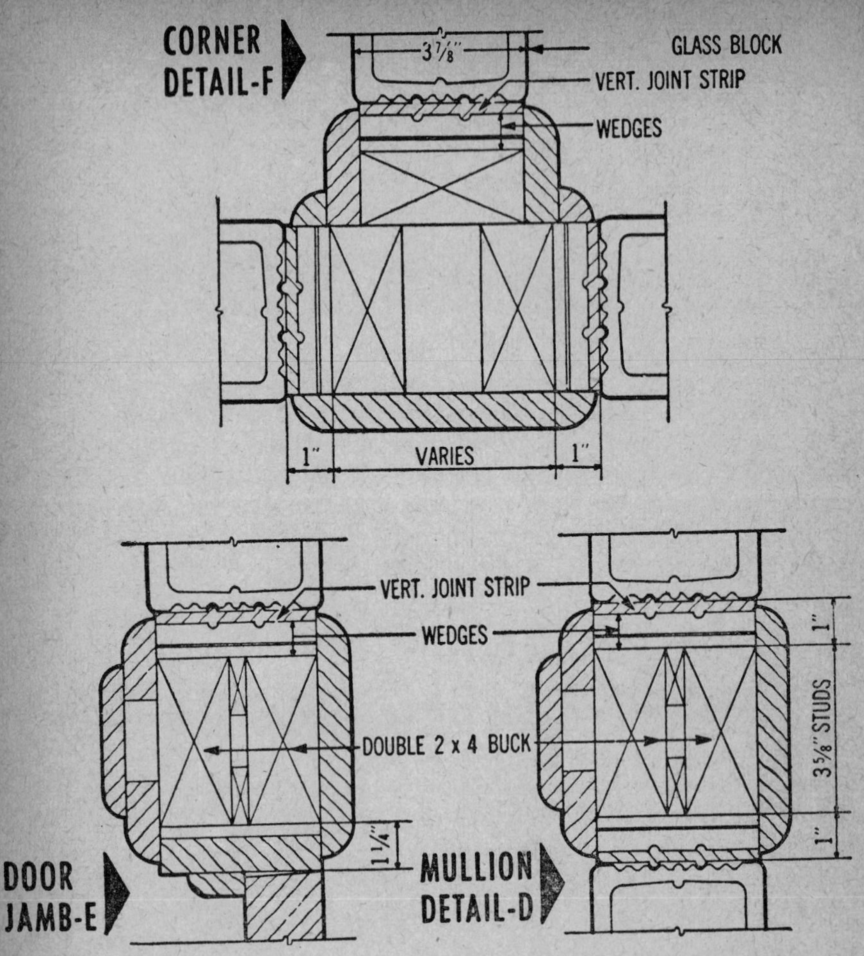

Fig. 77. Further details of glass block installation. Door jamb is 1 ¼" from rough buck, giving same trim-lap over door-jamb as over head of door.

should be obtained from a reliable manufacturer whose materials are to be used. It is advisable to experiment with the materials on a small upright surface before attempting the actual work. The method is not cheap, and if leaks do develop they may be difficult to locate and costly to repair.

The fabric generally used is a wool-and-cotton rag felt impregnated with asphaltic or coal-tar pitch saturating ingredients. The felt should be free of holes, rents, cracks, indentations, or ragged edges. Asphalt and coal-tar pitch in solid form are shipped in wooden barrels or steel drums. The compound as received from the manufacturer should be cut into small lumps with an ax and heated to about 300° F. in a kettle out of doors. Care should be

Three hinged pieces will stand alone as a screen.

Old furniture is refaced with sections of a panel.

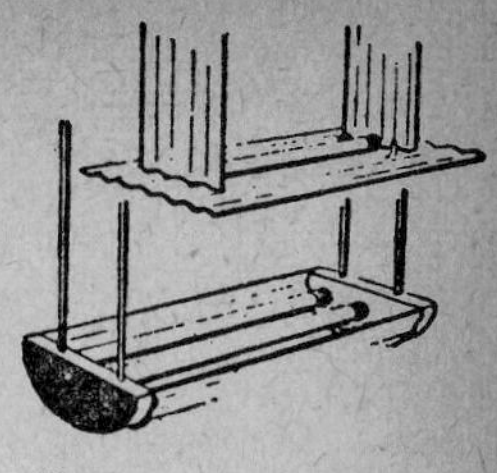

One panel is enough for several big light fixtures.

Fluorescent tubes behind panel light counter.

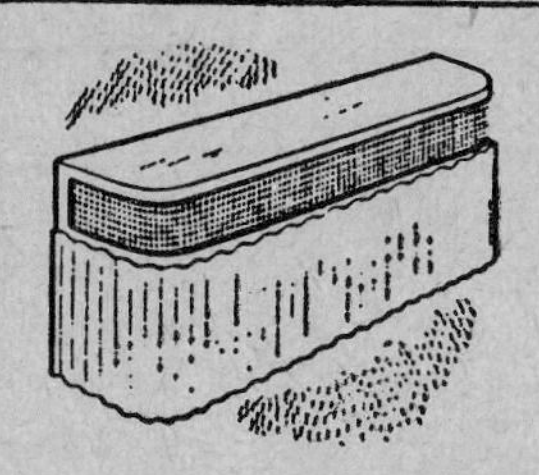

Prest-Glass forms handsome radiator enclosures.

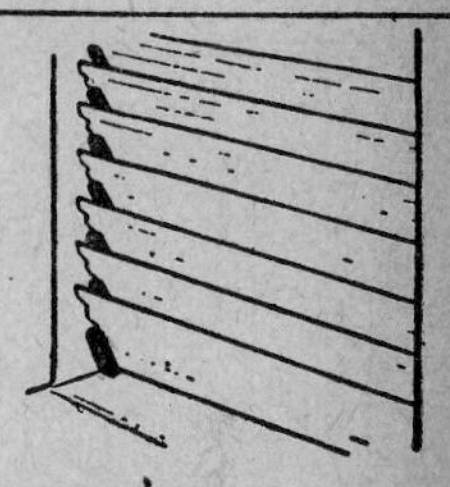

Narrow strips make airy, bright louvered windows.

Fig. 78.

used to avoid overheating which may make it brittle when cold and destroy its cementing properties. When the compound is fully melted and of uniform consistency it is an even glossy black. It should always be used when in this hot liquid condition and the mopping should be done rapidly.

The surface to which the felt is to be applied should be smooth, dry, and clean. Warm weather greatly favors the work. Brickwork should have struck joints, and holes and depressions in concrete or other masonry should be filled with portland-cement mortar. Projecting stones or bits of mortar that might punctuate the felt should be knocked off, and very sharp edges slightly rounded.

After the footing course is placed and the bottom of the excavation is compacted and smoothed a 1-inch underbed of cement mortar or, if the conditions are severe, a thin underbed of concrete should be evenly spread over the whole area to form a base upon which to lay the floor membrane. A 4-inch brick or concrete wall should then be built to such height as the conditions require to form a backing for the wall membrane. The floor and wall membrane should be laid as a unit. Each strip of felt, lapped and coated with the hot compound, should be laid across the floor and be continued without break at the wall angle up the inner face of the 4-inch veneer wall. After completion of the membrane a ¾-inch protecting layer of cement mortar should be spread over the whole floor area, and this should be covered with a 4 or 5 inch concrete floor recessed

Fig. 79.

along the edge to lap and bond with the side wall, as shown. The main wall should be built close to or against the membrane, and all space between the wall and the membrane should be solidly filled, by pouring, with the hot compound or with portland-cement grout.

Where it is not possible to waterproof the floor and wall in one operation special care is necessary so that later the strips of felt may be properly interlapped and interlocked. Usually, if the walls are constructed first, a 12-inch strip of the cement underbed is laid along the footing course, and the wall membrane is brought down and over the footing course and underbed leaving a 6 to 12 inch length of each strip of felt lying flat, and uncoated with compound, on the underbed. When the floor membrane is laid the uncoated laps are turned up, coated with hot compound, and interlocked with the floor sheets. Pending the main floor work, the membrane already placed, including the dry laps, should be covered with a waster sheet of dry felt and a thin protective coat of lean cement mortar. This covering is temporary and is removed when the floor membrane is laid, its purpose being to prevent injury to the felt by wheelbarrows, tools, or because of careless workmen.

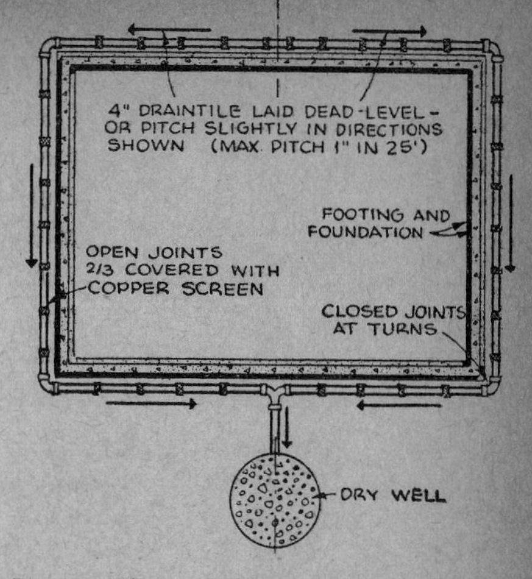

Fig. 80. Shows the layout for 4" agricultural drain tile around house footing to prevent water from entering the basement. Maximum pitch to the drain tile is 1" to 25'. Drain tile should be carried to dry well sufficiently far from the house to prevent seepage of water into basement. Best position for dry well is on ground sloping away from house and in soil containing sand or gravel.

LAYERS OF FELT

The number of layers of felt which may be needed varies with the drainage conditions and the ends to be attained. Two layers of felt are generally sufficient where there is little or no head and the main purpose is to damp-proof. From three to five layers, depending on the

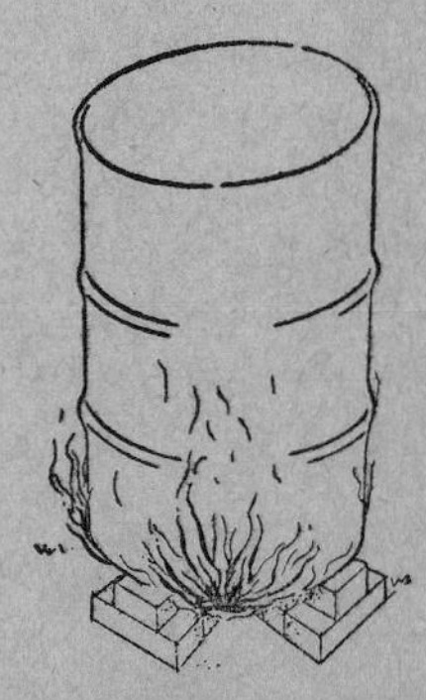

Fig. 81. A simple furnace for melting asphalt can be constructed out of a 55 gallon drum and a few bricks, concrete blocks or stones. The blocks or stones are used for the base and should be about 5 inches high.

height of the ground water are advisable for real waterproofing jobs.

Figure 83 shows how the felt may be run and lapped in two-layer and three-layer work. End laps should overlaps at least 6 inches. Each and every lap should be fully and evenly mopped with the hot compound, and the felt, closely following the mop, should be unrolled into the hot coating. This process, a strip at a time, is continued until every part of the surface to be treated has the required number of layers thoroughly cemented together.

With the intention of avoiding any seepage seam between the felt and the masonry, the two are sometimes united and bonded as effectively as possible, and in ordinary cellar work this is probably the better practice. For this purpose the masonry should first be given a suitable penetrating priming or bonding brush coat, applied cold, of about 1 gallon per 100 square feet. The use of a large, flat-bristle brush or a three-knot roof brush with long handle expedites the work. Without the priming coat the hot compound is unlikely to stick strongly to the masonry because of quick chilling and slight penetration, and the bond will be especially poor if the masonry is damp or cold. As soon as the priming coat sets, the surface should be mopped with hot compound, the felt being rolled into it as previously described.

The felt should lie perfectly smooth. Wrinkles and buckles should be smoothed out, and the sheets should be carefully pressed down and rubbed with the hand to remove air bubbles and to insure perfect bond between felt and felt. Special care is required to make the felt fit corners and angles neatly and snugly. To reinforce such places two strips of felt, cut to extend at least 6 inches each way from the angle, may be applied one strip before and one strip after placing the main waterproofing. After the several layers of felt have been cemented together the entire surface should be given a heavy mop coat of the hot compound. Five gallons per 100 square feet gives a top coating approximately five sixty-fourths inch thick. Each coat between layers of felt takes about 3 gallons per 100 square feet, and the mop coat over the primer on the masonry takes about 6 gallons per 100 square feet, making a total of 17 gallons of compound per 100 square feet for three-layer work and 14 gallons for two-layer work.

Thus there is built up a watertight, more or less pliable, yielding blanket or membrane approximately one-third inch thick in three-layer work and one-fourth inch thick in two-layer work.

PLASTER COATS

Plaster coats of portland-cement mortar have been much used to waterproof and damp-proof cellars. Sometimes the results have been successful and sometimes disappointing. Many failures with cement plaster are due to the sand being too fine or too coarse, too much water in the mix, plastering against seepage, poor preparation of the old surface, or poor bond between successive coats. Patches sag or slough off while the mortar is soft or scale off when it is hard. In other instances contraction cracks form, but this tendency may be partially offset by long wet curing of the plaster.

The surface to be plastered should be rough, thoroughly clean, and moist but not dripping. It should be kept wet by drenching with clean water for several hours prior to the application of the plaster. A dry surface will absorb moisture from the plaster and so prevent its proper setting and bonding. Just before the plaster is applied the moist surface should be given a brush coat of neat portland-cement grout. Each plaster coat should be applied before the coat beneath sets hard so that all will knit or bond together. Each of the undercoats should be lightly scratched or scored with a sawtooth paddle, piece of metal lath, or sharp stick, checkerboardlike, thus improving the mechanical bond with the next coat. All coats except the last on the outside of walls should be well worked with a wooden float to make the surface slightly granular. A steel trowel should be used on an outside finish coat because it produces a smooth impervious surface, but overworking should be avoided as it creates a rich surface skin liable to crack badly and scale off.

Floor plaster is usually applied in one coat about three-fourths inch thick. Wall plaster is applied in two or more coats each about three-eighths inch thick. A slight saving can generally be effected by making

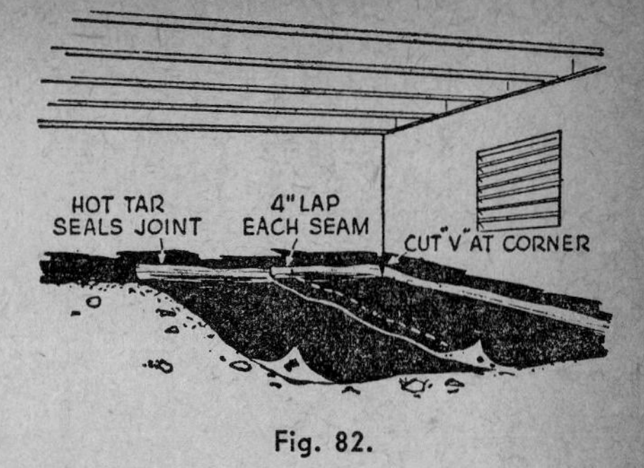

Fig. 82.

wall plaster a little thinner at the top than at the bottom. Damp-proofing plasterwork generally approximates three-fourths inch in thickness. Waterproofing plasterwork on the inside of walls generally tapers from 1½ to 2 inches in thickness at the bottom to three-fourths inch at the top. Waterproofing plasterwork on a floor liable to pressure from beneath should be underlaid with a properly reinforced layer of concrete from 2 to 4 inches thick.

Joints, angles, and corners are the weak places. There should be as few joints as possible, and they should be made on the wall or on the floor a foot or more from angle or corner. All angles and corners should be covered or rounded as a continuous part of the plastering. If the floor is to be plastered first and the walls must wait, the plastering should be carried up the walls about a foot, leaving a rough beveled edge which is later wet, brush coated with grout, and bonded with the wall plaster. Wall plastering should be started by making a rough vertical beveled edge on the flat surface, as it is difficult to make a tight closure at a corner. The plastering should be completed with

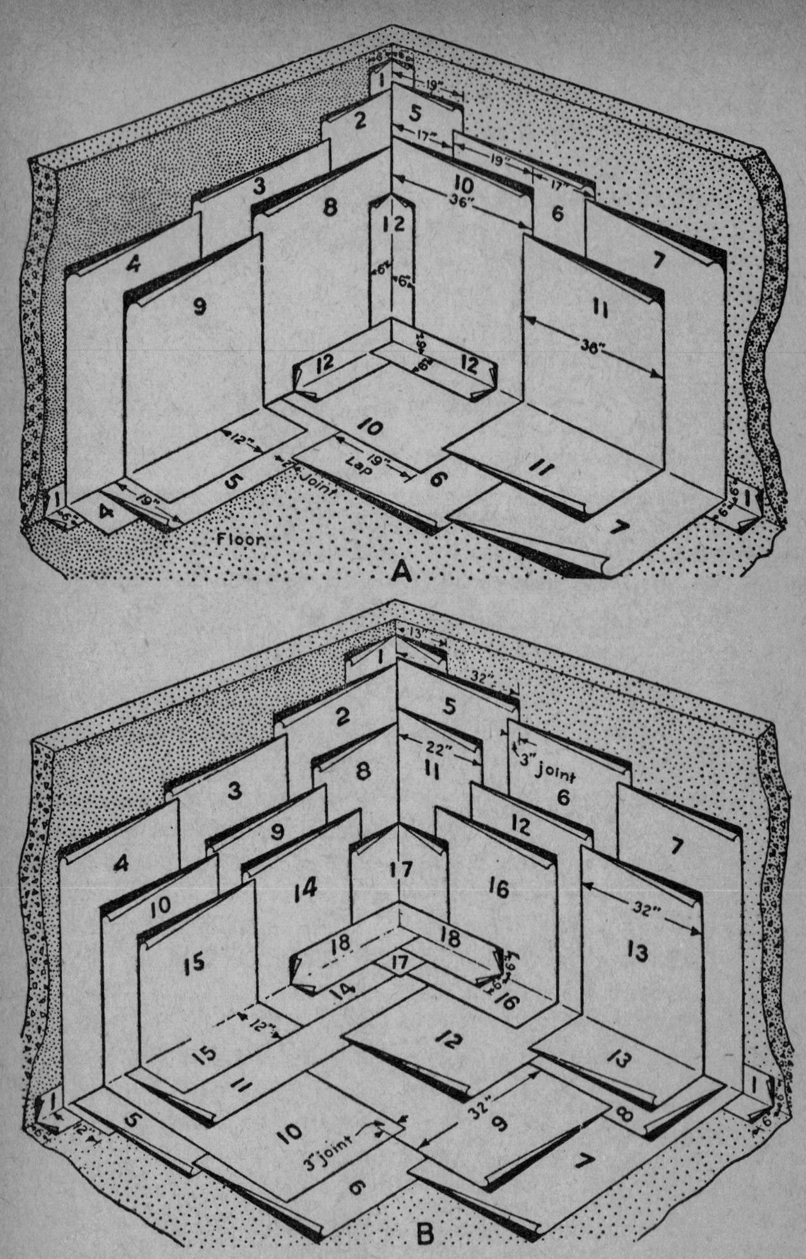

Fig. 83. Membrane waterproofing: **A,** Two layers of 3-inch felt, spaced 17 inches, overlapped 19 inches, jointed 2 inches; numbers show order if applying sheets. **B,** three layers of 32-inch felt, jointed 3 inches; intermediate floor layer crosswise of bottom and upper layers; wall sheets overlapped 22 inches, spaced 10 inches.

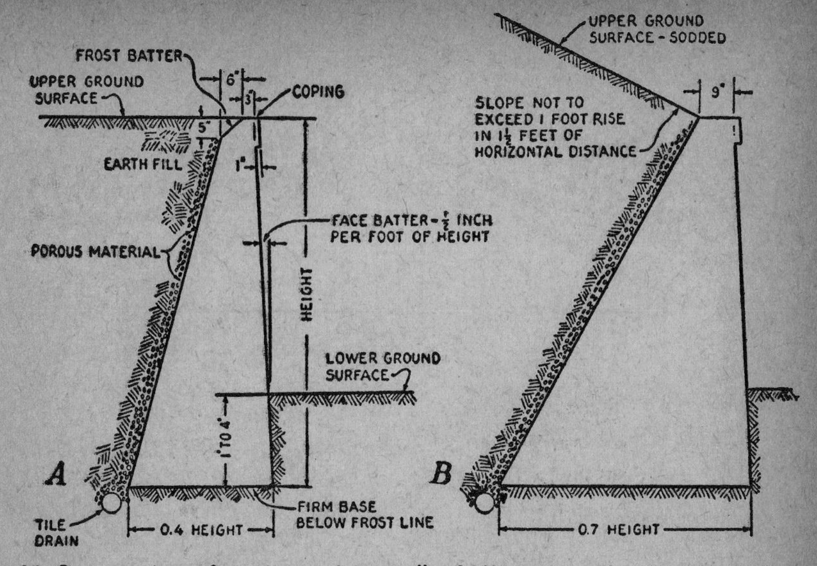

Fig. 84. Cross sections of gravity retaining walls: A, Upper ground surface level, showing frost batter and coping at the top of the wall; B, upper ground surface sloping, showing added thickness of base needed for the slope shown.

as few vertical joints as possible. If the walls are done first, the plastering should be carried out on the floor about a foot, leaving a rough beveled edge to be grouted and bonded with the floor plaster. The latter method (walls first) is usually more convenient, but the first method (floor first) is more likely to give a water-tight job because the joint work is at a higher level. Plastering dries quickly and may crack. Just as soon as it is sufficiently hard, so that the cement will not be washed away, it should be drenched and kept continuously wet or flooded for a period of at least a week.

Commercial bituminous mortars applied cold with a plasterer's trowel are used to damp-proof and to intercept shallow seepage. These plastic cements are usually asphalt or other bituminous material combined with asbestos fiber, mineral filler, and suitable volatile solvents. It is advisable before using such products to obtain explicit directions and specifications from the dealer or manufacturer.

The cement, ready for use, comes in containers holding from 30 to 500 or more pounds. It should spread smoothly and evenly, without drawing or pulling. A ⅛-inch coat requiring approximately 80 pounds for 100 square feet is usually applied to the outside of cellar walls and a ¼-inch coat to cellar floors. The wall excavation may be refilled after the plaster has dried 24 to 48 hours, care being taken not to injure it. Floor plaster should be given a heavy protective covering of portland-cement mortar or concrete.

Fig. 85.

RETAINING WALLS FOR STEEP DRIVEWAYS

Steep grades frequently cannot be avoided, as many homes have built-in garages that are several feet higher or lower than the street or alley. Drives that slope downward from the street or alley may have the following disadvantages:

1. In the winter the drive's surface may become coated with ice or snow, rendering the drive so slippery as to require removal of ice or snow, use of chains, or scattering sand or ashes over the surface.

2. There is some danger in backing out of the drive where the driver's view of the sidewalk and the street is blocked by retaining walls, shrubs, or trees, and on very steep grades by the back of the car itself.

3. Special drainage must be provided for the drive.

Drives that slope upward from the street also have the disadvantage that they may become slippery, but generally the driver's view is not obstructed in backing down them, and they drain to the street or alley.

Drives with grades as steep as 30 percent (the equivalent of a vertical drop of 30 feet in a horizontal distance of 100 feet) have been observed, and their owners considered them satisfactory. However, they were short (less than 25 feet long). Such steep grades are not recommended.

Drives that pitch downward on a grade of more than 25 percent have additional disadvantages. Low-hanging parts of the car may scrape on the surface of the drive where the grade begins. This can be prevented by dishing the center of the drive at the high point, or by rounding off the high point. Also, the front or rear fenders and bumpers may overhang enough to scrape on the surface of the drive at the bottom of a steep grade. This can be remedied either by making the entire slope flatter or by flattening the slope for a short distance at the bottom of the grade.

Wherever it is possible, sloping drives should be built straight. It is not easy to handle a car on a curved, sloping drive, especially when backing.

Most lawns are level or nearly so, and a downward-sloping drive will require a trough through the lawn. Vertical retaining walls are frequently built along the sides of the drive, with their tops flush with the lawn. An alternative method of construction is to slope the earth upward from the top of the wall. Slopes of 1 foot of rise to 1½ feet of horizontal distance may be used where a more gentle slope is not possible. In either case the slope must be sodded.

Retaining walls are constructed of concrete, brick, or stone. Concrete

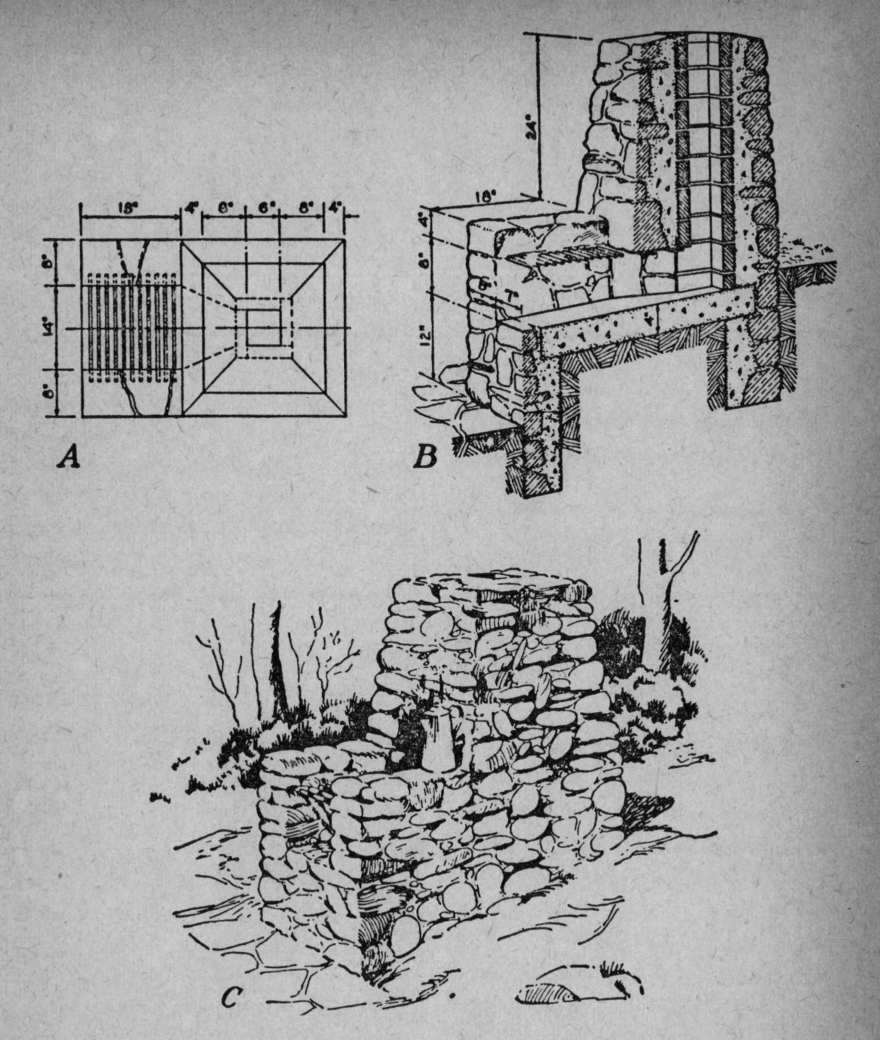

Fig. 86. **A**, Ground plan of a stone fireplace that can be built in different sizes to suit the landscape; **B**, vertical-section sketch; **C**, the completed fireplace. About 8 bushels of stones are used over a backing of concrete; 16 bushels are needed if the concrete is not used. The chimney is battered 4 inches in the 24-inch height.

is recommended for walls over 2 or 3 feet high. The thickness of a retaining wall at any point should be not less than 0.4 times the depth of the point below the top of the wall. In case the ground slopes up from the top of the wall, this factor should be increased. In no event should the ground above the wall have a steeper slope than 1 foot of vertical rise in 1½ feet of horizontal distance, and for a slope this steep the base thickness should be 0.7 times the height of the wall. The slope should be sodded to prevent erosion. A minimum top thickness of 6 inches is suggested for walls less than 5 feet high; for walls higher than 5 feet a minimum top thickness of 9 inches would be preferable.

Retaining walls should extend from 1 to 4 feet below the ground level at the base, as shown in figure 84, depending on the depth of the frost line in the particular locality or the depth to a firm base. The bottom of a retaining wall should be placed on firm, unyielding material, and should be slightly below the normal frost line.

The designs shown in figure 84 are merely suggested as a general guide. It would be preferable to build the wall upon a rectangular footing of concrete or masonry having a depth of approximately 8 inches and extending 6 inches beyond the face of the wall on each side.

Avoid high retaining walls in combination with poor drainage as the wall, no matter how well built, will be pushed out at the top by the freezing of saturated soil.

The appearance of a retaining wall can be improved by providing face batter of not less than one-half inch per foot of height. An absolutely vertical wall has the appearance of toppling, and this amount of face batter will make the wall appear to be vertical. A coping along the top of the wall will also improve its appearance.

When retaining walls are used, the slab type of drive is recommended, and the width should be at least 8½ feet between the walls for straight drives. This width is needed because, although the two front or rear wheels are only about 4.8 feet apart, the car's fenders and running board overhang about 8 inches on each side and there should be some additional width to permit easy handling of the car.

GRADING

The chance of moisture reaching the basement can be reduced by grading the soil around the foundation wall so that it slopes down and away from the foundation as illustrated in figure 85.

A good covering of sod over this fill should be installed immediately.

SECTION II

ROUGH CARPENTRY

Suitability of Woods for Various Uses—Standard Widths and Thicknesses of Rough and Surfaced Yard Lumber—Standard Thicknesses and Widths for Softwood Yard Lumber—Standard Hardwood Grades of Lumber—Standard Widths and Thicknesses of Lumber—Contents of Lumber—Cutting Down Waste—Methods of Seasoning Wood Posts—Inexpensive Incinerator—Fire Stopping—Installing an Extra Post—Plumbing Corner Posts —Method of Plumbing and Straightening Wall—Nailing Studding—Siding Sizes and Estimating Quantities—Figure in Wood —Bridging of Walls—Roof Trusses—Advantages of Roof Trusses Joining Roofs to Walls—Methods of Laying Out Rafters—Estimating Shingle Requirements—Application of Red Cedar Shingles —Mark Location of Studding—Spaces Let Sub-flooring Expand —Fitting Warped Boards.

SECTION II

ROUGH CARPENTRY

SUITABILITY OF WOODS FOR VARIOUS USES

Exterior trim

Usual requirements:

Medium decay resistance, good painting and weathering characteristics, easy-working qualities, and maximum freedom from warp.

Woods combining usual requirements in a high degree:

Cedars, cypress, redwood. (Heartwood only. Adapted to blinds, rails, and balcony and porch trim, where decay hazard is high.)

Northern white pine, sugar pine, western white pine, yellow poplar. (Heartwood only. Adapted to ordinary trim where decay hazard is moderate or low.)

Woods for special architectural treatments:

Chestnut, white oak. (Heartwood only. Used with natural finish.)

Woods combining usual requirements in a good degree:

Hemlocks, ponderosa pine, spruces, white fir. (When drainage is good.)

Douglas fir, western larch, southern yellow pine. (Special priming treatment advisable to improve paint-holding qualities.)

Grades used:

A, B, or B and Better finish is used in the best construction, C and D finish in more economical construction, and No. 1 or No. 2 boards where appearance is not important.

Living room and bedroom flooring

Usual requirements:

High resistance to wear, attractive figure or color, minimum warp and shrinkage.

Woods combining usual requirements in a high degree:

Hard maple, red and white oak. (Most commonly used hardwoods.)

Ash (white), beech, birch, walnut. (Not commonly used.)

Hickory, black locust, pecan. (Not commonly available. Hard to work and nail.)

Woods combining usual requirements in a good degree:

Cypress, Douglas fir, western hemlock, western larch, redwood, southern yellow pine. (Vertical grain.)

Cherry, red gum, sycamore (quartered). (Not commonly available. Highly decorative and suitable where wear is light and maintenance good.)

Grades used:

In beech, birch, and maple flooring the grade of Firsts is ordinarily used for the better class of homes and Seconds and sometimes Thirds in low-cost jobs. In oak the grade of Clear (either plain or quartered) is used in better class work and Selects and sometimes No. 1 Common in low-cost work. Other hardwoods are ordinarily used in the same grades as oak. When softwood flooring is used (without covering) in better class homes grade A or B and Better vertical grain is used. Grade D or C (vertical grain) is used in more economical and low-cost homes.

Kitchen flooring (uncovered)

Usual requirements:

Resistance to wear, fine texture, ability to withstand washing and wear without discoloring and slivering, minimum warp and shrinkage.

Woods combining usual requirements in a high degree:

Beech, birch, hard maple. (Fine textured.)

Woods combining usual requirements in a good degree:

Ash, red and white oak. (Open textured.)

Soft maple.

Woods combining usual requirements in a fair degree:

Cypress, Douglas fir, western hemlock, western larch, redwood, southern yellow pine. (Vertical grain preferred.)

Elm, hackberry, sycamore.

Grades used:

The flooring grades, Seconds in beech, birch, and hard maple, and Selects in the oaks are used in high-priced houses. In more economical construction Thirds in beech, birch, and hard maple, and No. 1 Common or No. 2 Common in the oaks are used. D (vertical grain) is the lowest grade of softwood that proves thoroughly satisfactory in high-class construction. A grade and B and Better grade (vertical grain) are used most extensively. No. 1 and 2 are serviceable in low-cost construction but wear unevenly around knots.

Porch flooring

Usual requirements:

Medium to good decay resistance, medium wear resistance, nonsplintering, freedom from warping.

Woods combining usual requirements in a high degree:

Cypress, Douglas fir (vertical grain), western larch (vertical grain), southern yellow pine (vertical grain), redwood, white oak. (If full drainage is not obtainable only the heartwood of cypress, redwood, and white oak can be given a high rating.)

Black locust, walnut. (Usually impractical except when cut from home-grown timber.)

Grades used:

Grades C to A are used in the better types of homes. No. 1 and No. 2 are used in lower cost homes and are serviceable, but wear unevenly around knots, and the maintenance of paint on the knots is difficult. The superior paint-holding qualities and uniform wearing surface of vertical grain makes it preferred in all grades. Hardwoods, if used at all, should be of Select or No. 1 Common quality.

Framing

Usual requirements:

High stiffness, good bending strength, good nail-holding power, hardness, freedom from pronounced warp. For this use dryness and size are more important factors than inherent properties of the different woods.

Woods combining usual requirements in a high degree:

Douglas fir, western larch, southern yellow pine. (Extensively used.)

Ash, beech, birch, maple, oak. (Sometimes used but more difficult to obtain in straight pieces and harder to nail and saw than preceding group.)

Cypress, redwood. (Seldom used.)

Woods combining usual requirements in a good degree:

Eastern hemlock, western hemlock, eastern spruce, Sitka spruce, white fir. (Extensively used.)

Northern white pine, ponderosa pine, sugar pine, western white pine. (Seldom used because of adaptability to more exacting uses. Low strength compensated for by use of larger members.)

Chestnut, yellow poplar. (Seldom used.)

Woods combining usual requirements in a fair degree:

Elm, red gum, sycamore, tupelo. (Seldom used.)

Grades used:

No. 1 Dimension is the usual softwood grade for all framing items in both high- and medium-class construction. No. 2 Dimension renders satisfactory service once it is in place, but is not so straight or easily fabricated as No. 1. No. 3 Dimension is serviceable for studs and joists in the more economical and low-cost homes, especially when warped pieces and short lengths resulting from cutting out defects can be used to advantage. When hardwoods are used for framing, sound square edge is used in the better types of construction and for such items as joists, rafters, and sills. Hardwood Common Dimension is used in the more economical type of buildings and for studding in all types of buildings.

Interior trim with natural finish

Usual requirements:

Pleasing figure, hardness, freedom from warp.

Woods combining usual requirements in a high degree:

Ash, birch, cherry, chestnut, oak, sycamore (quartered), walnut.

Woods adaptable to special selection and architectural treatment:

Pecky cypress; etched or special-grain cypress, Douglas fir, western larch, southern yellow pine, curly or bird's-eye maple.

Knotty cedars, ponderosa pine, spruces, sugar pine, white pine. (Lack hardness of the preceding group.)

Woods combining usual requirements in a good degree:

Cypress, Douglas fir, western hemlock, western larch, southern yellow pine, redwood, beech, maple, red gum. (With conventional treatment.)

Grades used:

High-class hardwood interior trim is usually of A grade. The softwood grade A or B and Better is commonly used in high-class construction. In the more economical types of construction C grade is serviceable. D grade requires special selection or some cutting to obtain clear material. Special grades of knotty pine, pecky cypress, and sound wormy oak and chestnut are available to meet special architectural requirements in some types of high-class construction.

Interior trim with paint finish

Usual requirements:

Fine and uniform texture, hardness, absence of discoloring pitch, freedom from warp and shrinkage.

Woods combining usual requirements in a good degree:

Birch, cherry, walnut, yellow poplar.

Northern white pine, ponderosa pine, sugar pine, western white pine. (Where liability to marring is negligible and special priming is used.)

Woods combining usual requirements in a good degree:

Hemlocks, redwood, spruce, white fir.

Basswood, beech, red gum, maple, tupelo.

Cypress, Douglas fir, western larch, southern yellow pine, ash, chestnut, oak. (Used satisfactorily where requirements for smoothness of finish are not exacting.)

Grades used:

C is the lowest softwood grade commonly used for high-class paint and enamel finish. D can be used but requires some selection or cutting. No. 1 is used for ordinary or rough-paint finishes. In cheaper and more economical homes No. 2 may be used for ordinary or rough-paint finishes. Smooth-paint finishes are difficult to obtain and maintain over knots in No. 1, No. 2, and No. 3 grades. The A trim grade in the hardwoods is used for exacting requirements of high-class paint and enamel finish in high-cost homes. The standard grade of Firsts and Seconds is also used but requires some selection or cutting. No. 2 Common hardwoods are used for interior trim in the low-cost home, but in this class of home softwoods are generally used for the interior trim that is to be painted.

Lath

Usual requirements:

Low shrinkage, easy nailing, nondiscoloration of plaster.

Woods combining usual requirements in a high degree:

Jack pine, lodgepole pine, northern white pine, sugar pine, ponderosa pine, western white pine, spruce, white fir, yellow poplar.

Woods combining usual requirements in a fair degree:

Cypress, Douglas fir, hemlocks, western larch, southern yellow pine, basswood.

Grades used:

Two grades of lath, No. 1 and No. 2, are available in practically all softwoods and in a number of hardwoods. In high-class and in the standard or medium types of construction No. 1 lath is usually used. No. 2 lath meets the less exacting requirements of cottages and the lower-cost types of home.

Roof boards

Usual requirements:

High stiffness, good nail-holding, small tendency to warp, ease of working.

Woods combining usual requirements in a high degree:

Douglas fir, western larch, southern yellow pine. (Commonly used.)

Cypress. (Not commonly used because of adaptability to more exacting uses.)

Ash, beech, birch, chestnut, elm, hackberry, maple, oak, tupelo. (Seldom used because not readily available and hard to work.)

Woods combining usual requirements in a good degree:

Hemlocks, ponderosa pine, spruce, white fir. (Commonly used.)

Northern white pine, sugar pine, western white pine, redwood, yellow poplar. (Seldom used because of adaptability to more exacting uses.)

Grades used:

No. 2 boards are used extensively in higher type homes. In more economical construction both No. 2 and No. 3 are used. No. 3 is serviceable but not so tight as No. 2. No. 4 and No. 5 are available in some species but entail waste in cutting. When hardwoods are used No. 2 Common is adapted to the better class houses and No. 3 Common to the more economical type of house.

Sash used in a dry location (low decay hazard)

Usual requirements:

Moderate shrinkage, good paint qualities, freedom from warping, ease of working, screw-holding power.

Woods combining usual requirements in a high degree:

Northern white pine, ponderosa pine, sugar pine, western white pine. (Principal woods used for sash.)

Cypress, redwood.

Woods combining usual requirements in a good degree:

Douglas fir, western larch, southern yellow pine. (Vertical grain. Use limited by milling and finishing characteristics.)

Sash used in a moist location

Usual requirements:

High decay resistance. Moderate shrinkage, good paint qualities, freedom from warping, ease of working, screw-holding power.

Woods combining usual requirements in a high degree:

Northern white pine, ponderosa pine, sugar pine, western white pine. (Principal woods used for sash. Require good preservative treatment.)

Cypress, cedars, redwood, chestnut. (Heartwood only or sapwood when treated.)

Woods combining usual requirements in a good degree:

Douglas fir, western larch, southern yellow pine. (Hardwood only.)

White oak. (Harder to work and higher shrinkage than the softwoods.)

Grades used:

Grades of lumber used for sash are primarily of interest to manufacturers rather than users.

Shelving with natural or high-class paint finish

Usual requirements:

Stiffness, good finishing qualities, freedom from pitch and warp.

Woods combining usual requirements in a high degree:

Ash, birch, maple, oak, walnut. (Suitable for natural finishes used principally to match interior trim.)

Cypress, redwood, yellow poplar. (Suitable for high-class paint finishes, but use limited.)

Northern white pine, ponderosa pine, sugar pine, western white pine. (Principal woods used for high-class paint finishes.)

Woods combining usual requirements in a good degree:

Douglas fir, hemlocks, western larch, southern yellow pine, spruces, white fir, basswood, chestnut. (May be used with either natural or paint finishes.)

Shelving with unfinished or plain paint coating

Usual requirements:

Stiffness, ease of working, freedom from pitch and warp.

Woods combining usual requirements in a good degree:

Northern white pine, ponderosa pine, sugar pine, western white pine. (Principal woods used.)

Cypress, hemlocks, redwood, spruces, white fir, basswood, chestnut, yellow poplar.

Douglas fir, western larch, southern yellow pine. (Softwoods with high stiffness.)

Birch, maple, oak. (Seldom used; difficult to work.)

Grades used:

The grade best adapted to use depends on the character of the shelving as well as on type of construction. C or a better grade is used for shelves that are to receive a high-class paint or enamel finish. D grade is serviceable but may entail some waste. No. 1 and No. 2 are used for shelving that is unpainted or receives only a rough-paint finish. No. 3 is serviceable, especially when cut into short lengths, but may entail some waste. When hardwoods are used for shelving in closets or storerooms No. 1 or No. 2 Common is used. These two grades are suitable for higher class shelving where short-length or narrow, clear cutting can be used to advantage.

Shingles

Usual requirements:

High decay resistance, small tendency to curl or check, freedom from splitting in nailing.

Woods combining usual requirements in a high degree:

Cedars, cypress, redwood. (Principal shingle woods; heartwood only, edge grain.)

Northern white pine, ponderosa pine, sugar pine, western white pine. (Hand-made shingles or shakes from locally grown timber; require good preservative treatment.)

Chestnut, white oak. (Hand-made shingles or shakes from locally grown timber: require care in nailing.)

Grades used:

In western red cedar, cypress, and redwood No. 1 shingles (all heart, edge-grain clear stock) should be used for the longest life and greatest ultimate economy in dwelling roofs. Other all-heart but not edge-grain grades, such as No. 2 in redwood and western red cedar and Bests in cypress, are frequently used to reduce the first cost. Other grades permitting sapwood and flat grain are available and are used where low initial cost is the determining factor.

Siding

Usual requirements:

Good painting characteristics, easy working qualities, freedom from warp.

Woods combining usual requirements in a high degree:

Cedars, cypress, northern white pine, sugar pine, western white pine, redwood.

Woods combining usual requirements in a good degree:

Western hemlock, ponderosa pine, spruce, yellow poplar.

Woods combining usual requirements in a fair degree:

Douglas fir, western larch, southern yellow pine.

Grades used:

Redwood and cypress are available in special siding grades of Clear Heart, and western red and Port Orford cedar in a siding grade of Clear. In other softwoods the B and Better siding is used in the highest class of construction. Siding in more economical types of construction is usually of C or D grade, but No. 1 and No. 2 are available in a number of species.

Stepping

Usual requirements:

High decay resistance, nonsplintering, good bending strength and wear resistance, freedom from warping.

Woods combining usual requirements in a high degree:
- Cypress, white oak (especially when quartersawn). (Heartwood only.)
- Black locust, walnut. (Usually impractical except when cut from home-grown timber.)

Woods combining usual requirements in a good degree:
- Douglas fir, western larch, redwood, southern yellow pine. (Vertical-grain heartwood only.)

Woods combining usual requirements in a fair degree:
- Cedar, Douglas fir, western larch, southern yellow pine. (Flat grain.)

Grades used:
- C or a higher grade of softwoods and Firsts and Seconds in hardwoods are used in high-class construction. In the less costly construction, No. 1 Common in hardwoods and as low as No. 2 grade in softwoods are used. No. 1 and No. 2 grades in softwoods are serviceable but wear unevenly around knots. Dense No. 1 southern pine is sometimes used in better type homes.

Subfloors

Usual requirements:
- Requirements are not exacting but high stiffness, medium shrinkage and warp, and ease of working are desired.

Woods combining usual requirements in a high degree:
- Douglas fir, western larch, southern yellow pine. (Commonly used.)
- Cypress, redwood, ash, yellow poplar. (Seldom used because of adaptability to more exacting uses.)

Woods combining usual requirements in good degree:
- Hemlocks, ponderosa pine, spruces, white fir. (Commonly used.)
- Northern white pine, sugar pine, western white pine. (Seldom used because of adaptability to more exacting uses.)
- Beech, birch, chestnut, elm, hackberry, maple, oak, tupelo. (Seldom used. Not readily available and hard to work.)

Grades used:
- No. 2 boards are used extensively in higher type homes. In more economical construction both No. 2 and No. 3 are used. No. 3 is serviceable but not so tight as No. 2. No. 4 and No. 5 are available in some species but entail waste in cutting. When hardwoods are used, No. 2 Common is adapted to the better class houses and No. 3 Common to the more economical.

Wall sheathing

Usual requirements:
- Easy working, easy nailing, moderate shrinkage. All woods can be used for sheathing with satisfactory results although some woods are less time-consuming to work than are others.

Woods combining usual requirements in a high degree:
- Cedar, cypress, hemlocks, northern white pine, ponderosa pine,

sugar pine, western white pine, redwood, spruce, white fir, basswood, chestnut, yellow poplar.

Woods combining usual requirements in a good degree:

Douglas fir, western larch, southern yellow pine, cottonwood.

Grades used:

No. 3 grade of softwoods makes a serviceable sheathing when covered with good building paper. No. 1 and No. 2 make a tighter coverage but do not warrant omitting use of building paper. No. 4 and No. 5 are used in low-cost homes but are not generally available. They both entail some waste in cutting. When a hardwood is used for sheathing, No. 2 Common is adapted to the better type homes, and No. 3 Common to the more economical.

STANDARD WIDTHS AND THICKNESSES OF ROUGH AND SURFACED YARD LUMBER

Lumber described as nominal—		Actual dimensions when surfaced shall not be less than—	Actual dimensions when rough dry[1] shall not be less than—
	Inches	Inches	Inches
Thickness	1	25/32	29/32
	1¼	1 1/16	1 5/32
	1½	1 5/16	1 13/32
	1¾	1 7/16	1 9/16
	2	1⅝	1¾
	2½	2⅛	2¼
	3	2⅝	2¾
	4	3⅝	3¾
Width of finish	3	2⅝	2¾
	4	3½	3⅝
	5	4½	4⅝
	6	5½	5⅝
	7	6½	6⅝
	8	7¼	7⅜
	9	8¼	8⅜
	10	9¼	9⅜
	11	10¼	10⅜
	12	11¼	11⅜
Width of boards and dimension	3	2⅝	2¾
	4	3⅝	3¾
	5	4⅝	4¾
	6	5⅝	5¾
	7	6⅝	6¾
	8	7½	7⅝
	9	8½	8⅝
	10	9½	9⅝
	11	10½	10⅝
	12	11½	11⅝

[1] In a shipment of rough dry lumber 20 percent may be not more than one-thirty-second of an inch under the thicknesses shown.

STANDARD THICKNESSES AND WIDTHS FOR SOFTWOOD YARD LUMBER

Including finish, boards, dimension, and heavy joist, siding, flooring, ceiling, partition, shiplap, and dressed and matched lumber

Product	Rough green or nominal sizes (board measure)		Minimum rough-dry dimensions			Dressed dimensions		
			Thickness			Thickness		
	Thickness	Width	Standard yard[1]	Standard industrial	Width	Standard yard	Standard industrial	Width (face when worked)
	Inches	Inches	Inches	Inches	Inches	Inches	Inches	Inches
Common boards and strips	1	3	29/32	[2] 15/16	2 3/4	25/32	25/32	2 5/8
	1 1/4	4	1 3/16	....	3 3/4	1 1/16	....	3 5/8
	1 1/2	5	1 7/16	....	4 3/4	1 5/16	....	4 5/8
	....	6	....	....	5 3/4	....	....	5 5/8
	....	7	....	....	6 3/4	....	....	6 5/8
	....	8	....	....	7 5/8	....	....	7 1/2
	....	9	....	....	8 5/8	....	....	8 1/2
	....	10	....	....	9 5/8	....	....	9 1/2
	....	11	....	....	10 5/8	....	....	10 1/2
	....	12	....	....	11 5/8	....	....	11 1/2
Bevel siding	....	4	....	....	....	[3] 7/16 by 3/16	....	3 1/2
	....	5	....	....	....	5/8 by 3/16	....	4 1/2
	....	6	....	....	....	....	....	5 1/2
Wide bevel siding	....	8	....	....	....	[3] 7/16 by 3/16	....	7 1/4
	....	10	....	....	....	9/16 by 3/16	....	9 1/4
	....	12	....	....	....	11/16 by 3/16	....	11 1/4
Rustic and drop siding (shiplapped)	....	4	....	....	....	9/16	....	3 3/8
	....	5	....	....	....	3/4	....	4 3/8
	....	6	....	....	....	....	....	5 1/16
	....	8	....	....	....	....	....	6 7/8
Rustic and drop siding (D. & M.)	....	4	....	....	....	9/16	....	3 1/4
	....	5	....	....	....	3/4	....	4 1/4
	....	6	....	....	....	....	....	5 3/16
	....	8	....	....	....	....	....	7
Flooring	....	2	....	....	....	5/16	....	1 1/2
	....	3	....	....	....	7/16	....	2 3/8
	....	4	....	....	....	9/16	....	3 1/4
	1	5	....	....	....	25/32	....	4 1/4
	1 1/4	6	....	....	....	1 1/16	....	5 3/16
	1 1/2	....	....	....	....	1 5/16	....	....
Ceiling	....	3	....	....	....	5/16	....	2 3/8
	....	4	....	....	....	7/16	....	3 1/4
	....	5	....	....	....	9/16	....	4 1/4
	....	6	....	....	....	1 1/16	....	5 3/16

[1] 20 percent may be 1/32-inch scant.
[2] 10 percent may be 1/32-inch scant.
[3] Minimum.

STANDARD THICKNESSES AND WIDTHS FOR SOFTWOOD YARD LUMBER (CONT.)

Including finish, boards, dimension, and heavy joist, siding, flooring, ceiling, partition, shiplap, and dressed and matched lumber

Product	Rough green or nominal sizes (board measure)		Minimum rough-dry dimensions			Dressed dimensions		
			Thickness			Thickness		
	Thickness	Width	Standard yard[1]	Standard industrial	Width	Standard yard	Standard industrial	Width (face when worked)
	Inches	Inches	Inches	Inches	Inches	Inches	Inches	Inches
Partition	....	3	....	....	....	¾	....	2⅜
	....	4	....	....	....	....	....	3¼
	....	5	....	....	....	....	....	4¼
	....	6	....	....	....	....	....	5 3/16
Shiplap	1	4	....	....	....	25/32	....	3⅛
	....	6	....	....	....	....	....	5⅛
	....	8	....	....	....	....	....	7⅛
	....	10	....	....	....	....	....	9⅛
	....	12	....	....	....	....	....	11⅛
Dressed and matched	1	4	....	....	....	25/32	....	3¼
	1¼	6	....	....	....	1 1/16	....	5¼
	1½	8	....	....	....	1 5/16	....	7¼
	....	10	....	....	....	....	....	9¼
	....	12	....	....	....	....	....	11¼
Dimension and heavy joist	2	2	1¾	1⅞	1¾	1⅝	1¾	1⅝
	2½	4	2¼	....	3¾	2⅛	....	3⅝
	3	6	2¾	....	5¾	2⅝	....	5⅝
	4	8	3¾	....	7⅝	3⅝	....	7½
	....	10	....	....	9⅝	....	....	9½
	....	12	....	....	11⅝	....	....	11½
Factory flooring, heavy roofing, heavy decking, and sheet piling	2	4	1¾	....	....	1⅝	....	[4]3
	2½	6	2¼	....	....	2⅛	....	[4]5
	3	8	2¾	....	....	2⅝	....	[4]7
	4	10	3¾	....	....	3⅝	....	[4]9
	....	12	....	....	....	....	....	[4]11

[4] Face width when shiplapped; when dressed and matched the face is ⅛-inch greater; when grooved for splines the face width is ½-inch greater.

STANDARD HARDWOOD GRADES OF LUMBER[1]

Grade, and lengths allowed (feet)	Widths allowed	Surface measure of pieces (square feet)	Percentage of each piece that must work into clear-face cuttings	Maximum cuttings allowed	Minimum size of cuttings required
	Inches		Percent	Number	
Firsts:[2] 8 to 16 (will admit 25 percent of 8- to 11-foot, half of which may be 8- and 9-foot).	6+	4 to 9	91⅔	1	4 inches by 5 feet, or 3 inches by 7 feet.
		10 to 14	91⅔	2	
		15+	91⅔	3	
Seconds:[2] 8 to 16 (will admit 25 percent of 8- to 11-foot, half of which may be 8- and 9-foot).	6+	4 and 5	83⅓	1	Do.
		6 and 7	83⅓	1	
		6 and 7	91⅔	2	
		8 to 11	83⅓	2	
		8 to 11	91⅔	3	
		12 to 15	83⅓	3	
		12 to 15	91⅔	4	
		16+	83⅓	4	
Selects: 6 to 16 (will admit 30 percent of 6- to 11-foot, one-sixth of which may be 6- and 7-foot).	4+	2 and 3	91⅔	1	Do.
		4+	(3)		
No. 1 Common: 4 to 16 (will admit 10 percent of 4- to 7-foot, half of which may be 4- and 5-foot).	3+	1	100	0	4 inches by 2 feet, or 3 inches by 3 feet.
		2	75	1	
		3 and 4	66⅔	1	
		3 and 4	75	2	
		5 to 7	66⅔	2	
		5 to 7	75	3	
		8 to 10	66⅔	3	
		11 to 13	66⅔	4	
		14+	66⅔	5	
No. 2 Common: 4 to 16 (will admit 30 percent of 4- to 7-foot, one third of which may be 4- and 5-foot).	3+	1	66⅔	1	3 inches by 2 feet.
		2 and 3	50	1	
		2 and 3	66⅔	2	
		4 and 5	50	2	
		4 and 5	66⅔	3	
		6 and 7	50	3	
		6 and 7	66⅔	4	
		8 and 9	50	4	
		10 and 11	50	5	
		12 and 13	50	6	
		14+	50	7	

[1] Inspection made on the poorer side of the piece, except in selects.

[2] Firsts and Seconds are combined as 1 grade (FAS). The percentage of Firsts required in the combined grade varies from 20 to 40 percent, depending on the species.

[3] Same as seconds.

STANDARD HARDWOOD GRADES OF LUMBER[1] (CONT.)

Grade, and lengths allowed (feet)	Widths allowed	Surface measure of pieces (square feet)	Percentage of each piece that must work into clear-face cuttings	Maximum cuttings allowed	Minimum size of cuttings required
	Inches		Percent	Number	
Sound Wormy:					
4 to 16 (will admit 10 percent of 4- to 7-foot, half of which may be 4- and 5-foot).	3+	....	[4]	....	
No. 3A Common:					
4 to 16 (will admit 50 percent of 4- to 7-foot, half of which may be 4- and 5-foot).	3+	1+	[5] 33⅓	[6]	3 inches by 2 feet.
No. 3B Common:					
4 to 16 (will admit 50 percent of 4- to 7-foot, half of which may be 4- and 5-foot).	3+	1+	[7] 25	[6]	1½ inches wide and containing at least 36 square inches.

[4] Cutting requirements same as in No. 1 Common, except that worm holes, bird pecks, sound stain, sound knots not over ¾ inch in diameter, and other similar sound defects will be admitted in the cuttings.

[5] This grade also admits pieces which grade not below No. 2 Common on the good face and have the reverse face sound.

[6] Not specified.

[7] The cuttings must be sound; clear face not required.

STANDARD WIDTHS AND THICKNESSES OF LUMBER

Type of lumber	Normal size (inches)		Actual size S4S[1] (inches)	
	Thickness	Width	Thickness	Width
Timbers	2	4	1⅝	3⅝
	2	6	1⅝	5⅝
	2	8	1⅝	7½
	2	10	1⅝	9½
	2	12	1⅝	11½
	2	14	1⅝	13½
	2	16	1⅝	15½
	3	6	2⅝	5⅝
	3	8	2⅝	7½
	3	10	2⅝	9½
	3	12	2⅝	11½
	3	14	2⅝	13½
	3	16	2⅝	15½
	4	4	3⅝	3⅝
	4	6	3⅝	5⅝

[1] Surfaced 4 sides.

STANDARD WIDTHS AND THICKNESSES OF LUMBER (CONT.)

Type of lumber	Normal size (inches)		Actual size S4S[1] (inches)	
	Thickness	Width	Thickness	Width
Timbers	4	8	3⅝	7½
	4	10	3⅝	9½
	4	12	3⅝	11½
	4	14	3⅝	13½
	4	16	3⅝	15½
	6	6	5½	5½
	6	8	5½	7½
	6	10	5½	9½
	6	12	5½	11½
	6	14	5½	13½
	6	16	5½	15½
	8	8	7½	7½
	8	10	7½	9½
	8	12	7½	11½
	8	14	7½	13½
	8	16	7½	15½
	10	10	9½	9½
	10	12	9½	11½
	10	14	9½	13½
	10	16	9½	15½
	12	12	11½	11½
	12	14	11½	13½
	12	16	11½	15½
	14	14	13½	13½
	14	16	13½	15½
	16	16	15½	15½
Common boards	1	4	$\frac{25}{32}$	3⅝
	1	6	$\frac{25}{32}$	5⅝
	1	8	$\frac{25}{32}$	7½
	1	10	$\frac{25}{32}$	9½
	1	12	$\frac{25}{32}$	11½
Shiplap boards	1	4	$\frac{25}{32}$	3⅛
	1	6	$\frac{25}{32}$	5⅛
	1	8	$\frac{25}{32}$	7⅛
	1	10	$\frac{25}{32}$	9⅛
	1	12	$\frac{25}{32}$	11⅛
Tongued and grooved boards	1	4	$\frac{25}{32}$	3¼
	1	6	$\frac{25}{32}$	5¼
	1	8	$\frac{25}{32}$	7¼
	1	10	$\frac{25}{32}$	9¼
	1	12	$\frac{25}{32}$	11¼

[1] Surfaced 4 sides.

Contents of Lumber

Number of board feet in various sizes for lengths given

Size of piece (inches)	Length of piece (feet)								
	8	10	12	14	16	18	20	22	24
2 by 4	5⅓	6⅔	8	9⅓	10⅔	12	13⅓	14⅔	16
2 by 6	8	10	12	14	16	18	20	22	24
2 by 8	10⅔	13⅓	16	18⅔	21⅓	24	26⅔	29⅓	32
2 by 10	13⅓	16⅔	20	23⅓	26⅔	30	33⅓	36⅔	40
2 by 12	16	20	24	28	32	36	40	44	48
2 by 14	18⅔	23⅓	28	32⅔	37⅓	42	46⅔	51⅓	56
2 by 16	21⅓	26⅔	32	37⅓	42⅔	48	53⅓	58⅔	64
3 by 6	12	15	18	21	24	27	30	33	36
3 by 8	16	20	24	28	32	36	40	44	48
3 by 10	20	25	30	35	40	40	50	55	60
3 by 12	24	30	36	42	48	54	60	66	72
3 by 14	28	35	42	49	56	63	70	77	84
3 by 16	32	40	48	56	64	72	80	88	96
4 by 4	10⅔	13⅓	16	18⅔	21⅓	24	26⅔	29⅓	32
4 by 6	16	20	24	28	32	36	40	44	48
4 by 8	21⅓	26⅔	32	37⅓	42⅔	48	53⅓	58⅔	64
4 by 10	26⅔	33⅓	40	46⅔	53⅓	60	66⅔	73⅓	80
4 by 12	32	40	48	56	64	72	80	88	96
4 by 14	37⅓	46⅔	56	65⅓	74⅔	84	93⅓	102⅔	112
4 by 16	42⅔	53⅓	64	74⅔	85⅓	96	106⅔	117⅓	128
6 by 6	24	30	36	42	48	54	60	66	72
6 by 8	32	40	48	56	64	72	80	88	96
6 by 10	40	50	60	70	80	90	100	110	120
6 by 12	48	60	72	84	96	108	120	132	144
6 by 14	56	70	84	98	112	126	140	154	168
6 by 16	64	80	96	112	128	144	160	176	192
8 by 8	42⅔	53⅓	64	74⅔	85⅓	96	106⅔	117⅓	128
8 by 10	53⅓	66⅔	80	93⅓	106⅔	120	133⅓	146⅔	160
8 by 12	64	80	96	112	128	144	160	176	192
8 by 14	74⅔	93⅓	112	130⅔	149⅓	168	186⅔	205⅓	224
8 by 16	85⅓	106⅔	128	149⅓	170⅔	192	213⅓	234⅔	256
10 by 10	66⅔	83⅓	100	116⅔	133⅓	150	166⅔	183½	200
10 by 12	80	100	120	140	160	180	200	220	240
10 by 14	93⅓	116⅔	140	163⅓	186⅔	210	233⅓	256⅔	280
10 by 16	106⅔	133⅓	160	186⅔	213⅓	240	266⅔	296⅓	320
12 by 12	96	120	144	168	192	216	240	264	288
12 by 14	112	140	168	196	224	252	280	308	336
12 by 16	128	160	192	224	256	288	320	352	384
14 by 14	130⅔	163⅓	196	228⅔	261⅓	294	326⅔	359⅓	392
14 by 16	149⅓	186⅔	224	261⅓	298⅔	336	373⅓	410⅔	448
16 by 16	170⅔	213⅓	256	298⅔	341⅓	384	426⅔	469⅓	512

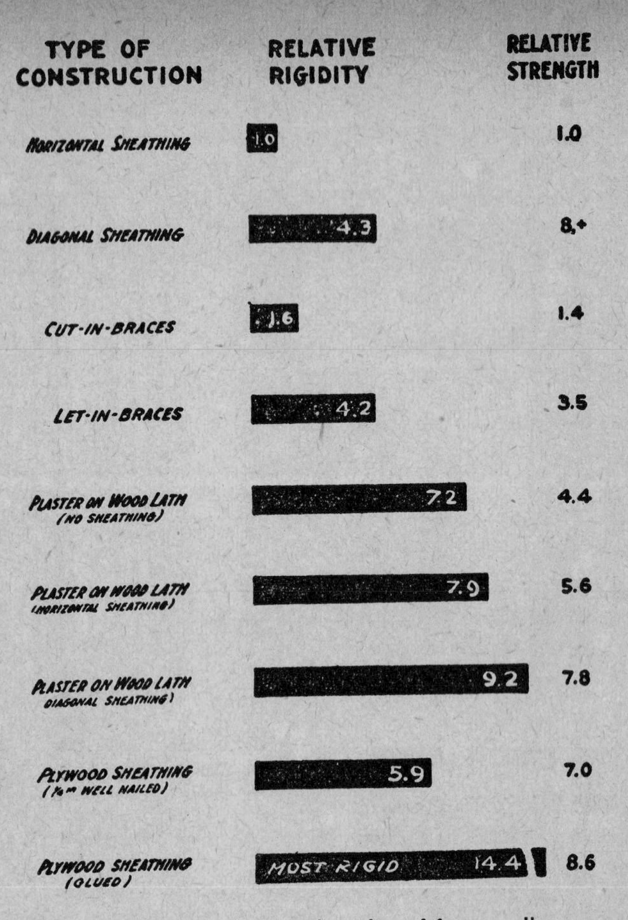

Fig. 1. Strength and rigidity of frame walls.

CUTTING DOWN WASTE

A considerable saving on every type of building job can be realized by reducing waste in materials to a minimum. One way to reduce waste is to take advantage of the fact, in planning the job, that more and more manufacturers of building materials are using 4-inch multiples as the standard unit of measurement. See figures 2 to 5. When all dimensions of a building are based on 4-inch multiples, it is possible to build with a minimum degree of waste material. Figure 4 shows interior wall studding placed at 4-inch multiples, allowing all types of standard insulation, plasterboard and wallboard to be installed with no waste at all.

Another method of reducing waste, especially in lumber, is to lay out the lumber requirements for a specific job before any cutting is done. Figure 5 shows how the gable end of a small cottage can be covered with sheathing or siding in two different ways. The top of the figure shows the usual method of cutting the lumber. In this particular case, the waste amounts to at least 4 feet and a total of 12 cuts had to be made. In the lower part, waste amounts to only 8 inches and only 8 cuts are necessary.

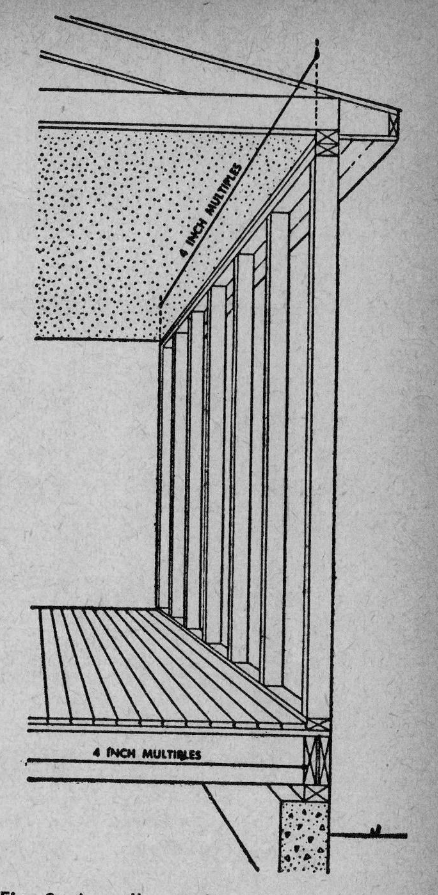

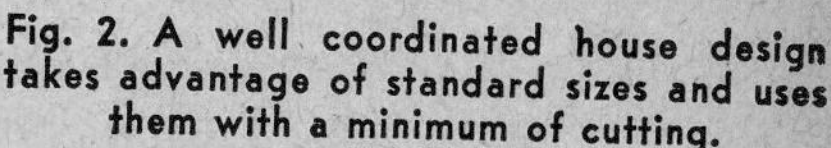

Fig. 2. A well coordinated house design takes advantage of standard sizes and uses them with a minimum of cutting.

METHODS OF SEASONING WOOD POSTS

The accompanying illustrations show several effective methods of seasoning wood posts. It has been proven to be a false economy to neglect proper seasoning. Any apparent saving of time at the moment is almost sure to be more than offset by subsequent untimely damage to the timbers involved.

INEXPENSIVE INCINERATOR

A safe and inexpensive incinerator for burning waste material during construction can be made out of a 55-gallon drum with the top removed (fig. 11). A few large holes are punched around the base of the steel drum to provide air for the fire. The top of the drum should be covered with wire mesh to prevent the escape of sparks.

FIRE STOPPING

The cavity between the inner and outer wall surface makes a perfect flue or chimney for a fire originating in the basement (fig. 12). This cavity should be stopped at each floor level with an incombustible material. Fire-resistant insulating materials filling the wall cavity will provide additional protection.

Doors and stairways

If a fire-resistant basement ceiling is built, a fire-resistant door leading to the basement is equally advisable. For other interior openings and with usual construction there is not much advantage in giving greater protection than that provided by an ordinary flush wooden door and frame.

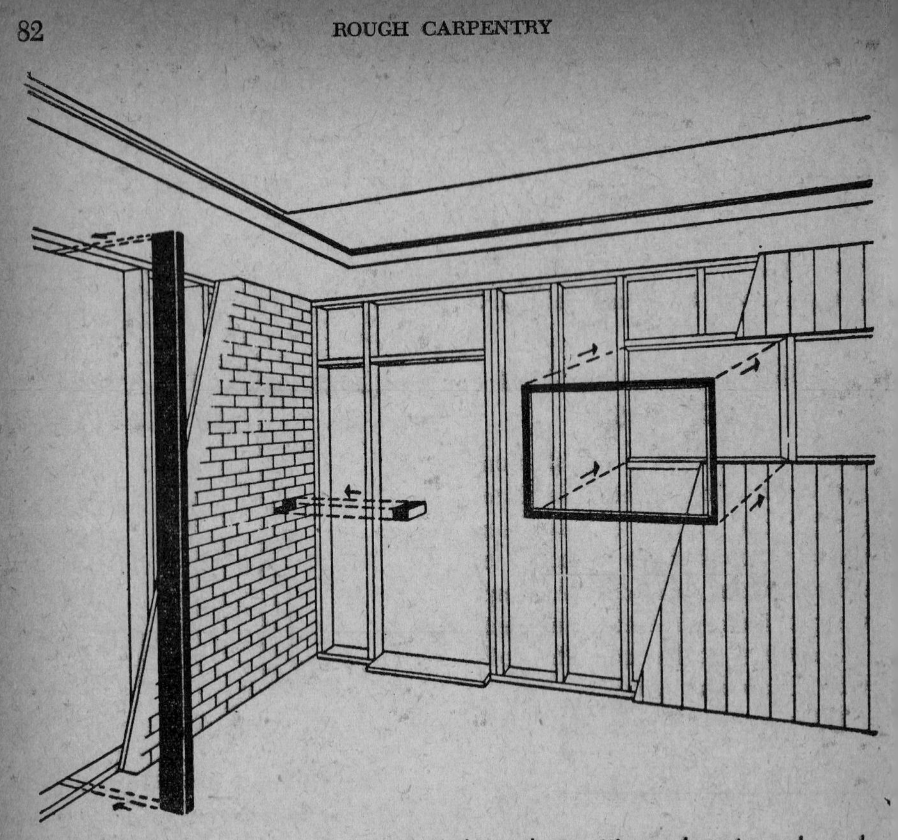

Fig. 3. Materials made in multiples of 4 inches reduce cutting and waste, and can be fitted together simply and orderly according to plan.

Inclosed stairways retard rapid spread of fire from floor to floor. If the interior design calls for an open stairway below, it can often be closed at the top with a flush door.

Coatings and surface treatments

Fire-retardant paints are of varying composition and properties but fall into two general classes, namely, special exterior paints usually made with an oil base or a binder, and interior paints, chiefly of the cold-water type. The cold-water paints, including sodium silicate, whitewash, and some casein products, are among the most effective fire-retardant coatings and are relatively cheap. Most of them, however, are nondurable in outside exposures and are suitable only for interior use.

A relatively thick, continuous film or coating of material is necessary to obtain a good fire-retarding effect. A thin coating of even the most effective materials does not add appreciably to the fire resistance of wood structures. Lack of a definite classification of the many kinds and brands of coating materials, as to effectiveness, permanence, and quantity required, precludes the giving of speci-

INSULATION

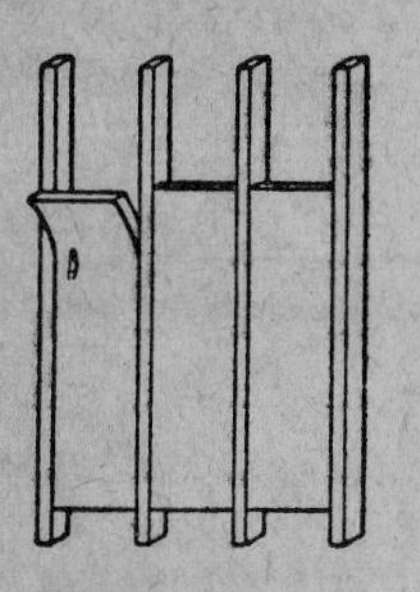

bat and blanket insulation
between studs spaced 16 inches on center

PLASTERBOARD

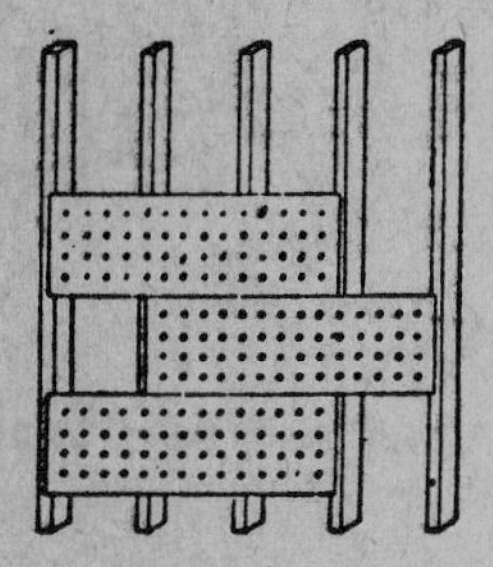

16- by 48-inch plasterboards fit
16- or 24-inch stud spacing

WALLBOARD

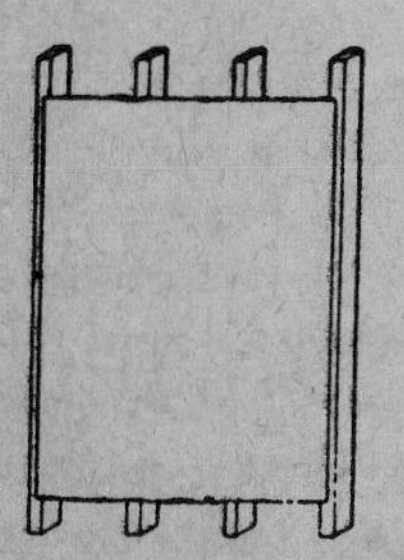

4- by 8-feet sheets fit
16- or 24-inch stud spacing

Fig. 4. A number of existing construction practices are generally based on a standard of 4 inch multiples.

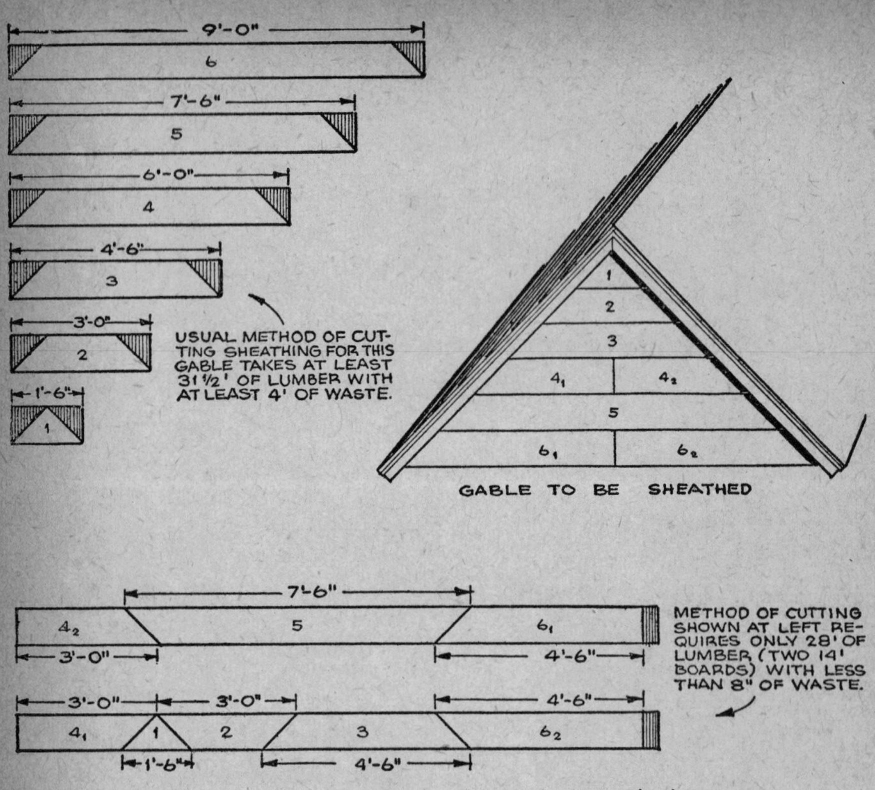

Fig. 5. Reducing waste to a minimum in cutting lumber.

fic recommendations. Effective fire-retardant coatings, properly applied, are of value in delaying ignition and checking the spread of flame originating from small sources. They are not nearly so suitable for protecting against high temperatures for a long time as are impregnation treatments. The best of these coatings are themselves noninflammable and form a protective film over the wood at high temperatures or emit noncombustible gases that dilute the inflammable gases from the wood or both.

The customary finishing materials for wood, such as ordinary stains, oil paints, varnishes, and lacquers are of no particular value in protecting wood against fire.

Impregnation methods

Wood is impregnated with fire-retardant chemicals by methods similar to those in use for the injection of preservatives. The wood is sealed within a treating cylinder and the treating solution forced in by means of pressure. While information on the permanence of treatments, their effect on the strength of wood, the amounts required for a specified performance, and other important points is still scant, it may be said that the

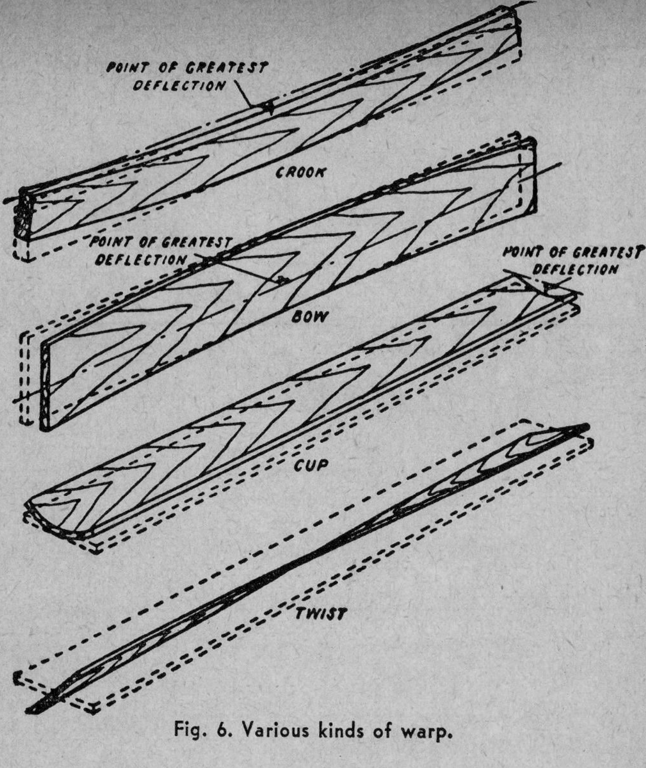

Fig. 6. Various kinds of warp.

Fig. 7. Seasoning a post against a stump.

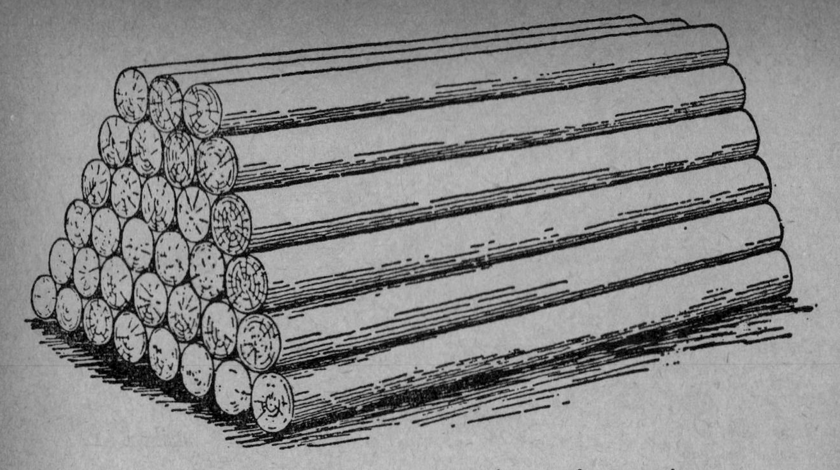

Fig. 8. A close pile; a poor way to pile posts for seasoning.

Fig. 9. A good way to season posts.

fire-retarding effect of impregnation treatments is closely related to the quantity of chemical injected into the wood. Absorptions of one-fourth to 1 pound of fire-retardant chemicals per cubic foot of wood, quantities such as are used with toxic chemicals for wood preservation, have only a small effect on the combustion of the wood. It is necessary to use several times as much chemical to obtain the best results. For a thorough impregnation and a high degree of effectiveness approximately 4 pounds of the more effective chemicals per cubic foot of wood are required, or something like 300 pounds per thousand board feet. Effectively fireproofed

Fig. 10. Another method of piling posts to season, not so satisfactory as that shown in figure 9.

wood can be charred or disintegrated by continuous exposure to intense heat from an outside source, but when the heating is discontinued the burning ceases. The principal effects of fireproofing treatments are to retard the normal increase in temperatures under fire conditions, to decrease the rate of flame spread and ignition of the wood, to lessen the rate of flame penetration or destruction of wood in contact with fire, and to make fires more easily extinguishable.

Impregnation treatments may be complete; that is, the treatment may extend completely through the piece, or they may be only partial, in which case only an outside zone of the piece is impregnated. Efficient, complete impregnation with an adequate quantity of fire-retardant chemicals makes wood sufficiently resistant to fire so that it will not of itself support combustion. Partial impregnation affords protection that may be adequate for many purposes and under many conditions although the central portion is unimpregnated. Only partial impregnation is possible with some species of wood and with large-sized timbers. When the lumber must be cut into smaller-sized pieces or machined after treatment in such a way that the interior is ex-

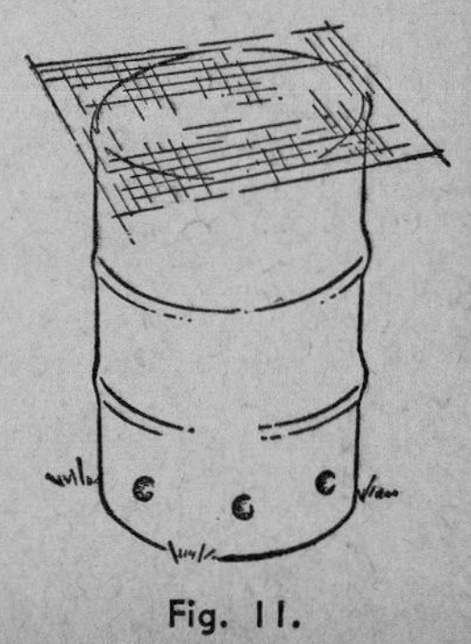

Fig. 11.

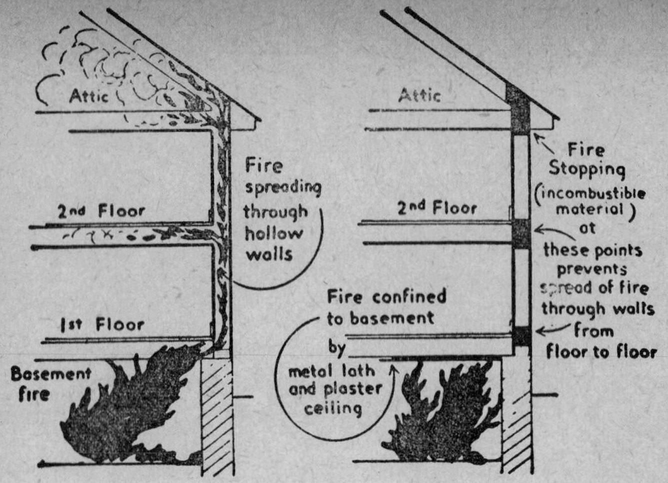

Fig. 12.

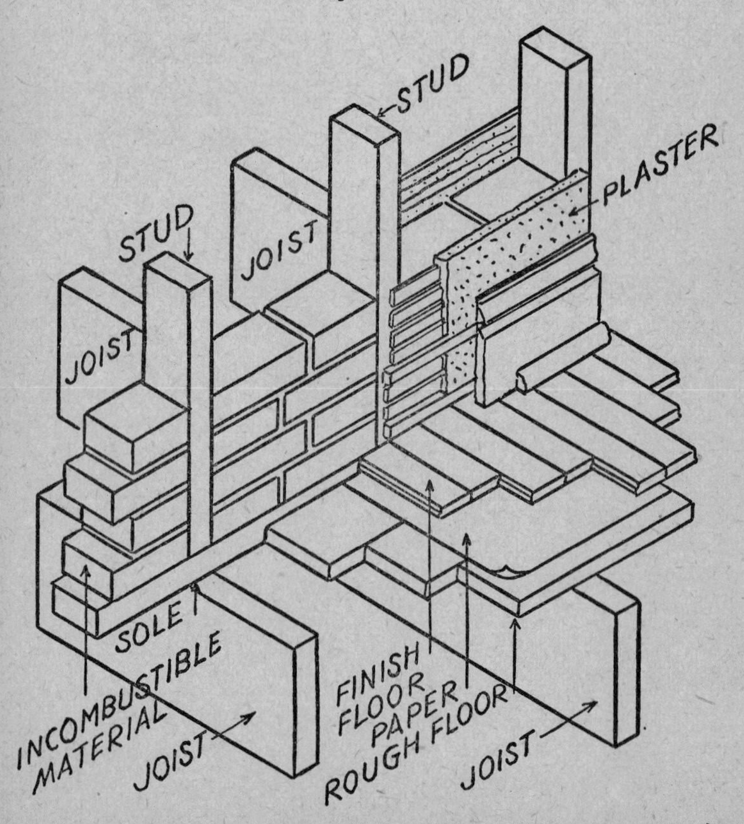

Fig. 13. A method of fire stopping at a partition which is not directly over another partition or support.

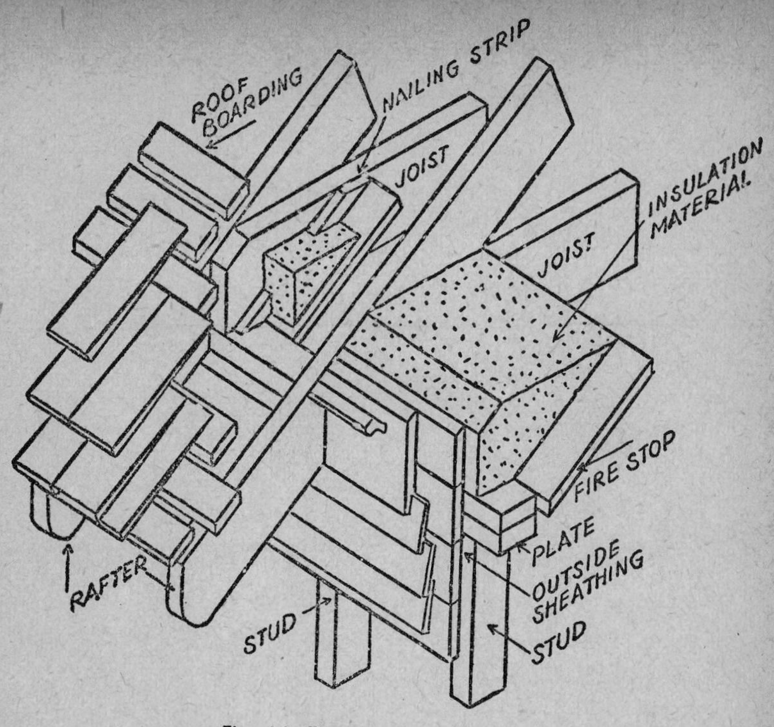

Fig. 14. Fire stopping at cornice.

posed, complete penetration is a necessity. Partial impregnation is obviously cheaper than complete impregnation.

When wood beams frame into a masonry wall, the ends should be beveled with a "fire cut" as in figure 15 so that in case of a fire burning through one or two joists before it is controlled, the joists can fall down without destroying the wall. With masonry walls, every fourth joist should be anchored to the wall with wrought-iron pin anchors.

INSTALLING AN EXTRA POST

The post should rest on a solid concrete footing and not on the basement floor. It should be several inches less than the required span from footing to girder. Heavy wood wedges are then driven in between the top of the post and the girder (fig. 16).

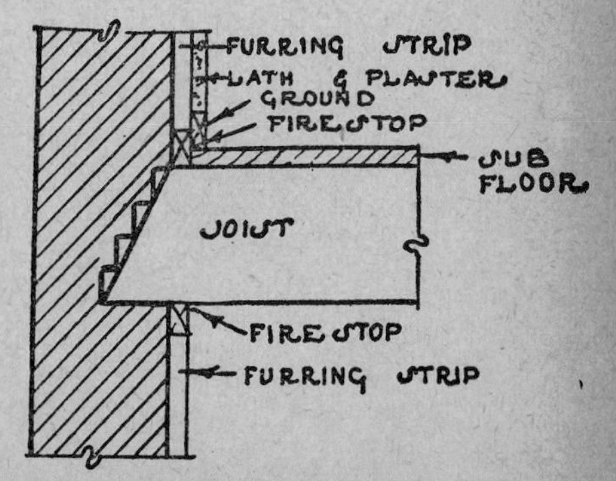

Fig. 15. Fire stopping of furred masonry wall.

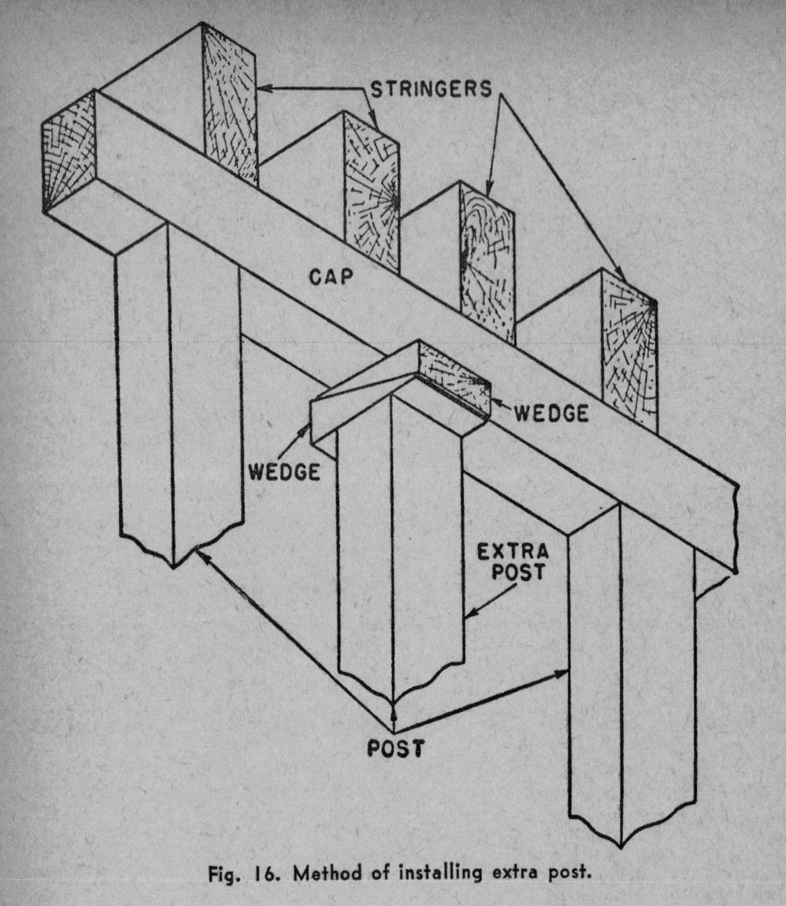

Fig. 16. Method of installing extra post.

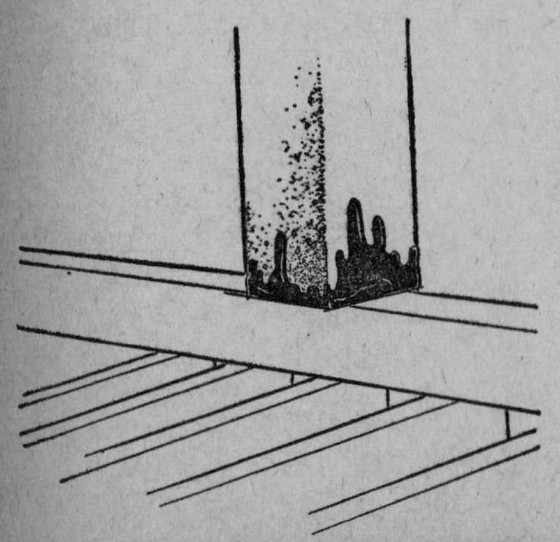

Fig. 17. To eliminate rot, tops of masonry piers should be coated with asphalt or tar.

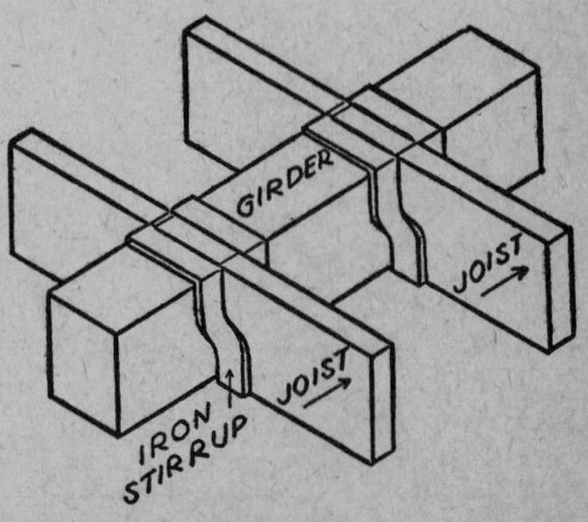

Fig. 18. Joists hung on girder with iron stirrups.

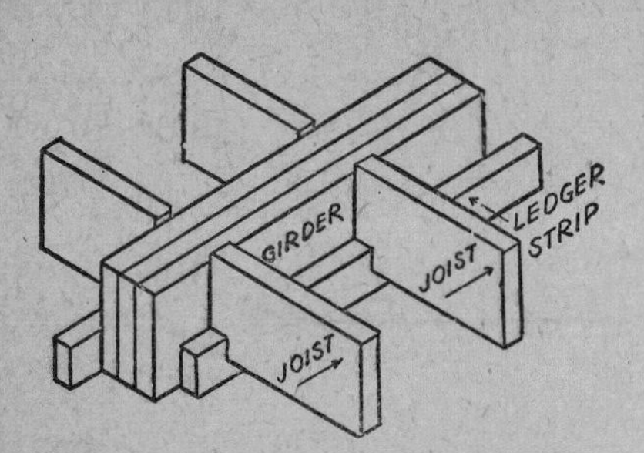

Fig. 19. Girder construction to equalize shrinkage (braced and western frame.)

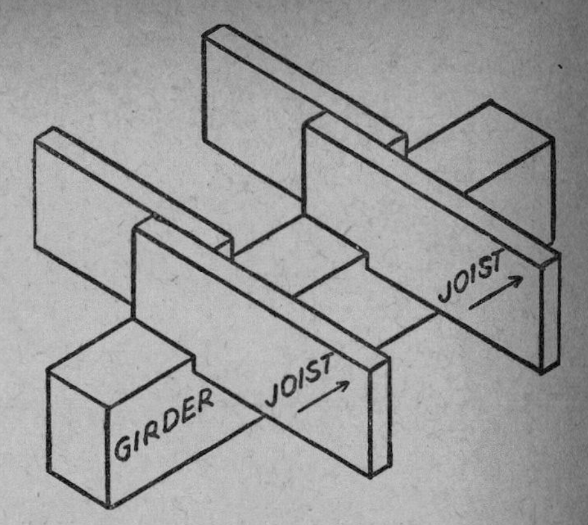

Fig. 20. Joists sized down 1 inch on girder with lap.

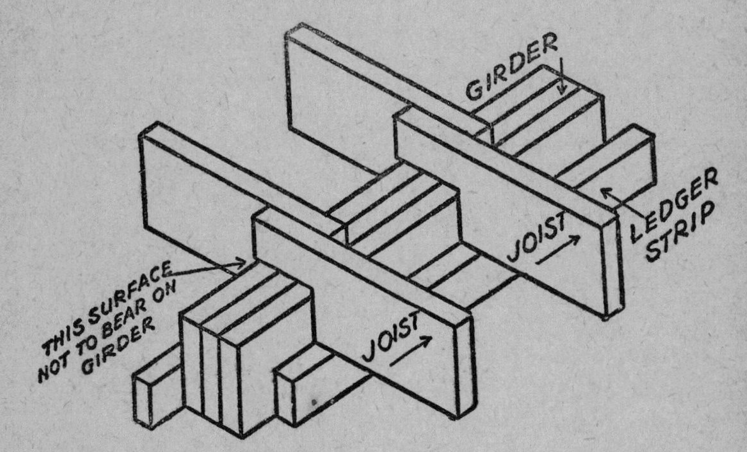

Fig. 21. Girder construction to equalize shrinkage (balloon frame).

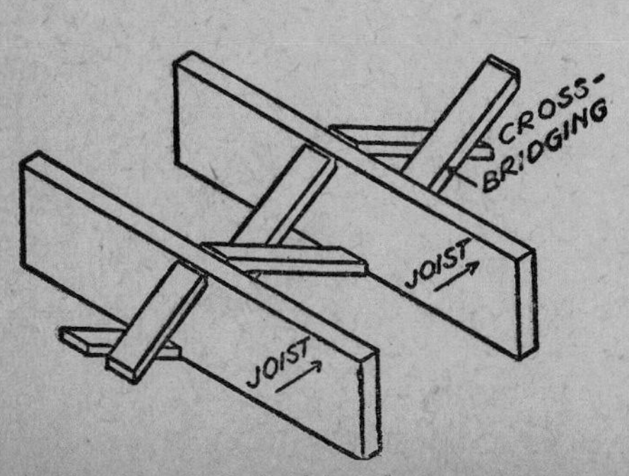

Fig. 22. Cross-bridging between joists.

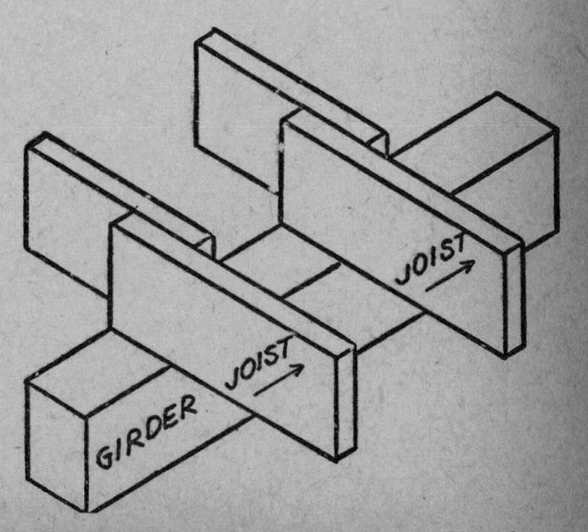

Fig. 23. Joists lapped on top of girder.

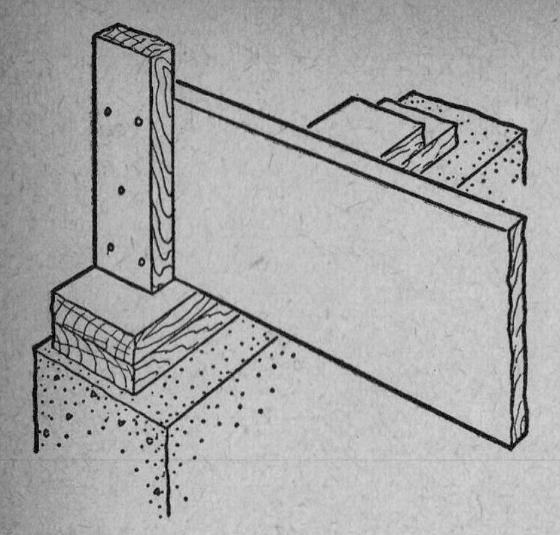

Fig. 24. A type of sill frequently used for small buildings and homes.

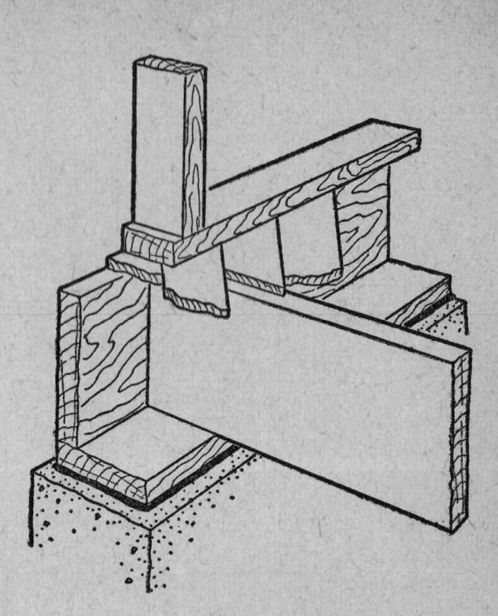

Fig. 25. Another type of sill suitable for small buildings.

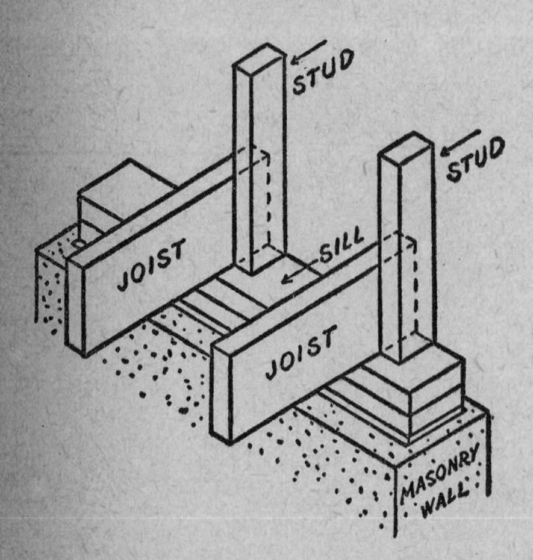

Fig. 26. Sill construction (balloon frame).

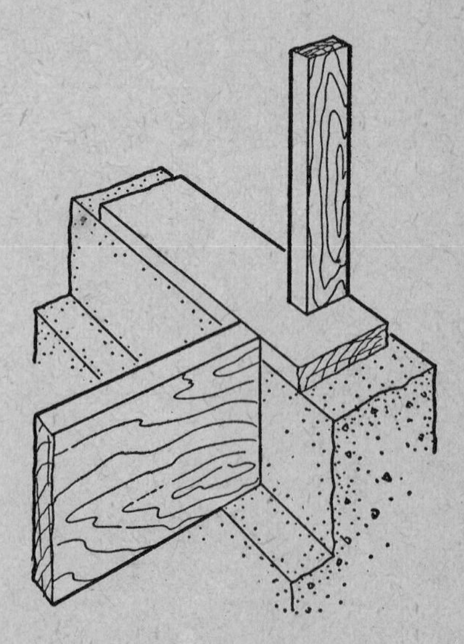

Fig. 28. A third type of sill, which may be used instead of those shown in figures 24 and 25.

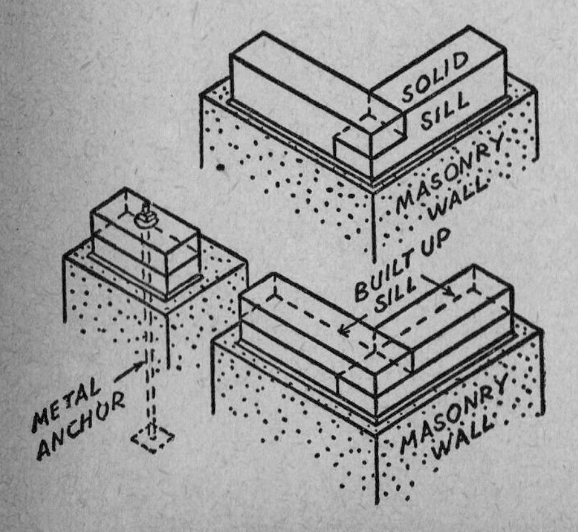

Fig. 27. Halving of sills at corner.

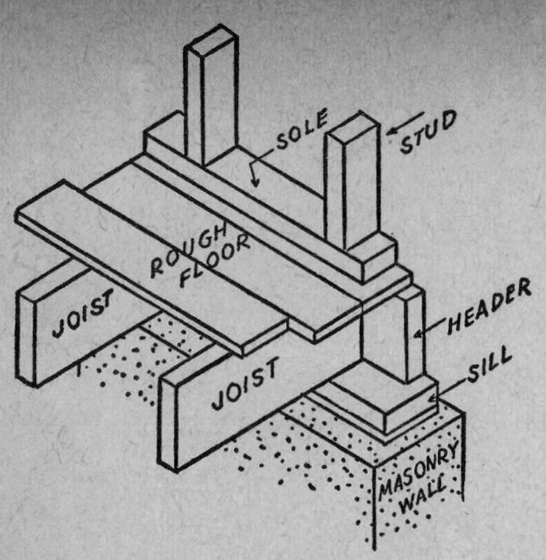

Fig. 29. Box-sill (western frame).

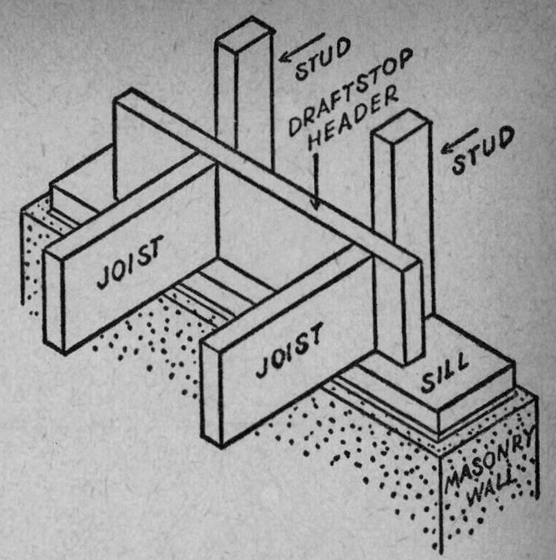

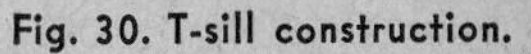

Fig. 30. T-sill construction.

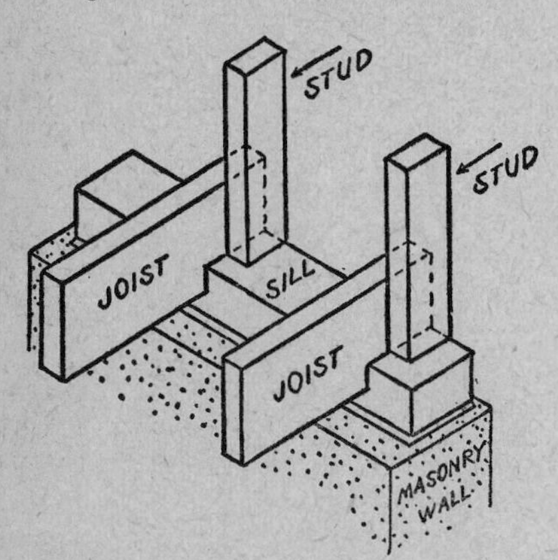

Fig. 31. Sill construction (braced frame).

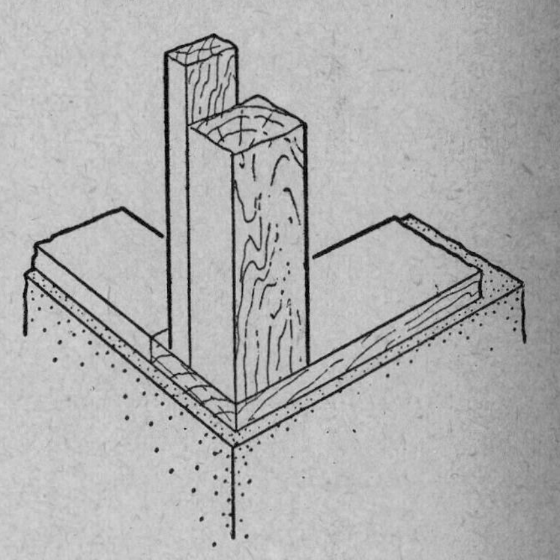

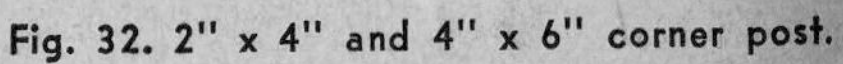

Fig. 32. 2" x 4" and 4" x 6" corner post.

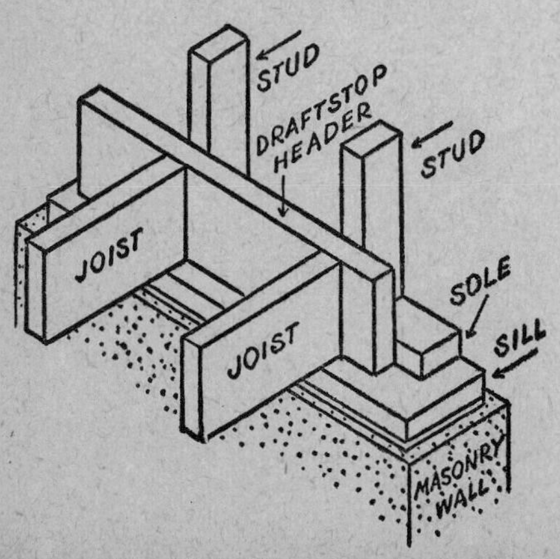

Fig. 33. R-sill construction.

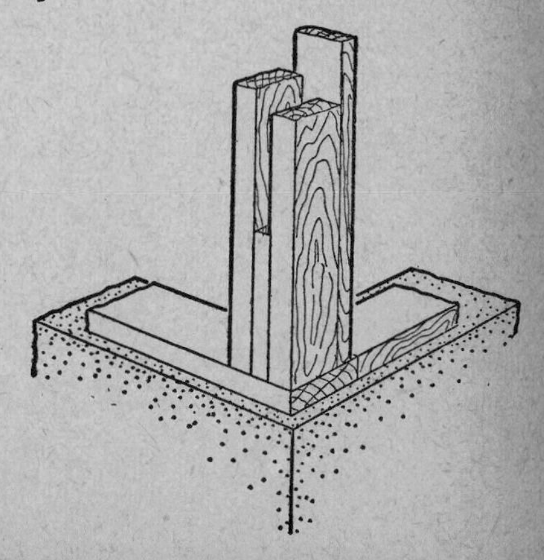

Fig. 34. A corner post of four 2" x 4"s.

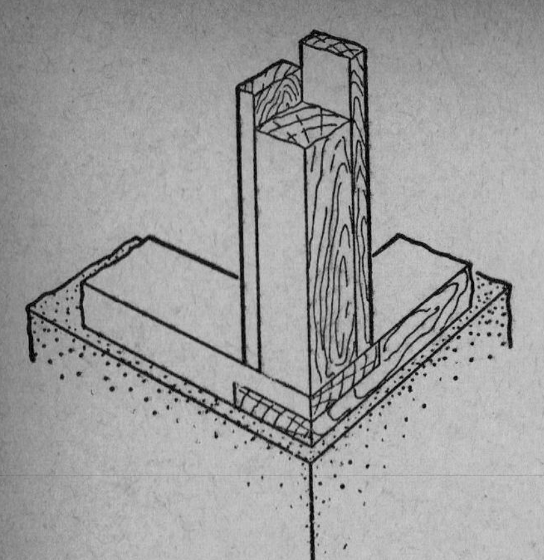

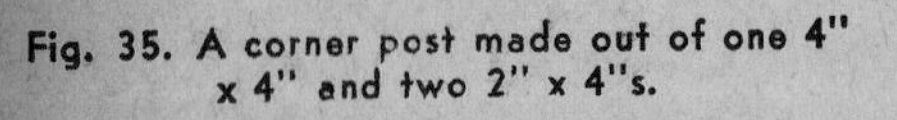

Fig. 35. A corner post made out of one 4" x 4" and two 2" x 4"s.

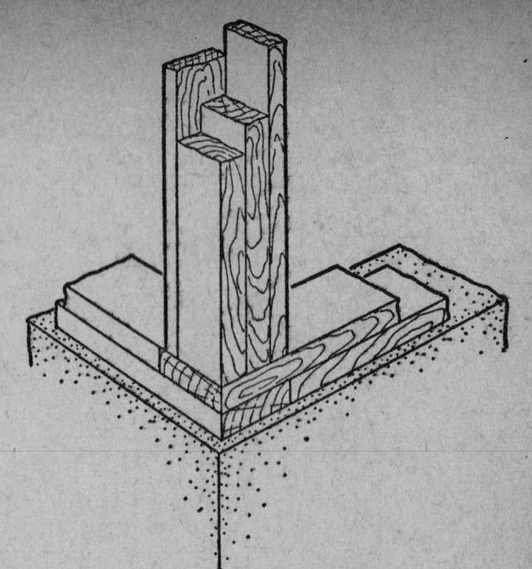

Fig. 36. A corner post made out of four 2" x 4"s in a different arrangement from that shown in figure 34.

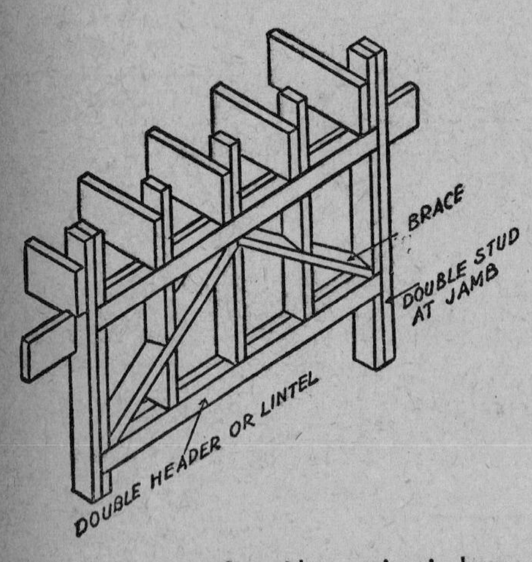

Fig. 37. Framing for wide opening in bearing wall or partition.

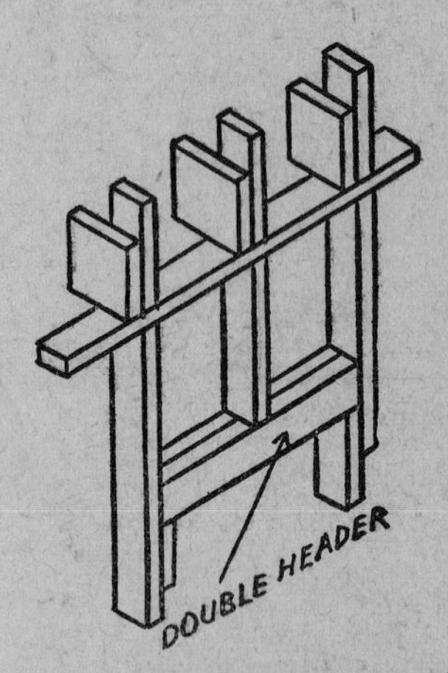

Fig. 38. Framing for narrow opening.

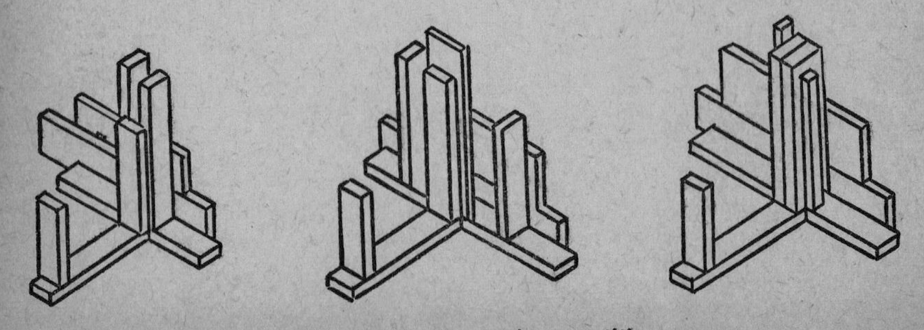

Fig. 39. Methods of framing studs at partition corners.

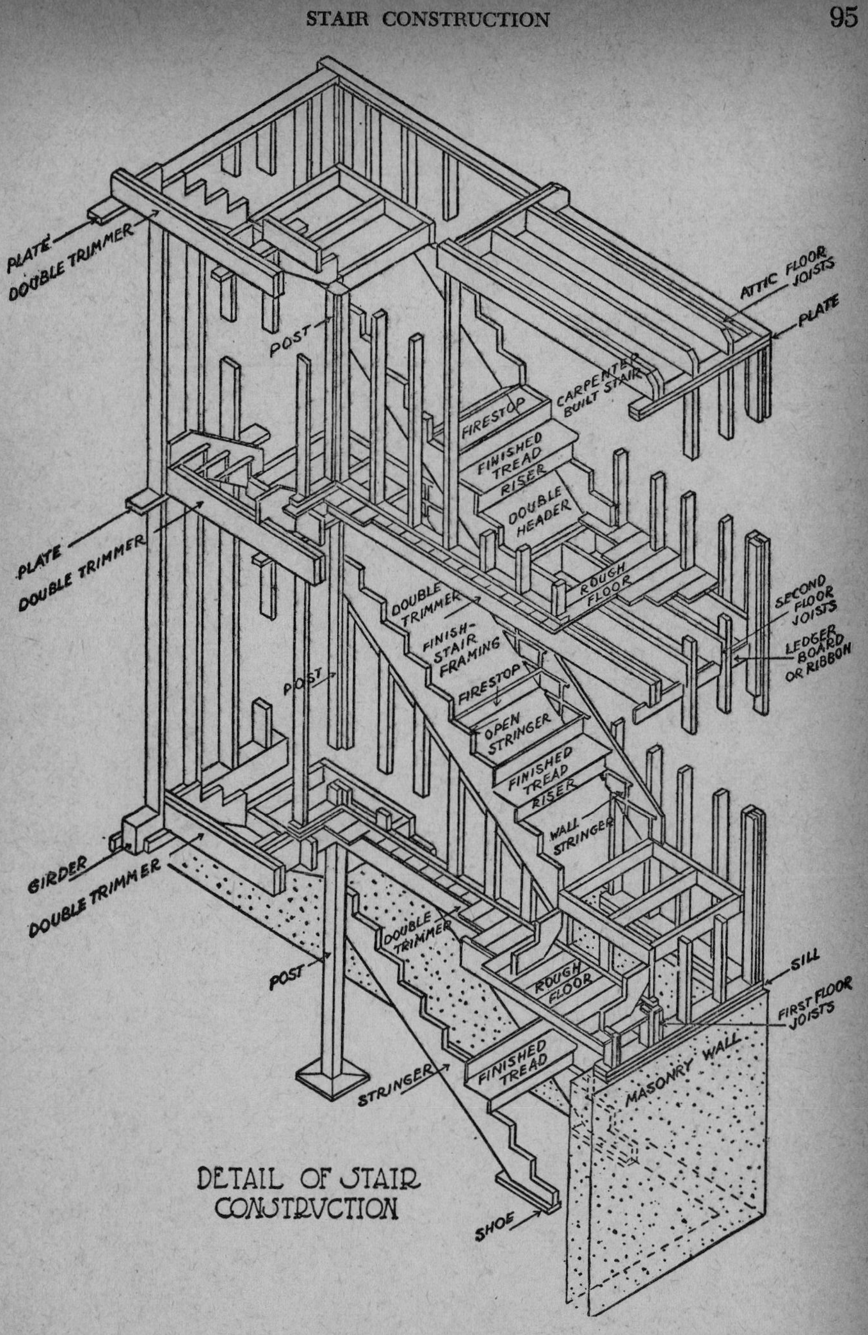

Fig. 40. Cutaway view showing nomenclature, position and assembly of good stair construction

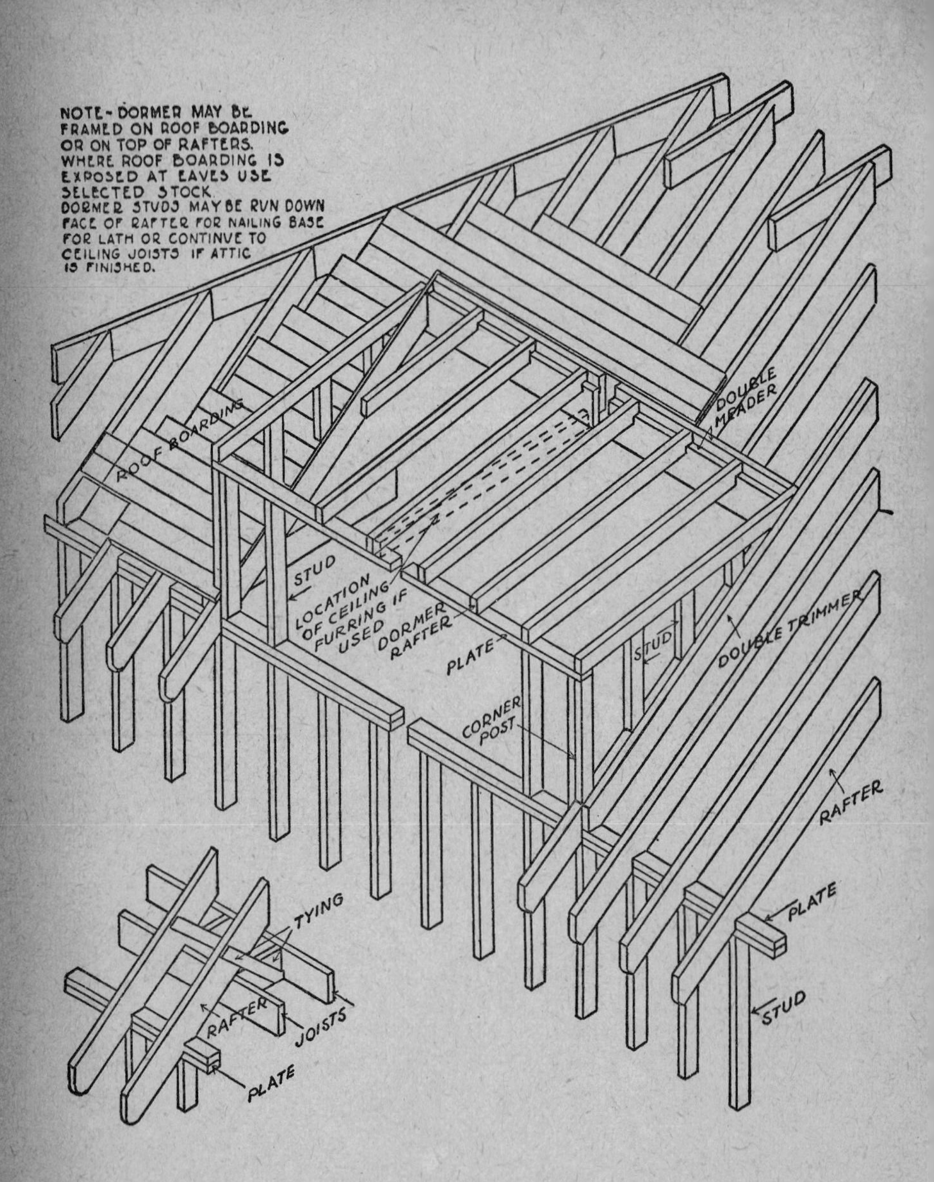
NOTE- DORMER MAY BE FRAMED ON ROOF BOARDING OR ON TOP OF RAFTERS. WHERE ROOF BOARDING IS EXPOSED AT EAVES USE SELECTED STOCK. DORMER STUDS MAY BE RUN DOWN FACE OF RAFTER FOR NAILING BASE FOR LATH OR CONTINUE TO CEILING JOISTS IF ATTIC IS FINISHED.
ROOF BOARDING
DOUBLE HEADER
STUD
LOCATION OF CEILING FURRING IF USED
DORMER RAFTER
PLATE
STUD
DOUBLE TRIMMER
CORNER POST
RAFTER
TYING
RAFTER
JOISTS
PLATE
PLATE
STUD

Fig. 41. Detail of dormer over stairwell. Inset shows method of bracing roof where rafters are at right angles to joists.

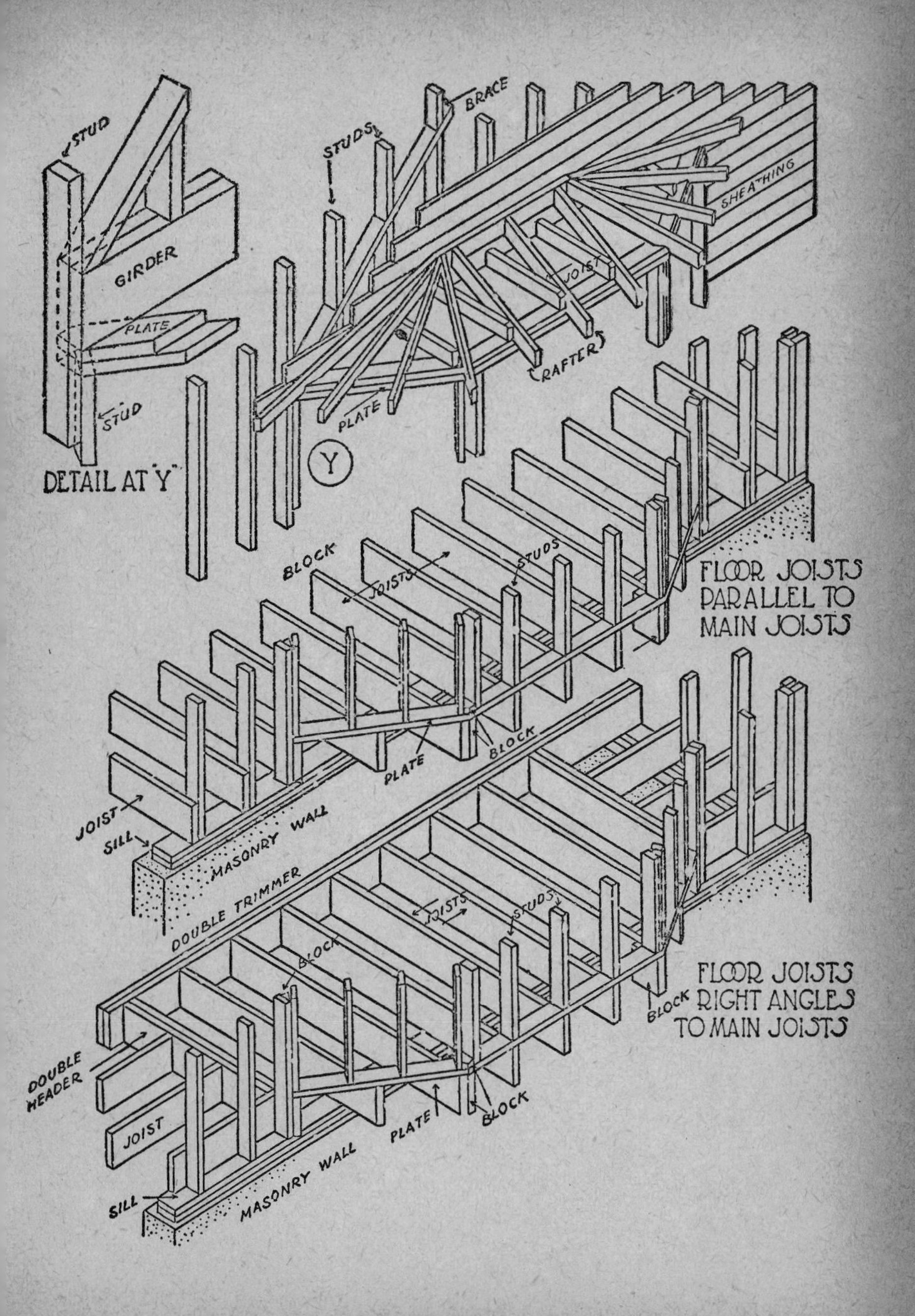

Fig. 42. Details of framing for bay in dining room.

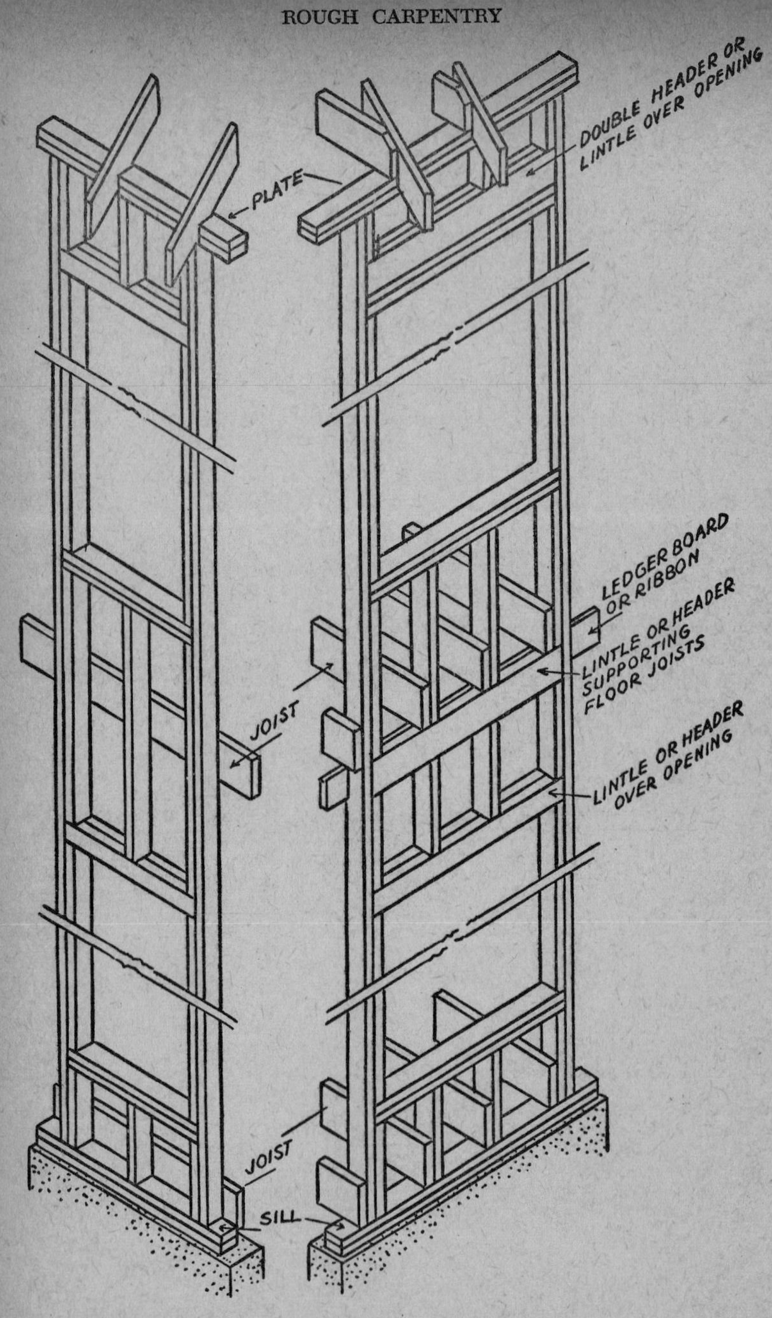

Fig. 43. Framing around openings. Left, for openings in walls or partitions parallel to joists; right, for average openings in bearing wall or partitions.

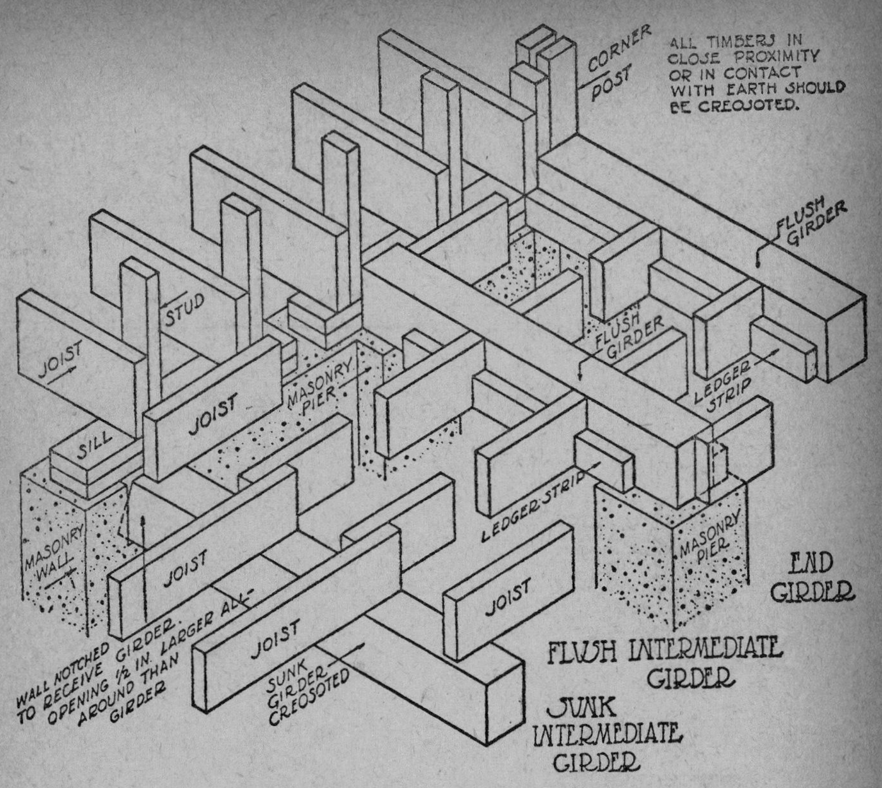

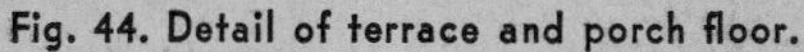
Fig. 44. Detail of terrace and porch floor.

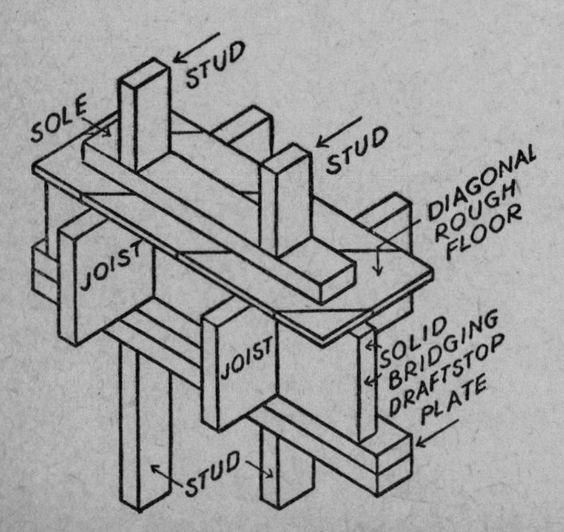

Fig. 45. Partition at right angles to joists (western frame).

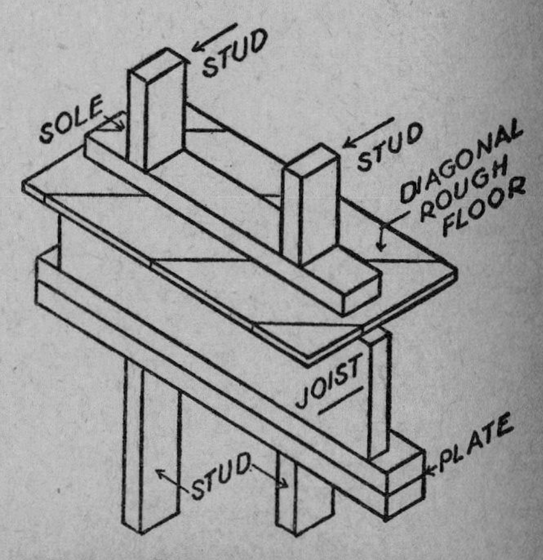

Fig. 46. Partition parallel with joists (western frame).

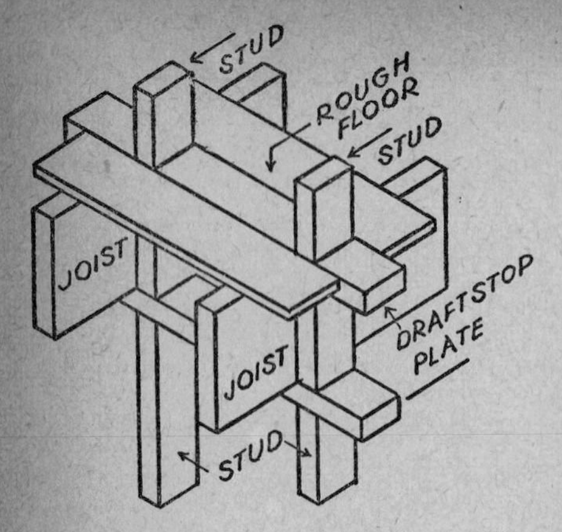

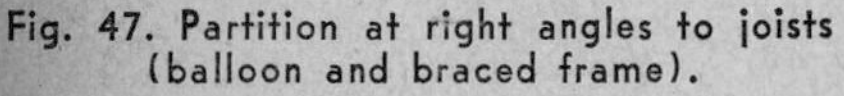
Fig. 47. Partition at right angles to joists (balloon and braced frame).

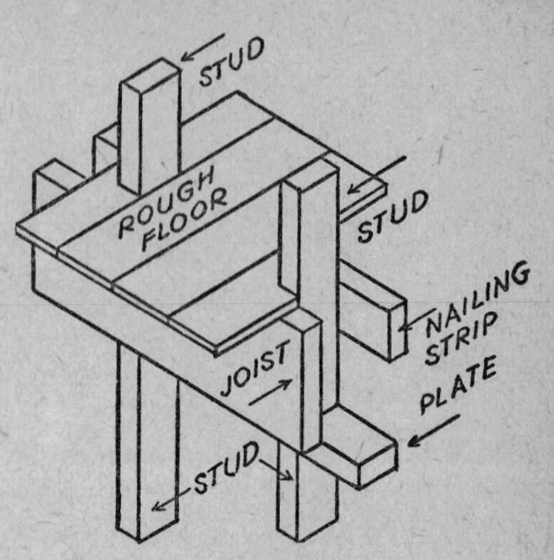

Fig. 48. Partition parallel with joists (balloon and braced frame).

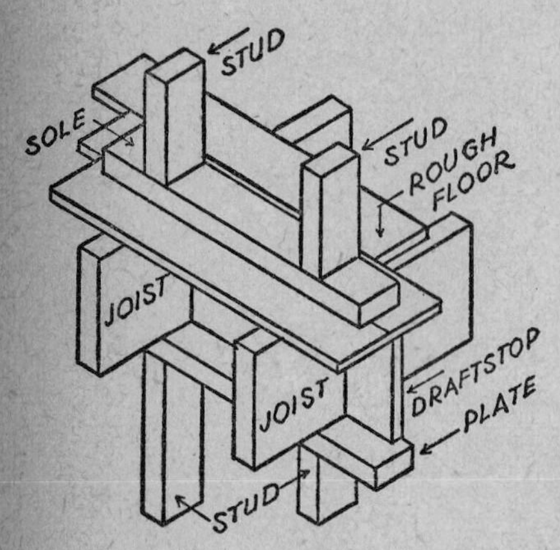

Fig. 49. Partition at right angles to joists (balloon frame).

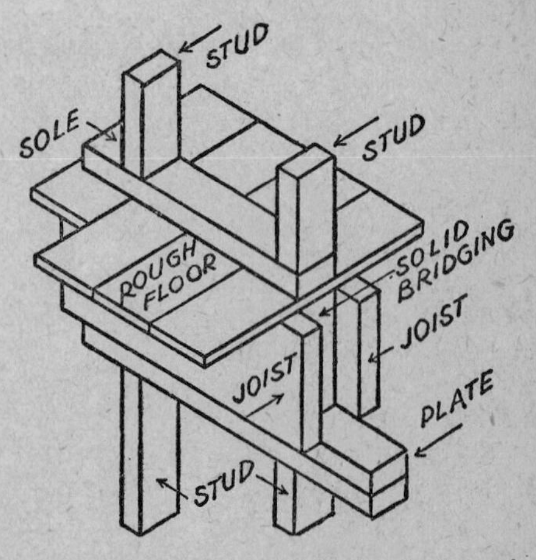

Fig. 50. Partition parallel with joists and joists spread for pipes, etc.

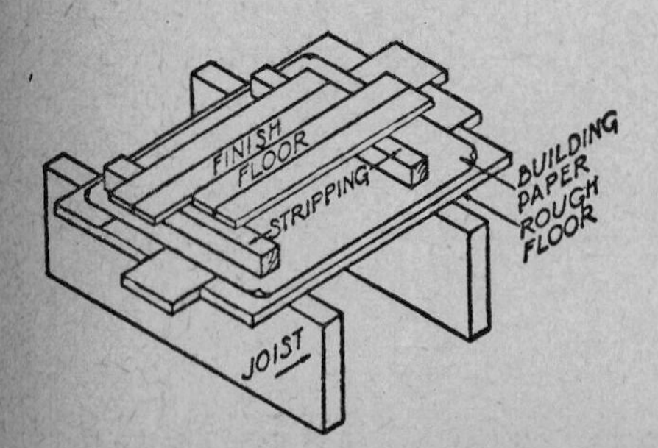

Fig. 51. Use of stripping in floors to provide space for conduits.

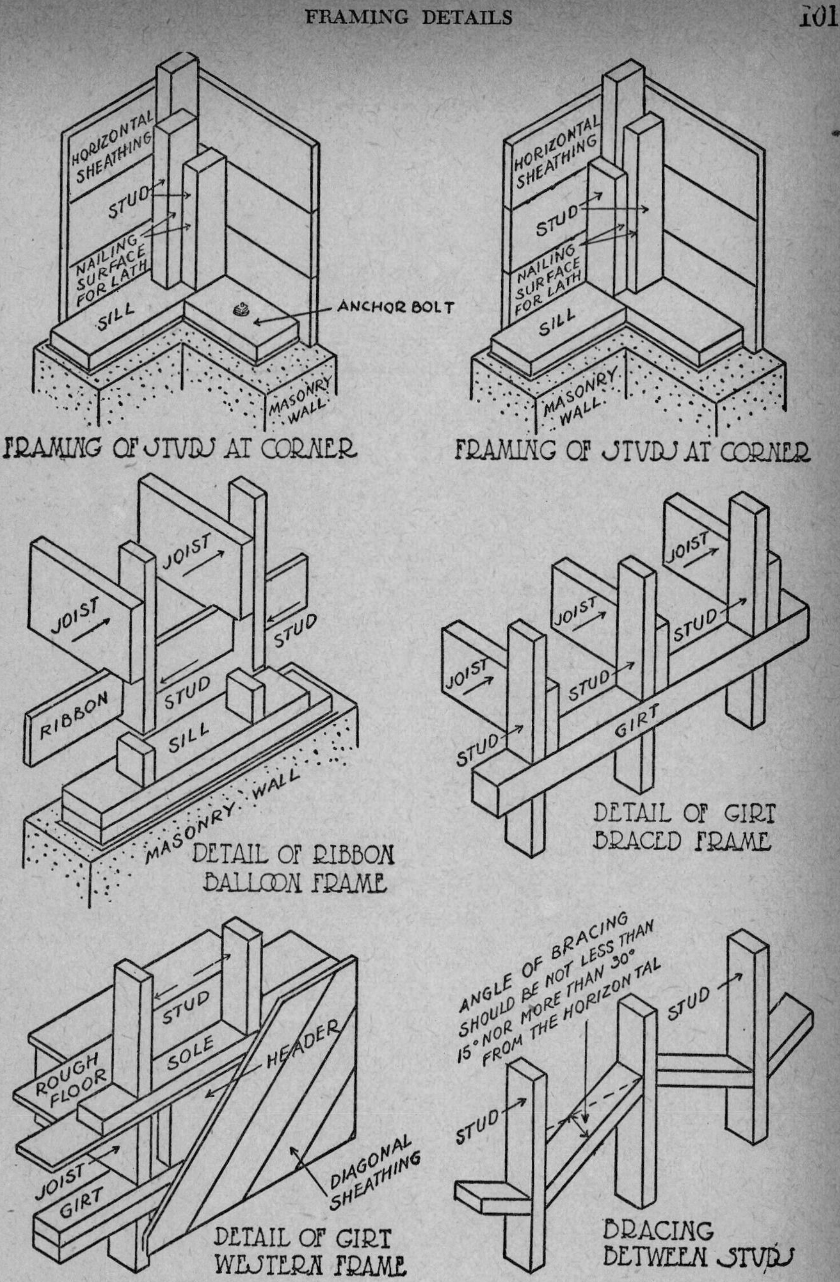
HORIZONTAL SHEATHING
STUD
NAILING SURFACE FOR LATH
SILL
ANCHOR BOLT
MASONRY WALL
FRAMING OF STUDS AT CORNER
HORIZONTAL SHEATHING
STUD
NAILING SURFACE FOR LATH
SILL
MASONRY WALL
FRAMING OF STUDS AT CORNER
JOIST
JOIST
STUD
RIBBON
STUD
SILL
MASONRY WALL
DETAIL OF RIBBON BALLOON FRAME
JOIST
JOIST
STUD
JOIST
STUD
STUD
GIRT
DETAIL OF GIRT BRACED FRAME
STUD
ROUGH FLOOR
SOLE
HEADER
JOIST
GIRT
DIAGONAL SHEATHING
DETAIL OF GIRT WESTERN FRAME
ANGLE OF BRACING SHOULD BE NOT LESS THAN 15° NOR MORE THAN 30° FROM THE HORIZONTAL
STUD
STUD
BRACING BETWEEN STUDS

Fig. 52.

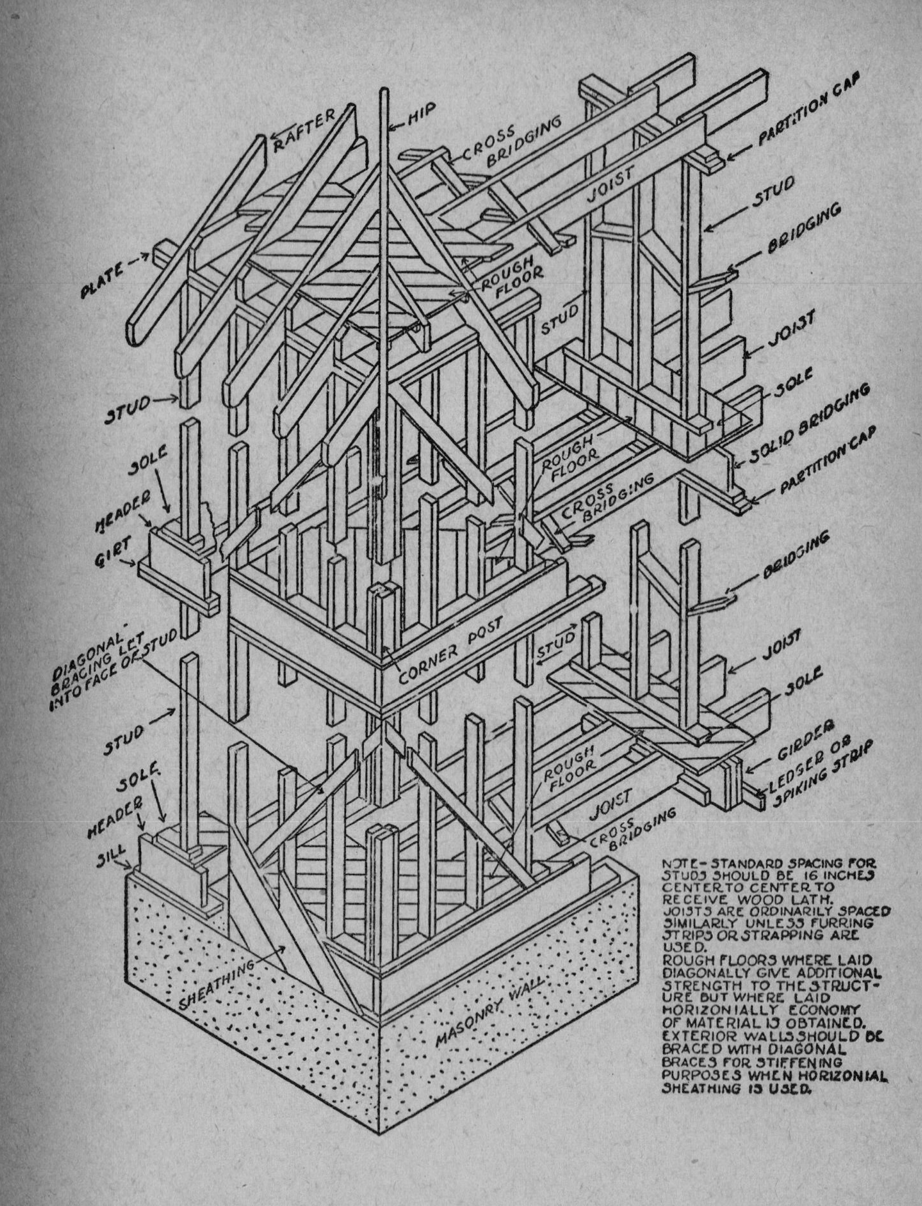

Fig. 53. Western frame construction.

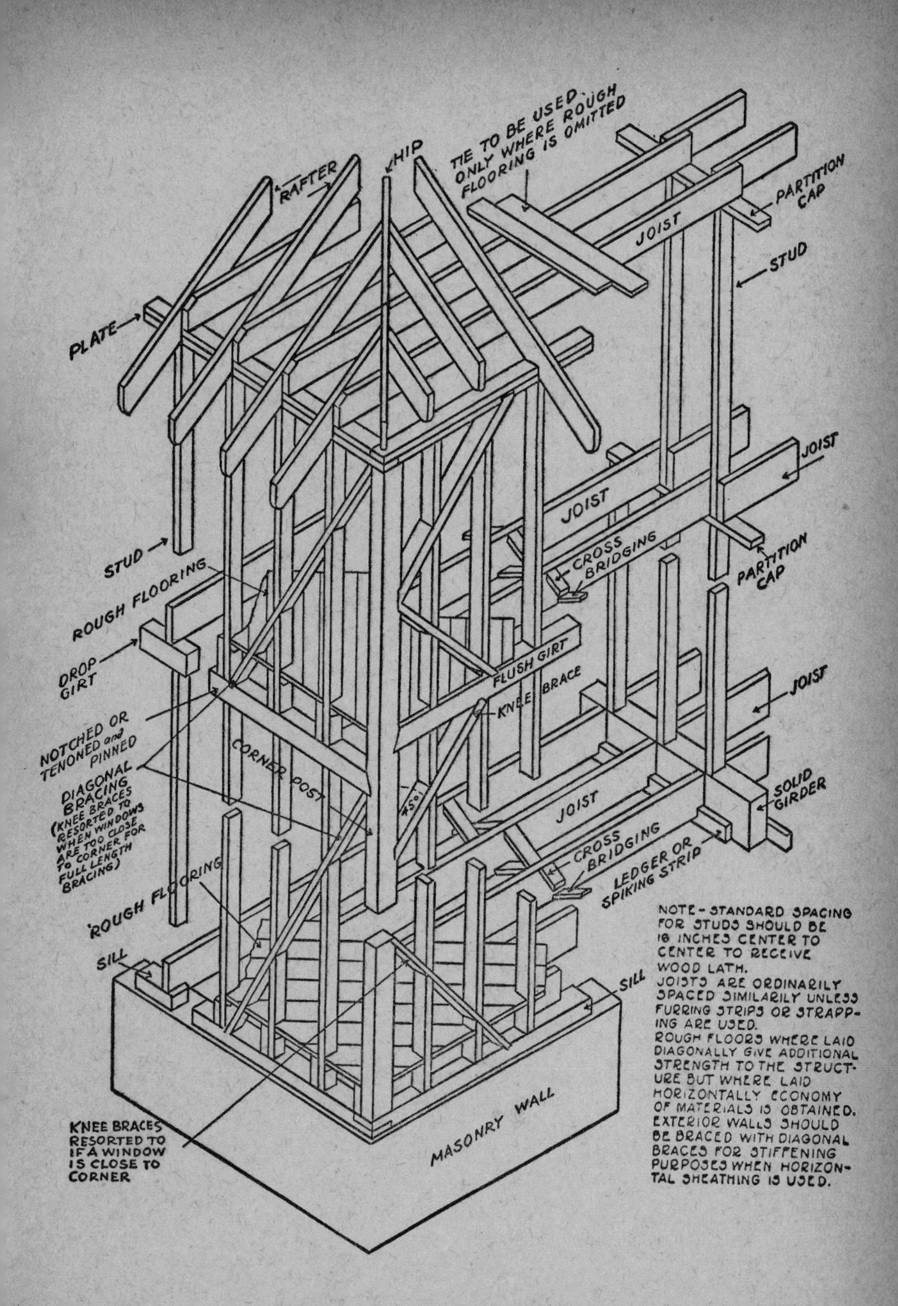
TIE TO BE USED ONLY WHERE ROUGH FLOORING IS OMITTED
RAFTER
HIP
PARTITION CAP
JOIST
STUD
PLATE
JOIST
JOIST
CROSS BRIDGING
PARTITION CAP
STUD
ROUGH FLOORING
DROP GIRT
FLUSH GIRT
KNEE BRACE
JOIST
NOTCHED OR TENONED and PINNED
DIAGONAL BRACING (KNEE BRACES RESORTED TO WHEN WINDOWS ARE TOO CLOSE TO CORNER FOR FULL LENGTH BRACING)
CORNER POST
45°
JOIST
SOLID GIRDER
CROSS BRIDGING
LEDGER OR SPIKING STRIP
ROUGH FLOORING
SILL
SILL
NOTE - STANDARD SPACING FOR STUDS SHOULD BE 16 INCHES CENTER TO CENTER TO RECEIVE WOOD LATH.
JOISTS ARE ORDINARILY SPACED SIMILARILY UNLESS FURRING STRIPS OR STRAPPING ARE USED.
ROUGH FLOORS WHERE LAID DIAGONALLY GIVE ADDITIONAL STRENGTH TO THE STRUCTURE BUT WHERE LAID HORIZONTALLY ECONOMY OF MATERIALS IS OBTAINED.
EXTERIOR WALLS SHOULD BE BRACED WITH DIAGONAL BRACES FOR STIFFENING PURPOSES WHEN HORIZONTAL SHEATHING IS USED.
MASONRY WALL
KNEE BRACES RESORTED TO IF A WINDOW IS CLOSE TO CORNER

Fig. 54. Braced frame construction.

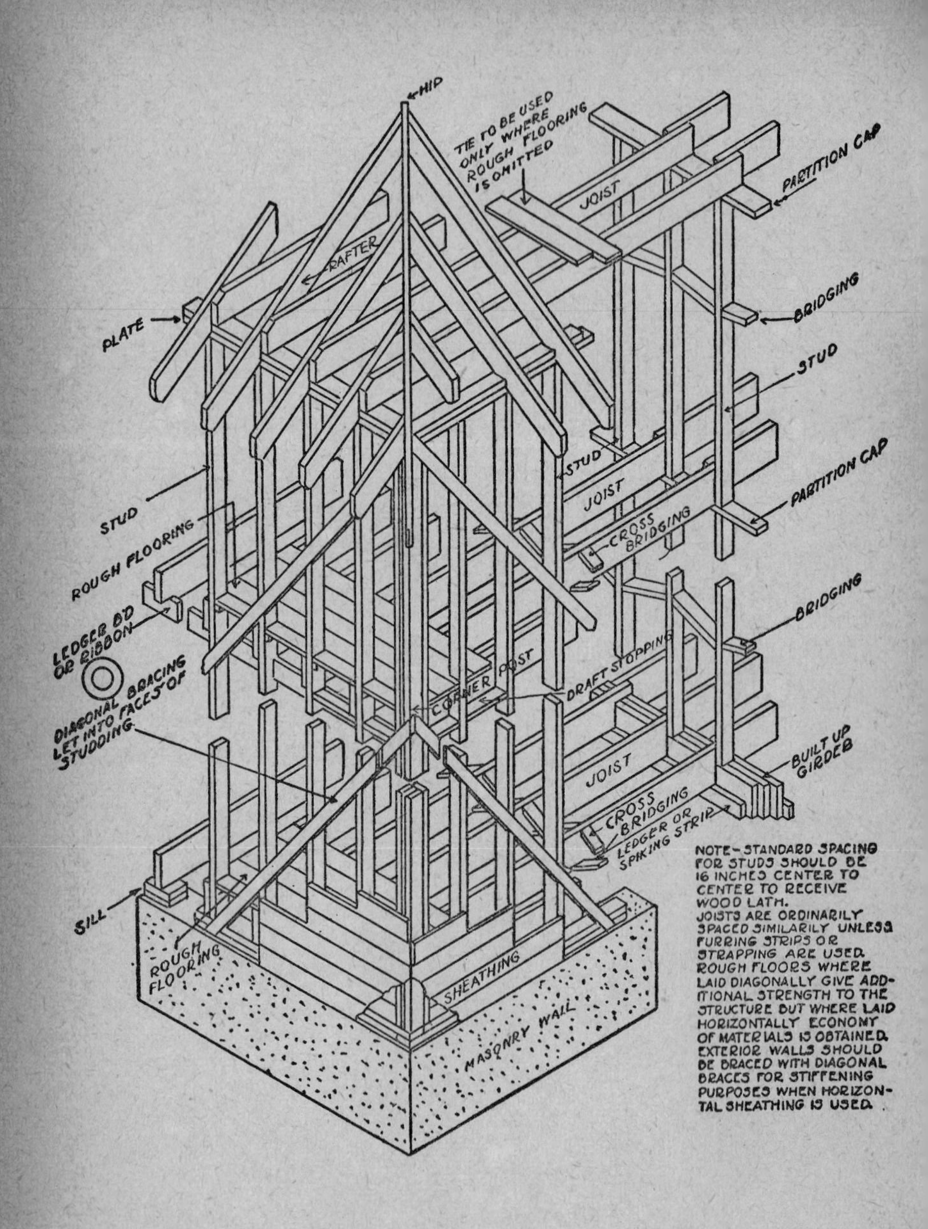

Fig. 55. Balloon frame construction.

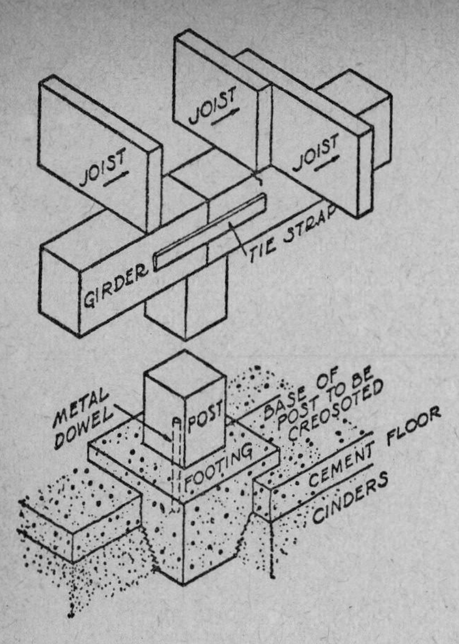

Fig. 56. Detail of posts in basement.

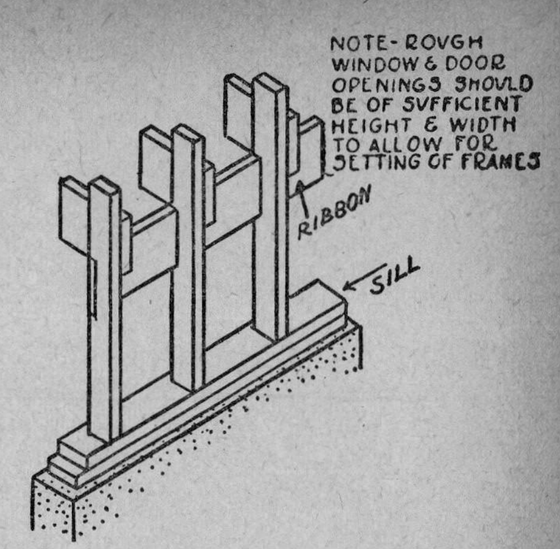

Fig. 57. Framing method reducing height of foundation.

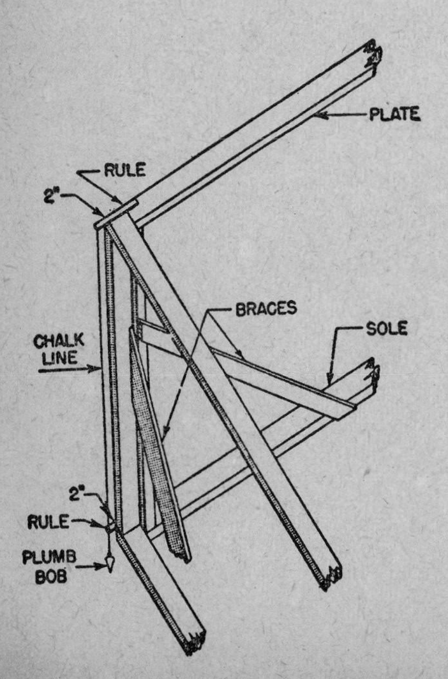

Fig. 58. Method of plumbing posts.

PLUMBING CORNER POSTS

To plumb a corner with a plumb bob, first attach to the bob a string long enough to extend to or below the bottom of the post. Lay a rule on top of the post so that 2 inches of the rule extends over the post on the side to be plumbed, then hang the bob-line over the rule so that the line is 2 inches from the post and extends to the bottom of it (fig. 58). With another rule, measure the distance from the post to the center of the line at the bottom of the post; if it does not measure 2 inches, the post is not plumb. Move the post inward or outward until the distance from the post to the center of the line is exactly 2 inches, then nail the temporary brace in place. Repeat this procedure for the other outside face of the post. The post is then plumb. This process is carried out for the remaining corner posts of the building. If a plumb bob or level is not available, a rock, a half-brick, or some small piece of metal may be used instead.

METHOD OF PLUMBING AND STRAIGHTENING WALL

After the corner post, T-post, and intermediate wall studs have been nailed to the plates or girts, the walls must be plumbed and straightened so that the permanent braces and rafters may be installed. This is done by using a level or plumb bob and a chalk line.

Plumb one corner post with the level or plumb bob and nail temporary braces to it to hold the post in place (fig. 60). Repeat this procedure for all corner posts. Fasten a chalk line to the outside of one post at the top and stretch the line to the post at the opposite end of the building, fastening the line to this post in the same manner as for the first post. Place a small ¾-inch block under each end of line as shown in figure 60 to give clearance. Place temporary braces at intervals small enough to hold the wall straight. When the wall is far enough away from the line to permit a ¾-inch block barely to slide between the line and the plate, the brace is nailed. This procedure is carried out for the entire perimeter of the building. Inside partition walls should be similarly straightened.

Fig. 59. Two types of wall bracing commonly used. A, cut-in bracing, consisting of 2" x 4" pieces fitted between the studs at an angle of approximately 45° with the horizontal and in a line from top to bottom plates; B, let-in bracing, consisting generally of a 1" x 4" piece set into notches in the studs and continuous from top to bottom.

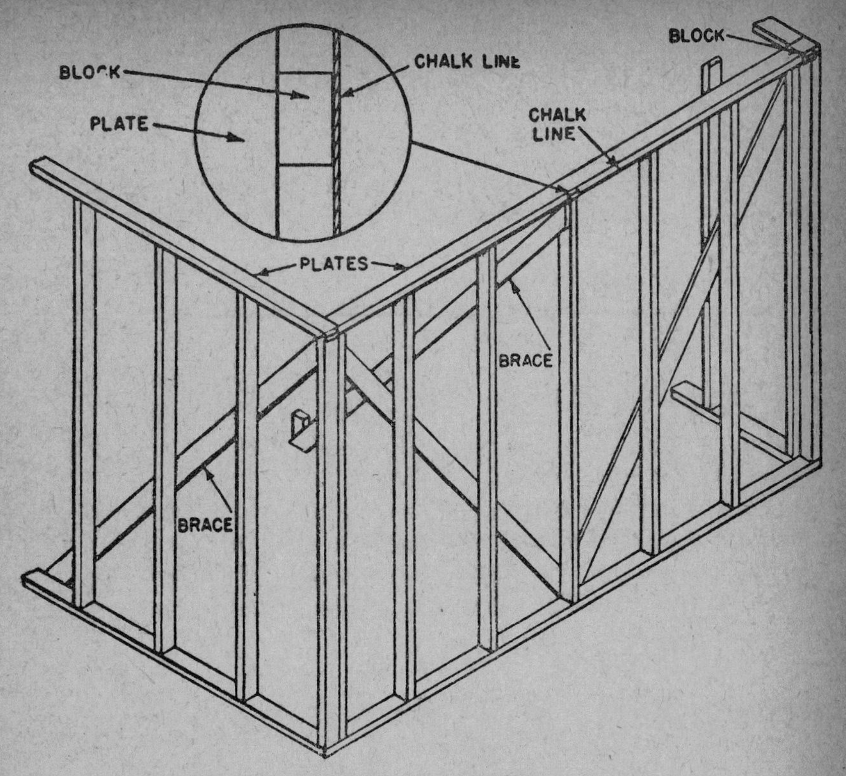

Fig. 60. Method of straightening walls.

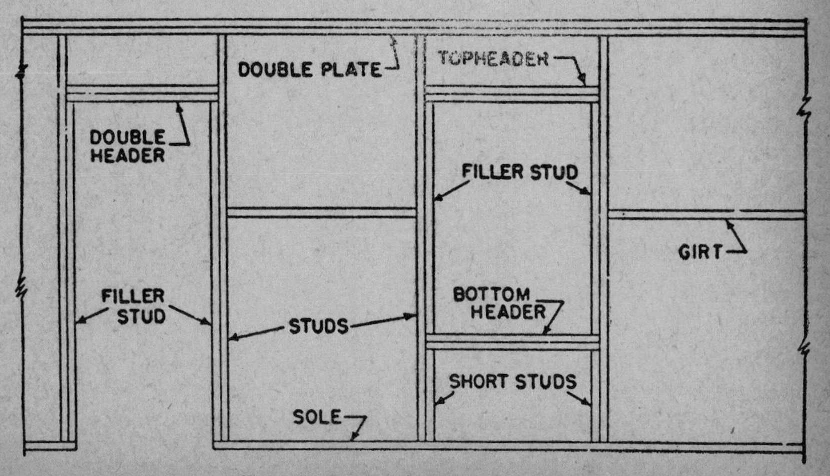

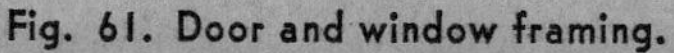
Fig. 61. Door and window framing.

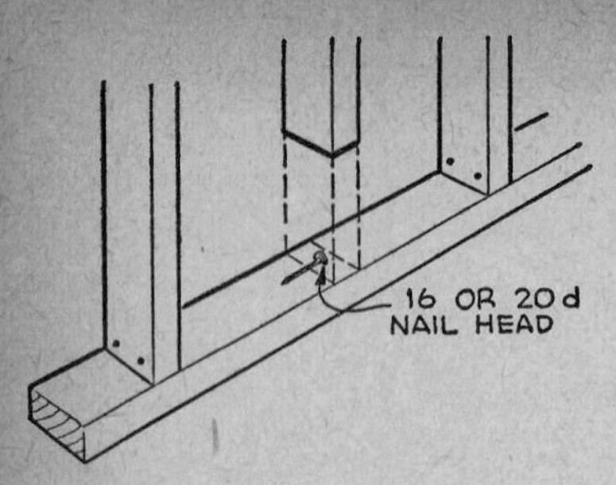

Fig. 62.

NAILING STUDDING

Difficulty is often encountered in nailing the bottom ends of studs to the sole plate due to the fact that in toe-nailing in the nails, the bottom of the stud tends to move out of position. This can be avoided by driving in one side of the head of a 16d nail along the line marking the location of the stud on the sole plate (fig. 62). The nail head will hold the stud in position so that it can be toe-nailed into place from the opposite side.

SIDING SIZES AND ESTIMATING QUANTITIES

The nominal sizes which are used in computing the footage of lumber are based upon the rough green sizes of boards which are cut from the logs. These rough green boards shrink somewhat in width and thickness as they dry, and their size is further reduced by machining to pattern. The following table is an ex-

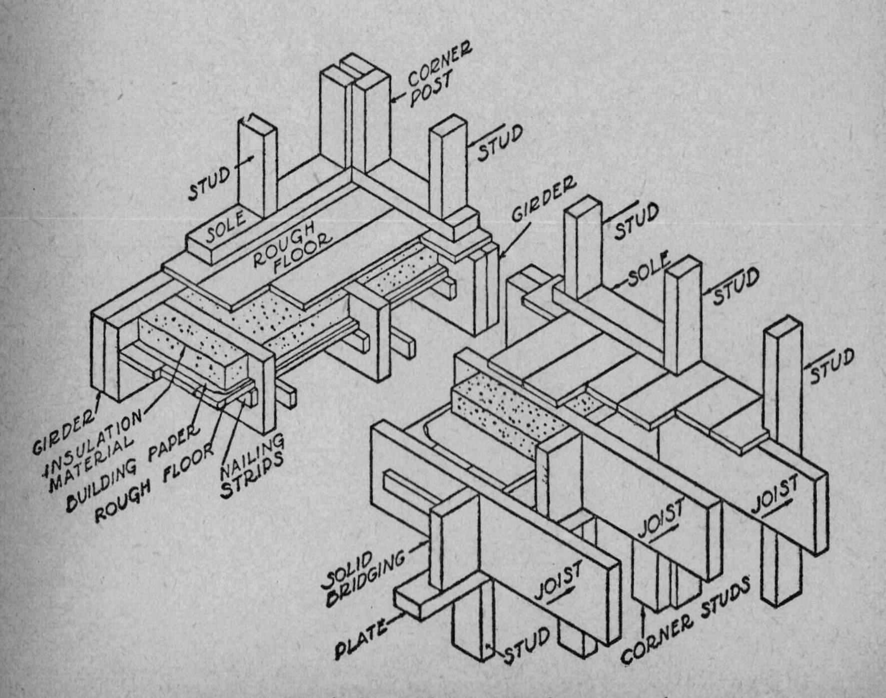

Fig. 63. Detail of second floor over the rear porch.

tract from the American Lumber Standards giving the nominal and finished sizes for siding to which, with minor variations, most siding is produced. It will serve as a sufficiently accurate guide for the design of exterior wall surfaces (the thicknesses apply to all widths and the widths to all thicknesses except as modified):

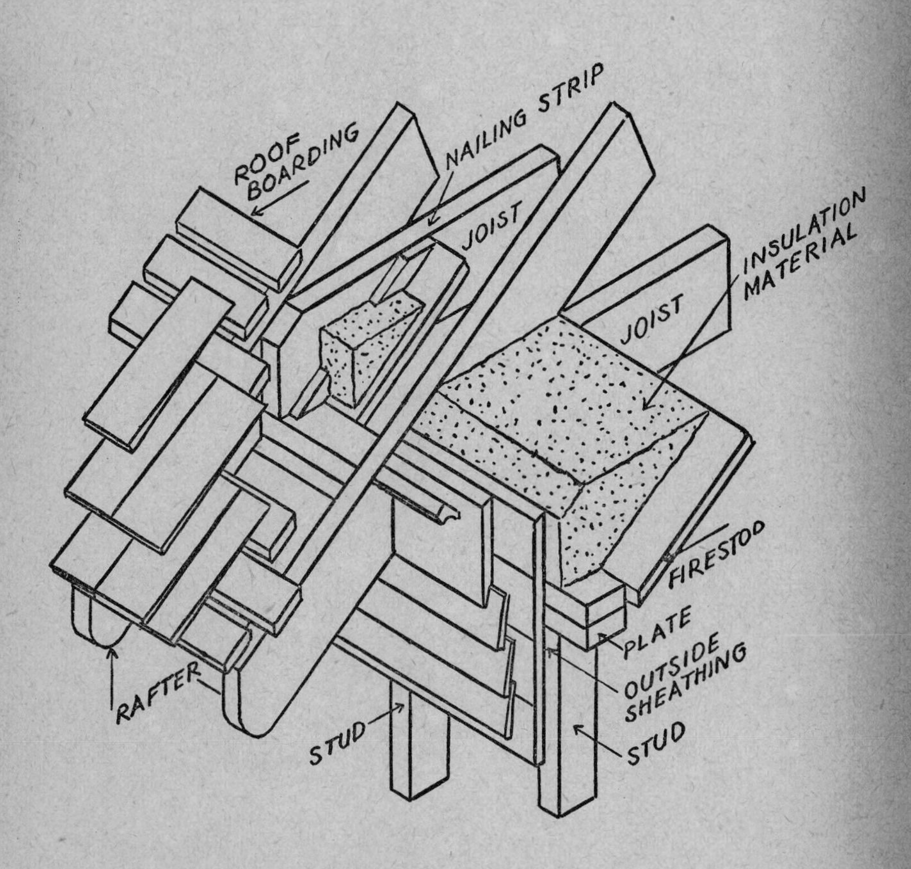

Fig. 64. Fire-stopping at cornice.

STANDARD SIDING SIZES

Siding	Size, board measure		Dressed dimensions	
	Thickness	Width	Standard thickness	Standard face width
	Inches	Inches	Inches	Inches
Bevel	....	4	$\frac{7}{16}$ by $\frac{3}{16}$	3½
	....	5	⅝ by $\frac{3}{16}$	4½
	....	6	....	5½
Wide beveled	....	8	$\frac{7}{16}$ by $\frac{3}{16}$	7¼
	....	10	$\frac{9}{16}$ by $\frac{3}{16}$	9¼
	....	12	$\frac{11}{16}$ by $\frac{3}{16}$	11¼
Rustic and drop (shiplapped)	....	4	$\frac{9}{16}$	3⅛
	....	5	¾	4⅛
	....	6	....	5$\frac{1}{16}$
	....	8	....	6⅞
Rustic and drop (dressed and matched)	....	4	$\frac{9}{16}$	3¼
	....	5	¾	4¼
	....	6	....	5$\frac{3}{16}$
	....	8	....	7

In patterned siding, $\frac{11}{16}$, ¾, 1, 1¼, and 1½ inches thick, board measure, the tongue shall be ¼ inch wide in tongued-and-grooved lumber, and the lap ⅜ inch wide in shiplapped lumber, with the over-all widths ¼ inch and ⅜ inch wider, respectively, than the face widths shown above.

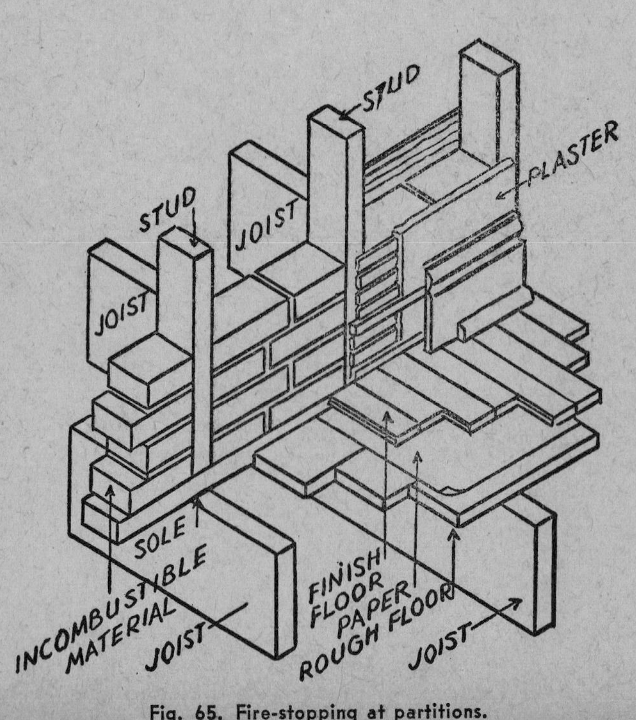

Fig. 65. Fire-stopping at partitions.

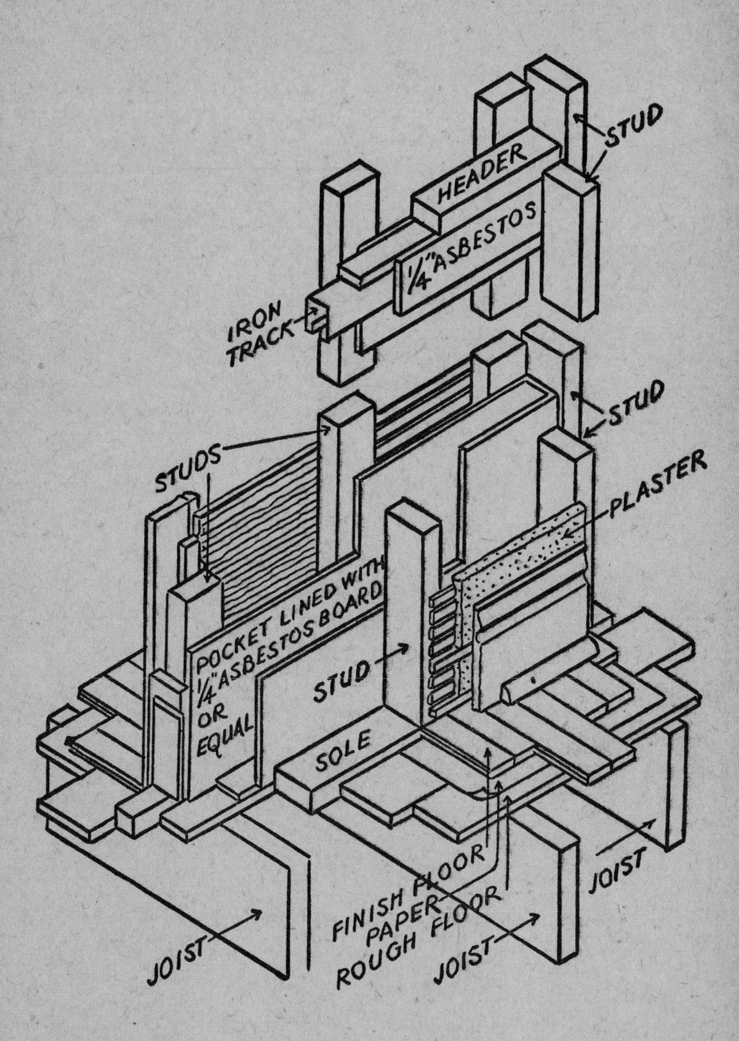

Fig. 66. Fire-stopping at sliding door.

In figuring the quantity of siding required for a home it is necessary to increase the square foot area of the walls, omitting openings, by enough to compensate for the machining of joints ship-lapped or dressed and matched and the overlap of bevel siding. The following allowances are approximately those that are usually made:

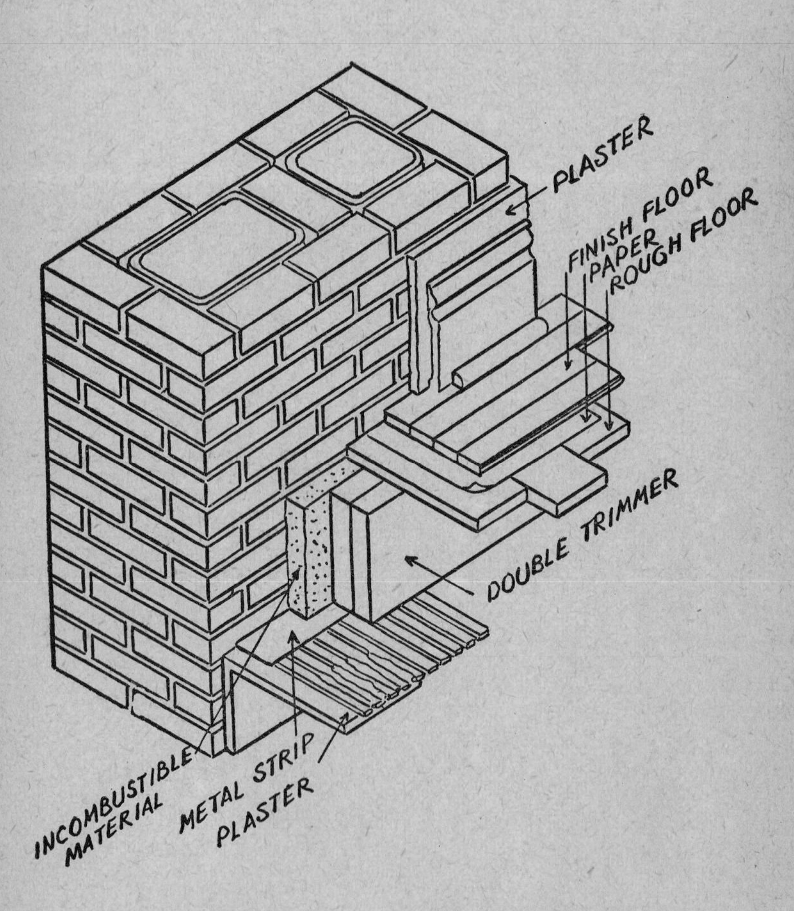

Fig. 67. Fire-stopping at chimney.

ALLOWANCES IN LAPPING SIDING

Bevel siding	1 x 4 with	3/4 lap	Add 45%
	*1 x 5	7/8 lap	38
	1 x 6	1 " lap	33
	1 x 8	1 1/4" lap	33
	1 x 10	1 1/2" lap	29
	1 x 12	1 1/2" lap	23
Rustic & drop siding (shiplapped)	1 x 4	Add 28%	
	*1 x 5	21	
	1 x 6	19	
	1 x 8	16	
Rustic & drop siding (dressed & matched)	1 x 4	23	
	*1 x 5	18	
	1 x 6	16	
	1 x 8	14	

* Unusual sizes.

An additional 3 to 5 percent should be allowed for cutting and fitting around openings and under the eaves.

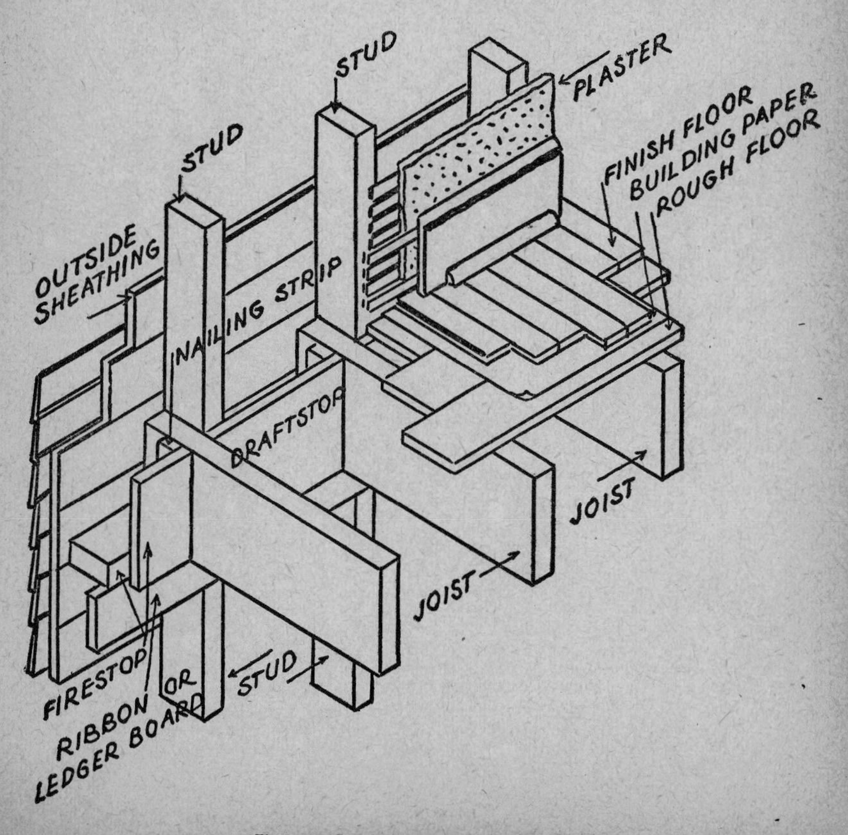

Fig. 68. Draft-stopping at ribbon.

FIGURE IN WOOD

The choice of wood for woodwork that is to be varnished or waxed is usually based largely upon the character of the figure in the wood. This figure is due to different causes in different woods. In woods like southern yellow pine and Douglas fir it results from the contrast within the growth rings; in others, such as oak, beech, or sycamore, it results from the flakes or rays in addition to the growth rings; in maple, walnut, and birch it results from wavy or curly grain; and in red gum it results from infiltrated coloring matter. Except where the figure in wood results from flakes or rays, the figure is more pronounced in plain-sawn lumber than in quarter-sawn. Figure resulting from wavy or curly grain or from infiltrated color does not occur in all lumber of a given species but only in lumber from occasional logs. To be certain of getting figured lumber in maple, walnut, or red gum special selection is necessary.

The color of wood has a decided influence on the figure. Stains, however, are so commonly and easily applied to practically all woods that the natural color is usually not of the first consideration except where a very light color is desired.

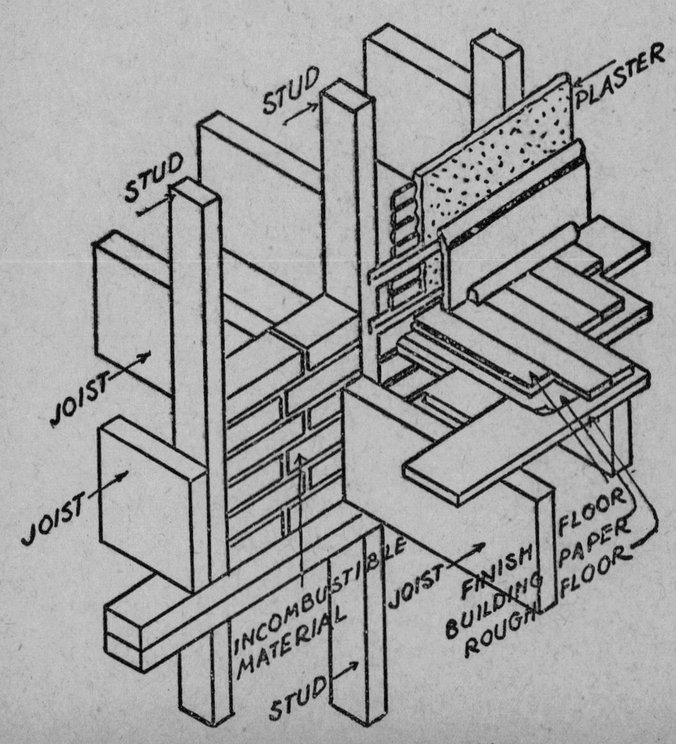

Fig. 69. Draft-stopping at partitions.

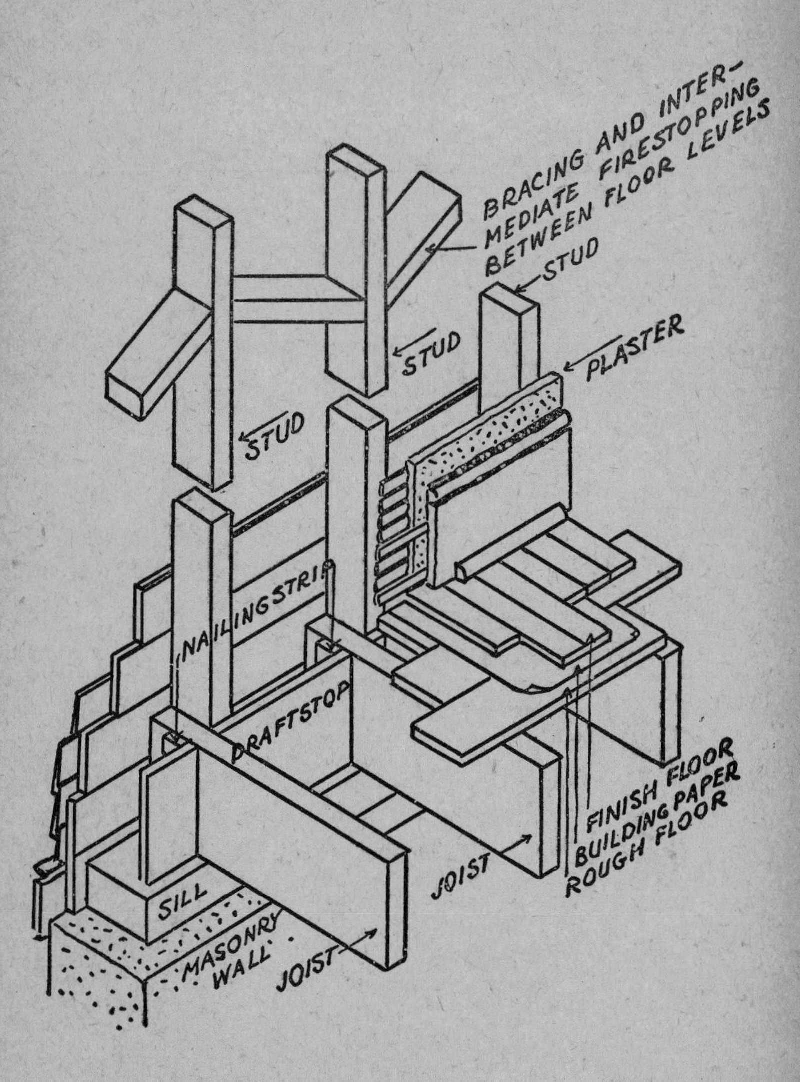

Fig. 70. Draft-stopping at sill.

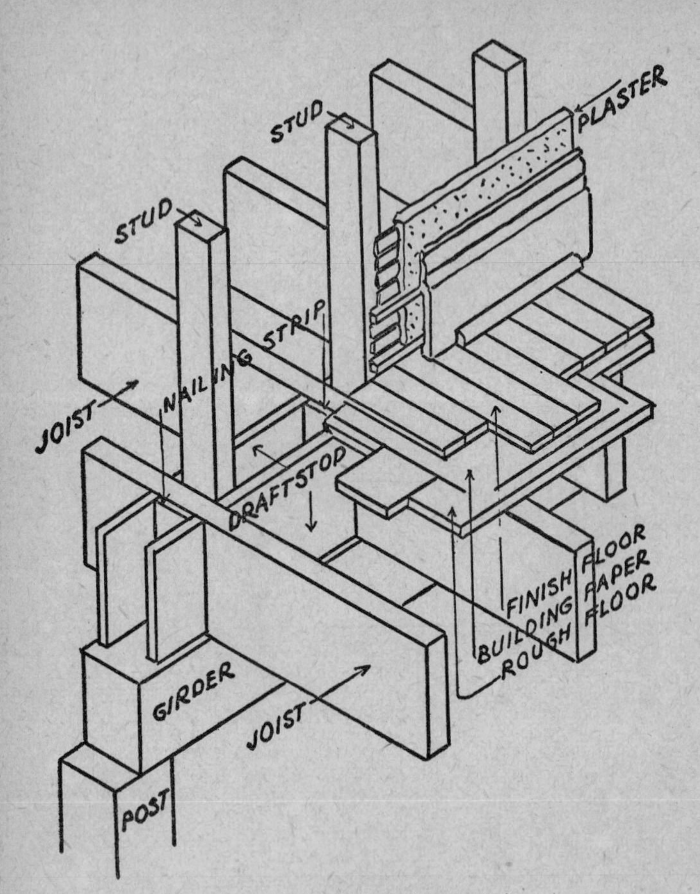

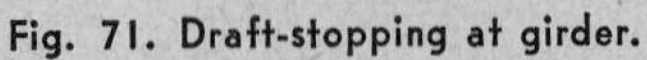
Fig. 71. Draft-stopping at girder.

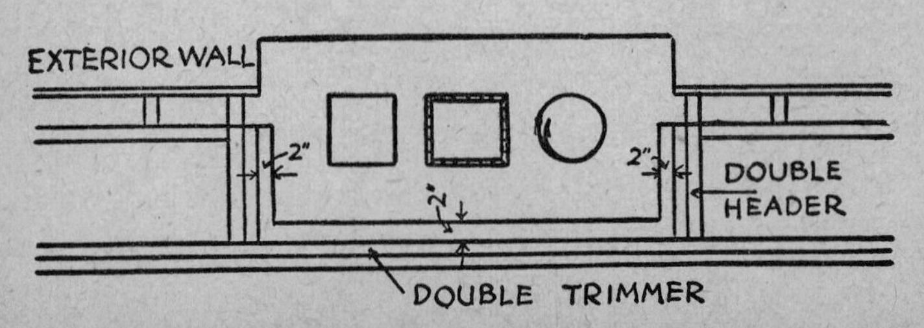

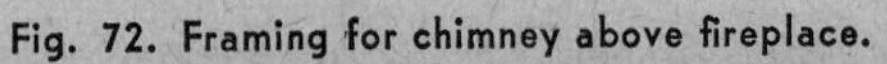
Fig. 72. Framing for chimney above fireplace.

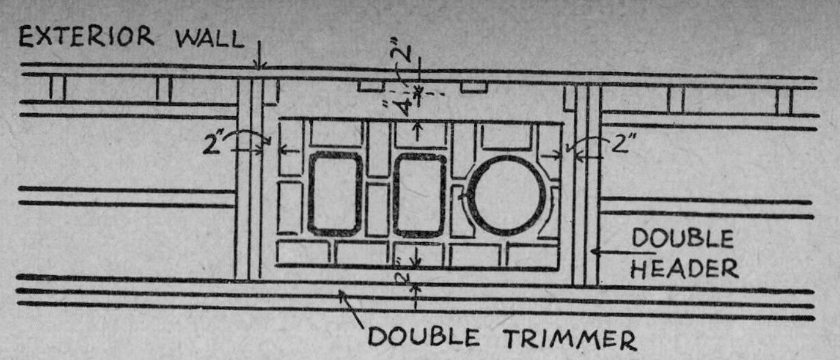

Fig. 73. Framing plan for brick chimney above fireplace.

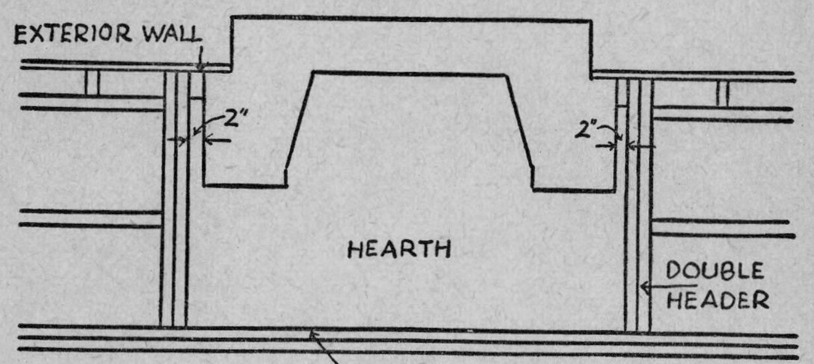

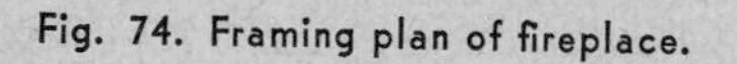

Fig. 74. Framing plan of fireplace.

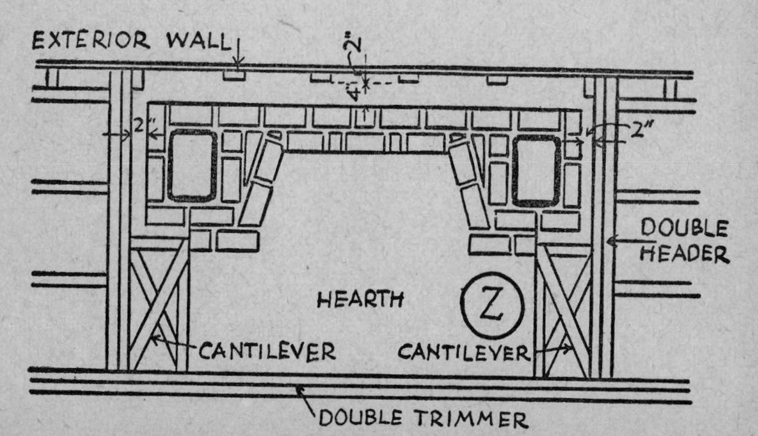

Fig. 75. Alternate plan of fireplace with additional flues shown.

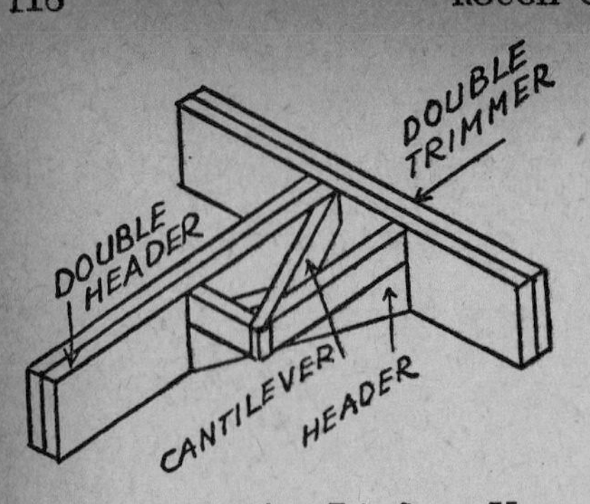

Fig. 76. Detail at Z in figure 75.

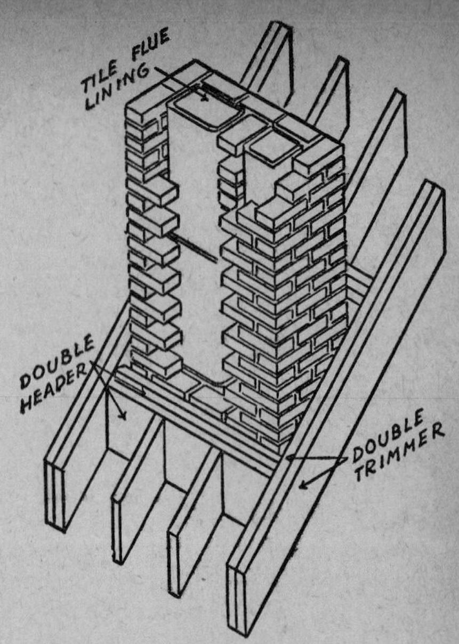

Fig. 77. Framing chimney at roof.

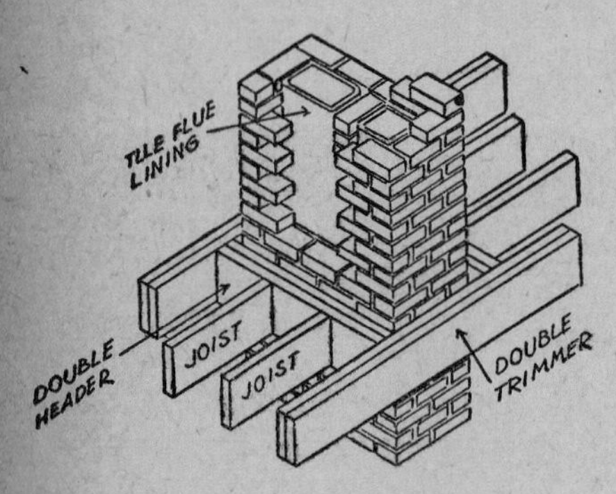

Fig. 78. Framing chimney at floors.

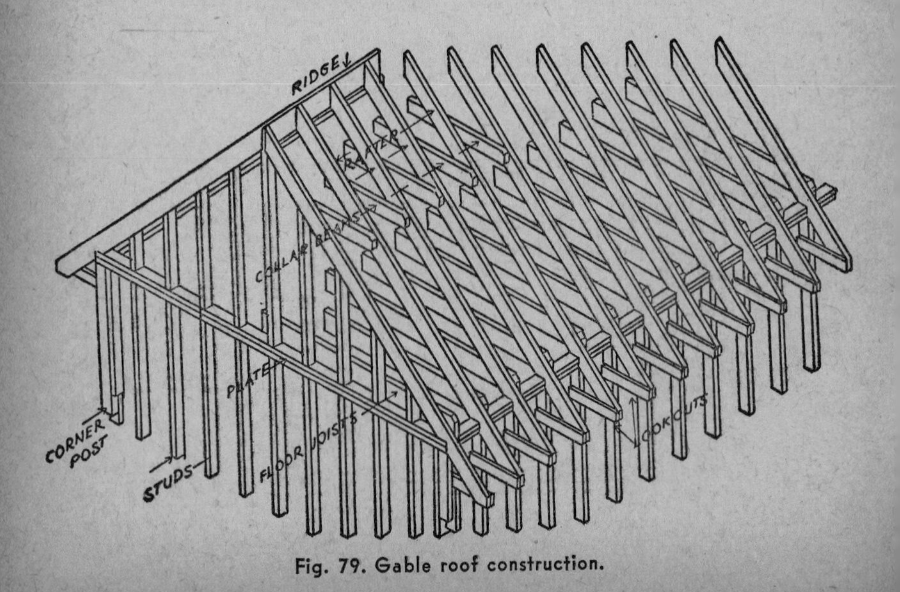

Fig. 79. Gable roof construction.

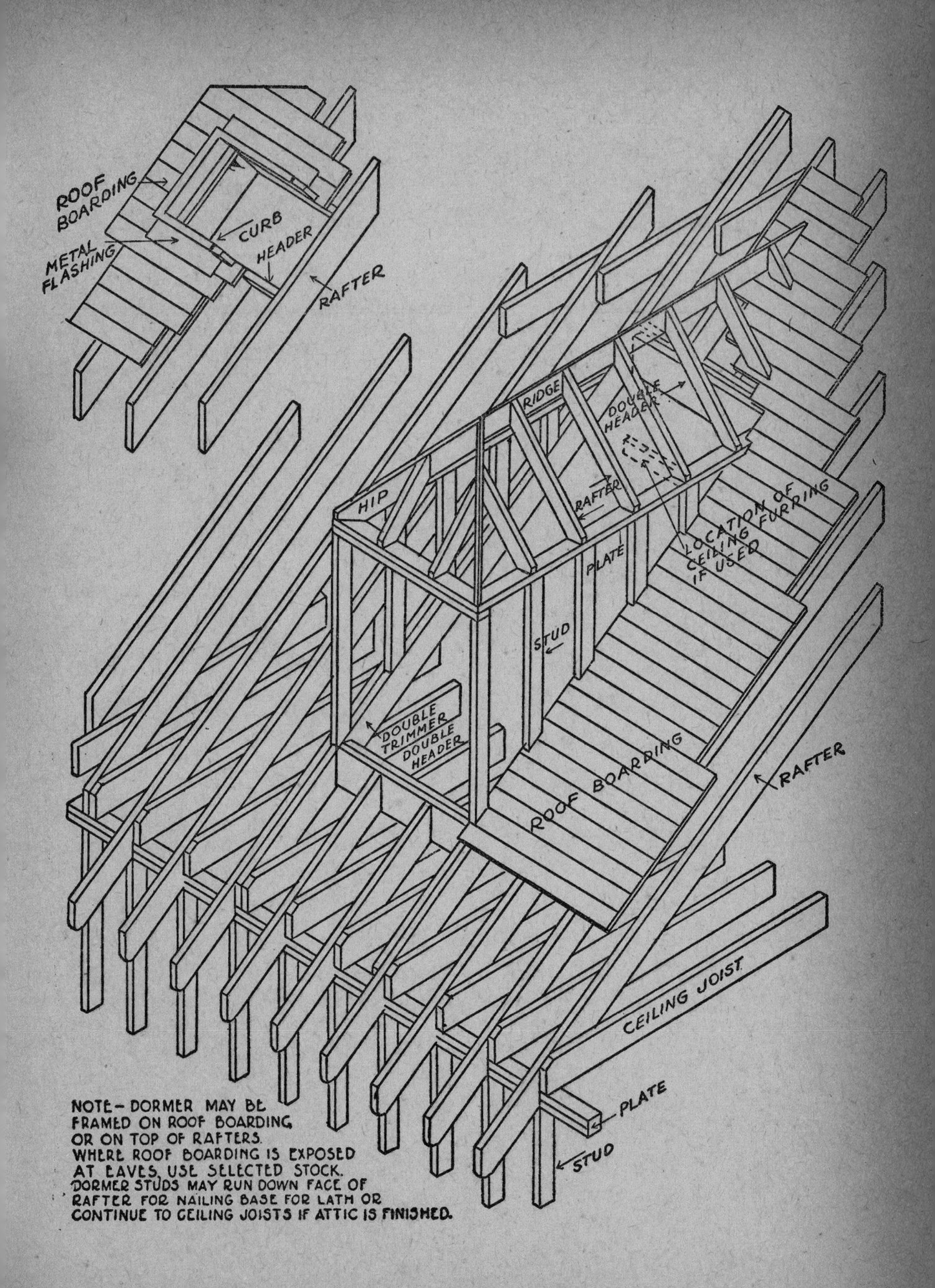
ROOF BOARDING
METAL FLASHING
CURB
HEADER
RAFTER
RIDGE
DOUBLE HEADER
HIP
RAFTER
PLATE
LOCATION OF CEILING FURRING IF USED
STUD
DOUBLE TRIMMER
DOUBLE HEADER
ROOF BOARDING
RAFTER
CEILING JOIST
PLATE
STUD
NOTE—DORMER MAY BE FRAMED ON ROOF BOARDING OR ON TOP OF RAFTERS.
WHERE ROOF BOARDING IS EXPOSED AT EAVES, USE SELECTED STOCK.
DORMER STUDS MAY RUN DOWN FACE OF RAFTER FOR NAILING BASE FOR LATH OR CONTINUE TO CEILING JOISTS IF ATTIC IS FINISHED.

Fig. 80. Detail of typical dormer. Inset shows framing at scuttle.

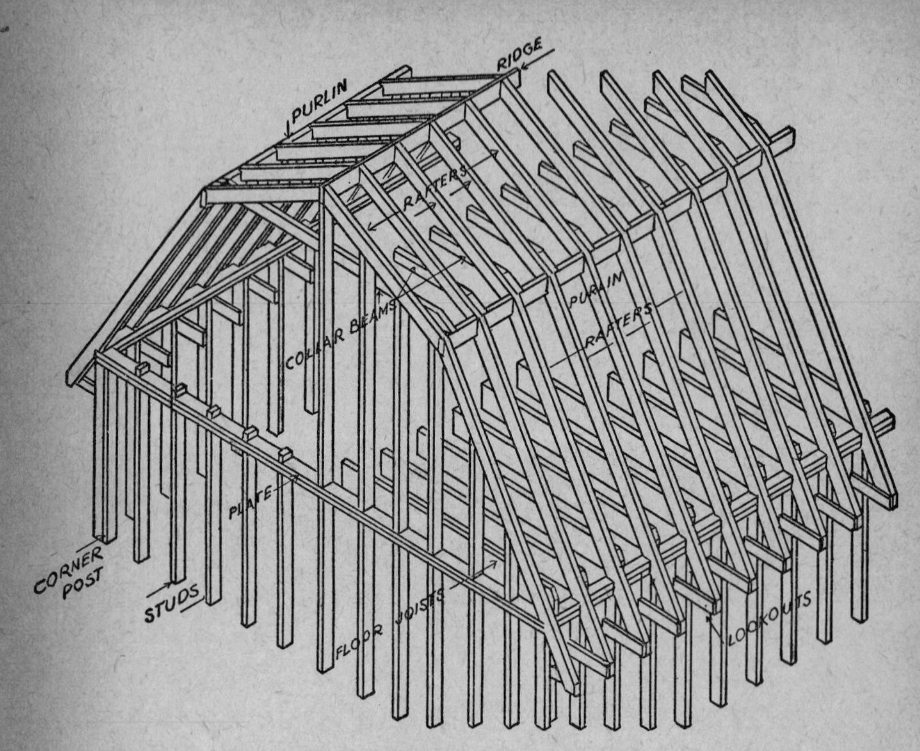

Fig. 81. Gambrel roof construction.

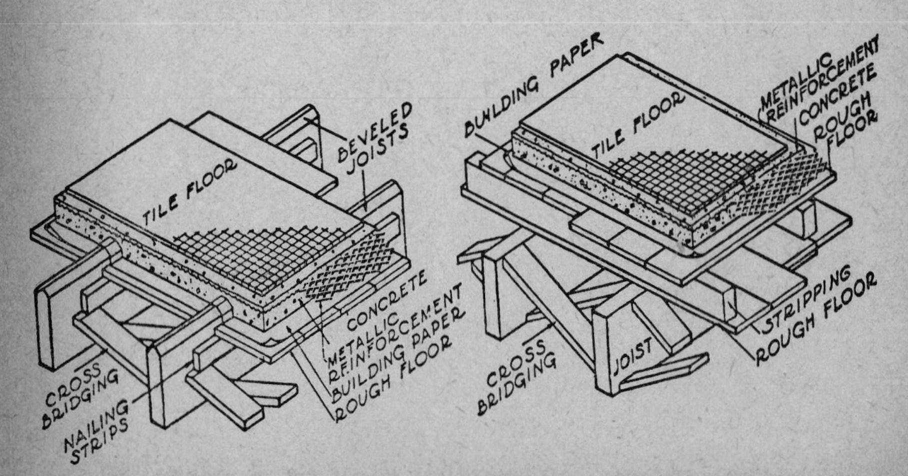

Fig. 82. Methods of laying tile floors. Left shows tile floor flush with main floor. Right shows tile floor stepped up.

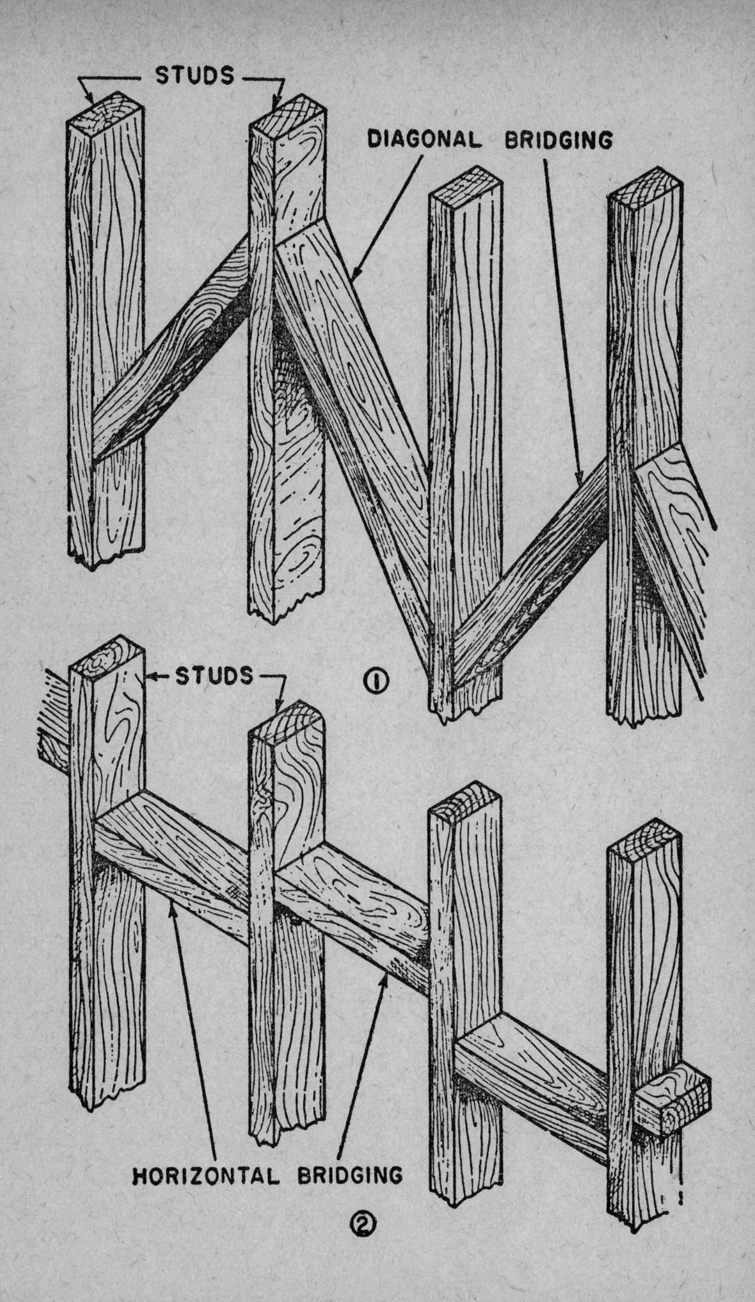

Fig. 83. Types of wall bridging.

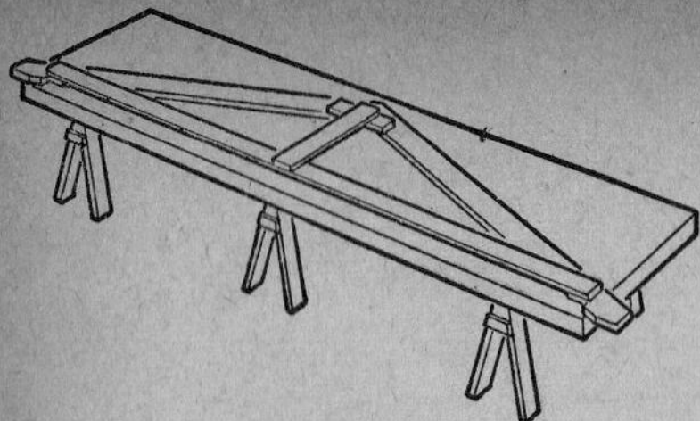

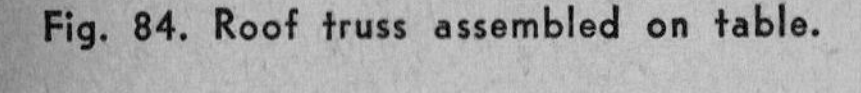

Fig. 84. Roof truss assembled on table.

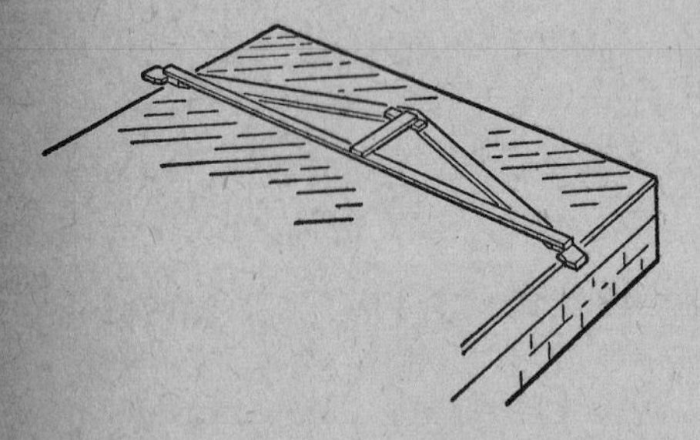

Fig. 85. Roof truss assembly on subfloor.

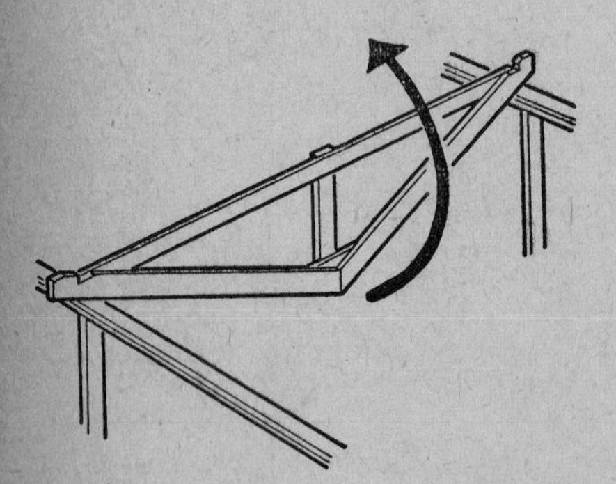

Fig. 86. Roof truss being put in position.

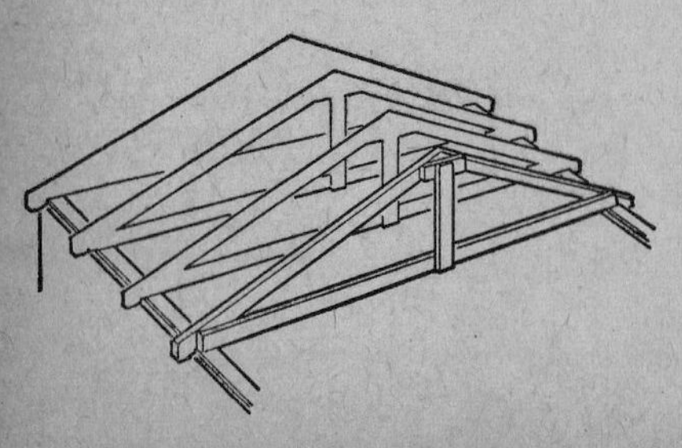

Fig. 87. Roof truss in position.

BRIDGING OF WALLS

Frame walls are bridged, in most cases, to make them more sturdy. There are two methods of bridging.

Diagonal bridging is nailed between studs at an angle (fig. 83, 1). It is more effective than the horizontal type since it forms a continuous truss and tends to keep the walls from sagging. Whenever possible, both inside and outside walls should be bridged alike.

Horizontal bridging is nailed between the studs horizontally and halfway between the sole and the plate (fig. 83, 2). This bridging is cut to lengths which correspond to the distance between the studs at the bottom. Such bridging not only stiffens the wall but will also help straighten studs.

ROOF TRUSSES

Roof trusses have several advantages over the conventional type of roof construction. Among these are the facts that the roof framework can be pre-assembled and that, in many cases, smaller size stock can be used. Figure 84 shows a section of truss being assembled on a large table. Figure 85 shows a truss assembly on the subfloor. Figure 86 shows how the truss is set into position; figure 87 shows truss in final position.

ADVANTAGES OF ROOF TRUSSES

Aside from direct benefits of reduced costs and savings in material

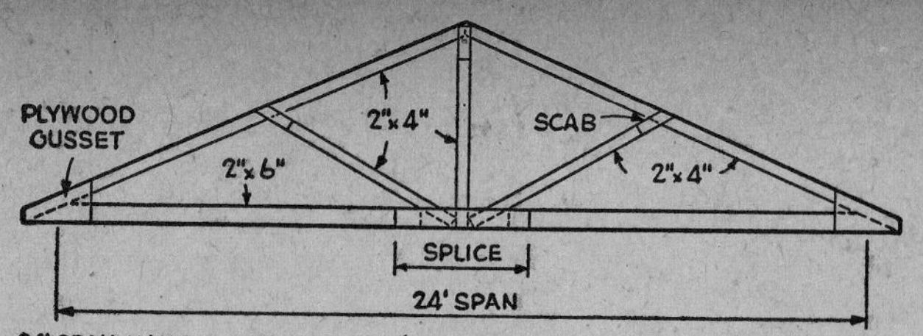

Fig. 88. Completed roof truss ready for installation.

and labor requirements, roof trusses offer special advantages in helping to speed up site erection and overcome delays due to weather conditions. These advantages are reflected not only in improved construction methods but also in further reductions in costs.

With pre-assembled trusses a roof can be put over the job quickly to provide protection against the weather. This offers advantages in all seasons and particularly in cold-weather building operations.

Because of the clear span afforded by trusses, fixed bearing partitions are not needed. This permits increased efficiency in laying floors and applying interior wall and ceiling finishes. Material can be brought in,

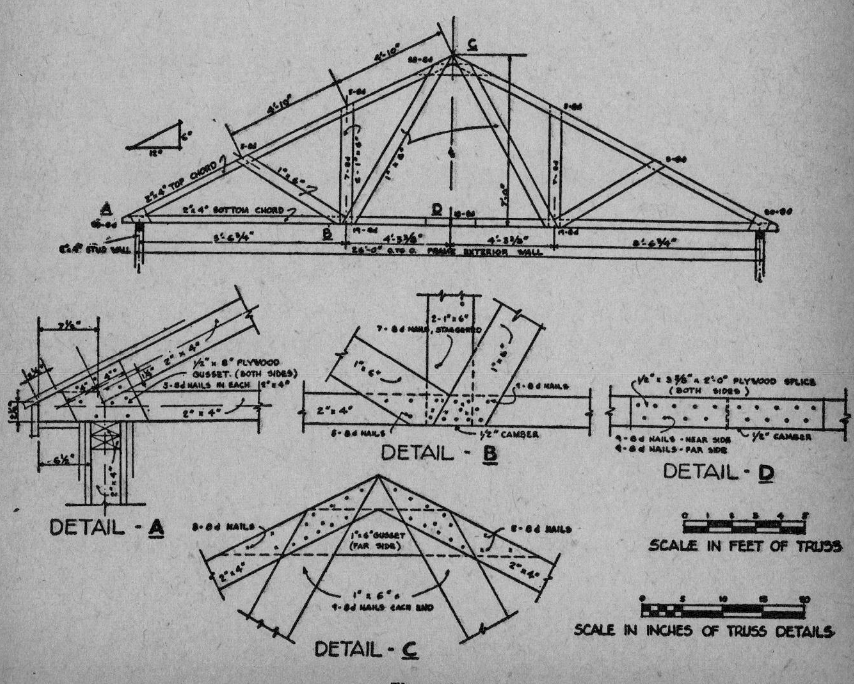

Fig. 89.

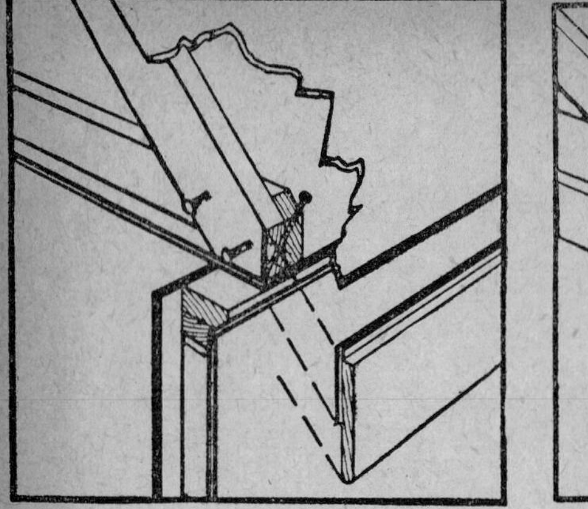

Fig. 90.

Fig. 91.

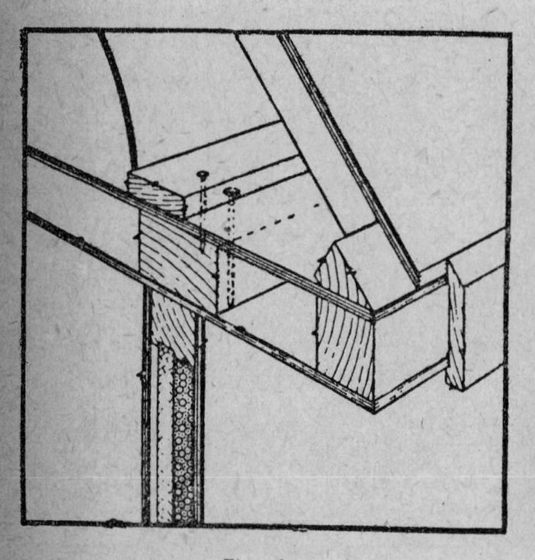

Fig. 92.

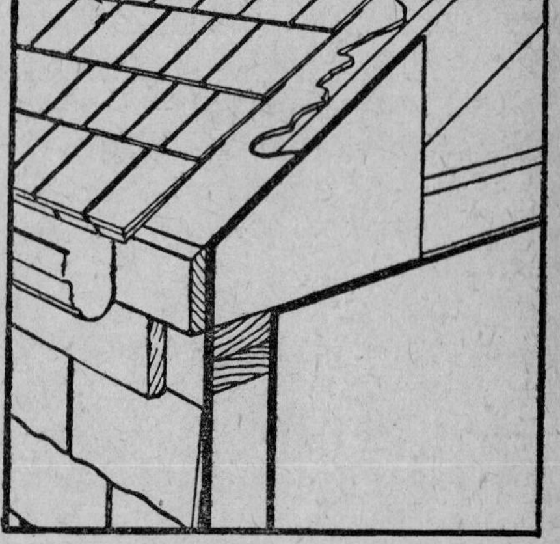

Fig. 93.

applied and trimmed conveniently without the waste of time and materials caused by having to fit materials around partitions. The fact that non-bearing partitions may be used considerably increases the flexibility of interior planning to provide for family activities.

In the case of houses built with insulation above crawl spaces, the quick roofing-over, made possible by the use of trusses, provides protection for insulation under the rough flooring. Without covering, the insulation material may get wet, impairing its value as insulation.

The trusses can be easily made on jig tables on the site or transported conveniently to the site ready for erection. They are relatively light in weight and can be readily set into place.

JOINING ROOFS TO WALLS

Figures 90 to 95 show various methods of joining roofs to walls. Figure 90 showed a pitched roof rafter fastened to the ceiling joist and the joist fastened to the top plate of the wall panel. Figure 91 shows a pitched rafter seated in the joist and the assembly fastened with a single lag screw to the panel plate. In figure 92 a block joint exerts its lateral thrust against a block attached to the second-floor panel, which is in turn fastened to the top wall plate. A truss type of roof is shown in figure 93; the rafter or upper chord is held firmly to the joist or lower chord of the truss with nail-glued gusset plates and the truss is fastened to the wall plate. Figures 94 and 95 show flat roofs consisting of stressed-cover panels that act as box beams.

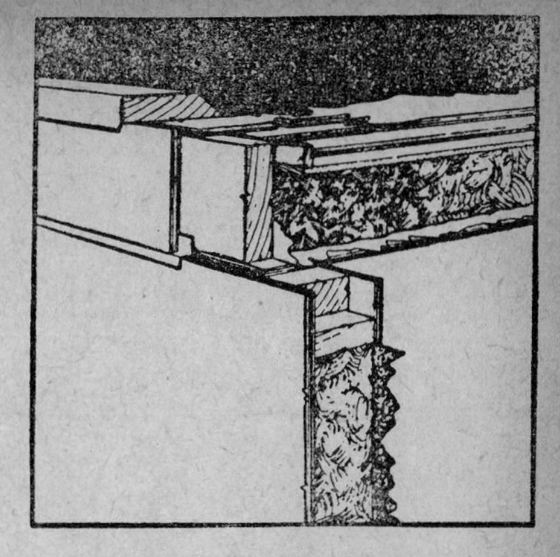

Fig. 94.

METHODS OF LAYING OUT RAFTERS

Rafters must be laid out and cut with slope, length, and overhang exactly right so that they will fit when placed in the position they are to occupy in the finished roof.

Scale or measurement methods.—The carpenter first determines the length of the rafter and the length of the piece of lumber from which the rafter may be cut. If he is working from a set of plans which includes a roof plan, the rafter lengths and the width of the building may be obtained from this plan. If no plans are available, the width of the building may be measured with a tape.

(1) To determine the rafter length, first find one-half of the distance between the outside plates. This distance is the horizontal distance which the rafter will cover. The amount of rise per foot has yet to be considered. If the building to be roofed is 20 feet wide, half the span will be 10 feet. For example the rise per foot is to be 8 inches. To determine the approximate over-all length

Fig. 95.

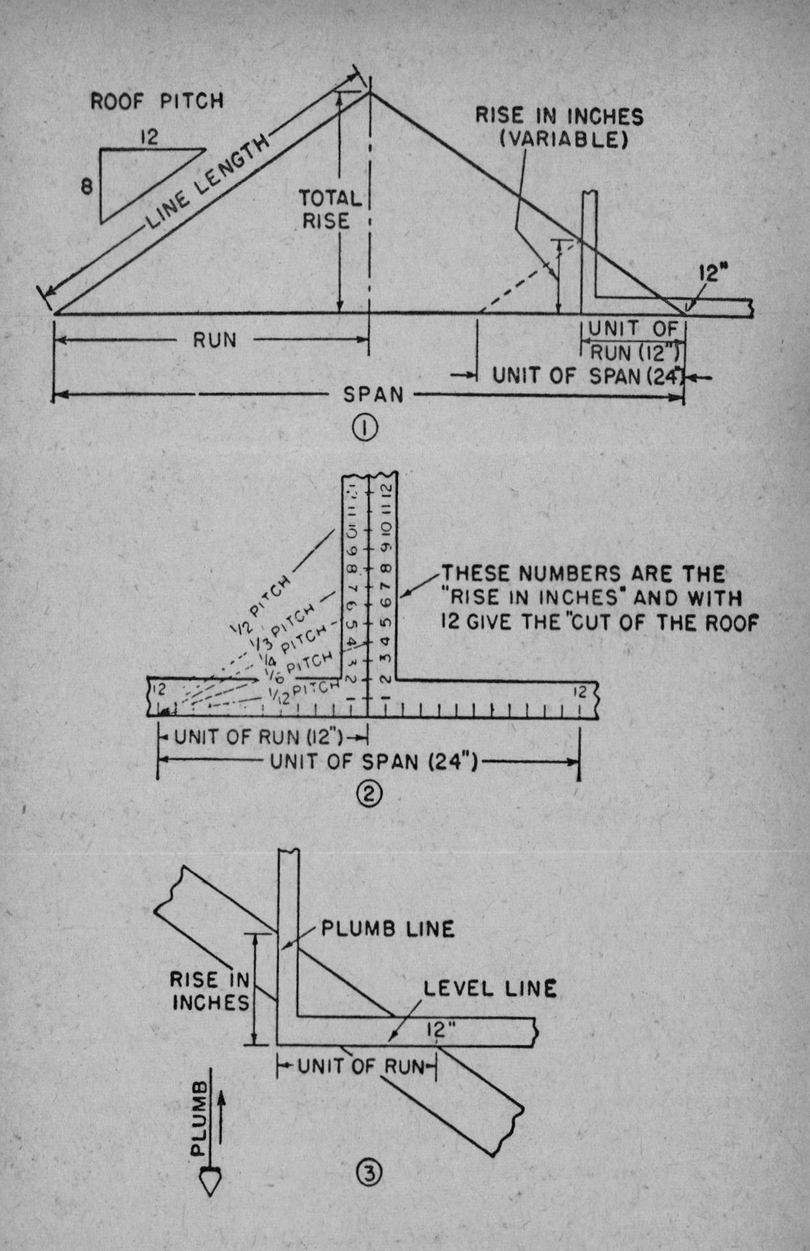

Fig. 96. Rafter layout terms.

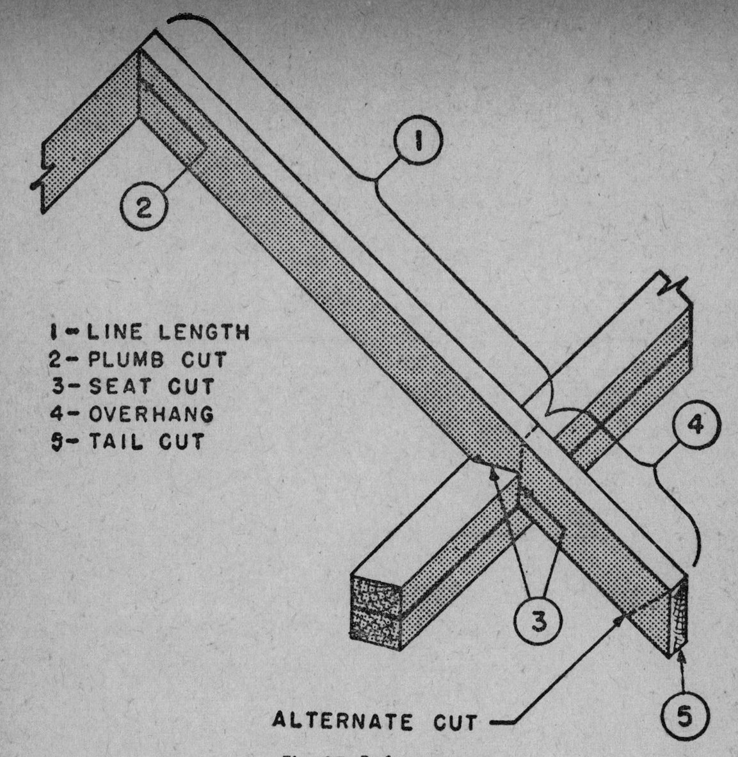

Fig. 97. Rafter terms.

of rafter, measure on the steel carpenter square the distance between 8 on the tongue and 12 on the blade, because 8 is the rise and 12 is the unit of run. This distance is 14 5/12 inches, and represents the line length of a rafter with a total run of 1 foot and a rise of 8 inches. Since the run of the rafter is 10 feet, multiply 10 by the line length for 1 foot. The answer is 144 2/12 inches, or 12 feet and 2/12 inches. The amount of overhang must be added if an overhang is to be used; it is often 1 foot. This makes a total of 13 feet for the length of the rafter; being an odd length for timber, 14-foot timber is used.

(2) After the length has been determined, the timber is laid on saw horses, sometimes called "saw-benches," with the crown or bow (if any) as the top side of the rafter. If possible, select a straight piece for the pattern rafter. If a straight piece is not available, have the crown toward the person laying off the rafter. Hold the square with the tongue in the right hand, the blade in the left, the heel away from the body, and place the square as near the upper end of the rafter as possible. In this case, the figure 8 on the tongue and 12 of the blade are placed along the edge of timber

which is to be the top edge of rafter as shown in figure 98-1. Mark along the tongue edge of square, which will be the plumb cut at the ridge. Since the length of rafter is known to be 12 feet, measure that distance from the top of the plumb cut and mark it on the timber. Hold the square in the same manner with the 8 mark of the tongue directly over the 12-foot mark. Mark along the tongue of the square to give the plumb cut for the seat (fig. 98-2). Next measure off, perpendicular to this mark, the length of overhand along the timber and make a plumb-cut mark in the same manner, keeping the square on the same edge of the timber (fig. 98-3). This will be the tail cut of the rafter; often the tail cut is made square across the timber.

(3) The level cut or width of the seat is the width of the plate, measured perpendicular to the plumb cut, as shown in fig. 98-4. Using the try

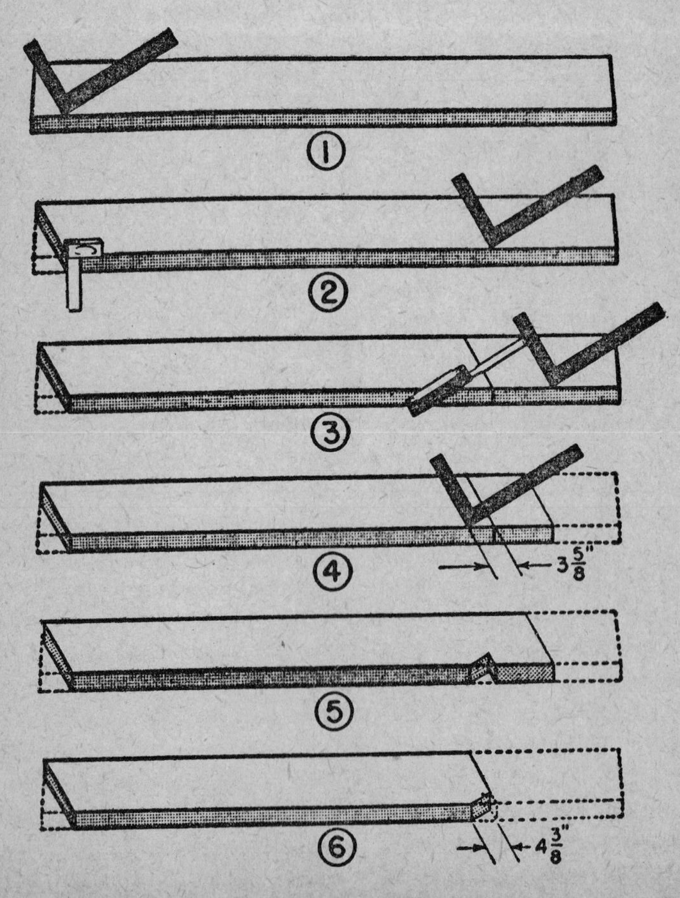

Fig. 98. Rafter lay-out.

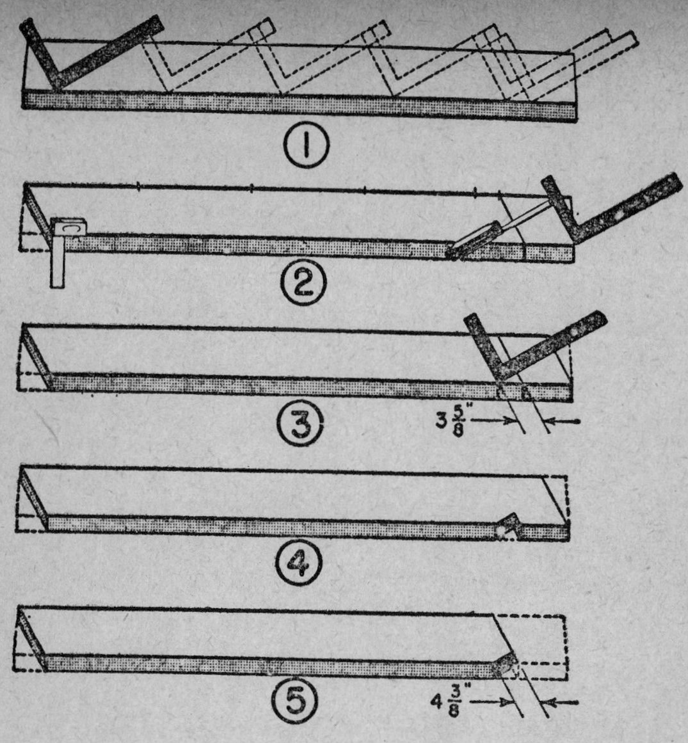

Fig. 99. Rafter lay-out.

square, square lines down on the sides from all level and plumb-cut lines (fig. 98-4). Now the rafter is ready to be cut.

Step-off method.—If a building is 20 feet 8 inches wide, the run of the rafter would be 10 feet 4 inches, or half the span. Instead of using the above method, the rafter length may be determined by *stepping it off* by successive steps with the square as shown in figure 99. Stake the same number of steps as there are feet in the run, which leaves 4 inches over a foot. This 4 inches is taken care of in the same manner as the full foot run, that is, with the square at the last step position, make a mark on the rafters at the 4-inch mark on the blade, then move the square along the rafter until the tongue rests at the 4-inch mark. With the square held for the same cut as before, make a mark along the tongue. This is the line length of the rafter. The seat-cut and hangover are made as described above. When laying off rafters by any method, be sure to recheck the work carefully. When two rafters have been cut, it is best to put them in place to see if they fit. Minor adjustments may be made at this time without serious damage or waste of material.

Table method, using rafter table on framing square.—The framing

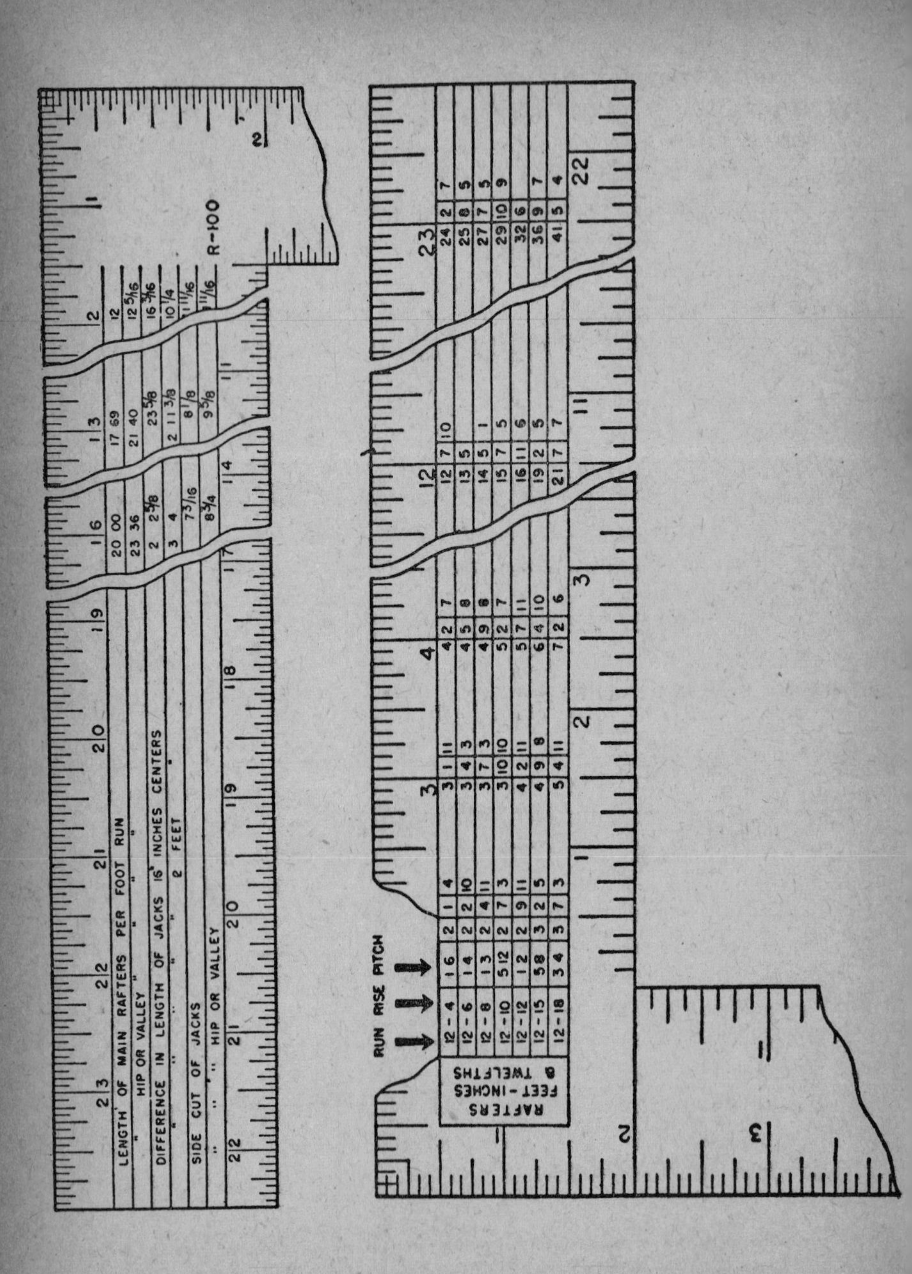

Fig. 100. Rafter table.

Fig. 101. Rafter table.

square may have one or two types of rafter tables on the blade. Figures 100 and 101 are illustrations of the two types. One type gives both the line length of any pitch or rafter per foot of run and the line length of any hip or valley rafter per foot of run. The difference in length of the jack rafter spaced 16 or 24 inches (on center) is also shown in the table. Where the jack rafter, hip, or valley rafter requires side cuts, the cut is given in the table. The other table gives the actual length of rafter for a given pitch and span.

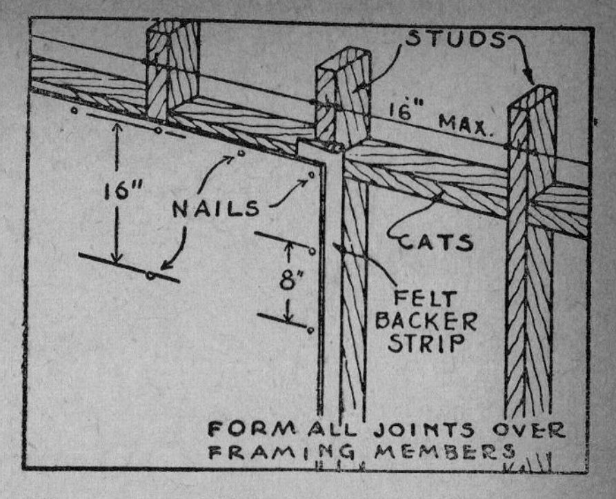

Fig. 102. Application of 3/16" asbestos board directly to studs on exterior walls. Maximum spacing of studs should be 16" and cats must be installed so that all joists are formed over framing members.

(1) The first type of table (fig. 100) appears on the face of the blade. It is used to determine the length of the common, valley, hip, and jack rafters, and the angles at which they must be cut to fit at the ridge and plate. To use the table, the carpenter first must become familiar with it and know what each figure represents. Study this table in figure 100. The row of figures in the first line represents the length of common rafters per foot of run, as the title indicates at the left-hand end of the blade. Each set of figures under each

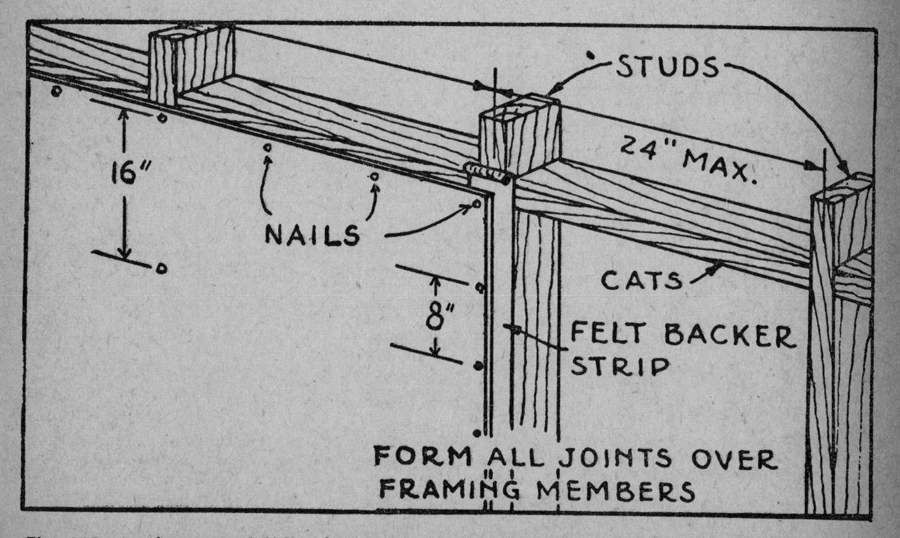

Fig. 103. Application of ½" asbestos board directly to studs on exterior walls. Maximum stud spacing here should be 24" and cats must be installed so that all joints are formed over framing members.

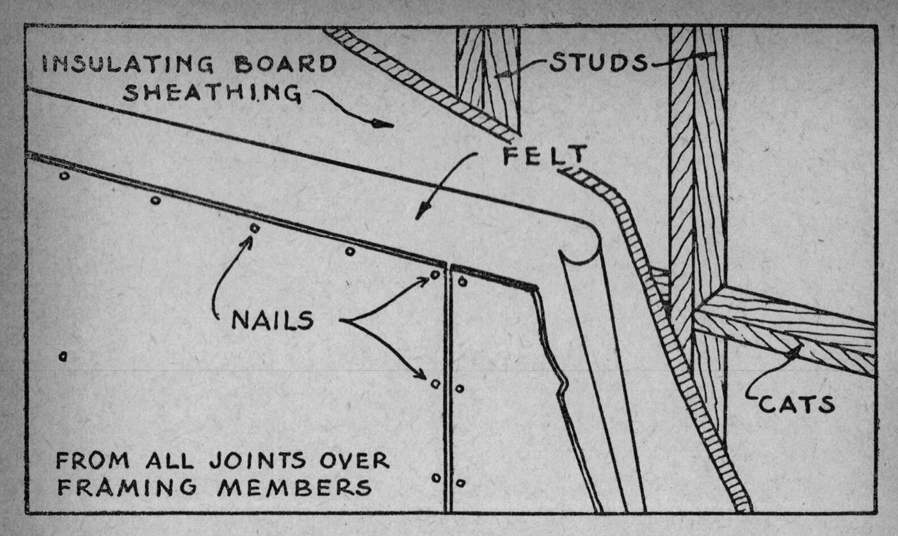

Fig. 104. Asbestos board over insulating board sheathing on exterior walls. Use 1/8" or 3/16" asbestos board, first applying a continuous felt underlayment. The felt should be a waterproof but not a vapor-proof membrane.

inch division mark represents the length of rafter per foot of run with a rise corresponding to the number of inches over the number. For example, under the 16-inch mark appears the number 20.00 inches. This number equals the length of a rafter with a run of 12 inches and a rise of 16 inches, or, under the 13-inch mark appears the number 17.69 inches which is the rafter length for a 12-inch run and a 13-inch rise. The other five lines of figures in the table will not be discussed as they are seldom used in the theater of operations.

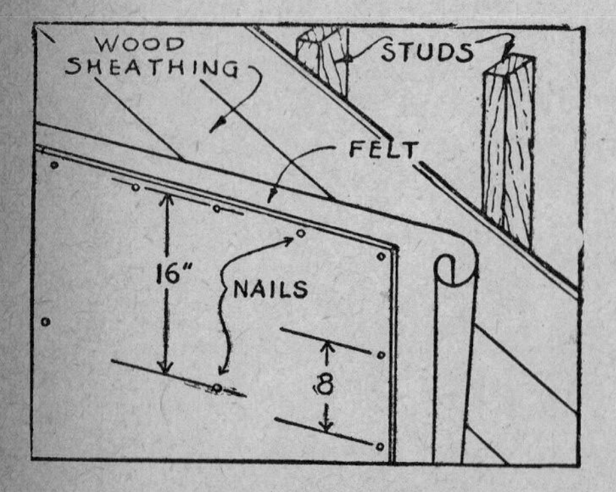

Fig. 105. Asbestos board over solid wood backing on exterior walls. Use 1/8" or 3/16" asbestos board over closely boarded wood, 3/8" (minimum) plywood, or old siding made reasonably smooth. Apply a water-proof but not vapor-proof felt underlayment first.

(2) To use the table for laying out rafters, the width of the building must first be known. Suppose the building is 20 feet 8 inches wide and the rise of the rafters is to be 8 inches per foot of run. The total run of the rafter will be 10 feet 4 inches. Look in the first line of figures; under the 8-inch mark appears the number 14.42, which is the length in inches of a rafter with a run of 1 foot and a rise of 8 inches. To find the line length of a rafter with a total run of 10 feet 4 inches, multiply 14.42 inches by $10\frac{1}{3}$ and divide by 12 so

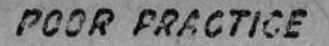

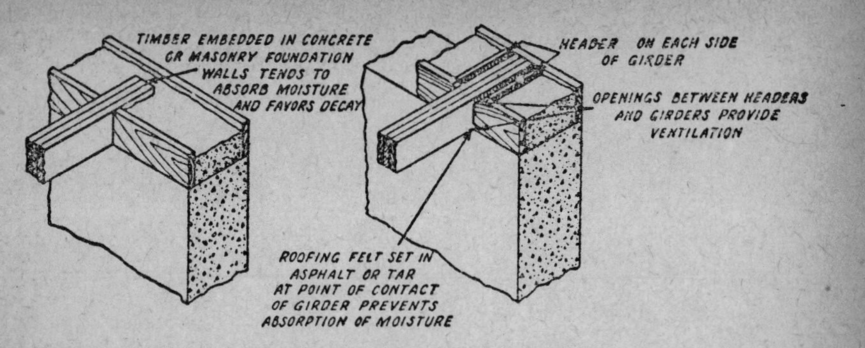

Fig. 106. Good and poor practice with girders embedded in concrete or masonry.

as to get the answer in feet. 14.42 inches by 10⅓ = 149.007 inches. 149.007 ÷ 12 = 12 5/12. Therefore 12 feet 5 inches is the line length of the rafter. The remaining procedure for laying out the rafters after the length has been determined is described above.

(3) The second type of rafter table appears on the back of the blade of some squares. This shows the run rise and the pitch of rafters of the seven most common pitches of roof (fig. 101). The figures are based on the length of the horizontal measurement of the building from the center to the outside. The rafter table and the outside edge of the back of the square, both the body and tongue, are in twelfths. The inch marks may represent inches or feet, and the twelfth marks may represent twelfths of an inch or twelfths of a foot. The rafter table is used in connection with the marks and figures on the outside edge of the square. At the left end of the table are figures representing the *run*, the *rise*, and the *pitch*. In the first column; the figures are all 12. These may be used as 12

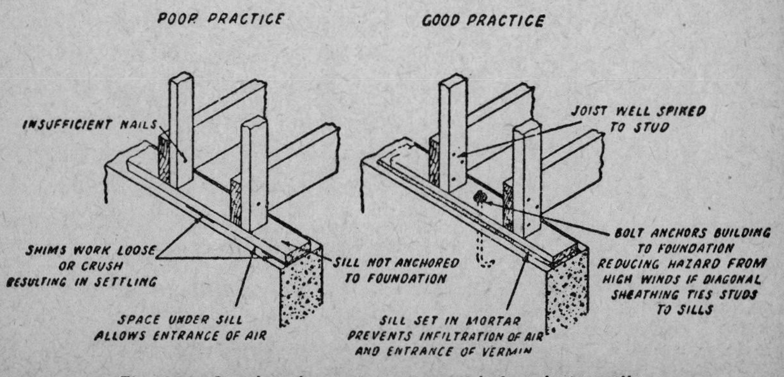

Fig. 107. Good and poor practice with foundation sills.

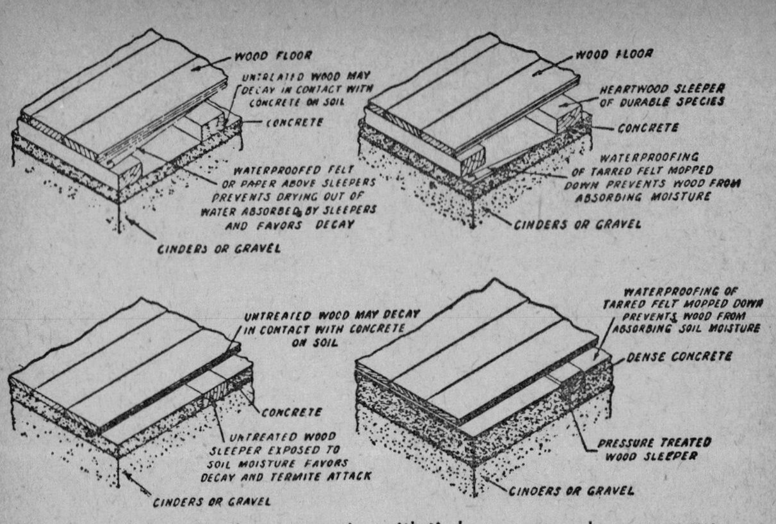

Fig. 108. Good and poor practice with timber on concrete or masonry.

inches or 12 feet as they represent the *run* of 12. The second column of figures represents various rises. The third column of figures, in fractions, represents the various *pitches*.

These three columns of figures show that a rafter with a run of 12 and a rise of 4 has one-sixth pitch, 12 and 6 has one-fourth pitch, and 12 and 12 has one-half pitch. To use this scale for a roof with one-sixth pitch (or the rise of one-sixth the width of the building) and a run of 12 feet, find 1/6 in the table, follow the same line of figures to the right until directly beneath the figure 12, which is the run of the rafter. Under the figure 12, appear the numbers 12, 7, 10, which is the rafter length required, and represents 12 feet, 7

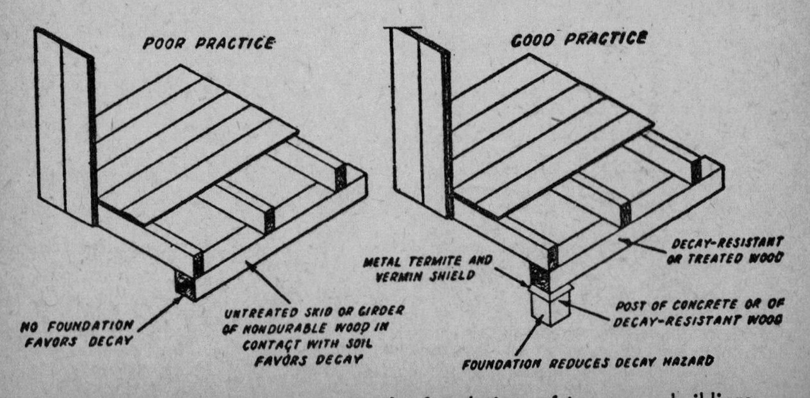

Fig. 109. Good and poor practice for foundations of temporary buildings.

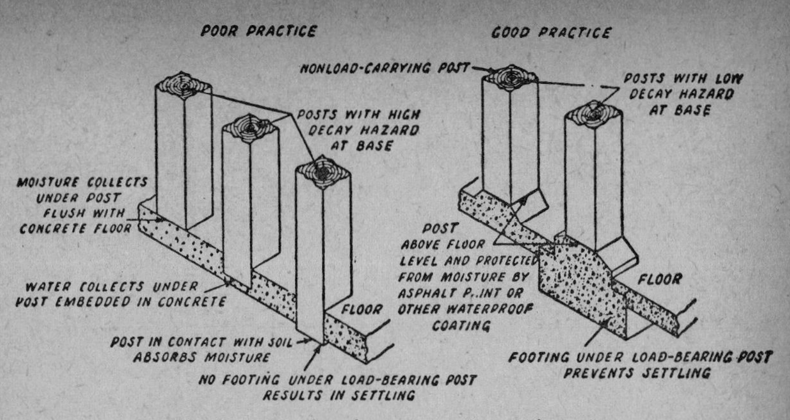

Fig. 110. Good and poor practice with posts.

inches, and $^{10}/_{12}$ of an inch. They are written as follows: 12 feet, 7 $^{10}/_{12}$ inches. For a pitch of one-half (or a rise of one-half the width of the building) and run of .12 feet, the rafter length is 16, 11, 6, or 16 feet, 11 $^{6}/_{12}$ inches.

If the run is over 23 feet, the table is used as follows: Using a run of 27 feet, find the length for a run of 23 feet, then find the length of 4 feet and add the two. The run for 23 feet with a pitch of one-fourth is 25 feet, 8 $^{5}/_{12}$ inches. For 4 feet, the run is 4 feet, 5¾ inches. The total run for 27 feet is 30 feet, 2 $^{1}/_{12}$ inches. When the run is in inches, the rafter table reads inches and twelfths instead of feet and inches. For example, if the pitch is one-half and the run is 12

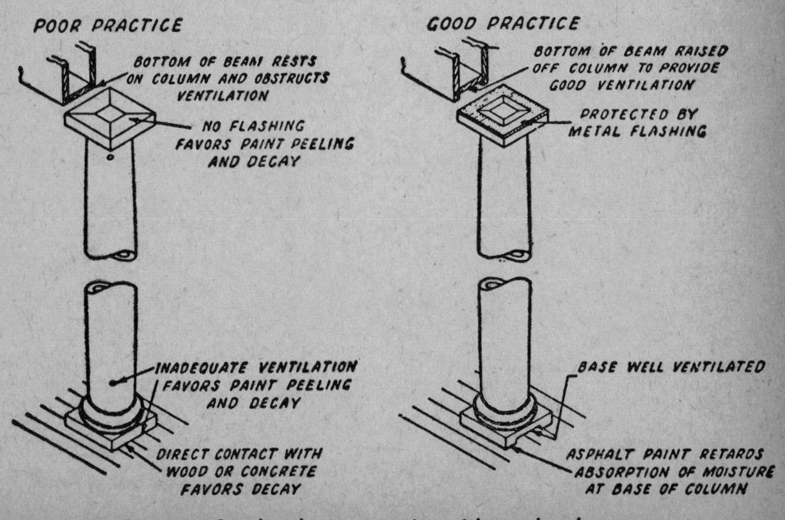

Fig. 111. Good and poor practice with porch columns.

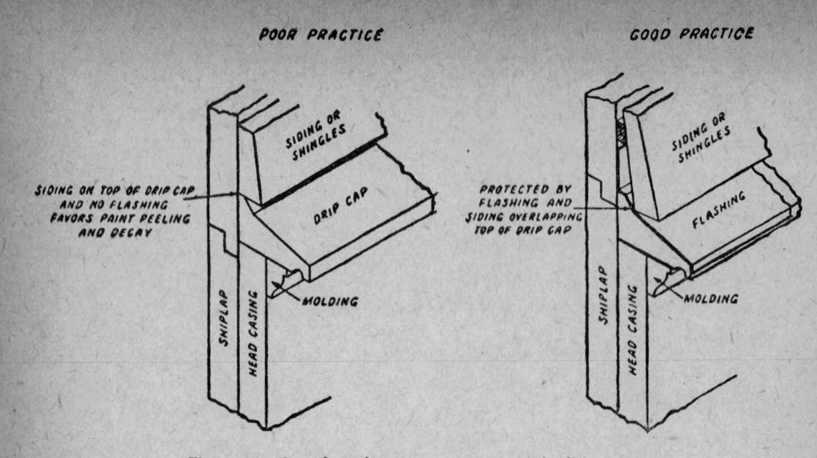

Fig. 112. Good and poor practice with drip caps.

feet, 4 inches, add the rafter length of 12-foot run to that of a rafter length of 4-inch run, as follows: For a run of 12 feet and one-half pitch, the length is 16 feet, 11 $^{6}/_{12}$ inches. For a run of 4 inches and one-half pitch, the length is 5, 7, 11. In this case the 5 is inches, the 7 is twelfths, the 11 is $^{11}/_{12}$ of $^{1}/_{12}$ which is nearly $^{1}/_{12}$. Add it to the 7 to make it 8, making a total of 5 $^{8}/_{12}$ inches, then add the two lengths together which totals 17 feet, 5 $^{2}/_{12}$ inches. The lengths that are given in the table are the line lengths; the overhang must be added. After the length of the rafter has been found, the rafter is laid out as explained above.

When the roof has an overhang (fig. 98), the rafter is usually cut square to save time. When the roof has no overhang, the cut is plumb, but no notch is cut in the rafter for a seat. The level cut is made long enough to extend across the plate and the wall sheathing. This type of rafter saves material, although little protection is given to the side wall.

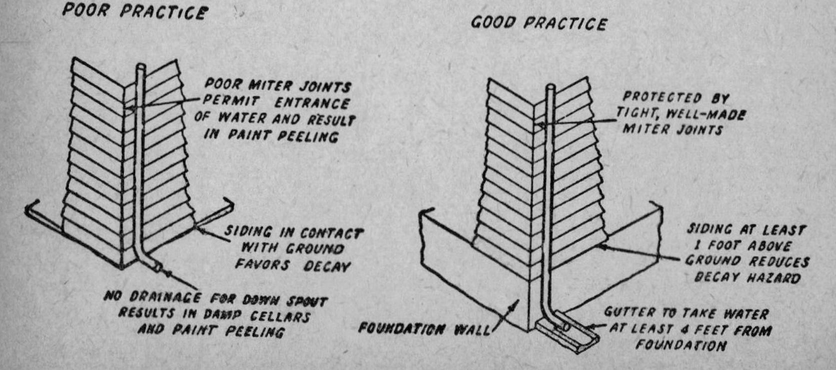

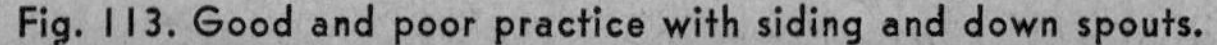
Fig. 113. Good and poor practice with siding and down spouts.

ESTIMATING SHINGLE REQUIREMENTS

To compute the quantity of shingles required to cover exterior walls, subtract the number of square feet of openings from the total number of square feet of wall surface. Most estimates disregard openings of less than 10 square feet.

When wood shingles are placed on side walls, there are usually two thicknesses compared with three for roofs; therefore fewer shingles are required to cover 100 square feet. The usual exposure for 16-inch shingles on side walls is 7½ inches for single coursing and 12 inches for double coursing. A four-bundle square of 16-inch shingles laid 7½ inches to the weather will cover 150 square feet; laid 12 inches to the weather, it will cover 238 square feet. As the latter exposure requires double coursing, another four-bundle square of No. 2 or No. 3 shingles would be required for the under course.

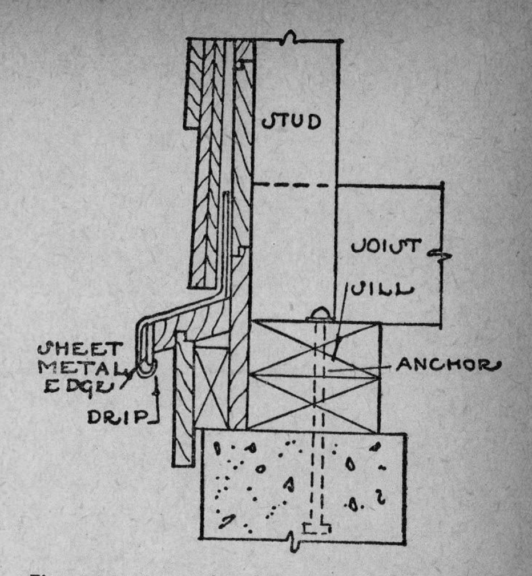

Fig. 114. A good method of keeping moisture away from the sills. Note sheet metal flashing.

Running-inch method of estimating.—Another method of figuring the quantity of shingles required is the running-inch method.

The length of each row in inches times the number of rows, as determined by the exposure and size of area, will give the running inches of shingles required for roofs or side

Side Wall Covering Capacities (Per 4-Bundle Square) in Square Feet for the Various Sized Shingles

Single Course				Double Course			
Exposure Inches	16″ shingles	18″ shingles	24″ shingles	Exposure double course	16″ shingles	18″ shingles	24″ shingles
7	140	......	......	......	......	......	......
7½	150	......	......	11½	226	......	......
8	......	146	......	12	238	218	......
8½	......	154	......	13	......	236	......
9	......	......	120	14	......	254	......
10	......	......	132	15	......	......	200
11	......	......	146	16	......	......	212
11½	......	......	152	......	......	......	......

Note: Quantities shown under "Double Course" are for each course.

walls. Allowance should be made for starters, hips, ridges, and valleys, and deductions made for window and door openings.

"RUNNING INCHES" PER 4-BUNDLE SQUARE OF SHINGLES

Length	Thickness—green	Number of running inches per 4-bundle square	
		Green	Dry
Inches	Inches		
16	5 butts, 2	2960	2880
18	5 butts, 2¼	2664	2620
24	4 butts, 2	1996	1920

APPLICATION OF RED CEDAR SHINGLES

Roof shingles should be spaced one-eighth to one-fourth inch apart. Wall shingles are laid without spacing. The first course of shingles at the eaves should be doubled, and for all first-class work a triple layer of shingles is recommended. The second layer in the first course should be nailed over the first in such a way that the joints in each course are not less than 1½ inches apart, the minimum "side lap" allowable, and if possible, should be "broken" by a greater margin. None of the joints in the three layers should match up (fig. 115).

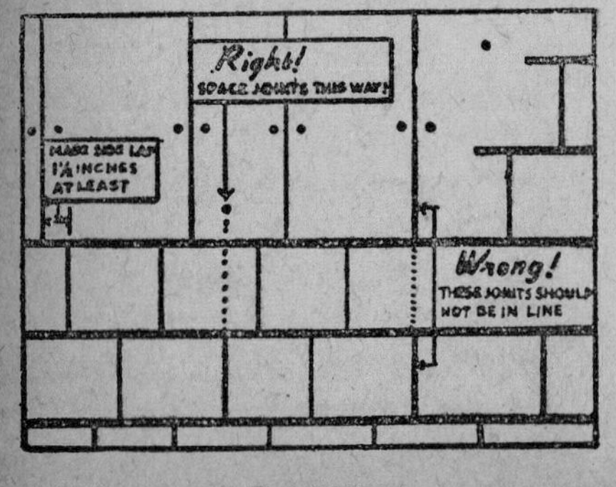

Fig. 115.

Butts should project from 1 to 1½ inches beyond the first roof board so that rain water will be spilled into the gutter and not down the side of the building and barge board.

In applying successive courses, correct exposure should be measured from the butts in the preceding course, and care should be taken to insure the proper side lap over joints between shingles (fig. 115).

It is a good plan to measure courses from the ridge at intervals, so that errors in the alignment of courses can be corrected by adjustments that will not be discernible to the unaided eye. This insures that the last or final course at the ridge will have shingles of the proper length of butt exposure. As the last course is nailed in place, that portion of the shingles projecting beyond the center line of the ridge should be sawed off.

When flat-grained shingles are used, greater service will be obtained if they are laid with the bark side (that which was nearest the bark in the tree) exposed, as this side weathers better than the heart side. Shingles so laid are not likely to be-

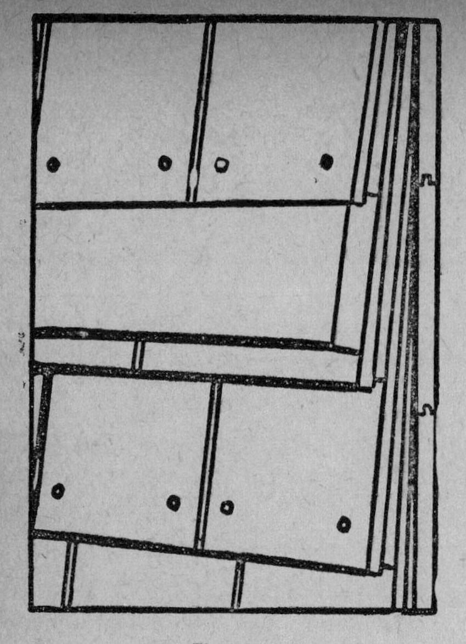

Fig. 116.

Fig. 117.

come waterlogged nor to turn up at the butt. Be careful not to place heart centers above or below cracks.

Application of shingles on exterior walls.—In applying red cedar shingles to the exterior walls of new buildings, tight sheathing should be used, preferably applied diagonally, unless insulation is not desired. Five-sixteenths inch plywood sheathing is an excellent base for shingles.

The application of a good grade of building paper on the sheathing before the shingles are applied will reduce air infiltration through the wall to a minimum.

When shingles are laid in single course, the weather exposure on exterior walls should never be greater than half the length of a shingle, less one-half inch, so that two layers of wood will be found at every point in the wall. When "double coursing" is employed, however, exposure up to three-fourths of the shingle becomes possible.

When "double coursing" a wall, the exposed shingles are usually No. 1 grade. The shingles that are covered in each course may be No. 2 or No. 3 grade. The double courses of shingles applied in this way provide a high degree of insulation against heat losses.

No special tools are required to apply double-coursed walls. The method is simple and requires only a good workman to cover the walls quickly and well (fig. 116).

Choosing proper exposure.—In choosing the exposure to be used on a side wall, to obtain the best effect and to avoid as much cutting of the shingles as possible, the butt lines, or so-called "shadow lines," should be even with the upper lines of the

Fig. 118. Two methods of making corners. **Left**, a "laced" corner, **right**, a mitered corner.

window openings, and also wherever possible, with the lower lines of such openings (fig. 117). It is also better to tack a temporary strip to the wall to use as a guide for placing the butts of the shingles squarely, rather than to attempt to shingle to a chalk line, when straight shadow lines are desired. In applying side-wall shingles with tight or closed joints, the butts should be placed squarely on the strip, and if the edges of some of the shingles, despite the care that is used in manufacture, are not exactly at right angles with the butts and are not strictly parallel, the edges can be shaved off straight with a knife.

Fig. 119. Monotony in large wall areas can be prevented.

Fig. 120. An unusual method of double coursing side walls.

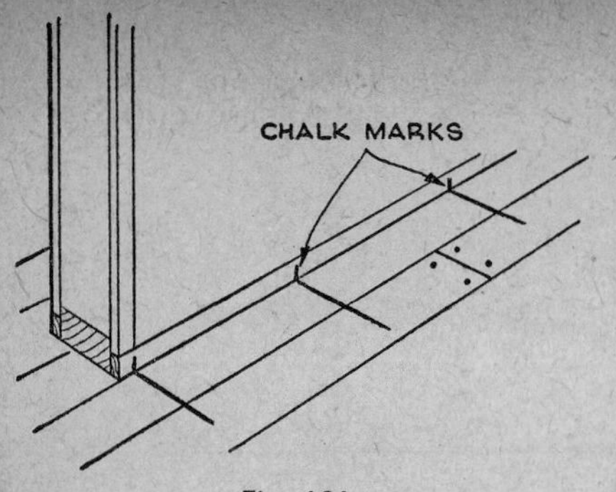

Fig. 121.

Fig. 122.

MARK LOCATION OF STUDDING

It is sometimes difficult to find the exact location of wall studding after the wall surfaces have been covered with wallboard. Much time can be saved by marking the location of each piece of studding on the subfloor as soon as the subfloor has been installed (fig. 121). In this way, there will be no difficulty in finding each piece of wall studding later.

SPACES LET SUBFLOORING EXPAND

Dry subflooring will become swollen if a prolonged rain occurs before the roof has been put on a new building. The tremendous pressure developed can cause serious displacement of walls and partitions, unless spaces are left to let subflooring expand.

One way of leaving such spaces that makes it easy to fill them in after the roof is on, and the danger of swelling is past, is to lay in common one-by-twos temporarily. Simply insert one between every seven or eight boards when laying the floor, and remove until the roof is on. Later, nail them.

Fig. 123.

FITTING WARPED BOARDS

In laying sheathing, subflooring or roofing boards, it is often difficult to bring a warped board in for a tight fit. A simple way to accomplish this is to nail a strip of 1″ x 3″ or larger to one of the joists or studs to act as a lever (fig. 123). The nail serves as a pivot, and by pulling on the top of the lever, the warped board will be brought in close for nailing.

SECTION III

MILLWORK, FLOORING, WINDOWS, DOORS, CLOSETS

Old Mortise Built Up with Shims—Rabbeting and Grooving by Hand—Standard Oak Flooring Grades—Beech, Birch, Hard Maple Flooring Grades—Pecan Flooring Grades—Standard Sizes, Counts and Weights—Standard Grades of Softwood Flooring—Nail Schedule for Flooring—New Strip Flooring over an Existing Finish Floor—Installation of Plank and Parquet Flooring—How to Estimate Amount of Hardwood Flooring Required—Edge Grain and Flat Grain Flooring—Hiding Cracks Between Flooring and Baseboard—Compression Set—Sub-floor Construction—Laying and Nailing Oak Floors—Finishing Oak Floors—Refinishing Hardwood Floors—Puttying Window Panes—Block Holds Glazier's Points—What's Wrong?—Hinge Locks Sliding Window—Combination Screen and Storm Door—A Quickly Built Door—Making a Door Stay Shut—Awnings for Casement Windows—Bedroom Closets—Shoe Racks—Business Closet—Dining-Room Storage—Easy-To-Build Kitchen Cabinets—Food Storage Room—Shelves and Cabinet Transform Extra Closet—Folding Table Seats Eight—Building Outdoor Stairs—How to Carpet Stairs—Jig Assures Square Corners When Assembling Picture Frames—Usual Dimensions and Spacings for Picket and Stretcher Fences.

SECTION III

MILLWORK, FLOORING, WINDOWS, DOORS, CLOSETS

OLD MORTISE BUILT UP WITH SHIMS

Sometimes you will find that old mortises have been so worn that it is impossible to get a tight joint. The problem can be solved by building up the mortises with shims as shown in figure 1.

After each old mortise has been cleaned out and enlarged slightly, shims are cut to build up the mortise to suit the existing tenon. The shims then are wedged in place while the glue is drying, the wedges being made by cutting short pieces of stock to the thickness of the finished mortise, taking slanting cuts on each side of one end as illustrated, and marking the mating pieces. The center piece is also shortened slightly so it will clear the bottom of the mortise when driven in.

If the shims have been cut the proper thickness, the mortise will be ready for the tenon as soon as the glue has set and the wedges are removed. The number of wedges required will depend on the length of the mortise.

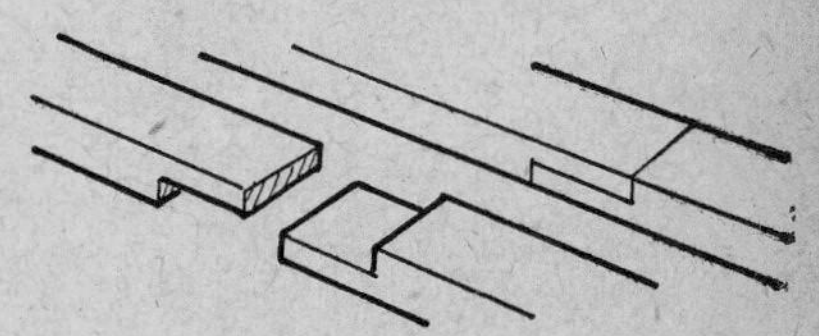

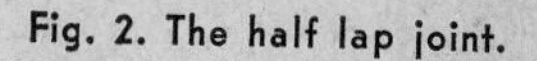

Fig. 2. The half lap joint.

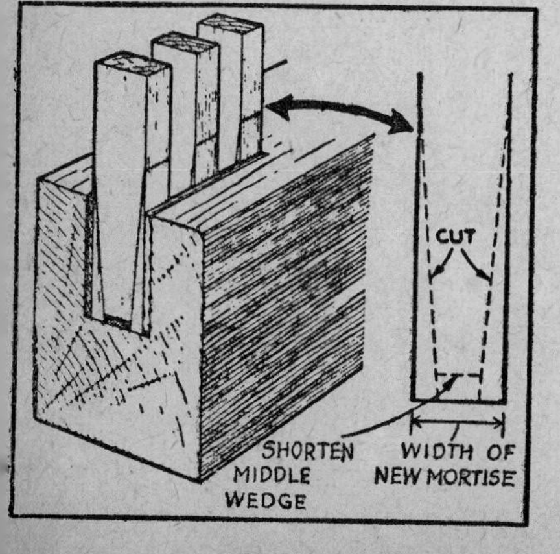

Fig. 1.

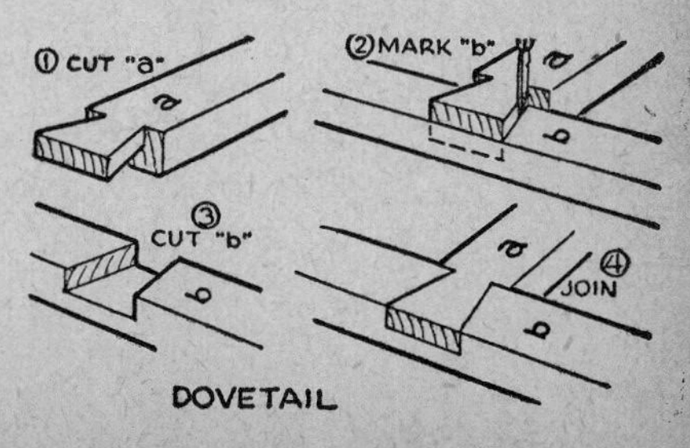

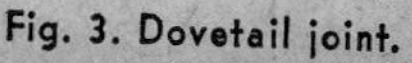

Fig. 3. Dovetail joint.

Fig. 4. Types of butt-joint construction: **A**, end to end; **B**, scarf; **C**, serrate or finger; **D**, end to side; **E**, miter; **F**, dowel; **G**, mortise and tenon; **H**, dado tongue and rabbet; **I**, slip or lock corner; **J**, dovetail; **K**, blocked; **L**, tongue and groove.

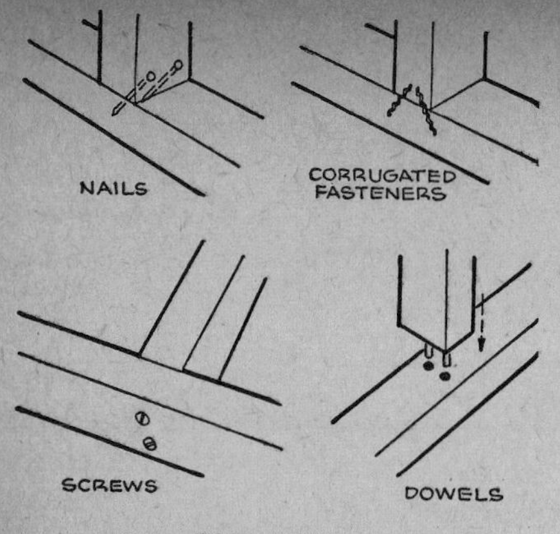

Fig. 5. Butt joints can be made with nails, corrugated fasteners, screws and dowels. This joint is used both in rough and finish carpentry.

"b" MARKED FOR GLUING BY NAIL DRIVEN THROUGH "a"
EACH JOINING END CUT AT 45°
GLUE - THEN DRIVE NAIL THROUGH "b"
MITER JOINT

Fig. 6. Steps in making a miter joint.

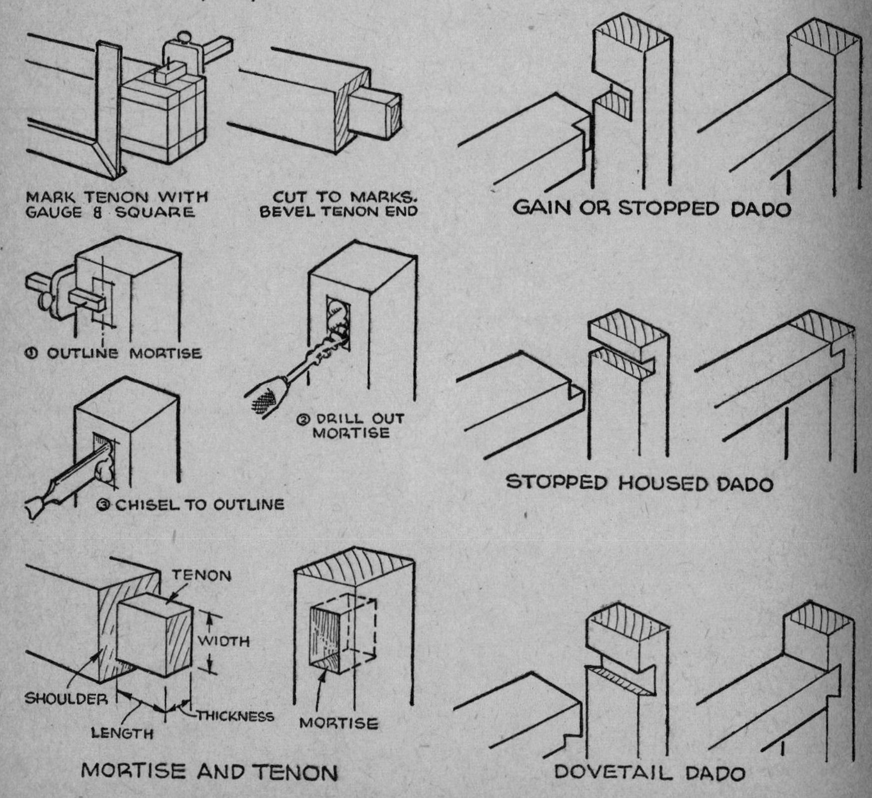

Fig. 7. Six steps in constructing a mortise and tenon joint.

Fig. 8. Three types of dado joints that will be found useful in all phases of carpentry.

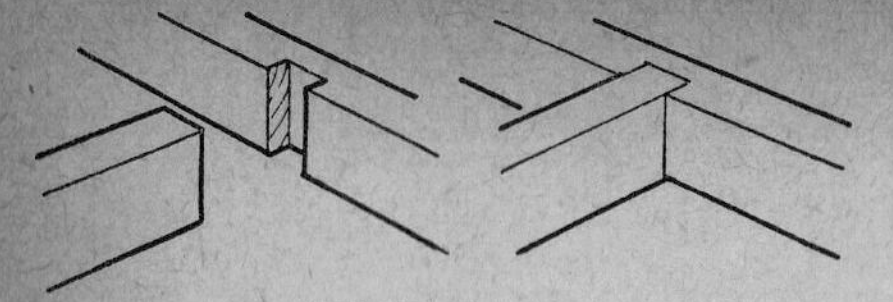

Fig. 9. The simple dado.

RABBETING AND GROOVING BY HAND

The first rabbet or dado joint is a real milestone in a novice craftsman's experience. Making butted or cleated joints is something that the noncarpenter does almost instinctively. But to make a well-executed rabbet joint is to take an unmistakable first step down the road toward woodworking craftsmanship.

Not that there's anything wrong with butting or cleating two pieces of wood together. In plenty of applications—the shelves in a kitchen closet, for example—cleated construction is simple, quick, and amply strong for the purpose. But in the case of a nicely finished piece of living-room furniture, say, a maple bookcase, nailing the shelves in from the sides is practically a workshop scandal, and cleats aren't much better. For looks, strength (especially against "cornering" stresses), and plain woodworking craftsmanship, a dado joint is in order here.

Rabbets, grooves, and dadoes are a way of creating two or more meeting surfaces where only one would exist without them. A rabbet is a recess in the end or edge of a piece of stock; a groove is a channel that runs along the grain of the board. Cross-grained or edge-to-edge channels are called dadoes. Grooved joints may employ any of these cuts in a variety of combinations.

Cutting end rabbets. Any shop, so long as it has saws and chisels, is equipped for rabbeting and grooving. To establish the dimensions of a rabbet, gauge lines along the face, end, and edge as illustrated in fig. 11.

End rabbets are usually sawed. While a backsaw (fig. 12) is most convenient, a rip saw is also satisfactory and is generally the choice of carpenters. Nudge the saw to the

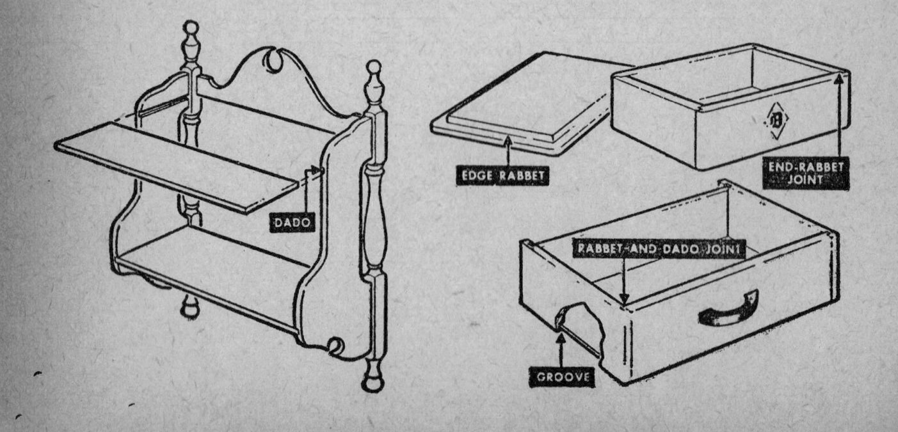

line with the extended thumb of the left hand. Start cutting at the near corner but level off when the kerf has been cut to the shoulder.

The standard method of cutting the shoulder is to square the line with the point of a knife, lay the work on a pair of bench hooks, and start sawing at the far end. Steady the saw with the thumb or forefinger and level out as the work progresses. If the cut is level the waste block will fall away as soon as it is severed, thus insuring against cutting into the bottom of the rabbet and spoiling the job.

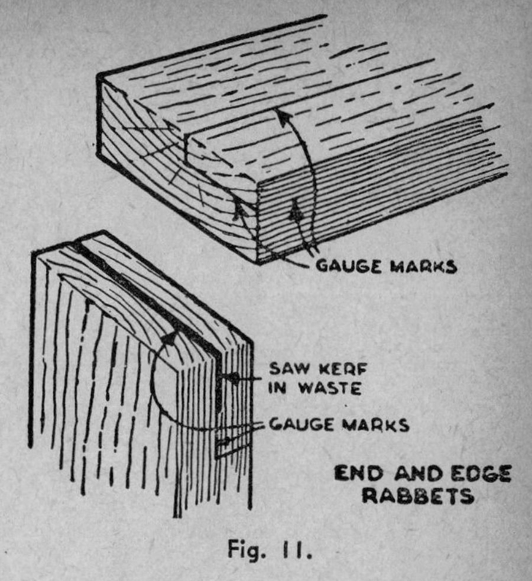

Fig. 11.

Edge rabbets are more commonly chiseled, although shorter and deeper ones can be sawed as described for end cuts. With the lines gauged, lay the piece on the bench, face up, and cross-score nearly to depth. Follow this by roughing the shoulder with a wide chisel. Rough out the waste with the chisel held horizontally, bevel up (the technique, in a different application, is pictured in fig. 16). Trim the shoulder and the bottom of the rabbet to the line.

A well-chiseled rabbet is ready for assembling, but sanding is needed if it is to serve as a molding. Fold a piece of coarse paper around a square-edged block for the first sanding, and follow with finer grits. Use a scraper to level off high spots.

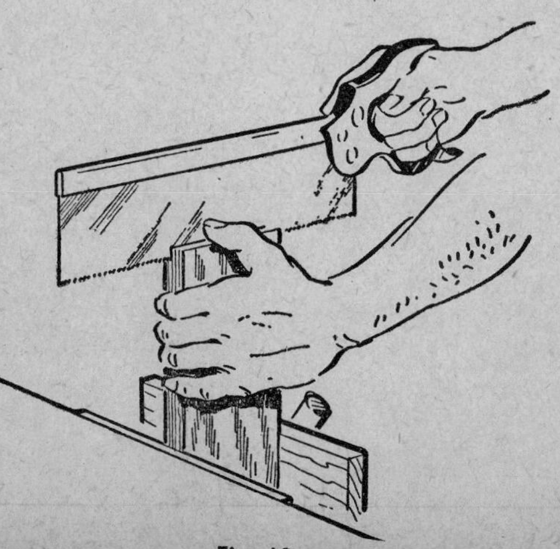

Fig. 12.

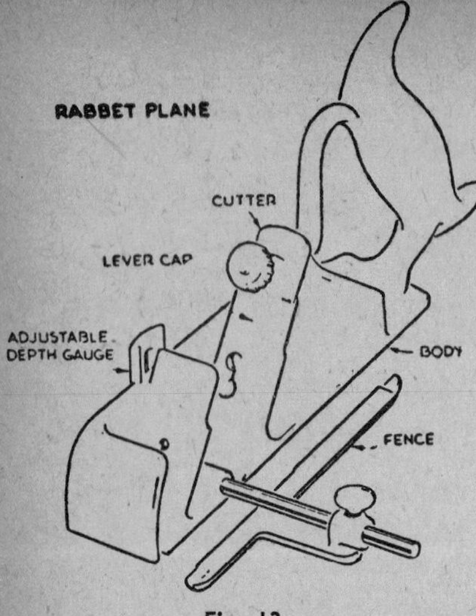

Fig. 13.

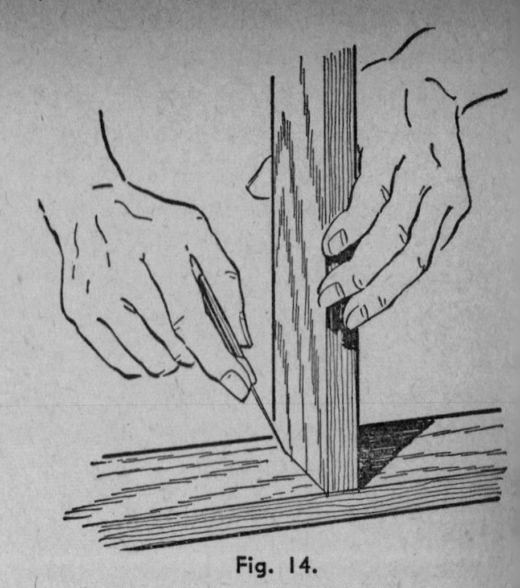

Fig. 14.

Rabbet planes. The saw-and-chisel combination is perfectly adequate for the occasional rabbeting or grooving job, but for a lot of this work it pays to have one of several special planes. One type of rabbet plane is shown in figure 13. The cutter is a single plane iron held in place by a lever cap. It is important that the cutter edge be sharp, straight, and square, and it must also be locked exactly flush with the side of the plane working against the rabbet shoulder. Adjust the iron for depth of cut by sighting along the sole, as with a jack plane, or by testing the edge projection with the finger. A spur screwed to the side of the plane slits the shoulder just ahead of the cutter. Depth of cut is regulated by a gauge on the spur side.

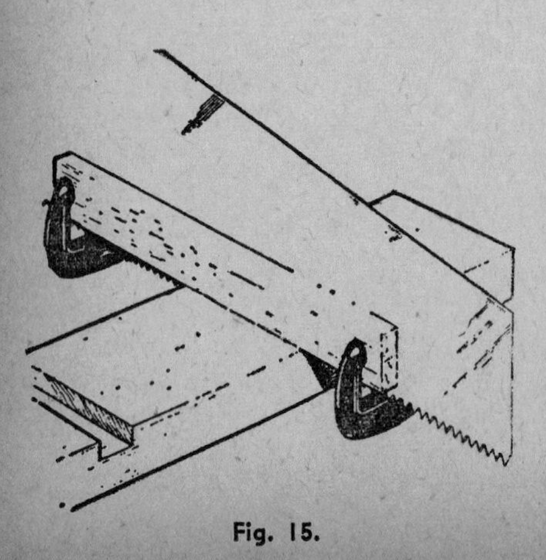

Fig. 15.

The simple rabbet plane has no fence; it is guided by a strip of wood nailed to the surface of the board. By tacking the fence strip obliquely it is possible to make the rabbet wider at one end than the other. The fence, of course, can be clamped on if you wish to avoid nail holes. Secure the work in a tail vise to keep it from sliding on the bench. In place of the vise, a strip clamped to the bench at the far edge of the board can be used to hold the work still.

A rabbet plane fitted with a fence is pictured in fig. 13. The thumb of the left hand can be hooked behind the front of the plane to steady it. With this tool no fence strip is needed so long as the shoulder of the rabbet is to be parallel with the edge.

A sloping or ragged shoulder may result if the plane iron is dull, out of square, or not flush with the side. Sharpen or adjust the cutter; then correct the rabbet with a chisel before continuing the work. While a rabbet plane can be used to cut across the grain, you will usually find it better and easier to saw to the shoulder, split out the waste with a chisel, and use the plane only for smoothing the bottom.

Grooves and dadoes. A groove can be chiseled in much the same manner as a rabbet. On short work the sides may be cut with a saw; since they must be perfectly straight and parallel, it is a good idea to clamp a strip of wood along the gauge mark to guide the saw.

Dadoes, which are grooves cut across the grain, are most often made to receive the ends of other members, as in joining a shelf to the side of a bookcase. The end to which a dado is joined may be plain or rabbeted as shown in figure 10. You can readily see the advantage of the rabbet and dado joint in this application: no ordinary pull on the drawer front can separate the two members.

If a dado is too big, the joint will be both weak and unsightly. Accurate layout is therefore the first essential of a good dado. Square a line across the face of the piece and scribe a line for the other side at a distance equal to the thickness of the joining member. Many woodworkers like to use the joining piece itself as a pattern (fig. 14) because it compensates for unequal thickness along its length. Gauge for depth and saw the sides accurately. A stop clamped to a saw blade as in figure 15 will guarantee the proper depth of cut. Bevel the edges of the waste toward the saw line and chisel out the bottom (fig. 16). To prevent splintering of the edges, chisel half way across

Fig. 16.

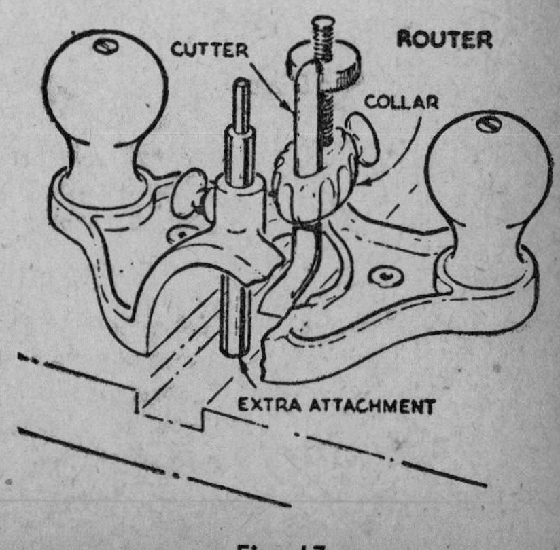

Fig. 17.

from one edge and finish from the other.

Router and combination plane. Dado planes are seldom seen except in production shops because each one will make a cut of only one width. More generally useful is a router (fig. 17), which planes the bottom of any groove after the sides are cut. One or two heavy cuts remove the waste, while smoothing results from another pass with a fine-shaving adjustment.

One of the best all-around tools—if somewhat on the expensive side for small shops—is a combination plane. A variety of cutters is provided to enable it to rabbet, plow (groove), match (tongue-and-groove), bead, and so on. For plowing, slide the adjustable stock into alignment with the side of the cutter. A rabbet is made by clamping the cutter to the main stock, adjusting the depth of cut and the depth gauge, and setting the fence. The cutter used should be somewhat wider than the rabbet to be made so that it will project beyond the wood and leave a clean edge.

FLOORING

GRADES, DESCRIPTION, AND DIMENSIONS OF OAK FLOORING

Kind of flooring	Grade		Standard worked dimensions		
	Name	Description	Thickness	Face width	Length, feet
			Inch	Inches	
Quarter-sawed	Clear	The face shall be practically clear of defects except ⅜ inch of bright sap. The question of color shall not be considered.	25/32 25/32 25/32 25/32 15/32 15/32 11/32 11/32	3¼ 2¼ 2 1½ 2 1½ 2 1½	2 and up, not to exceed 20 percent under 4. Average length 5.
Quarter-sawed	Sap Clear	The face shall be practically free from defects but will admit unlimited bright sap. The question of color shall not be considered.	25/32 25/32 25/32 25/32 15/32 15/32 11/32 11/32	3¼ 2¼ 2 1½ 2 1½ 2 1½	2 and up, not to exceed 20 percent under 4. Average length 5.
Quarter-sawed	Select	The face may contain sap, and will admit pin worm holes, streaks, slight imperfections in working or a small tight knot, not to exceed 1 to every 3 feet in length.	25/32 25/32 25/32 25/32 15/32 15/32 11/32 11/32	3¼ 2¼ 2 1½ 2 1½ 2 1½	2 and up. Average length 4.

GRADES, DESCRIPTION, AND DIMENSIONS OF OAK FLOORING

Kind of flooring	Grade: Name	Grade: Description	Standard worked dimensions: Thickness	Standard worked dimensions: Face width	Standard worked dimensions: Length, feet
			Inch	Inches	
Plain-sawed	Clear	The face shall be practically clear of defects except ⅜ inch of bright sap. The question of color shall not be considered.	25/32 25/32 25/32 25/32 15/32 15/32 11/32 11/32	3¼ 2¼ 2 1½ 2 1½ 2 1½	2 and up, not to exceed 20 percent under 4. Average length 5.
Plain-sawed	Select	The face may contain sap, and will admit pin worm holes, streaks, slight imperfections in working or a small tight knot, not to exceed 1 to every 3 feet in length.	25/32 25/32 25/32 25/32 15/32 15/32 11/32 11/32	3¼ 2¼ 2 1½ 2 1½ 2 1½	2 and up. Average length 4.

All flooring listed is kiln-dried and grade-marked, hollowed back and side, and end matched. "Hollowed-back" flooring has the back hollowed out to a depth of about ⅛ inch and about two-thirds the width of the piece. When hardwood flooring is manufactured, all dressing is done on the face side, and in order to relieve any tension that would make the piece cup from this unequal dressing, the back is hollowed out. Softwood flooring is usually manufactured in the same manner, although some of it is produced with merely a ⅛-inch V-shaped groove running down the middle of the back. Such flooring is referred to in the trade as "scratched-back." "Side- and end-matched" means flooring that has a tongue worked on one edge and one end and a groove worked on the other edge and the other end. This permits the pieces to be tightly interlocked both along the sides and at the ends when laid in place.

STANDARD OAK FLOORING GRADES

QUARTER SAWED

Clear. The face shall be practically free of defects except ⅜ of an inch of bright sap. The question of color shall not be considered. Bundles to be 2 ft. and up, not to exceed 25% under 4 ft. Average length 4½ ft.

Sap clear. The face shall be practically free from defects but will admit unlimited bright sap. The question of color shall not be considered. Bundles to be 2 ft. and up, not to exceed 25% under 4 ft. Average length, 4½ ft.

Select. The face may contain sap, and will admit pin worm holes, streaks, slight imperfections in working or a small tight knot, not to exceed one to every 3 ft. in length.

Bundles to be 2 ft. and up. Average length 4 ft.

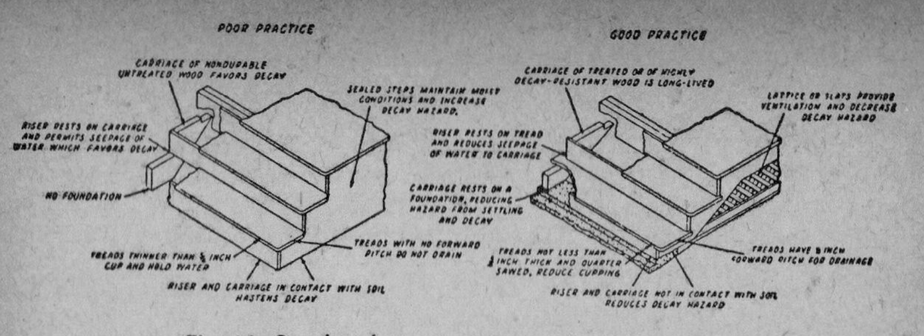

Fig. 18. Good and poor practice with porch steps.

Plain Sawed

Clear. The face shall be practically free of defects except ⅜ of an inch of bright sap. The question of color shall not be considered. Bundles to be 2 ft. and up, not to exceed 25% under 4 ft. Average length 4½ ft.

Select. The face may contain sap, and will admit pin worm holes, streaks, slight imperfections in working or a small tight knot, not to exceed one to every 3 ft. in length.

Bundles to be 2 ft. and up. Average length 4 ft.

No. 1 Common. Shall be of such nature as will make and lay a sound floor without cutting.

Bundles to be 2 ft. and up. Average length 3 ft.

No. 2 Common. May contain defects of all characters, but will lay a serviceable floor.

Bundles to be 1¼ ft. and up. Average length 2½ ft.

Square edge strip flooring is graded as above, but the Clear is bundled 2 ft. and up, average length 5½ ft.; Select bundled 2 ft. and up, average length 4½ ft.; No. 1 Common bundled 2 ft. and up, average length 3½ ft.

BEECH, BIRCH, HARD MAPLE FLOORING GRADES

First grade. Shall have the face practically free of all defects, but the varying natural color of the wood shall not be considered a defect. Bundles shall be 2 to 16 ft., as the stock will produce; the proportion of 2 and 3 ft. bundles shall be what the stock will produce up to 25%.

Second grade. Will admit of tight, sound knots and slight imperfections in dressing, but must lay without waste. Bundles shall be 1¼ to 16 ft., as the stock will produce; the proportions of 1¼ to 3 ft. bundles shall be what the stock will produce up to 40%.

Third grade. Must be of such character as will lay and give a good serviceable floor. Bundles shall be 1¼ to 16 ft., as the stock will produce; the proportion of 1¼ to 3 ft. bundles shall be what the stock will produce up to 60%.

PECAN FLOORING GRADES

First grade. Shall be practically free of defects, but the varying natural color of the wood shall not be considered a defect. Bundled 2 to 16 feet, not over 25% of the footage shall be 2 and 3 feet.

First grade red. Same as First Grade except shall be made from all heartwood.

First grade white. Same as First Grade except shall be made from all bright sapwood.

Second grade. Will admit of tight, sound knots, pin worm holes, streaks, and slight imperfections in working. Bundled 2 to 16 feet, not over 30% of the footage shall be 2 feet and 3 feet.

Second grade red. Same as Second Grade except shall be made from all heartwood.

Third grade. Shall be of such nature as will make and lay a sound floor without cutting. Bundled 2 to 16 feet, not over 50% of the footage shall be 2 and 3 feet.

Fourth grade. May contain defects of any character so long as will lay a serviceable floor. Bundled 1¼ to 16 feet.

STANDARD SIZES, COUNTS AND WEIGHTS

"Nominal" is the size designation used by the trade, but it is not always the actual size. Sometimes the actual thickness of hardwood flooring is 1/32-inch less than the so-called nominal size. "Actual" is the *mill* size for thickness and face width, excluding tongue width. "Counted" size determines the board feet in a shipment. Pieces less than 1 inch in thickness are considered to be 1 inch.

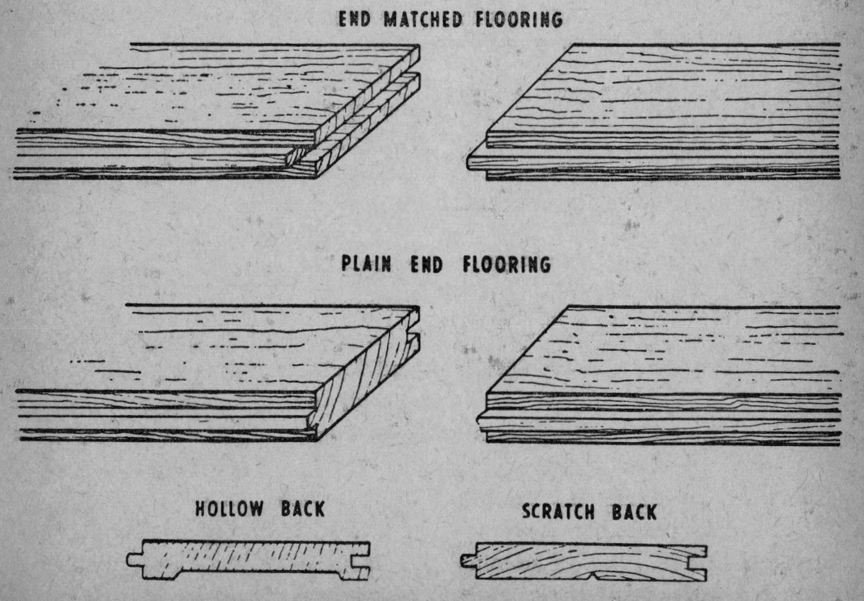

Fig. 19. Details showing the manner in which end-matching joins up in laying; the importance of accurate 90° trimming when squaring the abutting piece of plain end.

Oak

Nominal	Actual	Counted	Weights M Ft.
Tongued and Grooved-End Matched			
$\frac{25}{32}$ x 3¼ in.	$\frac{25}{32}$ x 3¼ in.	1 x 4 in.	2250 lbs.
$\frac{25}{32}$ x 2¼ in.	$\frac{25}{32}$ x 2¼ in.	1 x 3 in.	2000 lbs.
$\frac{25}{32}$ x 2 in.	$\frac{25}{32}$ x 2 in.	1 x 2¾ in.	2000 lbs.
$\frac{25}{32}$ x 1½ in.	$\frac{25}{32}$ x 1½ in.	1 x 2¼ in.	2000 lbs.
⅜ x 2 in.	$\frac{11}{32}$ x 2 in.	1 x 2½ in.	1000 lbs.
⅜ x 1½ in.	$\frac{11}{32}$ x 1½ in.	1 x 2 in.	1000 lbs.
½ x 2 in.	$\frac{15}{32}$ x 2 in.	1 x 2½ in.	1300 lbs.
½ x 1½ in.	$\frac{15}{32}$ x 1½ in.	1 x 2 in.	1300 lbs.
Square Edge			
$\frac{5}{16}$ x 2 in.	$\frac{5}{16}$ x 2 in.	face count	1200 lbs.
$\frac{5}{16}$ x 1½ in.	$\frac{5}{16}$ x 1½ in.	face count	1200 lbs.

Beech, Birch, Hard Maple and Pecan

Nominal	Actual	Counted	Weights M Ft.
Tongued and Grooved-End Matched			
$\frac{25}{32}$ x 3¼ in.	$\frac{25}{32}$ x 3¼ in.	1 x 4 in.	2250 lbs.
$\frac{25}{32}$ x 2¼ in.	$\frac{25}{32}$ x 2¼ in.	1 x 3 in.	2000 lbs.
$\frac{25}{32}$ x 2 in.	$\frac{25}{32}$ x 2 in.	1 x 2¾ in.	2000 lbs.
$\frac{25}{32}$ x 1½ in.	$\frac{25}{32}$ x 1½ in.	1 x 2¼ in.	2000 lbs.
⅜ x 2 in.	$\frac{11}{32}$ x 2 in.	1 x 2½ in.	1000 lbs.
⅜ x 1½ in.	$\frac{11}{32}$ x 1½ in.	1 x 2 in.	1000 lbs.
½ x 2 in.	$\frac{15}{32}$ x 2 in.	1 x 2½ in.	1300 lbs.
½ x 1½ in.	$\frac{15}{32}$ x 1½ in.	1 x 2 in.	1300 lbs.
Special Thicknesses (T and G, End Matched)			
$1\frac{1}{16}$ x 3¼ in.	$1\frac{1}{32}$ x 3¼ in.	1¼ x 4 in.	2400 lbs.
$1\frac{1}{16}$ x 2¼ in.	$1\frac{1}{32}$ x 2¼ in.	1¼ x 3 in.	2250 lbs.
$1\frac{1}{16}$ x 2 in.	$1\frac{1}{32}$ x 2 in.	1¼ x 2¾ in.	2250 lbs.
Jointed Flooring—i.e., Square Edge			
$\frac{25}{32}$ x 2½ in.	$\frac{25}{32}$ x 2½ in.	1 x 3¼ in.	2250 lbs.
$\frac{25}{32}$ x 3¼ in.	$\frac{25}{32}$ x 3¼ in.	1 x 4 in.	2400 lbs.
$1\frac{1}{16}$ x 2½ in.	$1\frac{1}{32}$ x 2½ in.	1¼ x 3¼ in.	2500 lbs.
$1\frac{1}{16}$ x 3½ in.	$1\frac{1}{32}$ x 3½ in.	1¼ x 4¼ in.	2600 lbs.

NOTE: Oak, Beech, Birch, Hard Maple and Pecan Flooring are bundled by averaging the lengths. A bundle may include pieces from 6 in. under to 6 in. over the nominal length of the bundle. No piece shorter than 9 in. admitted.

¾-in. allowance shall be added to the face length when measuring the length of each piece.

Flooring shall not be considered of standard grade unless the lumber from which the flooring is manufactured has been properly kiln-dried.

STANDARD GRADES OF SOFTWOOD FLOORING

Plain End		End-Matched	
Edge Grain	*Flat Grain*	*Edge Grain*	*Flat Grain*
A	A	A	A
B	B	B	B
C	C	C	C
D	D	D	D
	No. 2		
	No. 3		

(The common practice is for *A* and *B* grades to be combined into one grade designated as "B&Better.")

The principal uses for these grades of flooring are as follows:

A and B (B&Btr). Used mainly for the floors of fine residences, office buildings, ballrooms, department stores, schools and other floors that are not to be covered.

C. Used for the same purposes as "B&Btr," but where a less expensive floor is specified.

D. For bedrooms, upstairs halls, and for living rooms where rugs or carpets will predominate; also for play rooms, attics, summer cottages.

No. 2. For kitchens, bathrooms and service parts of the house. Usually either painted or covered with linoleum. Also used for attics, closets and other floors where appearance is not a factor.

No. 3. Used chiefly for temporary construction work and is discarded after serving its purpose.

By following this guide, builders and property owners will be able to get the most for their flooring dollars.

Standard sizes of softwood flooring are:

Rough or Nominal	*Dressed or Finished*
1″ x 2″	$\frac{25}{32}$″ x 1½″ face
1″ x 3″	$\frac{25}{32}$″ x 2⅜″ face
1″ x 4″	$\frac{25}{32}$″ x 3¼″ face

Also available in 1¼″ thickness, finished to $1\frac{1}{16}$″; and 1½″ finished to $1\frac{5}{16}$″; in same face widths as above. The most widely used sizes, however, are 1″ x 3″ and 1″ x 4″.

NAIL SCHEDULE FOR FLOORING

TONGUED-AND-GROOVED FLOORING. TO BE BLIND-NAILED.

Flooring Dimen., In.	*Size Nails, Spacing*
$\frac{25}{32}$ x 3¼ $\frac{25}{32}$ x 2¼	8d light flooring nail—wire or steel cut casing nail—(use cut nail when possible). 10 in. apart.
$\frac{25}{32}$ x 1½	Same nails as above. 12 in. apart.
½ x 2 ½ x 1½	6d bright wire casing nails. 10 in. apart.
⅜ x 2 ⅜ x 1½	4d bright wire casing nails. 8 in. apart. Must always be laid on subfloor.

SQUARE-EDGE FLOORING. FACE-NAILED.

$\frac{5}{16}$ x 2 $\frac{5}{16}$ x 1½	1⅛ in. barbed wire flooring brad. No. 16 heads countersunk and puttied. 2 nails every 7 in.

NEW STRIP FLOORING OVER AN EXISTING FINISH FLOOR

Strip flooring can be laid with equally effective results over an old finish floor of wood. This is often done in the modernization of old homes whose existing floors are of inferior quality. The same general principles of installation apply. Provision often must be made for the higher level of the new floor, of course. Interior doors, for example, should be lifted from their hinges, then planed if necessary. Ordinarily, the thinner sizes of flooring are adequate over an existing finish floor.

INSTALLATION OF PLANK AND PARQUET FLOORING

In general, plank flooring is installed much in the same manner as the strip style. The planks, however, are fastened at intervals along the length of the boards as well as at the ends. Screws usually are preferred for fastening because they add holding strength required for wide boards. Face-nailing, however, may be used along the length of the boards. Tongued and grooved planks also are blind-nailed at tongue edges.

Recommended procedures for installation of parquet flooring vary widely among the different manufacturers. Probably the best advice on this score is simply to make sure the flooring is laid according to the instructions of the manufacturer whose product you select.

Here are a few general points of information, though, which may

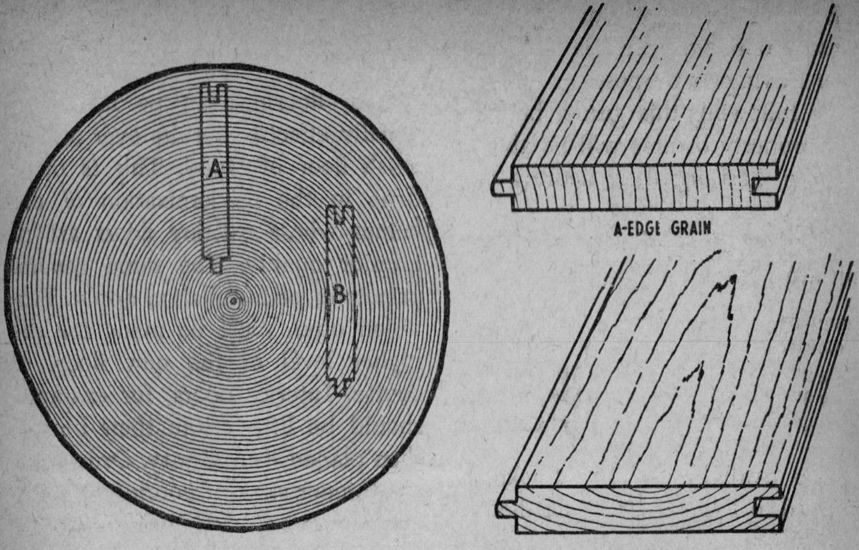

Fig. 20. Illustrating (**left**) the relation of edge and flat grain flooring to the angle of ring growth in the tree; and (**right**) how each appears in the piece, ready for installation.

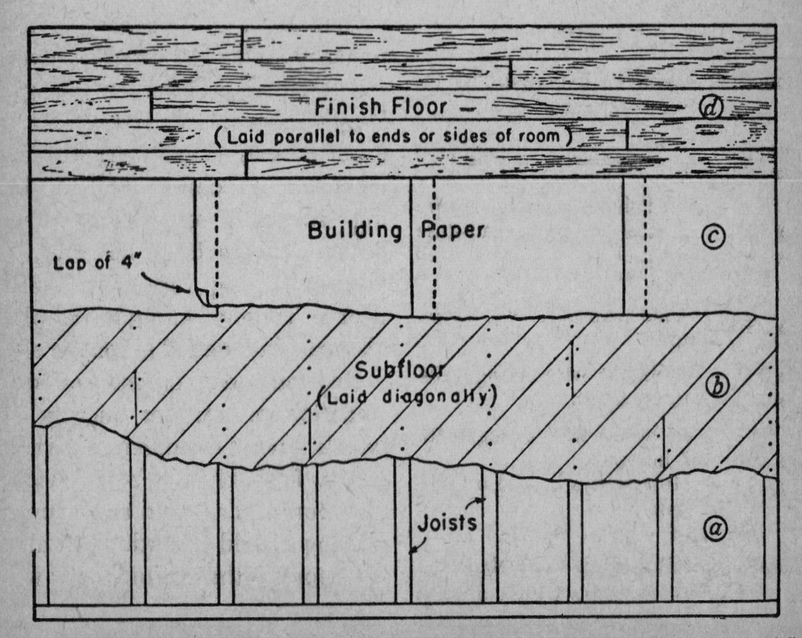

Fig. 21. Cut-away view of floor, showing details of construction: **a**, Joists; **b**, subfloor; **c**, building paper; **d**, finish floor.

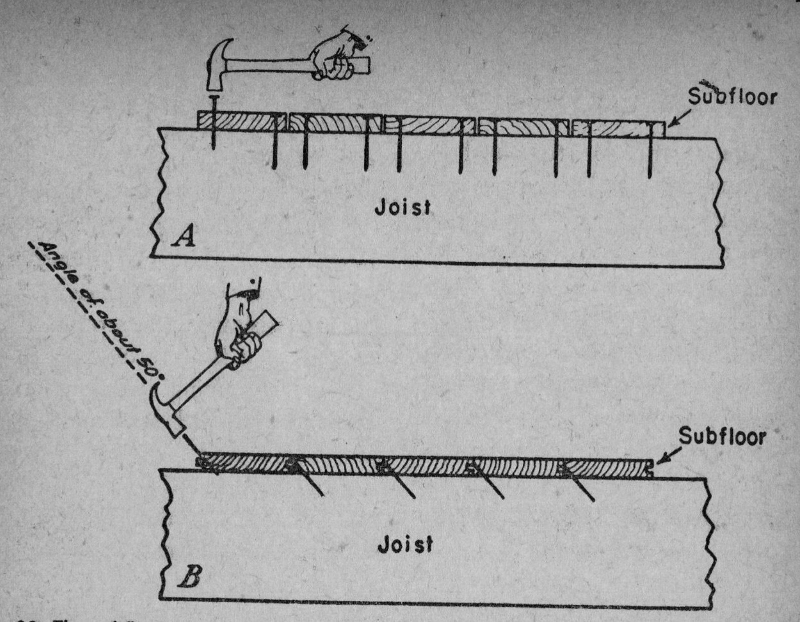

Fig. 22. The subfloor: A, Square-edge boards, face-nailed at every bearing point. For unheated houses and those in moist climates allow one-eighth to one-fourth inch between boards as shown, otherwise lay with flush-butted joints, close but not exceedingly tight. B, Matched boards (tongued and grooved), blind-nailed at an angle of about 50° at every bearing point.

serve as a preliminary guide. Either the individual parquetry pieces or the pre-assembled blocks may be laid in mastic or nailed to a wood subfloor. Laying in mastic is the method employed when the subflooring is of concrete. Advantages of this method include saving in floor thickness due to the absence of wood subflooring or screeds. The concrete should be smooth, level and dry before application of the mastic is begun. If conditions expose the concrete to dampness or do not permit adequate ventilation, a two-ply membrane waterproofing of coal tar pitch and asphalt felt usually is recommended. In such instances the concrete customarily is first treated with an ashalt primer to assure bond. Mastic usually is applied to an average thickness of about 3/32 inch.

HOW TO ESTIMATE AMOUNT OF HARDWOOD FLOORING REQUIRED

Strip Flooring. To determine the board feet of flooring needed to cover a given space, first find the area in square feet, then add to it the percentage of that figure which applies to the size flooring to be used, as indicated below:

50% for .... 25/32" x 1½"
37½% for .... 25/32" x 2"
33⅓% for .... 25/32" x 2¼"
24% for .... 25/32" x 3¼"

33⅓% for .... ⅜" x 1½"
25% for .... ⅜" x 2"
33⅓% for .... ½" x 1½"
25% for .... ½" x 2"

The above figures are based on laying flooring straight across the room. Where there are bay windows or other projections, allowance should be made for additional flooring. It is always well to order 5% additional flooring to take care of floor layers' cutting and possible damage if carelessly handled.

EDGE GRAIN AND FLAT GRAIN FLOORING

In edge grain flooring the wearing surface is at an angle of 45 degrees or more with the grain (ring growth). Also termed vertical grain and rift flooring, this type corresponds to quarter sawn in hardwood flooring (figure 20).

The surface of edge grain flooring averages six annual rings per inch throughout the area of each piece. In the finished floor, this grain shows in closely spaced parallel lines, formed by the alternating sequence of winter and summer growth. Both heart and sap which vary somewhat in color are included. For a thoroughly uniform color, it is necessary to use all-heart face stock.

Edge grain flooring has a hard surface which provides impressive resistance to wear. It stands up under such severe usage as in school rooms, stores, auditoriums, and when exposed to weather in open-air dance pavilions and porches.

Flat grain flooring disregards any designated angle with annual ring growth and may completely coincide with it. This accounts for the great variety in figure peculiar to flat grain flooring. Like edge grain it includes both heart and sap growth, although it, too, may be had in all-heart face when uniform color is desired. While not as resistant to severe wear as edge grain, it is a thoroughly practical material, giving splendid service in residential and apartment uses, either for scatter rugs or under carpets and linoleum. Costing somewhat less than edge grain, it affords an enduring value when economy must be considered.

In residential and apartment construction, edge grain flooring is often used in hallways, living and dining rooms, and flat grain in bedrooms, closets and service quarters.

HIDING CRACKS BETWEEN FLOORING AND BASEBOARD

Cracks appearing between finish flooring and baseboard are the result of improper nailing of the shoe. In figure 23, *A* shows the shoe nailed directly to the baseboard. Shrinkage of the baseboard will lift the shoe off the finish flooring. In *B* the shoe is nailed to the finish flooring and shrinkage of the flooring moves the shoe away from the baseboard exposing a crack. In *C* the shoe is nailed to the subflooring and even if both finish floor and baseboard shrink the shoe will remain in place to conceal the crack.

COMPRESSION SET

Where a succession of damp days follows immediately after the floor is laid (fig. 24, *A*) and before the finish can be placed upon it, a very important pick-up in moisture content is likely to occur. The pick-up, of course, is very much slower after a floor has received even the first coat of its final finish.

Even a moderate absorption of moisture from the air is sufficient to cause a perceptible bulging of certain boards where they resist one another in the natural tendency to swell. Some crushing of wood fiber is bound to result from moisture increase in a tightly laid floor, and we are then face to face with the common cause of all or nearly all cracking, technically known as compression set (fig. 24, *B*). If one were able to examine some well-laid flooring and see just how the edges go together, he would find that there is a relatively narrow edge that has to take the first results of the compression. After a board has been compressed it never completely recovers.

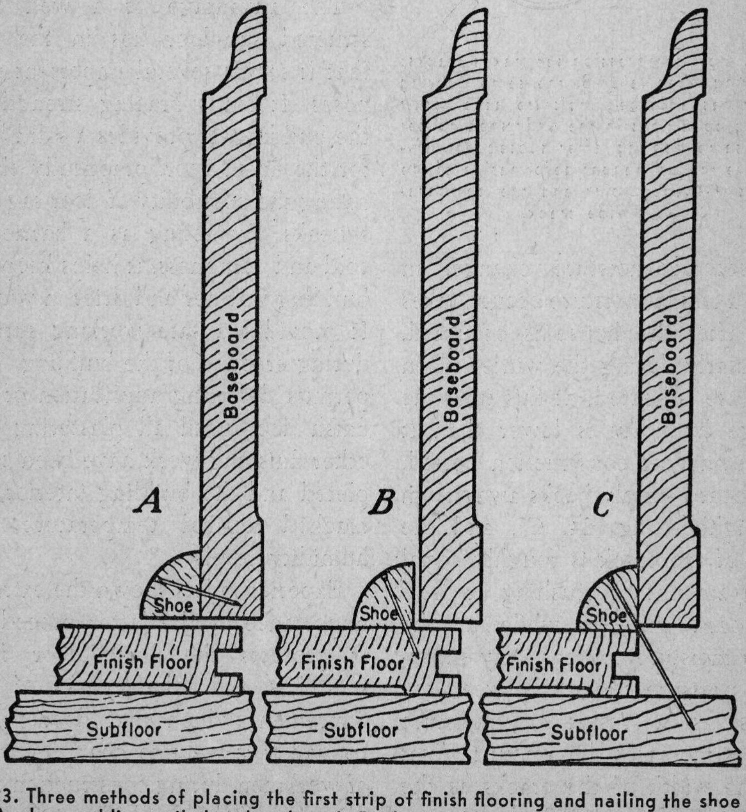

Fig. 23. Three methods of placing the first strip of finish flooring and nailing the shoe molding: A, shoe molding nailed to baseboard; B, shoe molding nailed to finish floor; C, shoe molding nailed to subfloor.

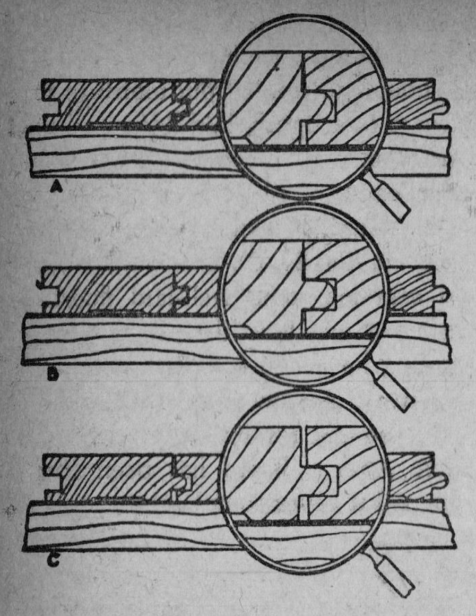

Fig. 24. How compression set makes cracks: **A**, flooring when laid; **B**, the same flooring after it has absorbed moisture as a result of damp conditions in the unfinished house; **C**, the same flooring after subsequent drying. Note the permanent deformation of the inverted V-shaped joint and the comparatively wide crack.

A second moisture change, in which a loss in moisture occurs, takes place after the house is occupied, particularly during the winter when the house is heated; at this time the average humidity is lower than it was during the construction period. Each board simply backs away from its neighbor (fig. 24, *C*), and the width of the crack is roughly equal to the amount of crushing or "set" the board suffered while at the higher moisture content. Any subsequent pressure contact between the boards as a result of moisture changes increases the amount of set and the width of the cracks as the wood again dries out. Such pressure may occur during a period when the house is unoccupied or unheated for several weeks during cold or damp weather or from contact with foreign matter in the cracks. Another example of this process is the typical kitchen floor, in which repeated scrubbing causes the cracks to grow wider and wider as the floor grows older.

SUB-FLOOR CONSTRUCTION

Sub-floors are so essential to good construction that most modern building codes specify them. Their omission usually is poor economy.

The advantage of a well constructed sub-floor lies in the fact that it serves several important purposes. It lends bracing strength to the building. It provides a solid base for the finish floor, practically eliminating the possibility of floor sag and squeaks. By acting as a barrier to cold and dampness, it helps keep the building warmer and drier in winter. It provides a safe working surface during erection of the building. This permits deferring application of the finish floor until all plastering and other finishing work have been completed and the building interior has reached normal temperature and humidity levels.

Experience has shown the extreme importance of the latter procedure. It protects the finish floor from scratches and other marks of disfigurement which that floor would receive if it were to bear the traffic of workmen during construction. Application of the finish floor after the building has reached proper temperature and humidity levels serves to guard against excessive expansion or contraction of the floor after installation.

Sub-flooring. In new buildings subfloors should be laid over joist construction before the finish flooring is applied. Sub-flooring should be of kiln-dried No. 1 Common or No. 2 Common grade lumber of any coniferous species customarily used for sub-flooring. The boards should be 1 inch thick and either 4 inches or 6 inches wide. Square-edge boards should be used.

It is best to avoid using boards which have served as forms for concrete work. They may be used only when they are sound, clean, dry and free of warps. Even then they should be extra nailed.

In some sections of the country, the tendency has been to use boards 10 to 12 inches wide. This practice has proved extremely unsatisfactory. Use of lumber more than 6 inches wide is not recommended, since expansion and contraction of such boards is out of proportion to that of the narrower finish flooring. This condition frequently gives rise to developments of squeaks, buckling and cracks between joints in the finish flooring. With use of 4-inch or 6-inch boards, this danger is averted. Under no circumstances should the boards be wider than 10 inches.

Square-edge boards, which are more economical, are generally preferred to tongued and grooved boards because the snug jointing effected by the latter is usually undesirable in sub-flooring. To allow for expansion, boards should be spaced slightly as directed in *3* and *4*. Square-edge sub-flooring is particularly recommended for buildings in moist climates and for summer homes which are not heated in winter.

Direction of sub-flooring. In new buildings of one story where strip finish flooring is to be used, the subfloor boards over joists or sleepers should be laid diagonally.

In new buildings of more than one story, where strip flooring is to be used, the sub-floor boards over joists or sleepers should be laid in opposite diagonal directions on alternate floors.

The purpose in laying sub-floors diagonally is twofold: to lend bracing strength to the building, and to permit the finish flooring to be laid in any direction. This practice is followed also where plank finish flooring is to be used. Where parquetry is to be installed as finish flooring, and sub-flooring is to be nailed on joists or sleepers, sub-floor boards should be laid at right angles to them.

Nailing sub-floors. When applied over joists, square-edge sub-floor boards should be spaced approximately one-fourth inch apart to allow for expansion. Boards of 4 or 6-inch width should be face-nailed solidly at every bearing with two 10-penny nails. All butt joints of square-edge boards should rest on bearings.

When it is necessary to use boards wider than 6 inches, extra nailing should be employed at each bearing. Thus, 8-inch boards require three 10-penny nails at each bearing; 10-inch boards, four nails.

Sub-floor boards over sleepers should be nailed according to directions above, except that they shall be spaced ½-inch apart.

It is of paramount importance that plenty of nails be used in sub-floors. Good nailing keeps the boards rigid, holding them in place and preventing the creeping sometimes caused by shrinkage and expansion in subfloor lumber. Without adequate nailing, it is impossible to obtain compact, non-squeaking finish floors.

Sub-floors over concrete. A two-course membrane waterproofing consisting of hot asphalt and 15-lb. asphalt felt should be applied directly over the concrete as follows: Hot asphalt is mopped onto the concrete to form an adhesive for the first layer of asphalt felt, and is applied between the first and second layer of asphalt felt. On top of the second layer of waterproofing, 2 x 4-inch sleepers are laid in mastic. They should be flat pieces 12 to 15 inches long and laid diagonally 12 inches on centers, with space between the butts to allow for air circulation. Subflooring then should be laid diagonally across the sleepers and nailed.

If laid on a grade, the concrete should have a fill which may consist of cinders, broken mortar or broken concrete.

LAYING AND NAILING OAK FLOORS

The specifications below are concerned principally with strip flooring, although instructions regarding plank flooring also are given. General information concerning the parquet and block flooring installation is offered as a preliminary guide for those considering their use.

Finish flooring. Strip oak flooring is generally available in three grades of quarter-sawed and four of plain-sawed flooring. In descending order the quarter-sawed grades are: Clear, Sap Clear and Select. Plain-sawed grades are: Clear, Select, No. 1 Common and No. 2 Common. Most strip flooring for residential use is tongued and grooved, although the square-edge type is available. Tongued and grooved flooring fits together more snugly, forming a "welded" unit which possesses greater strength than a floor of square-edge pieces. Both types are manufactured in various widths and thicknesses, and are used either in uniform or in random widths.

Preparation. Before laying of the finish floor over a sub-floor is begun, care should be taken that the subflooring surface has been properly leveled, smoothed and cleaned. Building paper also should be laid.

Time of installation. Finish flooring should be laid only after the plaster and cement work have dried thoroughly, and all but the final woodwork and trim have been completed. The building interior should have dried and seasoned by means of heat and ventilation. The flooring should be delivered to the site four or five days before installation and be piled loosely in the building. During that period a temperature of at least 70 degrees should be maintained in the building.

Laying and finishing the finish oak floors should be the last construction operation in a building. Except for the finish details, all other work should already be completed, so that the new finish floor will receive a minimum of traffic from workmen. Thus the floor is better protected against dirt, scratches and scars which might be difficult to remove.

It is extremely important that the flooring be kept warm and dry before installation, and that the temperature of the building interior be maintained at about 70 degrees. This is particularly true of winter construction jobs. If these precautions are not observed, the flooring may absorb an excessive amount of moisture. Then, after it has been in use for several months, it may contract noticeably. The result of such contraction usually is the development of cracks between the pieces of flooring.

Direction of finish flooring. In new construction, strip flooring in each room should be laid in the direction of the longest dimension of the building. The flooring should run continuously between adjoining rooms, and door sills between such rooms should be omitted.

Interior door sills or thresholds generally are omitted in modern construction to give the advantage of a flush floor throughout the building. The direction of the flooring must be uniform, therefore, in order to avert the unsightly break that would occur between rooms if the direction were varied. In some cases it may be desirable to lay the flooring crosswise instead of lengthwise of the building. This is permissible if the rooms are not exceptionally narrow.

Use of short strips. The shortest pieces of flooring should be used in closets and in the general floor area. When possible, avoid using short pieces at entrances and doorways. Do not use ripped strips at doors or other places where they may mar appearances.

Starting to lay the finish floor. In laying tongued and grooved strip flooring, begin at the junction of a sidewall and an endwall. The first piece in each one should be laid parallel to the sidewall, with the groove edge nearest the wall. A space of not less than ½-inch should be left between the flooring and the wall, but the space should be no wider than will be covered by the base-shoe, quarter-round or saddle. The baseboard should be so installed that the lower edge will be slightly above the finish floor level.

Leaving space between the walls and baseboard and the piece of flooring nearest to the wall allows room for expansion and contraction of the flooring without ill effects. Since the space later is covered, it does not mar the appearance of the floor.

Nailing. The groove edge of the first piece of tongued and grooved flooring should be face-nailed, with the nails driven so that later they will be concealed by the shoe moulding. Then the tongue edge should be blind-nailed, with the nails driven at an angle of about 50 degrees at the point where the tongue leaves the shoulder. In blind-nailing, the head of each nail should be countersunk with a steel nail set or a nail. After the first piece of flooring has been nailed, begin laying the other pieces, following the above directions regarding spacing and nailing for the first piece along either sidewall. Observe the spacing direction for the first piece nearest the endwall in each course. Each succeeding piece should be blind-nailed at the tongue end in the direction of the preceding piece.

Square-edge strip flooring should be used only over a sub-floor. It should be face-nailed. Otherwise specifications for tongued and grooved flooring should be followed.

Proper nailing is absolutely essential in the finish floor as well as the sub-floor. Inadequate nailing may easily result in loose or squeaky flooring.

Joints. End joints either of tongued and grooved or square-edge strip flooring should be staggered to avoid having several of them grouped closely together.

It is not necessary that the end joints either of square-edge or tongued and grooved finish flooring occur over joist or sleeper bearing points when a sub-floor is used. This applies also when the sub-floor is omitted, which may sometimes be done, provided the finish flooring is tongued and grooved and is at least 25/32-inch thick.

When a sub-floor is used, nails through the finish floor should not strike sub-floor joints. Care also should be taken, when the sub-floor is laid at right angles to the finish floor, that ends of the finish flooring do not meet directly over sub-floor joints.

Drawing up. Do not try to hammer each piece of tongued and grooved strip flooring into its final position as soon as it is nailed. After laying three or four pieces, place a short piece of straight-edge hardwood against the tongue of the outside piece and drive the pieces up snugly, taking care not to break the tongue. Repeat this after every three or four pieces have been laid. This operation drives the pieces into their final position.

Nailing shoe moulding. The shoe moulding should be nailed to the sub-floor at an angle through the crack between the baseboard and the finish floor. This should be done after the entire floor has been laid.

When the shoe moulding is nailed in the above manner, any movement either of the baseboard or the flooring, due to seasonal moisture changes, is less likely to affect the moulding and open unsightly cracks. If the moulding is nailed to the baseboard, however, shrinkage may result in a crack between the moulding and the finish floor. If the moulding is nailed to the finish floor, shrinkage may cause a crack to develop between the moulding and the baseboard.

Laying new strip flooring over old floor. The old floor may serve as a sub-floor. Examine it carefully and correct any defects. Any existing thresholds should be removed to allow the new floor to run flush through doorways. Interior doors should be lifted from their hinges. The base-shoe or moulding strip at the baseboard should be removed. Building paper should be laid. Then the new flooring is installed, with the pieces laid at right angles to the old floor boards. In other respects laying and nailing, as well as replacing the moulding, is done in the same manner as in new construction. The bottoms of doors should be planed if this becomes necessary due to the higher level of the new floor.

Ordinarily, the thinner sizes of strip flooring are used over an existing finish floor. Thicker flooring usually is unnecessary because strength is not a factor when the old flooring is structurally sound.

Plank flooring. Plank flooring should be nailed over wood sub-floors of the type used as a foundation for strip flooring. It is laid according to the same general specifications as strip flooring with regard to selection, preparation, time of installation, direction, use of short strips, joints and nailing shoe moulding. Each tongued and grooved plank should be blind-nailed.

Additionally, it should be fastened to the sub-floor with two countersunk screws at each end and other screws at intervals along the length of the plank. The screws should be covered with walnut plugs glued into the holes. Screws and plugs are placed at intervals frequent enough to hold the plank securely without marring its appearance. The same types and sizes of nails are employed as those used for corresponding thicknesses of strip flooring. The planks should not be driven tightly together.

Sometimes nails, instead of screws, are used along the length of the plank, although screws are recommended because of their superior holding qualities. If nails are employed, they should be the small-headed type. Driven vertically through the face of the plank, they should be countersunk and covered by walnut plugs, as is done when screws are used. The frequency of the fastening lengthwise of the plank is somewhat a matter of individual preference. Some authorities recommend screws or nails at 30-inch intervals.

In specifying that planks shall not be driven tightly together, some authorities recommend leaving a slight crack, about the thickness of a putty knife, between planks.

Parquet and block flooring. The styles and types of hardwood parquet and block flooring, as well as the recommended procedures for application, vary so widely among different manufacturers that it is impractical to set forth specifications applying to all. The manufacturer of the pattern flooring to be used will furnish all the necessary specifications upon request. A few points of information, however, may serve as a general preliminary guide.

Either the individual parquetry pieces or the prefabricated blocks of parquetry may be laid in mastic or nailed to a wood sub-floor. Laying in mastic is the method employed when the sub-floor is of concrete. Each piece of parquetry or each block is embedded in mastic individually. Advantages of this method include saving in floor thickness due to absence of wood sub-floor or screeds, and eliminating the danger of settling of sub-floor or screeds.

The concrete must be smooth, level and dry before application of the mastic is begun. Where conditions expose the concrete sub-floor to dampness or do not permit adequate ventilation, a two-ply membrane waterproofing of coal tar pitch and asphalt felt usually is applied. In such instances, the concrete customarily is first treated with an asphalt primer to assure bond. Mastic usually is applied to an average thickness of about 3/32-inch. The flooring manufacturer or dealer will specify whether hot or cold mastic should be used.

Most parquetry is manufactured in 25/32-inch thickness. It comes in various widths, the most extensively used being 2¼-inches. Lengths are in multiples of widths. Prefabricated blocks are made in several widths and thicknesses.

Quarter-sawed oak of Clear grade is widely recommended for parquet or block flooring, although other grades of oak, as well as other species of wood, are frequently used for this type flooring.

FINISHING OAK FLOORS

Oak flooring may be obtained either in unfinished or finished form. The unfinished type receives the final finishing treatment on the job after the flooring has been installed.

The instructions here are designed to point out the approved methods of finishing oak floors in such a way as to bring out the full richness of the wood. Some steps in the finishing operation are similar for all oak flooring, while others may vary with the grade of wood or the type of finish desired. For example, all unfinished flooring must be sanded or scraped before any finishing materials are applied. This is necessary to remove the scars or scratches which usually appear as a result of handling before and during installation. On the other hand, some floors are stained and others are not, depending upon the shade of finish preferred.

Pre-finished flooring is completely finished at the mill, even to the final polishing. Thus it is ready for service immediately after installation. In saving the time otherwise required for finishing the floors after they have been installed, pre-finished flooring hastens completion of a home by several days.

When to begin surfacing. Sanding is done just before application of the final coat of finish to the base moulding and after all other interior work has been completed.

Preparation. Immediately before the sanding operation is begun, the floor is swept clean. Use no water.

Method. Surfacing should be done with an electric sanding machine. The floor should be traversed at least four times. On the initial traverse the floor is sanded crosswise of the grain, then lengthwise. All succeeding traverses are lengthwise of the grain. Sandpaper employed should be No. 2 for the first traverse, No. ½ for the second, and No. 0 or No. 00 for the third and fourth. The floor then receives a final buffing by hand with No. 00 or No. 000 sandpaper.

Two or three traverses may be sufficient for some floors, but floors of high quality should receive four or even five traverses if one desires to bring out their full beauty.

In many cases steel wool, rather than fine sandpaper, is used effectively for the final buffing. It should never be used, however, when paste filler is to be applied to the floor immediately after; nor should it be used for cleaning the floor after application of the filler.

Most floors nowadays are sanded by electrically operated sanding machines. This method is faster, easier and more economical than sanding by hand. It requires only a fraction of the time and effort involved in the manual operation, yet produces an adequately smooth surface.

For especially fine floors, however, handscraping by expert mechanics often is recommended, because it produces an even smoother surface.

Large sanding machines are not sufficiently effective near walls, in corners or in small closets. Such places, therefore, should be sanded manually or with a small, power-driven hand sander.

Protecting the surface. After the final buffing the floor should not be walked on until the floor stain, filler or first coat of finish has been applied and is dry.

Final sanding and first finish Coat. The first coat of stain, filler or other finish should be applied the same day as the final sanding and buffing.

Application of the first coat of finish immediately after the final buffing is an important detail in procedure. If there is a longer interval between the two operations, the grain of the wood will rise and the finished surface will not be as smooth as it should be. Application of the finish immediately prevents the grain from rising.

Stain. If a dark colored floor is desired, one coat of a good oil stain is applied before any filler or other finish. A flat varnish brush 3 or 4 inches wide should be used for application. Prepare samples of the required color on pieces of scrap flooring or on an inconspicuous part of the floor, such as a closet, where variations in shade will not be noticed. When the desired shade has been achieved, begin in the farthest corner of the room from the exterior door and work lengthwise of the room, applying the stain in a width of approximately 36 inches. Care must be taken that the stain is applied evenly and that excess stain is wiped off with a soft cloth before it has had time to "set."

Unless the stain is applied evenly, some parts of the floor will be darker than others.

Colored wood filler often is used in place of a stain because it saves the cost of one coat. It is not recommended, however, since it produces a cloudy effect and does not wear well. Stain, on the other hand, not only develops the beauty of the wood but is long-lasting.

Oak floors can be finished in a wide diversity of colors. Brown, dark and natural tones are generally preferred, although some interesting bright color effects can be achieved by employing brilliant color stains and bright fillers.

All grades of oak flooring take dark stains well. Natural colored shades, however, are recommended for all grades except No. 1 Common and No. 2 Common, which should receive only medium or dark tones.

Wood filler. One coat of good quality paste wood filler should be applied after the stain has dried thoroughly. Apply with a short bristled 4-inch flat brush, or as directed by the manufacturer. Brush across the grain first, then with the grain. Care should be taken to avoid covering too large an area at once. Before the filler in each new area becomes hard, the excess should be wiped off so that the coat of filler is uniformly even with the surface of the wood. Using excelsior or burlap, wipe across the grain first, then with the grain. The filler should be allowed to "set" or dry for 24 hours before other finish materials are applied.

Wood filler is recommended for most residential oak floors, although it sometimes is omitted when floor seal is to be used. Specifications of floor seal manufacturers vary in this regard. The purpose of wood filler is to fill the minute surface crevices in oak and other hardwoods having large pores. By making the surface perfectly smooth, it prevents the top coating of finish from sinking into the pores, a condition which would cause a comparatively rough finish, particularly if floor seal were not used. In short, it aids in imparting a mirror-smooth sheen or luster to the finished floor. For a natural or light-colored floor, use colorless wood filler; for a dark-stained floor, use the colored type.

Finish materials. Specifications for application of finish materials vary with the manufacturers of the different brands. Care should be taken that the finish used is applied according to the directions printed on the containers.

In the absence of exact specifications covering all types and brands of finish, a brief discussion of the various types should prove helpful in selecting the type best suited. Following this are general recommendations regarding the application of each type.

The ideal qualities of a finish for oak or other hardwood floors are: attractive appearance; durability; ease of maintenance; and capacity for being retouched in worn spots without revealing a patched appearance. Some finishes are transparent, others are not. As a rule, the transparent type should be used on high grade flooring to accentuate its natural beauty. The three kinds of finish employed most extensively nowadays are floor seal, varnish and shellac. Lacquer, too, is sometimes employed.

Floor seal. Floor seal, a relatively new type of material, is being used on an increasingly large scale for residential as well as heavy duty flooring. It differs from other finishes in this important respect: instead of forming a surface coating, it penetrates the wood fibers, sealing them together. In effect it becomes a part of the wood itself. It wears only as the wood wears, does not chip or scratch and is practically immune to ordinary stains and spots. While it does not provide as shiny an appearance as other finishes, it has the advantage of being easily retouched. Worn spots may be refinished without revealing a patched appearance. Floor seals are available either colorless or in color.

Generally, floor seal is put on with a wide brush, a squeegee or a wool applicator. It is applied first across the grain, then with the grain. After a period of 15 minutes to 2 hours, depending upon the specific instructions of the manufacturer, excess seal should be wiped off with clean cloths or a rubber squeegee. For best results the floor should then be buffed with No. 2 steel wool. An electric buffer makes this task relatively simple. If a power buffer is not available, a sanding machine equipped with steel wool pads may be used; or the buffing may be done by hand. Although one application of seal sometimes is sufficient, a second coat frequently is recommended for new floors or floors that have just been sanded.

Varnish. Varnish presents a glossy appearance, is quite durable, fairly resistant to stains and spots, but will show scratches. It is difficult to patch worn spots, however, without leaving lines of demarcation between the old and the new varnish. New types of varnish dry in eight hours or less. Like the other types of finish, it gives satisfactory results if properly waxed and otherwise maintained.

Varnish made especially for floors is preferred. So-called all-purpose varnishes ordinarily are not so durable when used on floors. As a rule, three coats of floor varnish are required when it is applied to bare wood. Two coats usually are adequate, however, when wood filler has been used or when a coat of shellac has been applied first, as is sometimes the case. Cleanliness of both the floor and the applicator is essential to a smooth finish. Drying action is hastened when room temperature of at least 70 degrees F. is maintained and plenty of ventilation is provided.

Shellac. Two of the chief reasons shellac is so widely used are its quick drying property and its ease of application. Starting with floors in the front of a house and shellacking toward the rear, you may begin applying the second coat by the time you have finished the first. Shellac has moderate resistance to water and other types of stains, but will spot if liquids remain on it for an extended period. It is transparent, has a high gloss, and does not darken with age as quickly as varnish. If kept waxed and not subjected to extreme wear, it will give satisfactory service.

Shellac to be used on floors should be fresh or be packaged in a glass container. If it remains too long in a metal container, it may accumulate salts of iron, which discolor oak and other hardwoods containing tannin.

Shellac should not be adulterated with cheaper resins, but before use it should be thinned with 188-proof No. 1 denatured alcohol. Usual recommended proportion is 1 quart of thinner to 1 gallon of 5-pound cut shellac. A wide brush that covers the width of three strip flooring pieces is the most effective and convenient size for application. Strokes should be long and even, with laps joined smoothly.

The first coat on bare wood usually will dry in 15 to 20 minutes, after which the floor should be rubbed lightly with steel wool or sandpaper, then swept clean. A second coat then should be applied and allowed to dry 2 to 3 hours. Then the floor should be rubbed again with steel wool or sandpaper and be swept a second time. A third coat then is applied. If necessary, the floor may be walked on about 3 hours after being finished. Preferably, it should remain out of service overnight.

Lacquer. Lacquer provides a glossy finish and possesses about the same durability as varnish. One of the advantages of a lacquered floor is that worn spots may be retouched with good results. Lines of demarcation are not noticeable because the new lacquer dissolves the old coat rather than forming an additional layer.

Lacquer is rather difficult to apply, chiefly because it dries so rapidly. It is important to observe rigidly the manufacturer's instructions.

Wax. After the final coat of finish has dried thoroughly the floor should be treated with a good quality of floor wax recommended for use on hardwood floors. The wax may be either the paste or the liquid type known as rubbing wax. It should be applied according to the manufacturer's directions.

Wax not only imparts a lustrous sheen to a floor, but also forms a protective film that prevents dirt from penetrating the wood pores. When it becomes dirty, it is easily removed and new wax applied.

In some cases one coat is sufficient, although in many instances two or three are recommended for best results. Here again the directions of the manufacturer should be followed closely.

Self-polishing liquid wax is not recommended, because it has a water base. Frequent use of water on a hardwood floor will cause the grain to rise, a condition that results in a rough surface. The rubbing type of liquid wax, on the other hand, is generally considered equal to paste wax in performance. Both types are applied in much the same manner. Usually the wax is mopped on with a cloth, then polished after an interval of 15 to 30 minutes with a soft cloth, a weighted floor brush or an electric polisher. Some electric polishers apply wax and polish the floor in one operation.

REFINISHING HARDWOOD FLOORS

If the existing finish is floor seal or lacquer, it may be necessary merely to retouch worn spots with the same type of finish. This is not advisable with other finishes, nor when the worn areas are large, numerous or in particularly conspicuous parts of a room. More pleasing results in such cases can be obtained by refinishing the entire floor.

Before applying new finish, sweep the floor clean and remove all wax and spots. Recommended cleansing agents for this purpose are mineral spirits and naphtha, either of which can be secured at most large paint stores. An alternative is to use a water-dampened cloth and mild soap. To remove grease spots, laundry soap containing lye may be substituted for mild soap. It is important that use of such soap be restricted to the spots. Especially stubborn spots which do not yield to soap treatment, mineral spirits or naphtha usually will disappear when rubbed with steel wool. When the damp cloth-and-soap method of cleaning is employed, only a small area should be worked at a time. Immediately after the area has been cleaned it should be wiped dry so the grain of the wood will not be affected.

In applying the new finish, follow the manufacturer's directions closely. Usually the finish should be the same type as the old. An exception to this rule is that varnish can be applied over shellac. One coat of new finish generally is sufficient. The manufacturer's directions customarily indicate conditions wherein more than one coat is desirable.

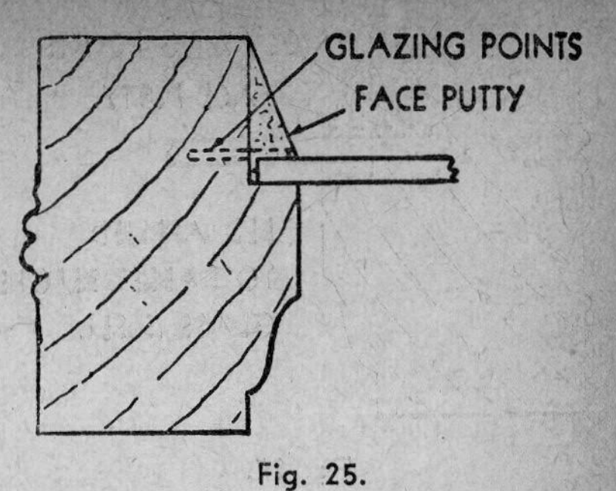

Fig. 25.

PUTTYING WINDOW PANES

Face puttying. Glass is inserted in the glass rabbet and securely wedged where necessary to prevent shifting. Glazing points are also driven into the wood to keep the glass firmly seated. The rabbet is then filled with putty, the putty being beveled back against the sash and muntins with a putty knife. (Fig. 25.)

Back puttying. After the sash has been face puttied, it is turned over and putty is run around the glass opening with a putty knife, thus forcing putty into any voids that may exist between the glass and the wood parts. (Fig. 26.)

Bedding. A thin layer of putty or bedding compound is placed in the rabbet of the sash and the glass

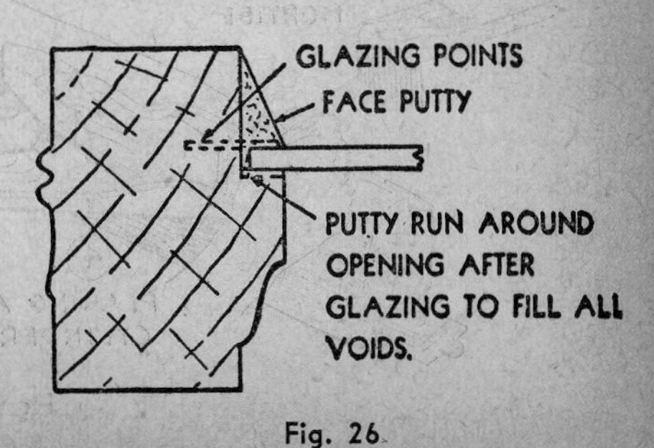

Fig. 26

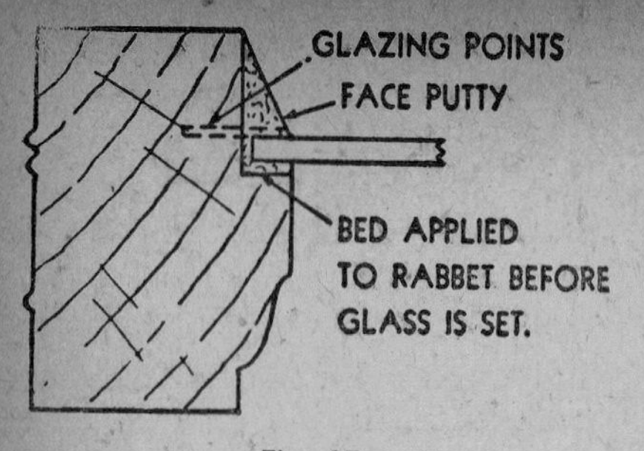

Fig. 27.

pressed onto this bed. Glazing points are then driven into the wood and the sash is face puttied. The sash is then turned over and the excess putty or glazing compound which emerged on the other side is cleaned away by running the putty knife around the perimeter of the glass opening as illustrated in figure 27.

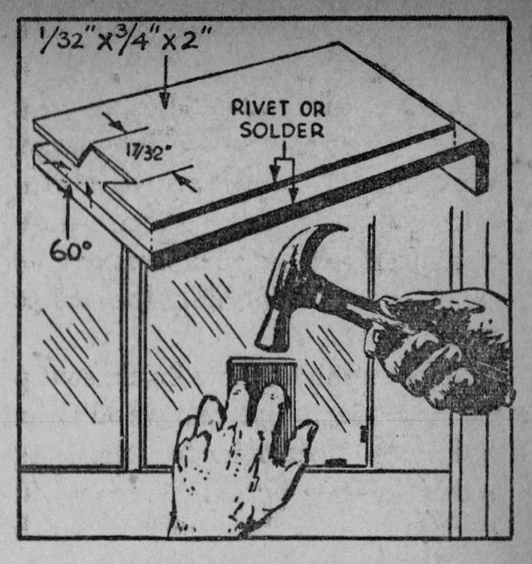

Fig. 28.

BLOCK HOLDS GLAZIER'S POINTS

When putting in window panes or framing pictures, the device

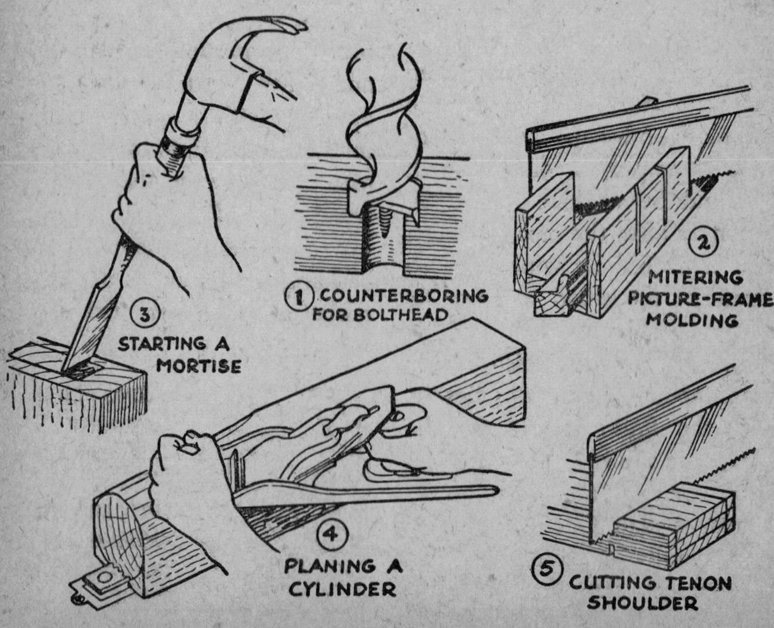

Fig. 29.

POOR PRACTICE

GOOD PRACTICE

NO PUTTY BACK OR UNDER GLASS ALLOWS RAIN FROM OUTSIDE AND CONDENSATION FROM INSIDE TO FIND ENTRANCE

LACK OF PRIMING, AND POOR, UNPAINTED PUTTY RESULTS IN CRACKS THAT PERMIT ENTRANCE OF MOISTURE FROM OUTSIDE

PRIMED AND BACK PUTTIED TO PREVENT ENTRANCE OF MOISTURE

PUTTY MIXED WITH WHITE LEAD AND PROTECTED BY PAINT REDUCES CRACKS

Fig. 30. Good and poor practice with window glass.

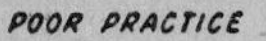

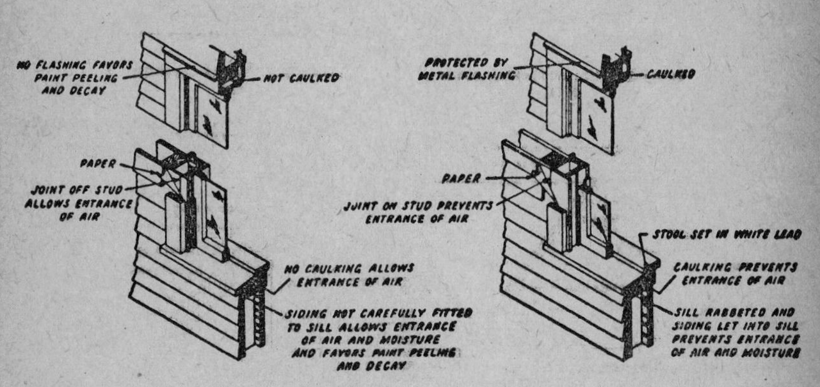

Fig. 31. Good and poor practice with window sash and frame.

sketched in figure 28 is a great time saver. The dovetail slot holds the point firmly against the glass and frame while the other end is tapped with a hammer. Another advantage of the holder is that points may be moved to position without slipping.

WHAT'S WRONG?

Woodworking technique isn't just a set of rules invented by the experts in order to make things tough. There's a reason for practically every "right" and "wrong" way. Usually the right way prevents damage to the work or the tools, and does the job better.

See if you can spot the errors shown in figure 29.

Fig. 32.

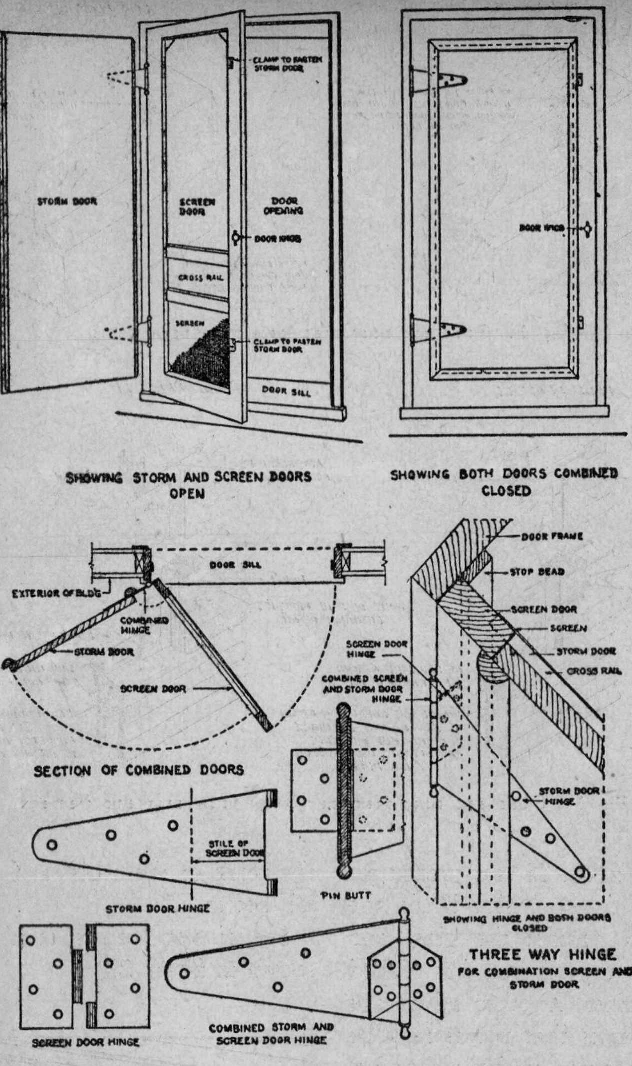

Fig. 33.

Answers.

1. When the smaller hole is bored first, the bit has no center and may tear or scar the wood. The fore-sighted craftsman counterbores first. If this isn't possible, use a dowel centering plug on the bit.

2. The back saw cuts on the push stroke, so hold the work against the far edge of the miter box. Wherever possible a true rather than a molded edge should bear against the wall. Sawing the second miter parallel to the first will make it impossible to

put the frame together. Reverse the angle of cut.

3. What happened to the mallet? If you don't have one, the side of the hammer head may be less likely to damage the chisel handle.

4. For evenness in rounding rectangular work, plane the full length into an octagon and keep cutting down the corners. Bring the entire plane sole into contact with the work.

5. Check cuts are always made first. This allows the waste to support the saw so there's less danger of cutting into the tenon.

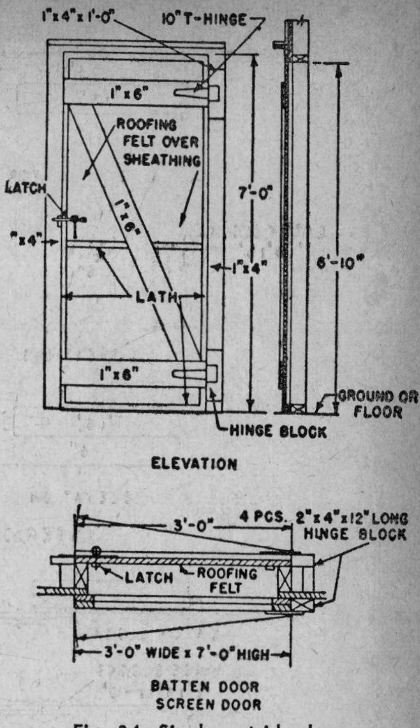

Fig. 34. Single outside door.

HINGE LOCKS SIDING WINDOW

Automatic locking of the horizontally sliding type of window often found in summer camps can be achieved with a common strap hinge. The end of one leaf is ground or filed to a sharp point, and the other leaf is screwed to the side of the window. (Fig. 32.)

COMBINATION SCREEN AND STORM DOOR

Combination screen and storm doors can be easily and inexpensively made out of an ordinary standard screen door, a sheet of exterior plywood and a three-way hinge (fig. 33). This hinge allows the storm door to be left open during mild weather while the screen door is in the closed position. In cold weather, the storm door is fastened in place to the screen door frame so that they move as one unit. The three-way hinge can be easily made out of an ordinary butt hinge and a strap hinge.

A QUICKLY BUILT DOOR

For hasty construction, you can make a door from several boards with battens and braces as shown in figure 34. These boards are 1 x 6's, laid close together and nailed to battens. The battens are placed with their edges 6 inches from the ends of the door boards. A brace is placed between the battens, beginning at the top batten end opposite the hinge side of the door, and running to the lower batten diagonally

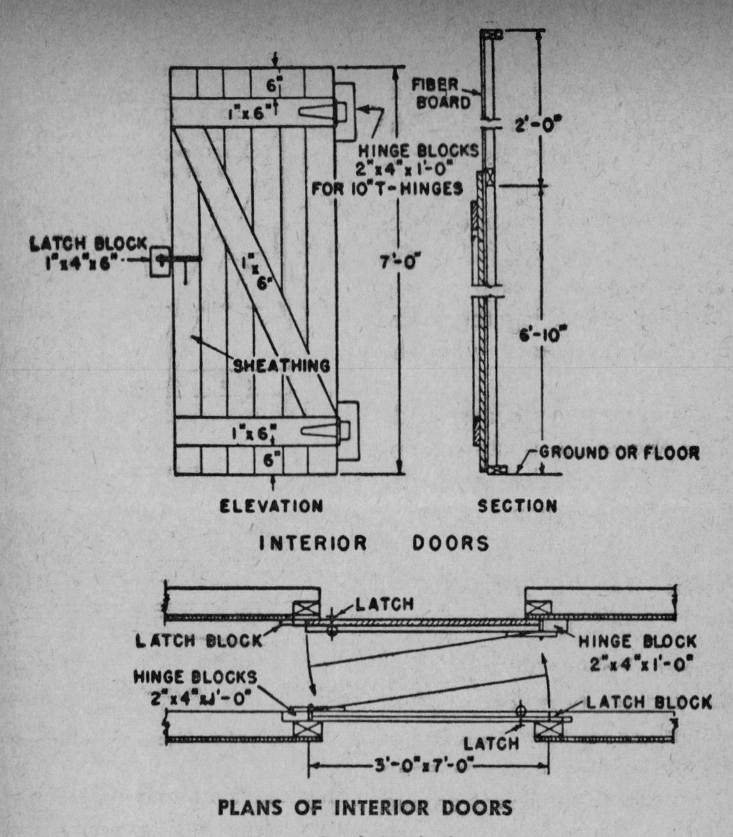

Fig. 35. Single inside door.

across the door. The battens and braces should be well nailed. If the door is used as an outside door, roofing felt is used to cover the boards on the weather side. The battens and braces are nailed over the felt. Figure 35 shows an interior door.

MAKING A DOOR STAY SHUT

Much easier than resetting an offending strike, when the latch of a door lock will not catch properly, is the alternative of filing the slot a little larger. Don't try to do this on the jamb, but remove the strike and clamp it in a vise for the job. It can then be replaced and the screws put in the same holes without plugging and respotting them, or enlarging the mortise. (Figure 37.)

Wear marks on the strike usually show whether it was too high or too low for the latch. If these are lacking, the latch has not been passing far enough inward, in which case the outer edge of the slot needs to be enlarged. Frequently no more than $\frac{1}{16}$″ of metal need be filed.

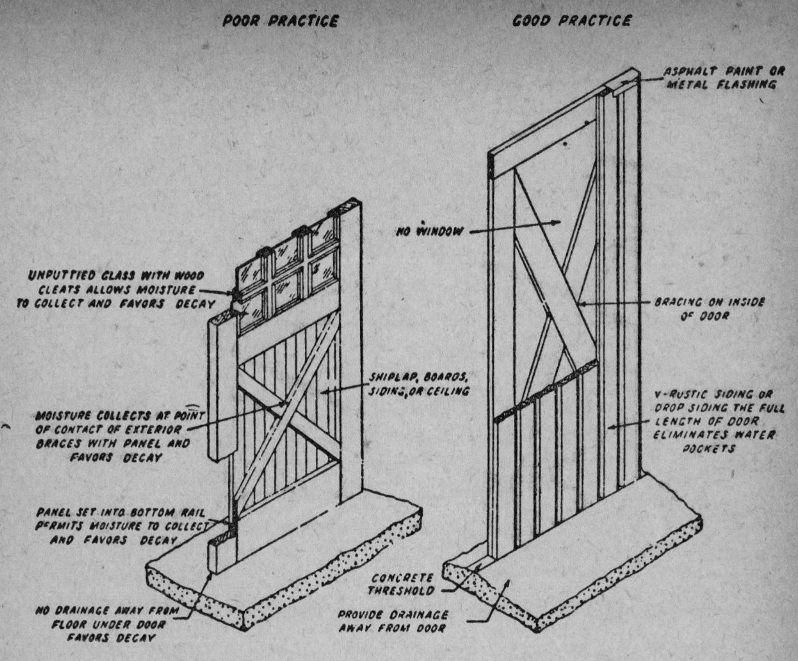
POOR PRACTICE
GOOD PRACTICE
ASPHALT PAINT OR METAL FLASHING
NO WINDOW
UNPUTTIED GLASS WITH WOOD CLEATS ALLOWS MOISTURE TO COLLECT AND FAVORS DECAY
BRACING ON INSIDE OF DOOR
SHIPLAP, BOARDS, SIDING, OR CEILING
MOISTURE COLLECTS AT POINT OF CONTACT OF EXTERIOR BRACES WITH PANEL AND FAVORS DECAY
V-RUSTIC SIDING OR DROP SIDING THE FULL LENGTH OF DOOR ELIMINATES WATER POCKETS
PANEL SET INTO BOTTOM RAIL PERMITS MOISTURE TO COLLECT AND FAVORS DECAY
CONCRETE THRESHOLD
NO DRAINAGE AWAY FROM FLOOR UNDER DOOR FAVORS DECAY
PROVIDE DRAINAGE AWAY FROM DOOR

Fig. 36. Good and poor practice with garage doors.

AWNINGS FOR CASEMENT WINDOWS

Besides adding comfort and a pleasant bit of color to your home, you'll find these homemade awnings a considerable saving over ready-made ones (fig. 38). They're easy to put up and take down, and they're especially suited for casement windows that swing outward. The hip gives ample clearance without requiring a frame mounted high over the window, as is usually necessary with conventional casement-window awnings.

Fittings can be bought at a hardware store. Some ¼″ galvanized pipe with the end tips hinged in brackets screwed to the wall will do nicely. Hems are sewn in the fabric as indicated in the stitching diagram. After the pipes and ½″ rod are inserted in the hems, the arms are screwed in place.

To keep the fabric taut from side to side, the edges are wired to the arms through grommets. Sash cord, or clothesline of good quality, is

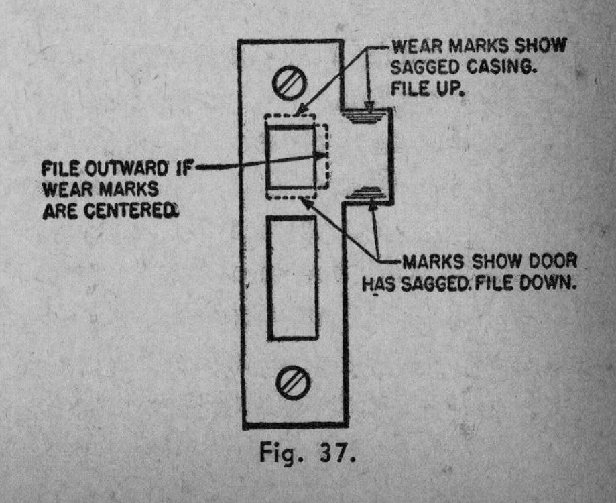
WEAR MARKS SHOW SAGGED CASING. FILE UP.
FILE OUTWARD IF WEAR MARKS ARE CENTERED.
MARKS SHOW DOOR HAS SAGGED. FILE DOWN.

Fig. 37.

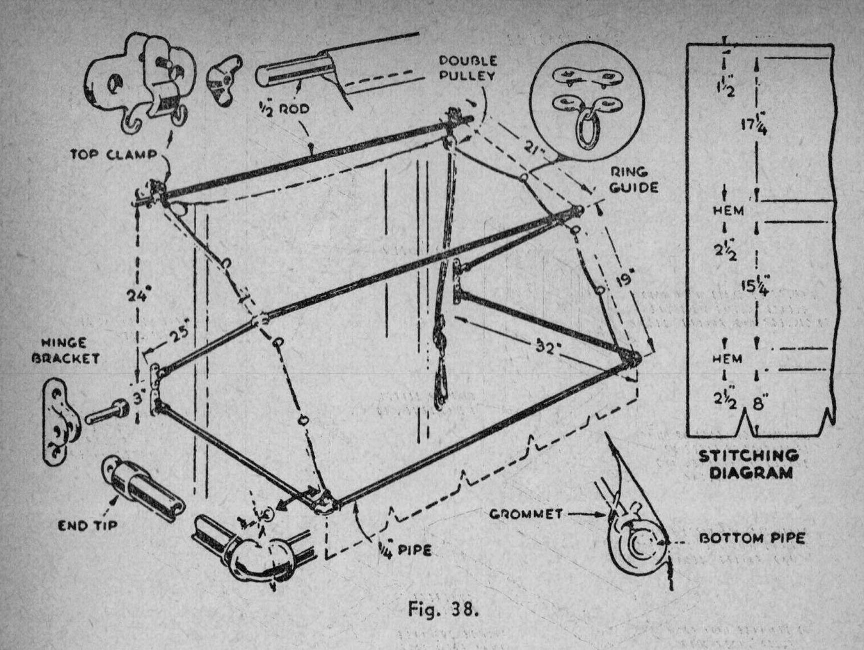

Fig. 38.

tied to each end of the lower pipe and carried through the grommets and pulleys. Use a double pulley on the side of the awning where the pull cord hangs down. A cleat, screwed to the window frame or wall, holds the cord.

BEDROOM CLOSETS

At least one closet in every bedroom is the rule for modern houses. Ideally, there is a separate closet for each person.

Of the basic closet arrangements shown in figure 39, the shallow reach-in type is the most economical of space and the most convenient for removing articles. Figure 40 shows a version of this type of closet designed for the wardrobe of one adult. It may also be used as a child's closet if hooks and rods are placed low.

In this closet a rod provides 24 to 27 inches of hanging space. Two feet of rod length is about the minimum to allow for each person. The tops of both the rod and the hooks on the closet door are 63 inches from the floor, a good height for the garments of most adults. Just above the rod, 65½ inches from the floor, is a shelf 18 inches from front to back. The second shelf above the rod is narrower and may be omitted if height is limited.

On the right-hand side is a section of shelves and drawers, 18 inches wide. The two lowest shelves for shoes are spaced 7 inches apart. The two drawers for ties, handkerchiefs, and toilet articles are 4 inches deep. Four movable shelves for

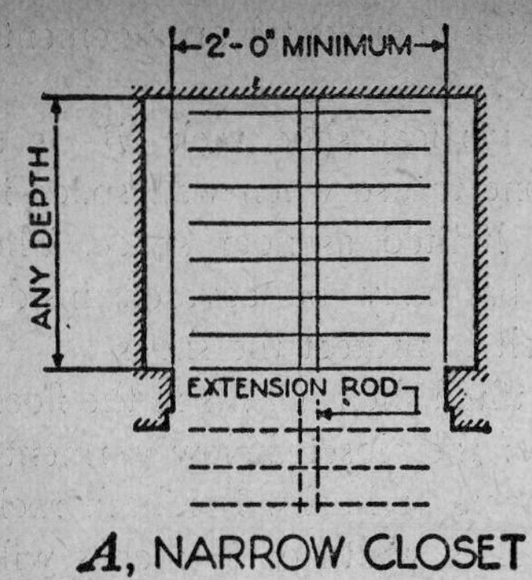

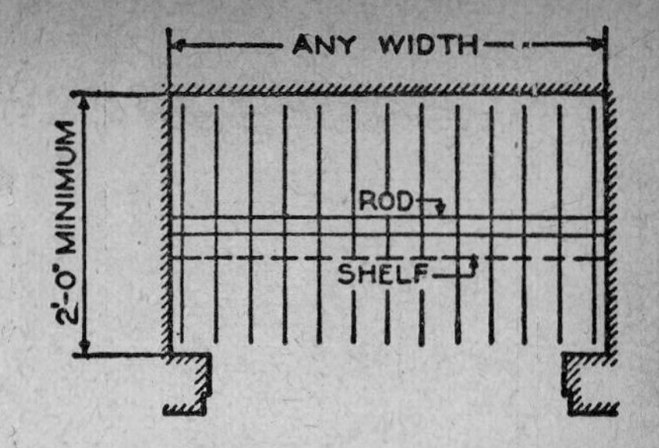

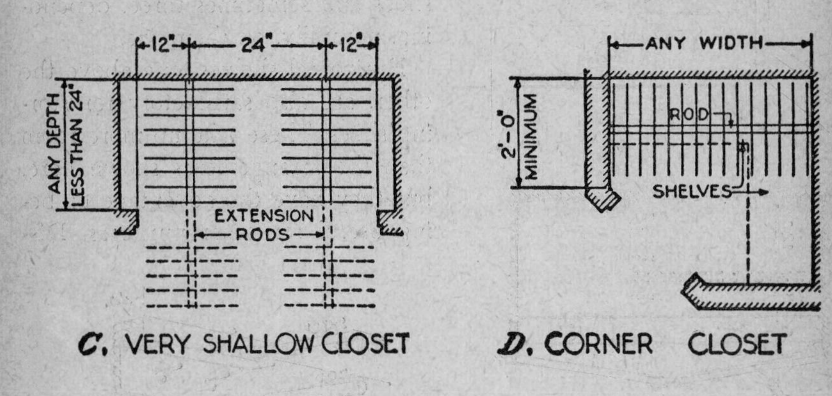

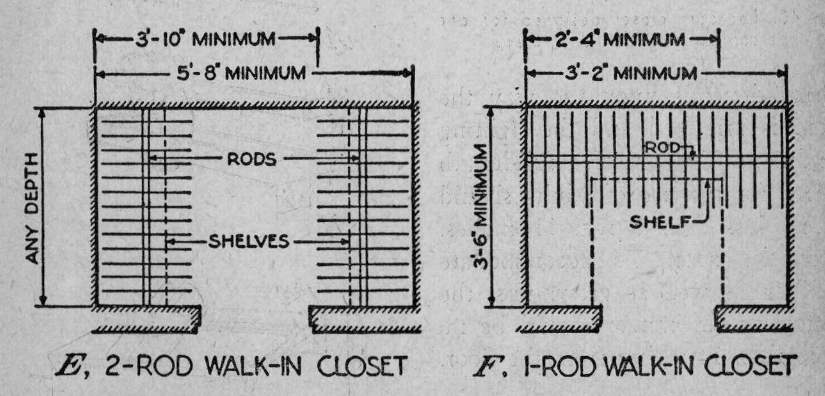

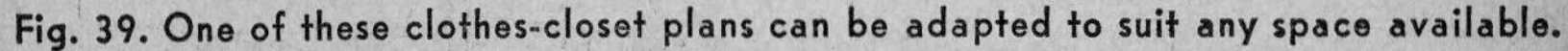
Fig. 39. One of these clothes-closet plans can be adapted to suit any space available.

folded articles are spaced 9 inches apart and have guards on the front to keep articles from falling off.

One of the closet doors is a handy place to put a full-length mirror. Which door is the better one for the

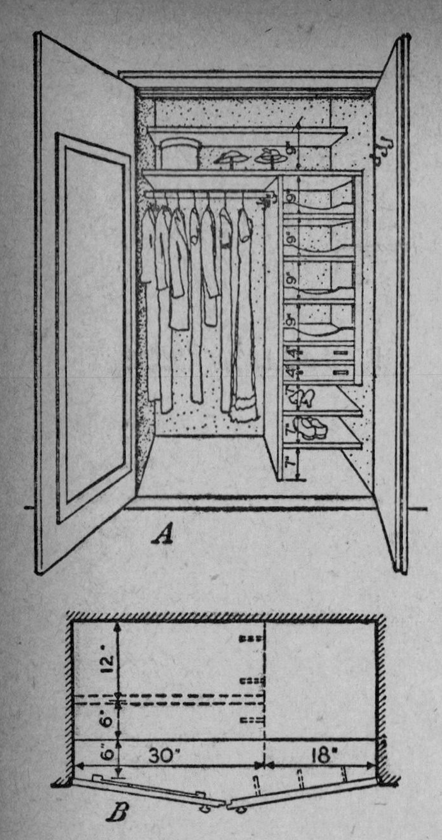

Fig. 40. Bedroom closet designed for one person: **A**, perspective; **B**, plan.

mirror depends upon the way the room is arranged and the lighting conditions. The top of a full-length mirror for the use of adults should be no less than 5 feet 11 inches, from the floor. To accommodate children as well as grown-ups, the bottom of the mirror should be no more than 14 inches from the floor.

SHOE RACKS

There are several convenient ways to store shoes. The rack and the shelf at the right take up less floor space than horizontal arrangements (fig. 41, *A*).

The vertical shoe rack (*B*) is a good one to use when wall space is not so limited as floor space. The lower bar may be covered inside with felt to protect the shoes.

The tilted shelf (*C*) fits in the floor space of the closet, below garments on hangers or hooks. For both rack and shelf a width of 18 inches will accommodate at least two pairs of shoes and sometimes three, depending, naturally, on their size.

Horizontal shelves, one above the other, are also satisfactory for storing shoes. These take up more room than the arrangements shown here, but they have the advantage of being useful for other purposes. Dis-

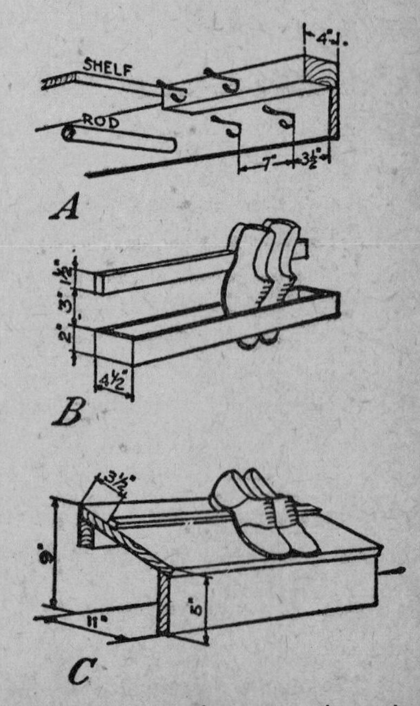

Fig. 41. **A**, a good way to place closet hooks; **B**, vertical rack for shoes; **C**, tilted shelf for shoes.

tance between shelves for storing shoes should be at least 7 inches.

BUSINESS CLOSET

It is usually convenient and efficient to have an "office headquarters" somewhere in the house. In this one place important letters, bulletins, catalogues, and reference books may be kept so that they are always available and easy to find.

A small closet off the living room or the dining room may be fitted up inexpensively to meet these needs (fig. 42). Trays or drawers may serve as files for receipts and records. Also stationery and other supplies can be

Fig. 42. Closet for business materials: **A**, perspective, **B**, detail of drawer for receipts.

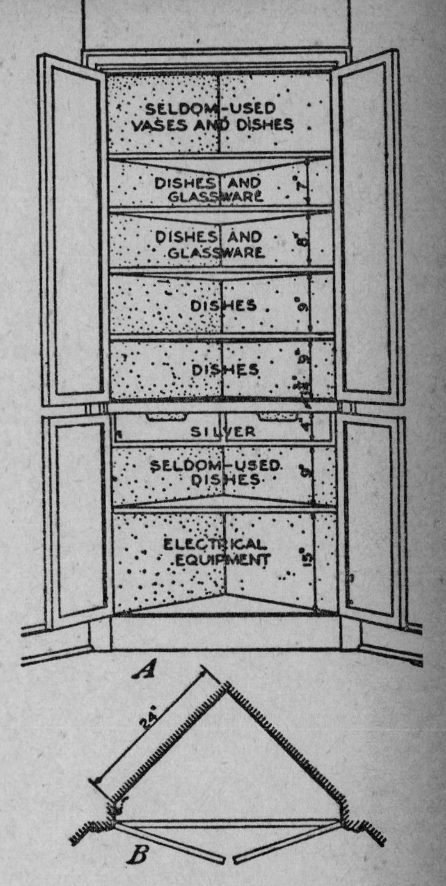

Fig. 43. Corner cupboard: **A**, perspective, **B**, plan.

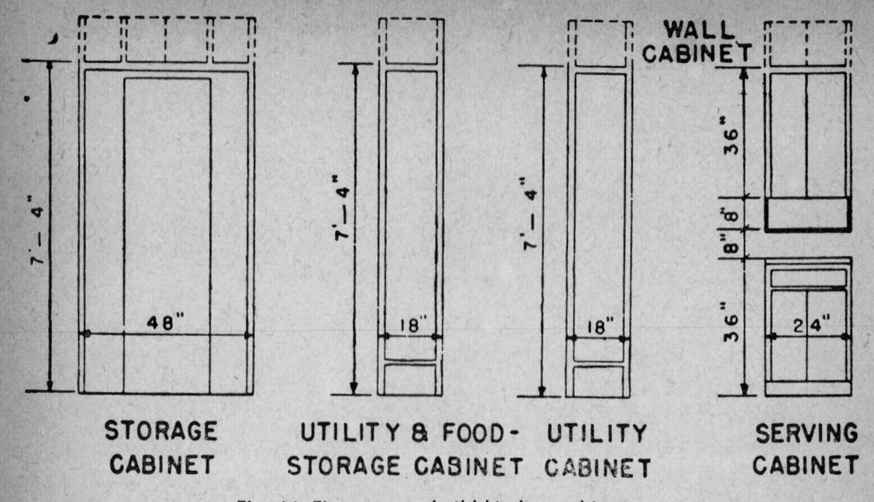

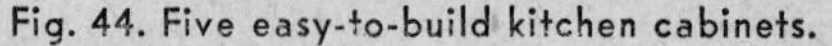
Fig. 44. Five easy-to-build kitchen cabinets.

kept handy in them. Shelves may be partitioned for bulletins and pigeonholes provided for unanswered letters. A shelf at the bottom of the closet is a good place to keep a strongbox for valuable papers.

A convenient depth for such a closet is about 18 inches. That is the depth of the closet shown in *A*. This closet is 18 inches wide and has space for practically everything needed in connection with correspondence and record keeping.

The detail (*B*) shows the upper drawer, sectioned to take care of receipts, unanswered letters, canceled checks, bills, and similar papers. The drawer is 15 inches deep and 16 inches wide. It is 2½ inches from center to center of the partitions fitted into the drawer.

DINING-ROOM STORAGE

For storing dishes and silver, especially the "best," used for entertaining, it is handy to have a closet or a cupboard in the dining room. This closet is also a good place to keep other articles used in serving meals, such as electrical equipment.

Figure 43 shows an inexpensive corner cupboard that may be built without tearing out any partitions. It may be any depth, but the size shown here will accommodate most articles that the average family uses in serving meals. Frequently cupboards are placed in two adjacent corners of the dining room.

Silverware should be kept in a separate drawer. Three inches is a satisfactory depth for the drawer unless more than 12 pieces are stored in a section. If the drawer has a separate section for forks, knives, and spoons, these sections should be at least 2½ inches wide.

Shelves for china need to be at least 11 inches wide. In estimating the distance between shelves, allow 1 inch above stacks of plates, which

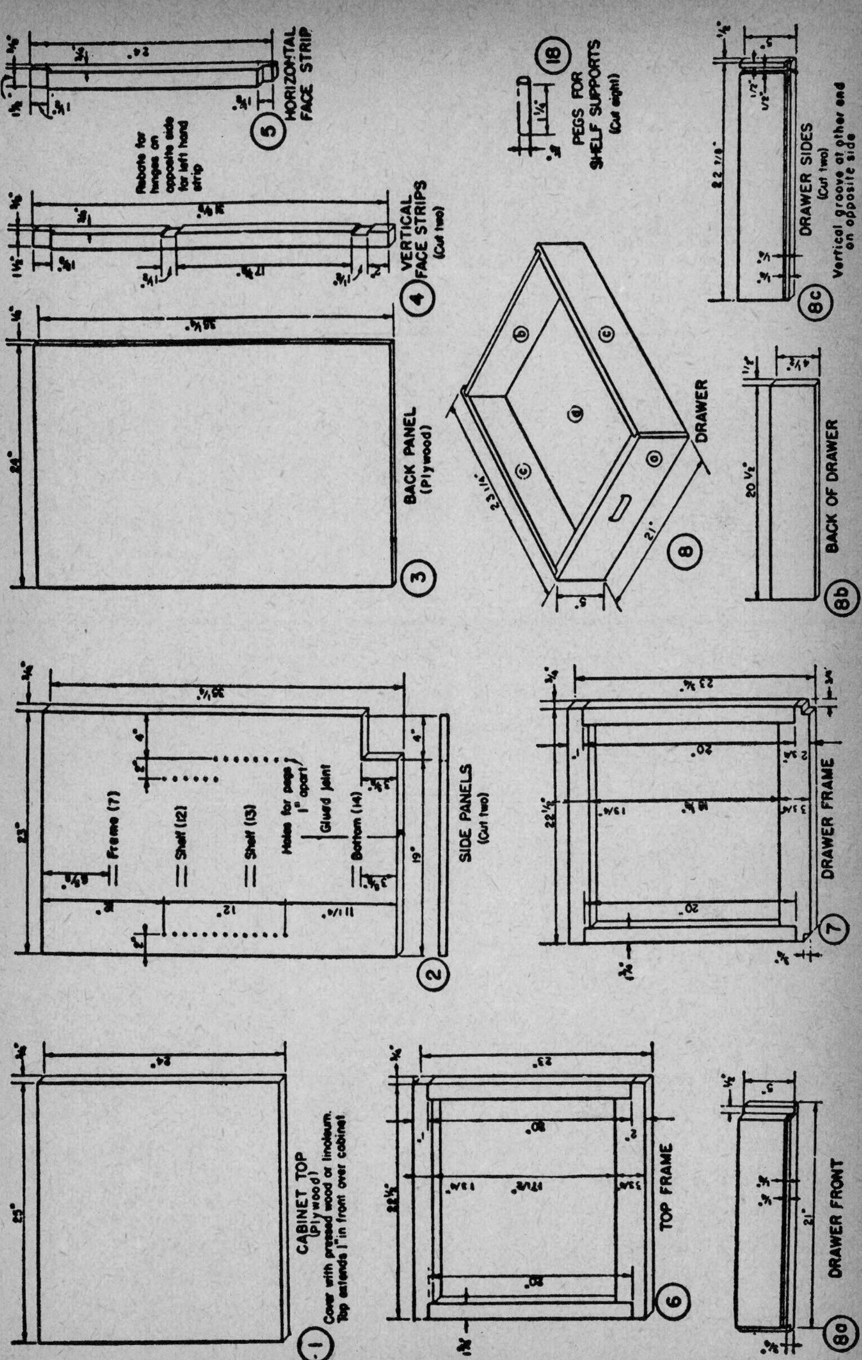

Fig. 45A. Serving cabinet.

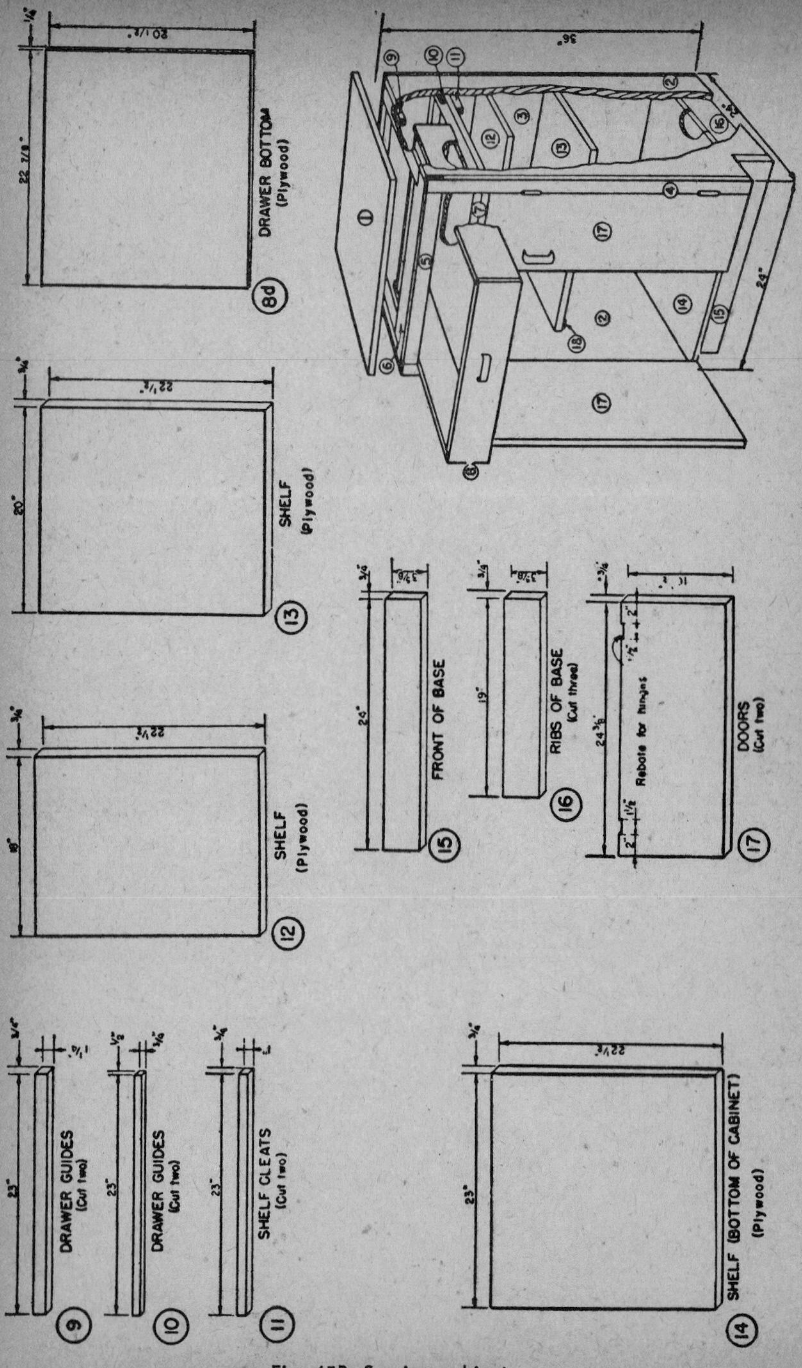

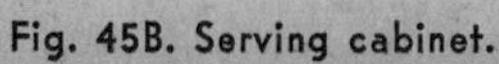
Fig. 45B. Serving cabinet.

are handled from the side, and 2 inches above articles, such as cups, handled from the top. The accompanying table may serve as a guide.

SHELF HEIGHT ALLOWANCE FOR DISHES IN COMMON USE

Article	*Inches*	*Article*	*Inches*
Dinner plates, stack of 6	7	Platters, stack of 2	4
Soup plates, stack of 6	7	Sugar bowl and creamer	6
Salad plates, stack of 6	6	Covered vegetable dishes	6
Saucedishes, stack of 6	6	Open vegetable dishes	5
Bread-and-butter plates, stack of 6	5	Glasses	6
Saucers, stack of 6	5	Sherbet glasses	6
Cups, stack of 2	5	Goblets	8

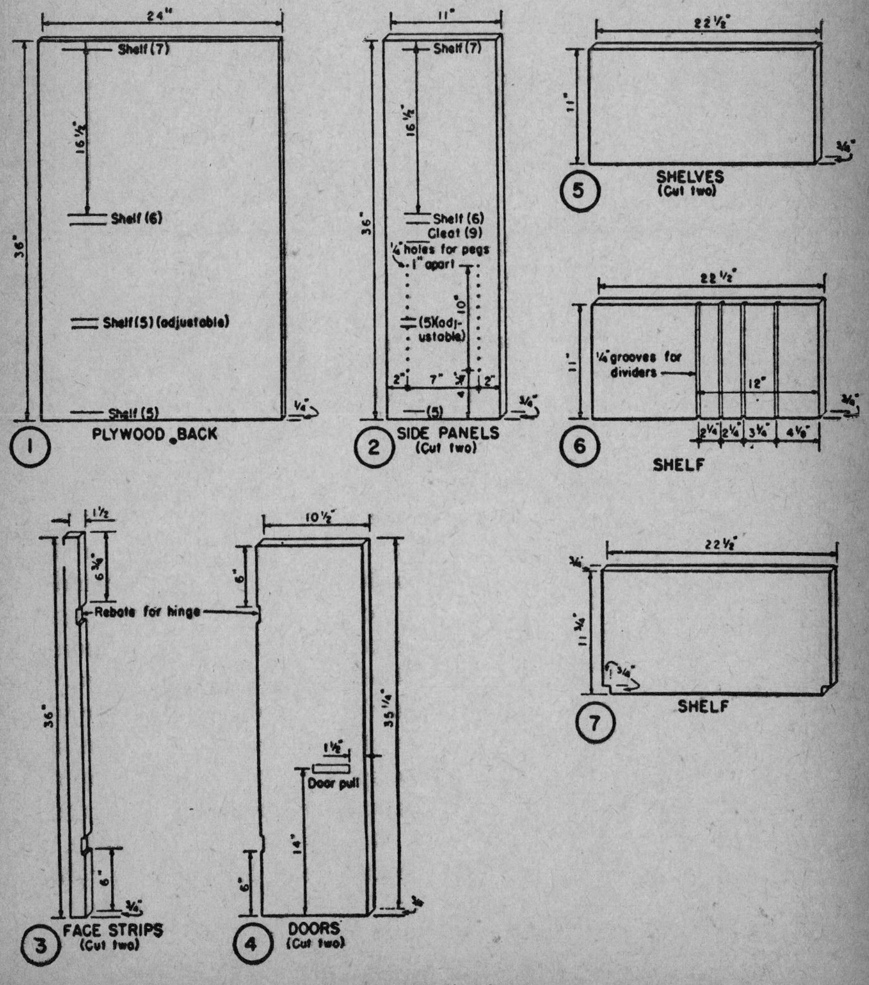

Fig. 46A. Wall cabinet.

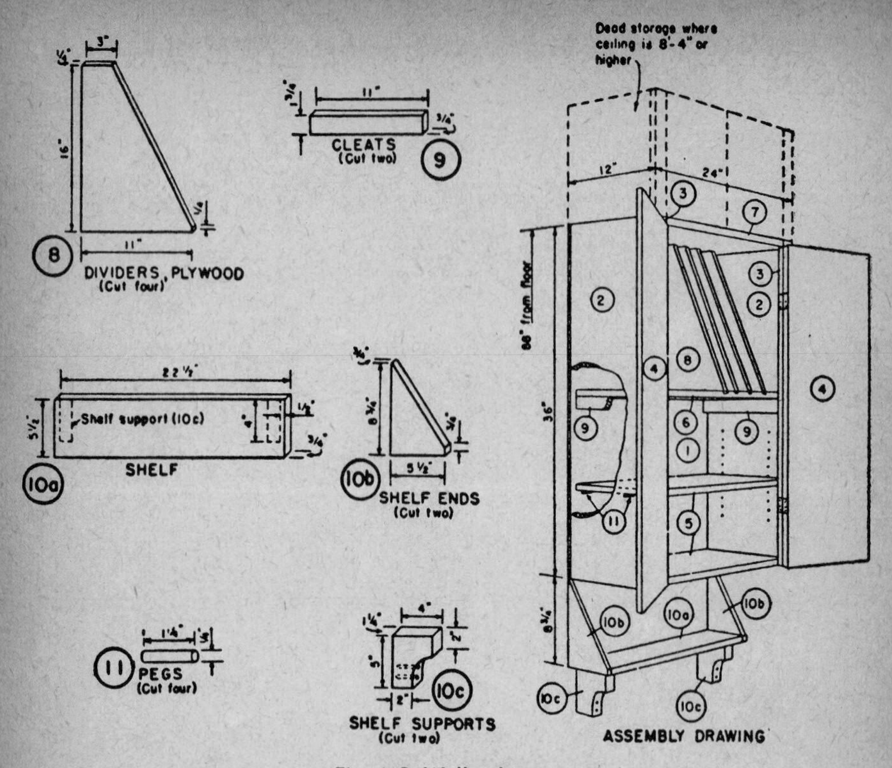

Fig. 46B. Wall cabinet.

EASY-TO-BUILD KITCHEN CABINETS

These easy-to-build kitchen cabinets, shown in figures 44 to 49, are especially suitable for remodeling where continuous work areas cannot be used, but they are suitable for new as well as remodeled kitchens.

The cabinets include five different units, each designed to serve a specific need: Serving cabinet; wall cabinet; storage cabinet; food-storage cabinet; and utility cabinet.

Old kitchens often have many doors and windows, and in remodeling it may be impossible, or too expensive, to move them. These cabinets can be used in groups or singly to fit between doors and windows.

For each cabinet, each piece is shown in detail with all necessary dimensions, and is numbered. The numbered pieces are also shown put together in an assembly drawing or perspective so that the location of each individual part is easily seen.

Materials needed. Materials and tools needed to build the cabinets are generally familiar to the amateur carpenter. The cabinets as shown are built of plywood and pine "shelving." In some of the

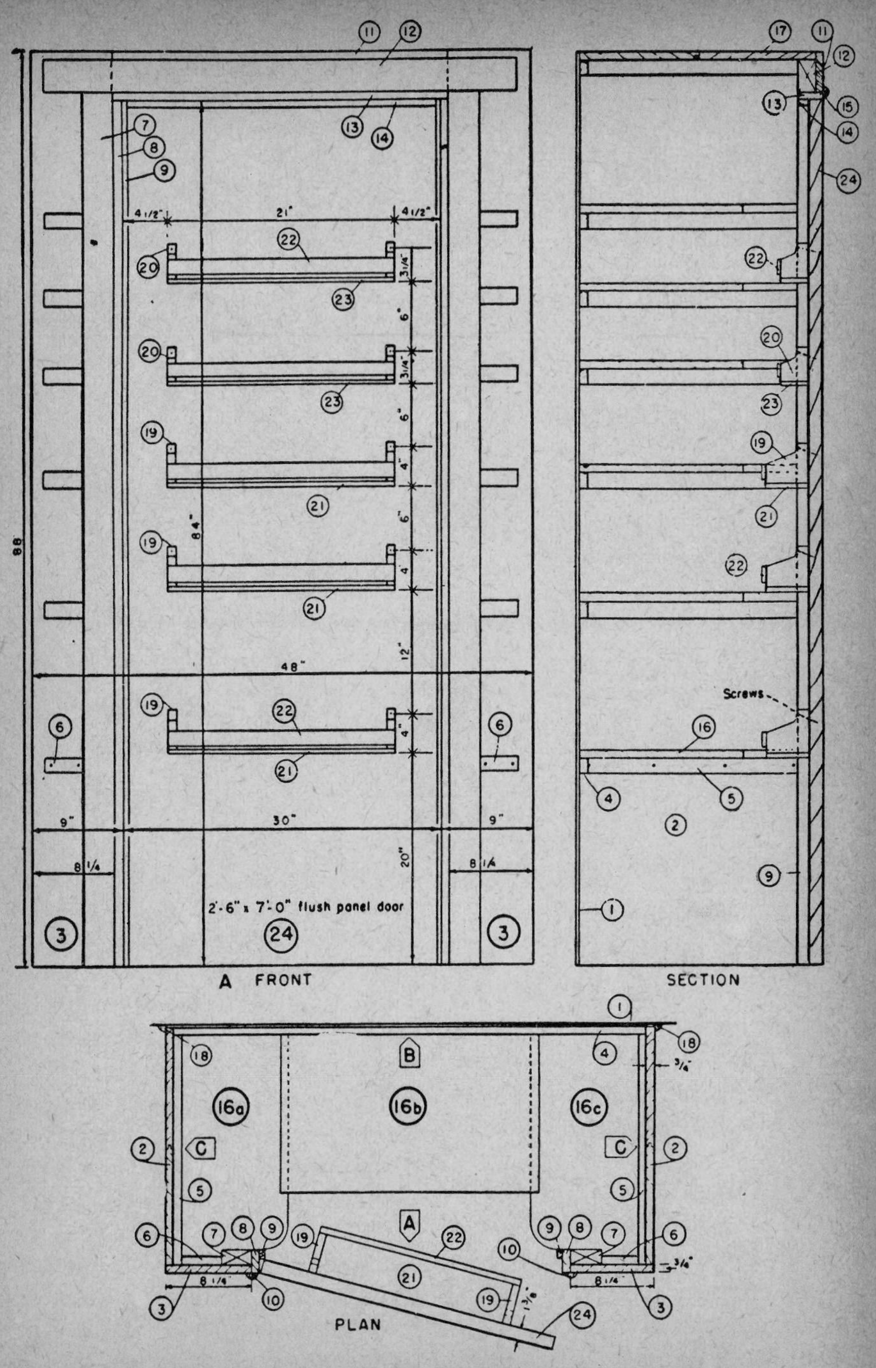

Fig. 47A. Storage cabinet.

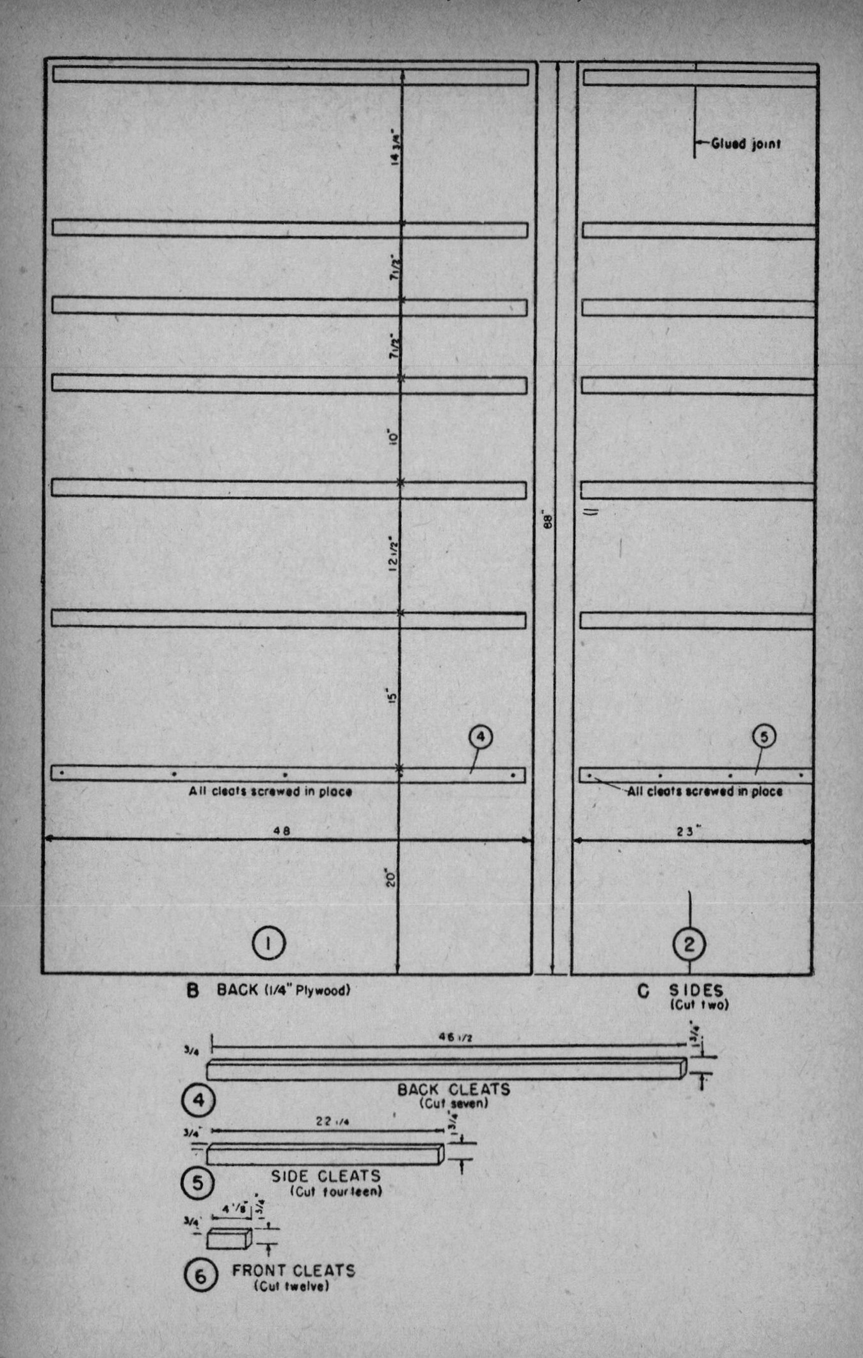

Fig. 47B. Storage cabinet.

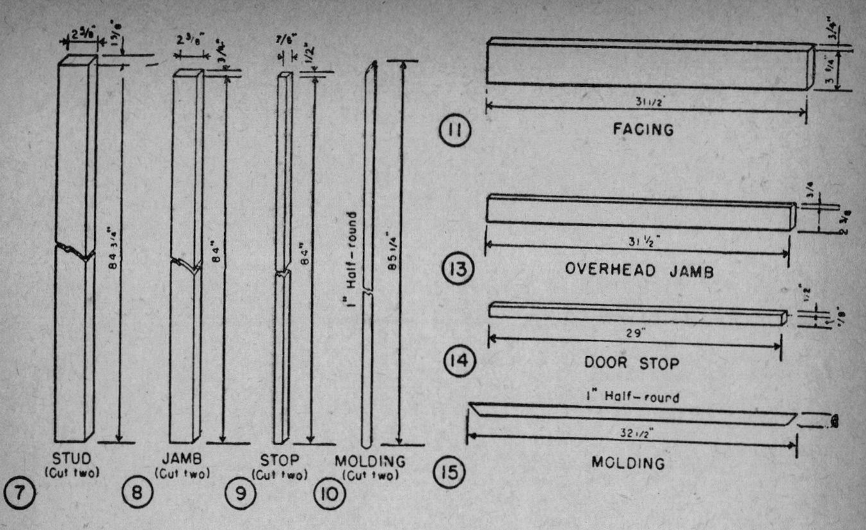

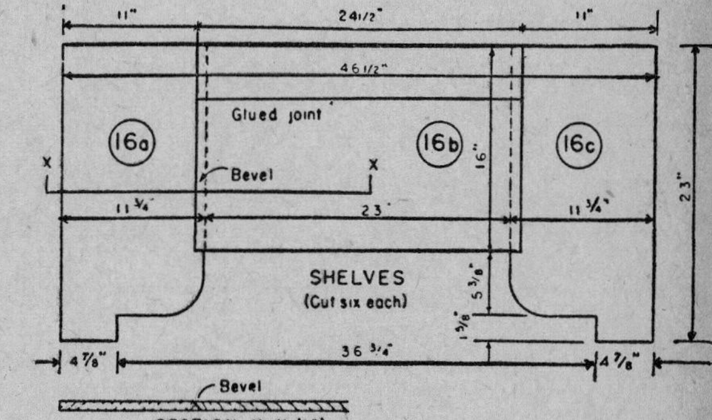

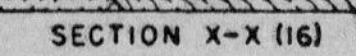

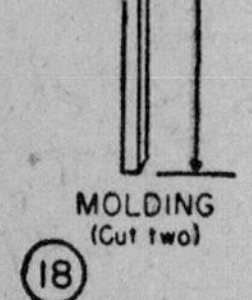

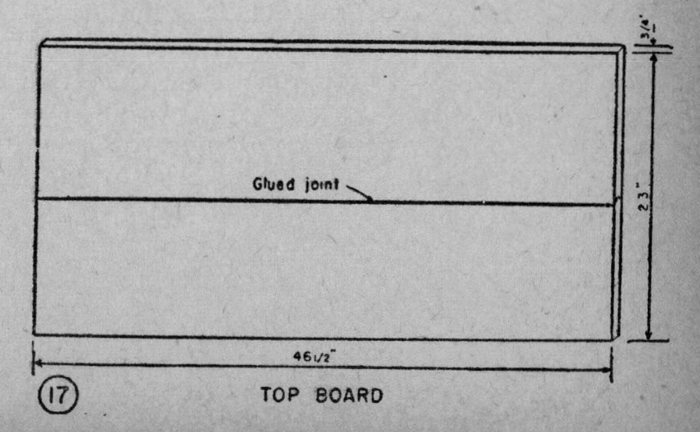

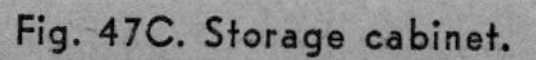
Fig. 47C. Storage cabinet.

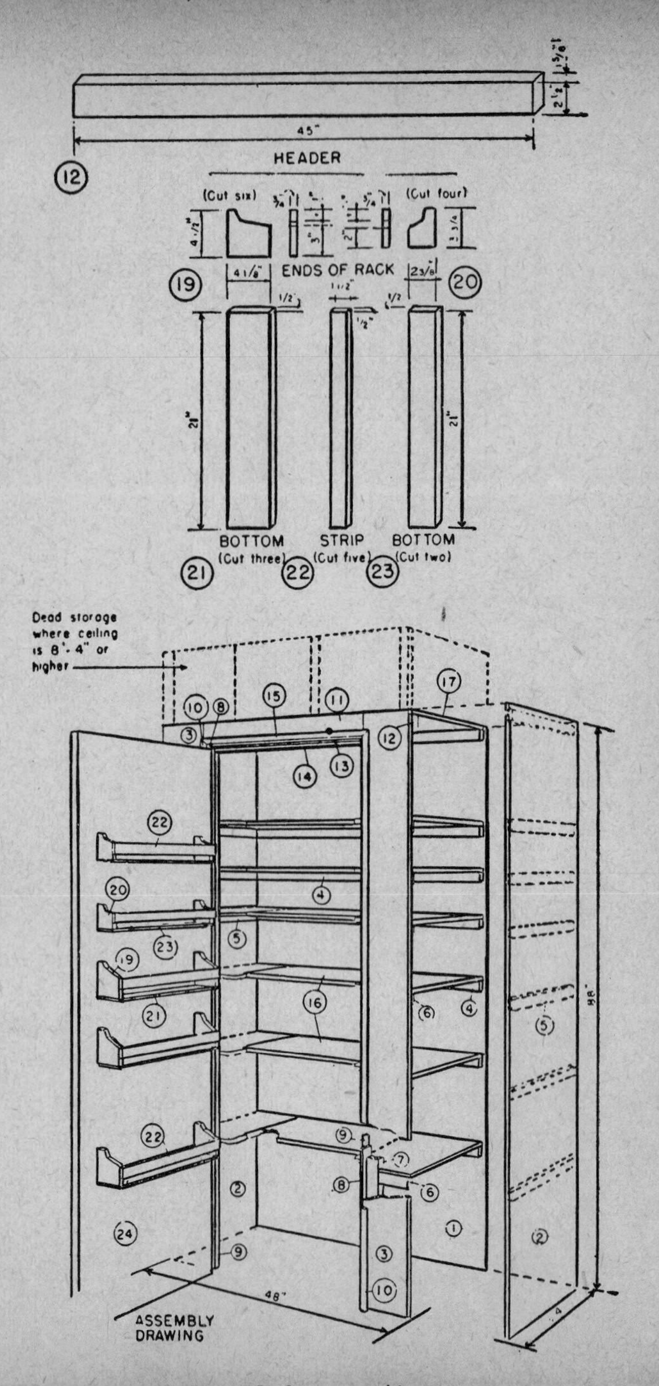

Fig. 47D. Storage cabinet.

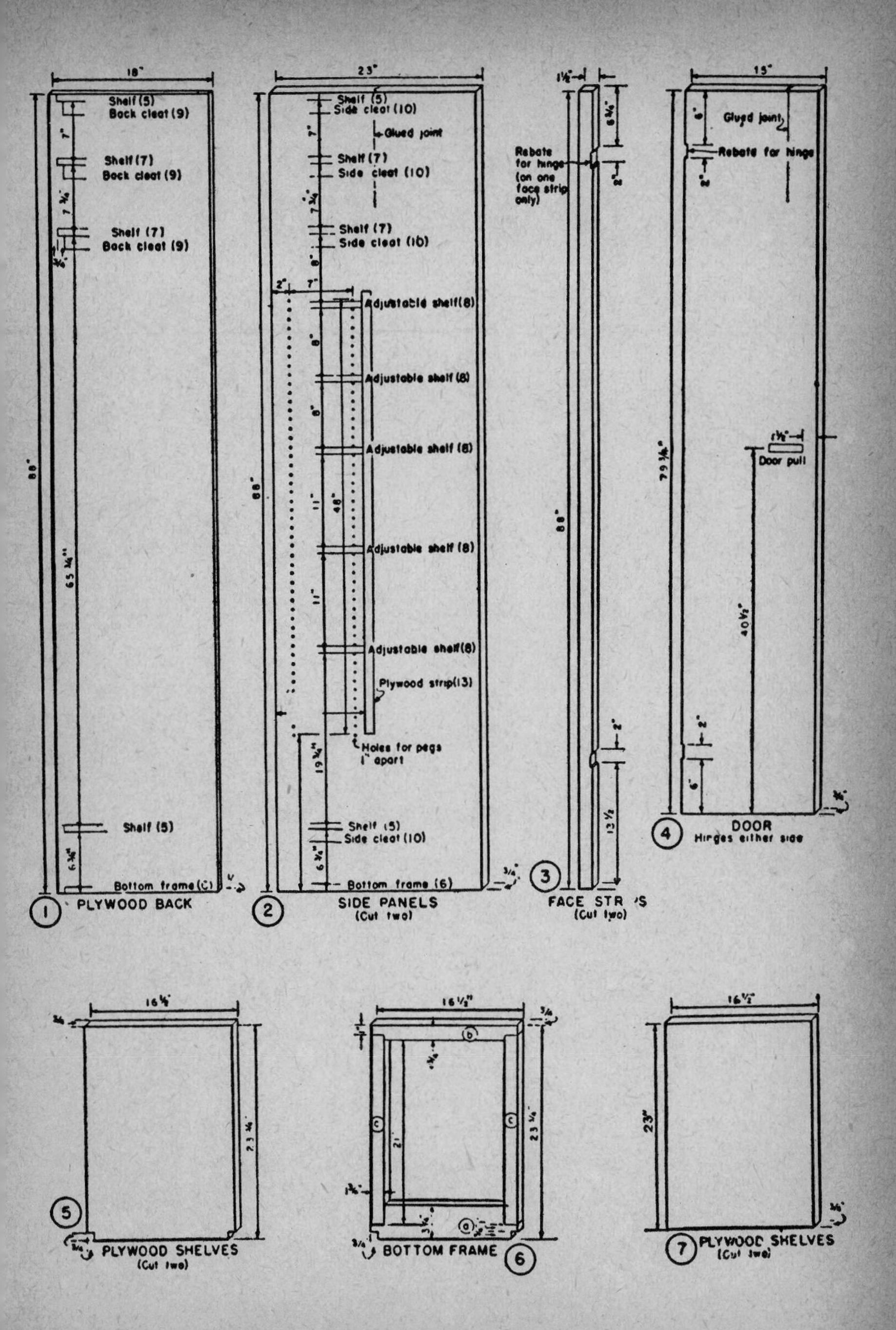

Fig. 48A. Utility and food storage cabinet.

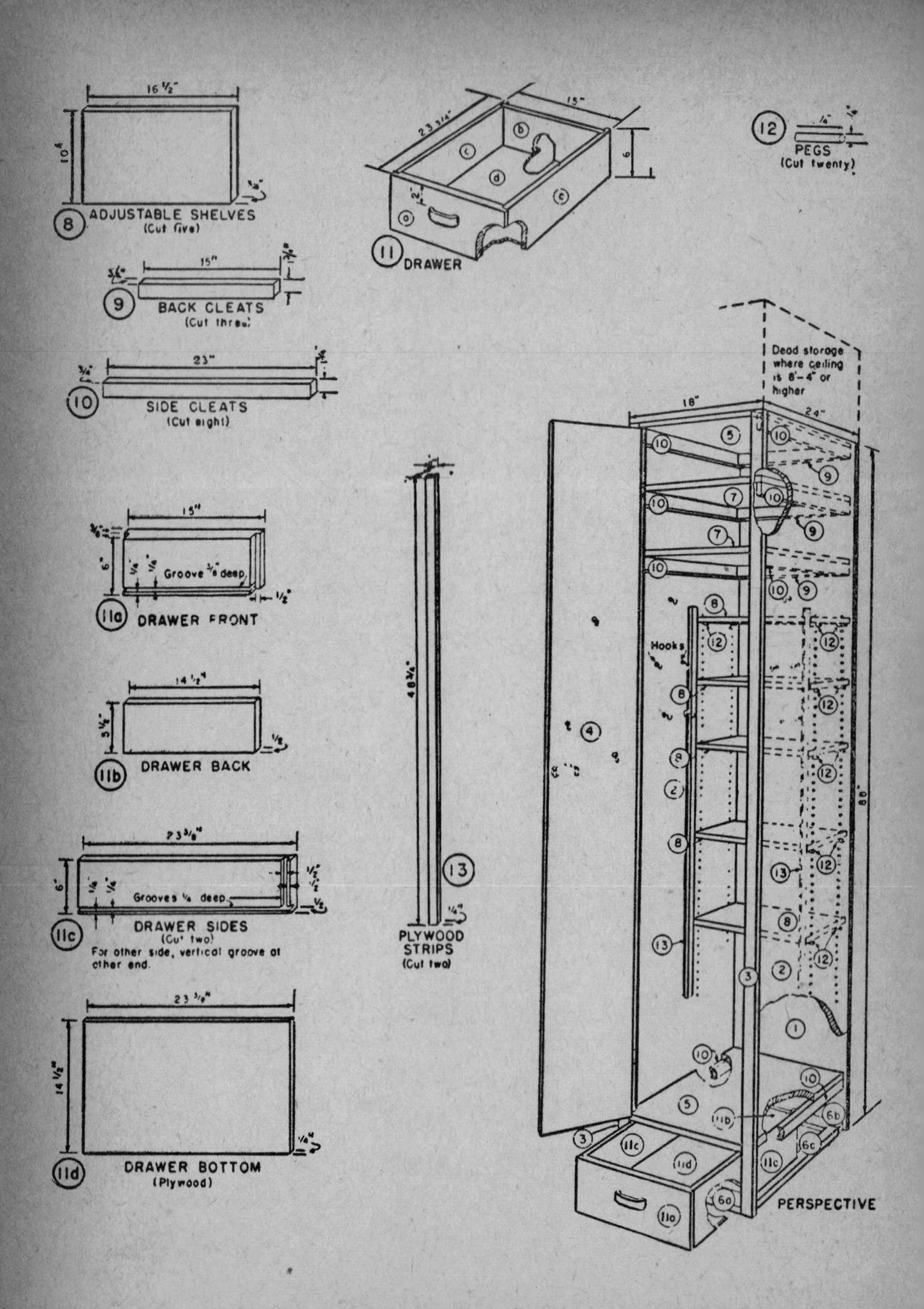

Fig. 48B. Utility and food-storage cabinet.

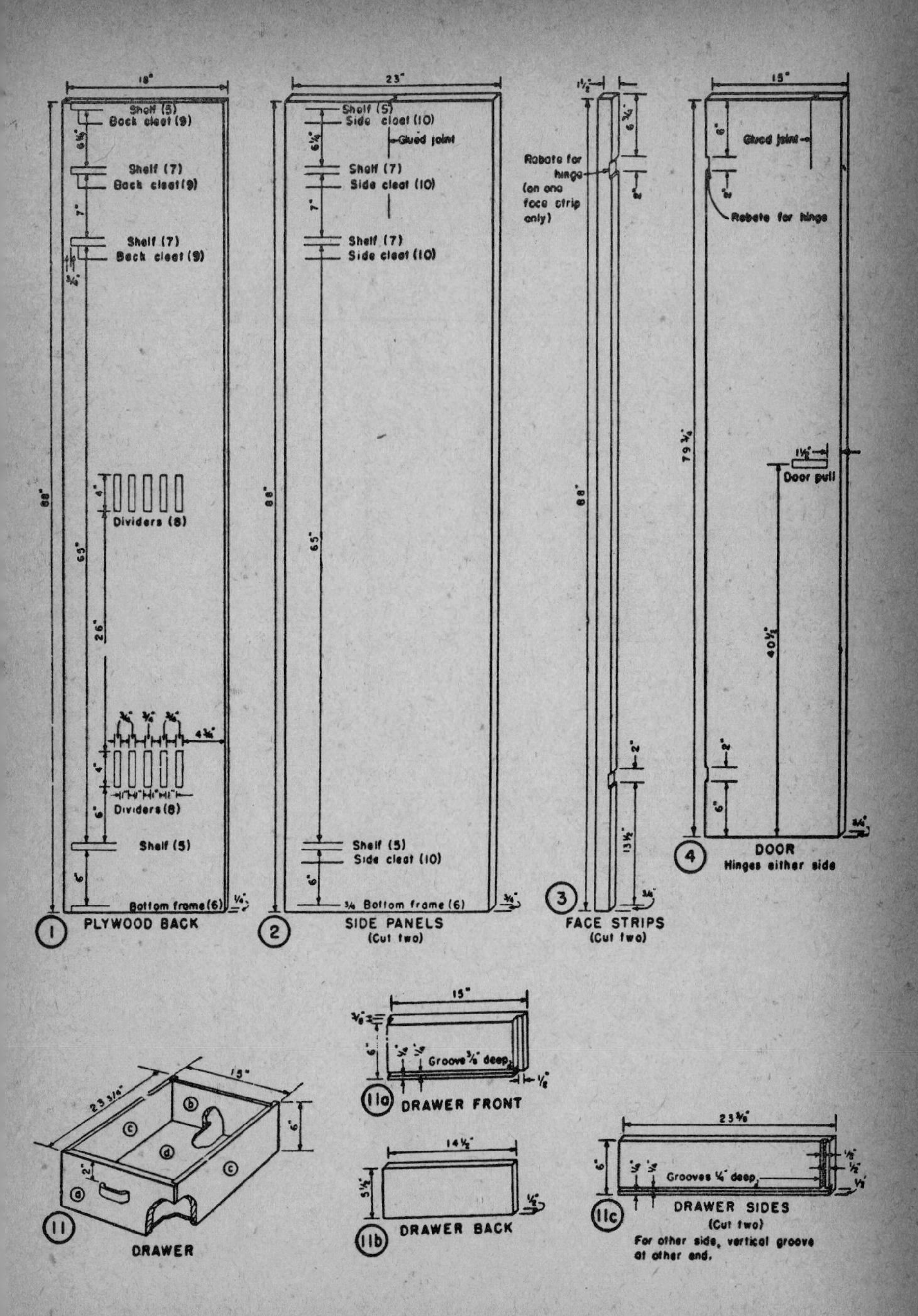

Fig. 49A. Utility cabinet.

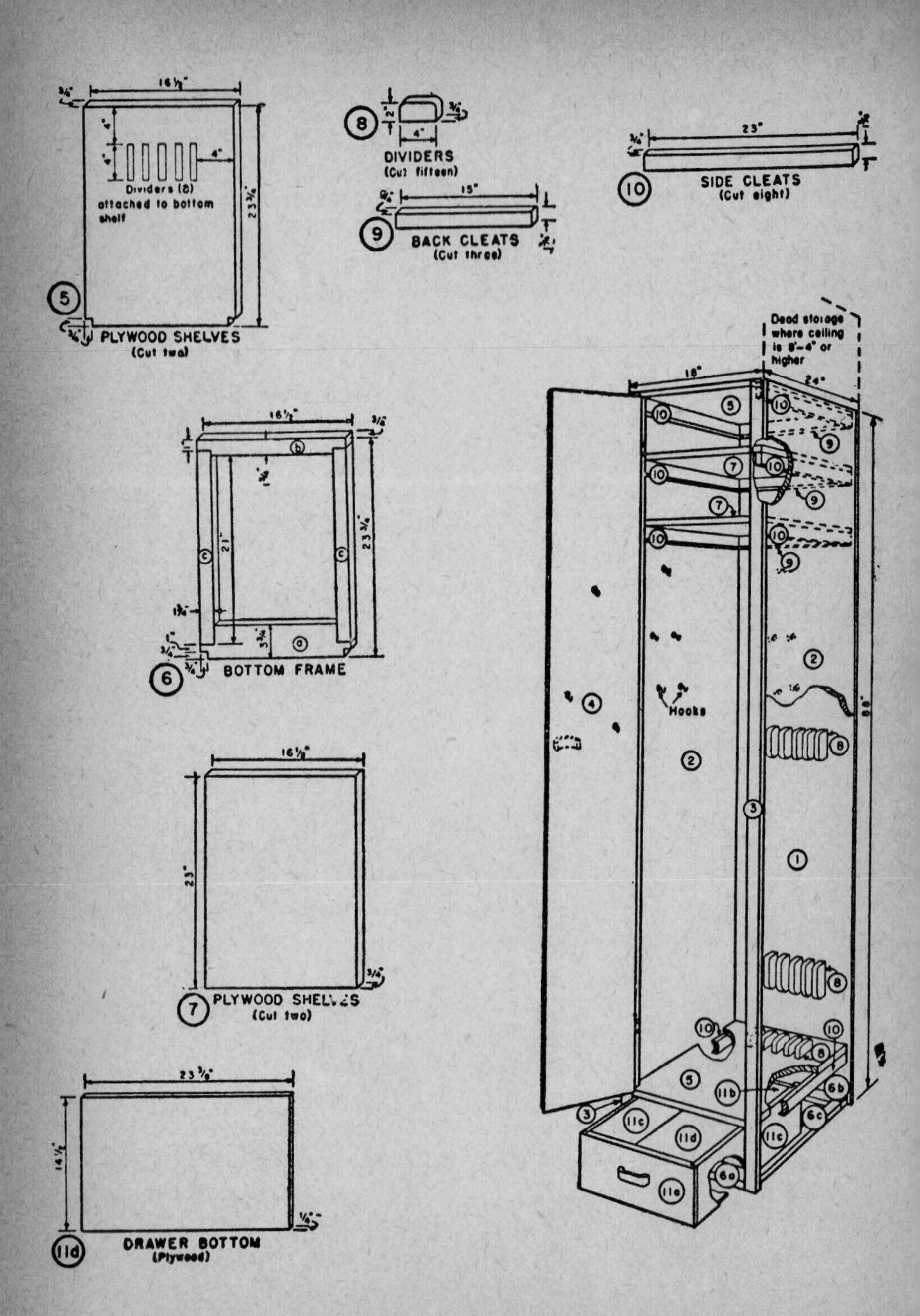

Fig. 49B. Utility cabinet.

larger pieces such as ends of cabinets, pine boards are shown tongued and grooved and glued together to form the necessary width. Plywood is specified for pieces too large to warrant gluing boards together or where it is needed for stiffening, as in the backs of cabinets. Other materials of sufficient strength may be used.

Wherever possible, standard-dimension boards, such as 1″ x 4″, 1″ x 6″, 1″ x 12″, have been used full width to avoid ripping and planing. On the working drawings the actual rather than the nominal dimensions are given. A nominal 1″ x 4″ board, for example, measures about ¾″ x 3⅝″.

Suggestions on building. Seven feet 4 inches high, the cabinet will fit in most houses. If a space of less than a foot is left between cabinet top and ceiling, it is best to close it in with a board or to nail furring strips between ceiling and top of cabinet and apply lath and plaster. A space of 12 inches or more may be used for additional cabinets for dead storage.

No space is wasted between the top of the base cabinets and the top of the first drawers. The front rim of the sink is kept close to the counter edge. Nonsupporting partitions and molding are omitted; facing strips are of minimum width.

Shelves and dividers on shelves and in drawers are adjustable in all cabinets except the large storage cabinet. Dividers are cut without waste of material. Wherever practicable, the same drawer size is used in different cabinets so that drawers can be interchanged.

Shelf heights shown on the drawings suggest good use of space. These heights provide for storage of the heaviest and the most often used supplies and dishes in locations that are most easily reached.

Serving cabinet. The top provides a serving counter, and there is drawer and cupboard space underneath for utensils used at the range.

Lumber and hardware

No. 1 Pine	
1″ x 12″ x 18′	1 pc.
1″ x 4″ x 12′	1 pc.
1″ x 2″ x 14′	1 pc.
1″ x 6″ x 4′	1 pc.
½″ x 6″ x 6′	1 pc.
Plywood	
¾″ x 4′ x 4′	1 pc.
¼″ x 4′ x 4′	1 pc.
Pressed wood or linoleum	
24″ x 25″	1 pc.
Wood dowels ¼″ x 12″	1 pc.
Hinges, 1½″ x 1½″	2 pr.
Door pulls	2
Drawer pull	1
Friction catches	2
Finishing nails, 4d	½ lb.
Finishing nails, 6d	1½ lb.
Wood screws, No. 8-1½″	1 doz.
Wood screws, No. 4-1¼″	1 doz.
Metal edging lin. ft.	1½

Wall cabinet. At the top of this cabinet, planned for use at the range, a file compartment with dividers (8) holds serving dishes and lids. With two adjustable shelves (5) space in the bottom section can be adapted to different storage needs. The narrow shelf (*10*) below the cabinet, designed for seasonings, may be omitted.

The wall cabinet can be used with the base serving cabinet.

Lumber and hardware

No. 1 Pine
- 1″ x 12″ x 12′ .... 1 pc.
- 1″ x 12″ x 8′ .... 1 pc.
- 1″ x 6″ x 3′ .... 1 pc
- 1″ x 2″ x 8′ .... 1 pc.
- 2″ x 6″ x 1′ .... 1 pc.
- ¼″ dowel 5″ long .... 1 pc.

Plywood
- ¼″ x 3′ x 4′ .... 1 pc.

Hinges, 1½″ x 1½″ .... 2 pr.
Finishing nails, 4d .... ½ lb.
Finishing nails, 6d .... ½ lb.
Wood screws, No. 8-¼″ .... 2 doz.
Toggle bolts, ⅛″ x 3″ 6
Door pulls 2
Friction catches 2

Storage cabinet. In this floor-to-ceiling cabinet may be stored extra food supplies, canning equipment, and numerous other articles not in frequent use.

The cabinet can be used in the kitchen itself or in an alcove or wide hall. The dimensions, 48″ x 24″ x 88″, can easily be changed to fit available space. If space in front of the cabinet is limited, a double instead of a single door may be used.

The shelves as shown are fixed. If cut from plywood, they can be made adjustable. Racks on the door provide a handy place for small articles.

The floor of the cabinet is the room floor, so heavy articles can be slid in and out without lifting. For reaching the top shelves, a small sturdy step box is shown in the plan.

Lumber and hardware

No. 1 Pine
- 1″ x 12″ x 12′ .... 3 pc.
- 1″ x 12″ x 10′ .... 1 pc.
- 1″ x 12″ x 8′ .... 4 pc,
- 1″ x 10″ x 8′ .... 2 pc.
- 1″ x 6″ x 16′ .... 1 pc.
- 1″ x 4″ x 4′ .... 1 pc.
- 1″ x 3″ x 10′ .... 1 pc.
- 1″ x 3″ x 8′ .... 1 pc.
- 1″ x 2″ x 12′ .... 2 pc.
- 1″ x 2″ x 10′ .... 3 pc.
- 1″ x 2″ x 8′ .... 1 pc.
- 2″ x 3″ x 12′ .... 1 pc.
- 2″ x 3″ x 8′ .... 1 pc.
- ½″ x 6″ x 10′ .... 1 pc.

Plywood ¼″ x 4′ x 8′ .... 1 pc.
Molding
- 1″ half-round 17 lin. ft.
- ¾″ quarter-round 15 lin. ft.

Door, flush panel, 2′-6″ x 7′ 1
Hinges, 3½″ x 3½″ .... 1 pr.
Lock set 1
Finishing nails, 4d .... 1 lb.
Finishing nails, 6d .... 1 lb.
Screws, No. 8-2″ .... 1 doz.
Screws, No. 8-1¼″ .... 1 gross

Utility and food storage cabinet. This cabinet, planned especially for storage of extra staple foods, also provides space where the kitchen apron and a sweater or two can be hung. The drawer at the bottom of the cabinet can be used for paper or seldom used articles.

Lumber and hardware

No. 1 Pine
- 1″ x 12″ x 8′ .... 5 pc.

1″ x 8″ x 2′ .... 1 pc.
1″ x 4″ x 10′ .... 1 pc.
1″ x 2″ x 8′ .... 4 pc.
1″ x 2″ x 10′ .... 1 pc.
½″ x 8″ x 6′ .... 1 pc.
¼″ dowel 26″ long .... 1 pc.
Plywood
¾″ x 3′ x 4′ .... 1 pc.
¼″ x 3′ x 8′ .... 1 pc.
Hinges, 1½″ x 2″ .... 1 pr.
Door pull 1
Drawer pull 1
Friction catches 2
Finishing nails, 4d .... 1 lb.
Finishing nails, 6d .... 1 lb.
Wood screws, No. 8-1¼″ .... 3 doz.
Small hooks 13

Utility cabinet. Designed with dividers (8) for storage of table leaves and the ironing board, this cabinet also has hooks for mops and brooms and shelf and drawer space for other articles.

Lumber and hardware

No. 1 Pine
1″ x 12″ x 8′ .... 5 pc.
1″ x 8″ x 4′ .... 1 pc.
1″ x 4″ x 8′ .... 1 pc.
1″ x 2″ x 8′ .... 4 pc.
1″ x 2″ x 10′ .... 1 pc.
½″ x 8″ x 6′ .... 1 pc.
Plywood
¾″ x 3′ x 4′ .... 1 pc.
¼″ x 3′ x 8′ .... 1 pc.
Hinges, 1½″ x 2″ 2
Door pull 1
Drawer pull 1
Friction catches 2
Finishing nails, 4d .... 1 lb.
Finishing nails, 6d .... 1 lb.
Wood screws, No. 8-1¼″ 3 doz.
Small hooks 13

FOOD STORAGE ROOM

Figure 51 shows the layout for a simple food storage room that can be either on the ground floor or in the basement.

The dimensions of the room can, of course, be varied to suit particular conditions, but the individual measurements given below may be considered minimum.

Shelves for small containers should measure at least 12 inches from front to back. Shelves for stone jars, crocks, or flat pans need to be at least 18 inches deep.

There should be free floor space of about 24 by 24 inches at the minimum so that one person can enter. If only canned goods are stored, the width of the doorway need be only about 2 feet 4 inches. If kegs or crates are stored, increase the door width at least 4 inches.

The length of shelving needed varies with both the size and the number of containers. Allow 19 feet

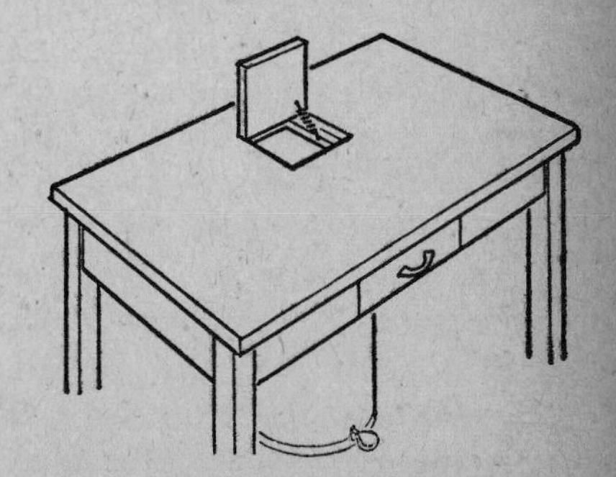

Fig. 50. Kitchen tables and work counters can be easily fitted with this simple type of trap door for garbage-disposal purposes. The inside of the opening in the table is lined with non-corrosive metal with smooth soldered joints to prevent any accumulation of waste matter.

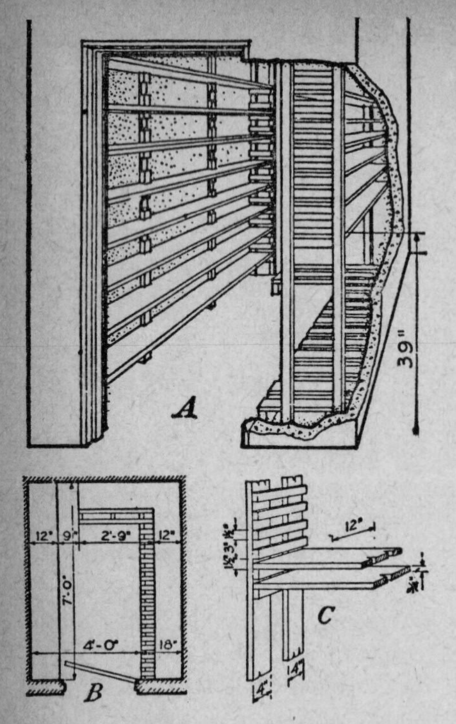

Fig. 51. Room for storing food: **A**, perspective, **B**, plan, **C**, detail of slots for shelves.

per 100 pint or quart glass jars, stored 2 rows to the shelf. Allow 20 feet per 100 half-gallon jars, stored 2 rows to the shelf. Allow 9 feet per 100 No. 2½ tin cans, 2 deep, 2 rows to the shelf. Allow 9 feet per 100 pint bottles stored 3 rows to the shelf.

It is best to have adjustable shelves. An interval of 3 inches between the slots for adjusting them is satisfactory. The lowest slot should be at least 9 inches from the floor—the highest not more than 72 inches. When shelves are long there should be intermediate supports spaced about 3 feet apart to prevent sagging. For heavy articles there should be movable platforms constructed of slats on two-by-fours as shown in the closet above.

The food storage room shown here has a capacity of about 525 glass jars or 1,165 tin cans. For each additional foot added to the length of the room there will be an increase in the capacity of the closet of 75 glass jars or 165 tin cans. There is 10 feet of platform or bin space for kegs and crocks.

SHELVES AND CABINET TRANSFORM EXTRA CLOSET

When a bedroom is made over into a den and its shallow closet no longer needed for ordinary purposes, a few shelves and panels will convert it into a combination bookcase

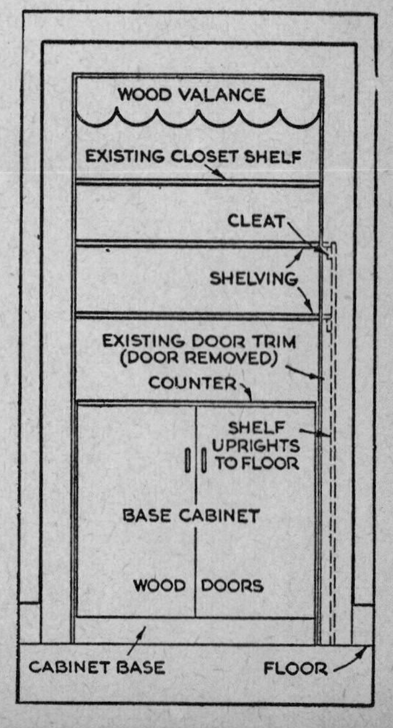

Fig. 52.

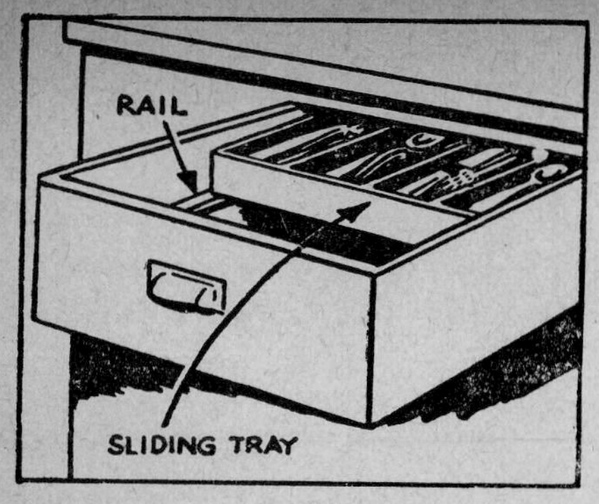

Fig. 53. Storage space can be saved in a cabinet drawer if the knives, forks, and spoons are kept in a tray built to fit inside width of the drawer. It should slide on rails nailed to the two sides.

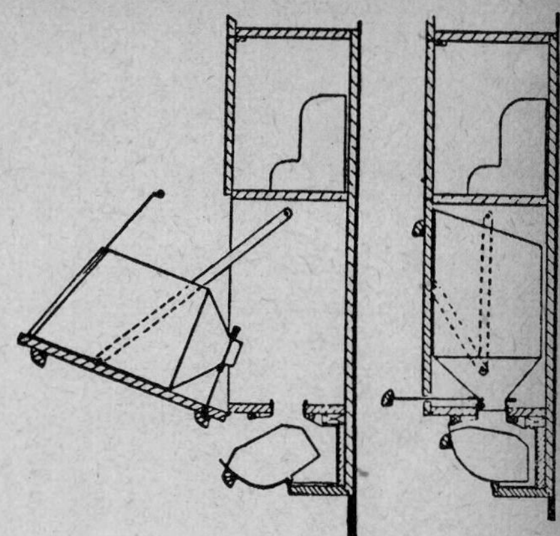

Fig. 55. Diagrammatic layout for a space- and time-saving double-deck flour bin.

and storage cabinet. The installation can be made so as to allow painless reconversion should that be necessary. (Fig. 52.)

First step is the removal of the door and hinges. Cleats are nailed to uprights inserted at both sides to support the 1″ by 12″ pine shelves. The cabinet—which does not have

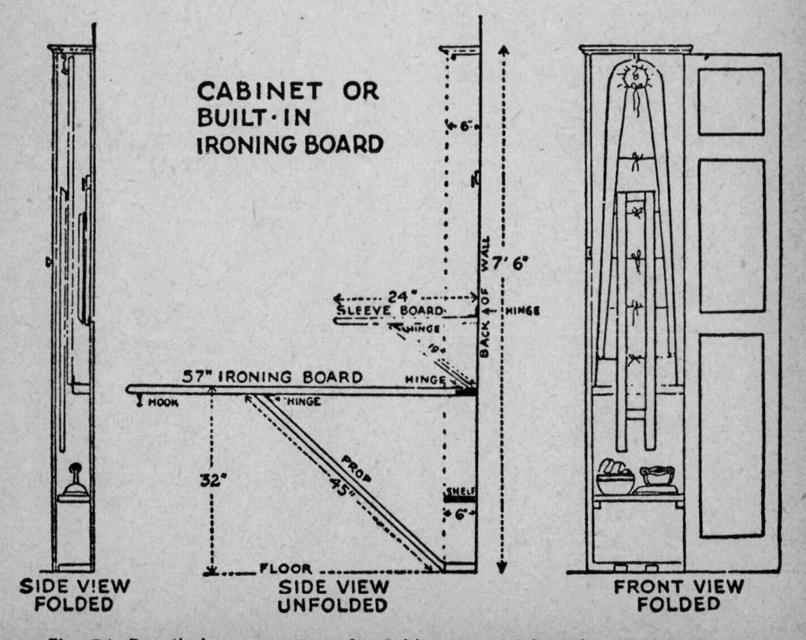

Fig. 54. Detailed construction of a folding ironing board and its wall case.

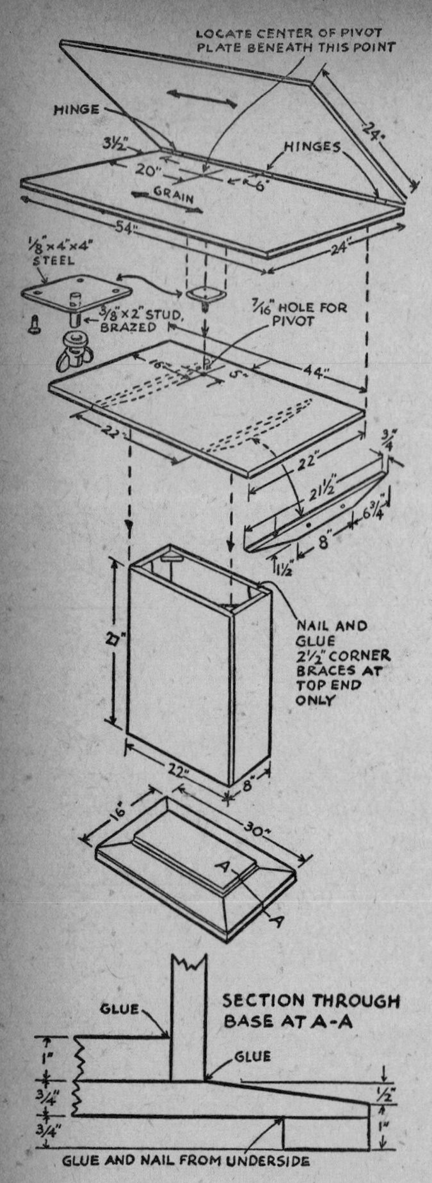

Fig. 56. Construction is in four pieces, with the lower three—base, column, and column top—glued and screwed together as a rigid unit. The folding leaves forming the table top are held in place loosely with a pivot bolt and wing nut.

to have a back—is measured to fit inside the door opening. When the cabinet doors are closed, the front of the unit does not extend over the jamb.

A valance is jigsawed from wood and tacked into place by means of small corner strips. Pieces of cardboard are cut out to fill the hinge mortises and are fastened in place with rubber cement. Painting over the cardboard will make it virtually impossible to detect the places where the hinges had been, but the cardboard can be peeled off without difficulty. With care, the same stunt can be used to disguise the strike mortise on the lock side. Remove the strike and cut cardboard to fit in its place.

FOLDING TABLE SEATS EIGHT

Accommodating six to eight persons for dinner, this table nevertheless folds so that it can be placed against a wall, where it projects no more than 2′. Its leaf may be folded over completely or supported vertically against the wall in the style of a console table in a living room or an entrance hall. To convert it for use as a dining table, the leaves are swung around at right angles and opened.

Solid stock is used for the base, and ⅝″ or ¾″ plywood for the column, top, and table leaves. If suitable plywood isn't available, satisfactory panels can be glued up from boards, provided dowel or spline reinforcement is employed and enough clamping equipment is

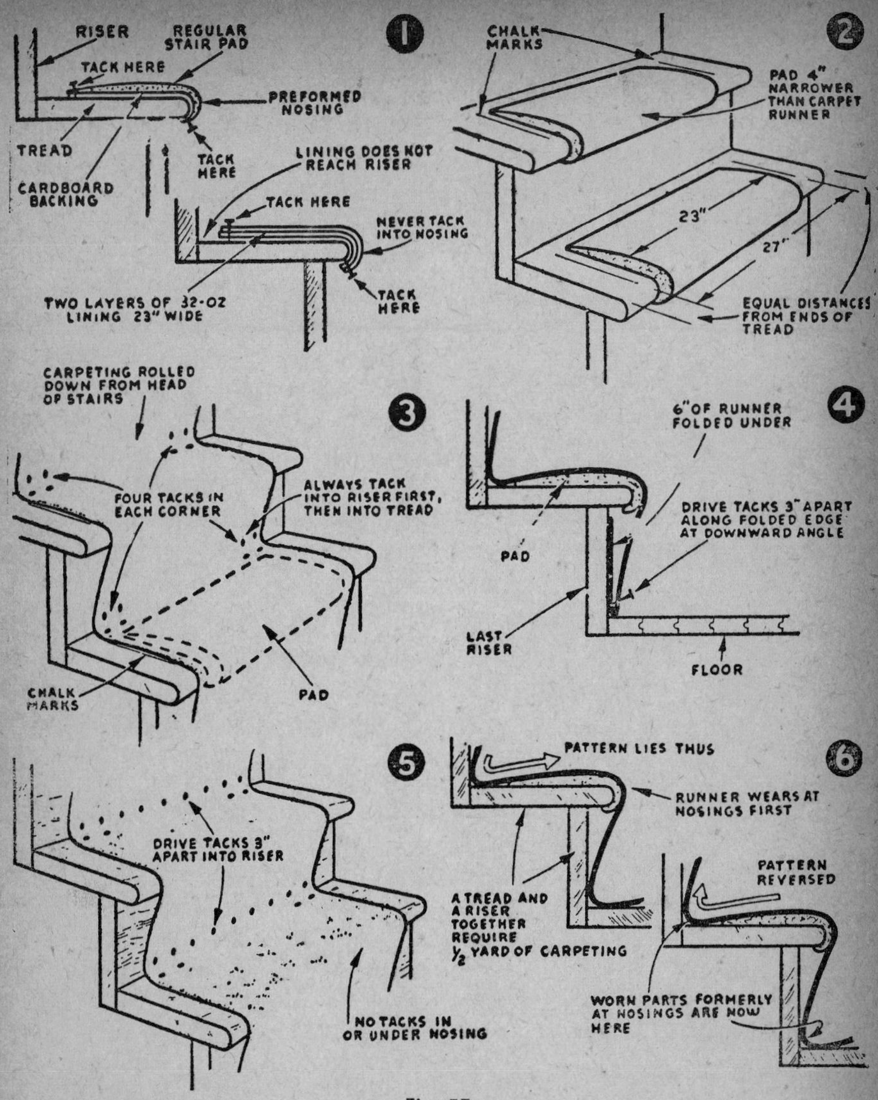

Fig. 57.

at hand. Located as shown in the drawing (fig. 56), the hole and pivot will come just outside the column. A steel plate with a stud brazed on is recessed into the lower leaf. A similar plate without the bolt may be let into the column top. Round the outer edge of both plates. Use three so-called invisible cabinet hinges on the leaves, mortising them into the edges. Dome casters are used under corners of base for feet.

The base, column, and outer part of the folding leaf take any finish, but use only a nonsticking finish on touching leaf surfaces and on the upper surface of the column top. Lacquer, enamel, and wax stains are practical for these parts.

BUILDING OUTDOOR STAIRS

The rule almost universally observed in stair building is that the height of two risers plus the length of one tread is equal to 24″ to 25″. A riser is a vertical strip that separates successive steps, and a tread is a horizontal footboard. To accommodate the longer stride most people use out of doors, outside stairs are generally built with relatively shorter risers and longer treads. As against a standard of 7⅝″ for indoor stairs, garden risers vary only about 1″ on either side of the 5½″ mark. If the slope is so steep that risers greater than 6¾″ are required, build ladder-type steps; if treads of more than 16″ will be needed for 4½″ risers, abandon the idea of steps and use a ramp instead.

Assume that you are going to use an equal number of treads and risers for a rise of 30″ and a run of 84″. Rise is always fixed by circumstances, but since it is not necessary to consider headroom, run can be quite variable on outdoor stairs. Dividing 30″ by 5½″, to obtain the number of steps needed, indicates a choice of five or six. Five steps require risers of 6″ and treads of 16 4/5″ to cover the two dimensions. But two of these plus a 16 4/5″ tread would equal 28 4/5″, considerably more than the 24″ to 25″ check measurement. The alternative of six steps calls for 5″ risers and 14″ treads, totaling up to a check measurement of 24″. If the total run were 90″ instead of 84″, treads of 15″ could be used and still conform to the formula.

The following table is given as a means of quickly checking calculations; best results are obtained by keeping to these standards.

Riser	*Tread*	*Twice Riser*	*Check Measure*
4½	15	9	24
4½	16	9	25
4¾	14½	9½	24
4¾	15½	9½	25
5	14	10	24
5	15	10	25
5¼	13½	10½	24
5¼	14½	10½	25
5½	13	11	24
5½	14	11	25
5¾	12½	11½	24
5¾	13½	11½	25
6	12	12	24
6	13	12	25
6¼	11½	12½	24
6¼	12½	12½	25
6½	11	13	24
6½	12	13	25
6¾	10½	13½	24
6¾	11½	13½	25

HOW TO CARPET STAIRS

There is no trick to laying carpet runners—but a few kinks will assure you a professional look on your stairway and make the job quicker and easier. Allow ½ yard per tread and riser in ordering your runner plus an extra 6″ over-all for shrinkage when the carpet has to be taken up and cleaned. Buy ready-made pads for the treads or sufficient 32-oz. carpet lining for cutting up and double-padding each tread.

Clean and examine the stairs before going to work and remove nails that might cause snags or wear and tacks left from previous carpeting. Then nail down all loose or squeaky steps, driving three 8d finishing nails through the tread into the riser.

Install the pads next, as in *1,* figure 57, leaving a space between the far end of each pad and riser and carrying the pad over the nosing. The padding should be about 4″ narrower than the runner (standard runners are 27″ wide) and centered between the sides of the steps, as shown in 2. Fasten them with No. 16 carpet tacks or blued lath nails, driving the front tacks under the nosing, not directly into it where they would wear through the carpet rapidly.

Begin laying the runner from the top of the stairway, first carpeting the hall or landing at the top. Chalk guide lines for the edges of the runner on each step, measuring them accurately so the runner won't go awry. Tack the end of the runner snugly against the edge of the hall carpet, and then roll the carpet down the stairs, pushing it loosely into each step.

Go back to the head of the stairs and tack the carpet in at the top step with four No. 16 tacks in each corner (3), making sure to pull the carpet taut before tacking. Put two tacks into the riser first and follow with two in the tread. Then tack into each riser and tread in turn, working from top to bottom and

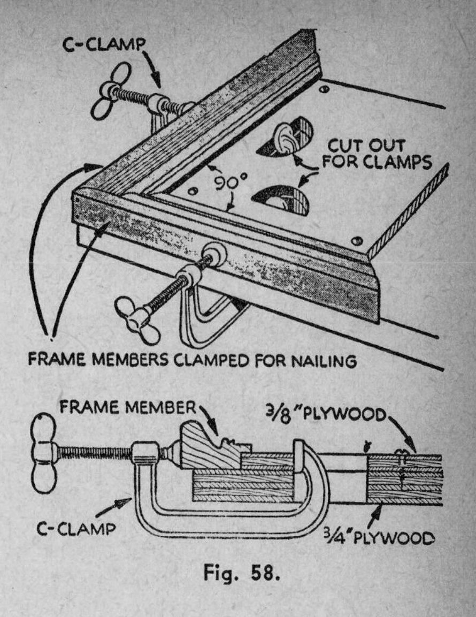

Fig. 58.

keeping the edges aligned with the chalk guide lines.

When you reach the bottom riser, fold under the last 6″, as in *4,* and tack all the way across the lower edge of the riser with tacks spaced about 3″ apart. Then go back to the top step, tack across the riser there, as indicated in 5, and proceed down, tacking across the lower or "inside" corner of each riser. This will stretch the carpet tight and keep it from "riding" on the steps. Put no tacks into the carpet under the nosing as this would destroy the "waterfall" effect that is the hallmark of the professional.

In addition to providing extra material for shrinkage, the 6″ folded under at the bottom riser permits reversing the runner on the stairway, as shown in *6,* when wear begins to show at the nosings. When this is done, the previously turned-under part goes up to the head of

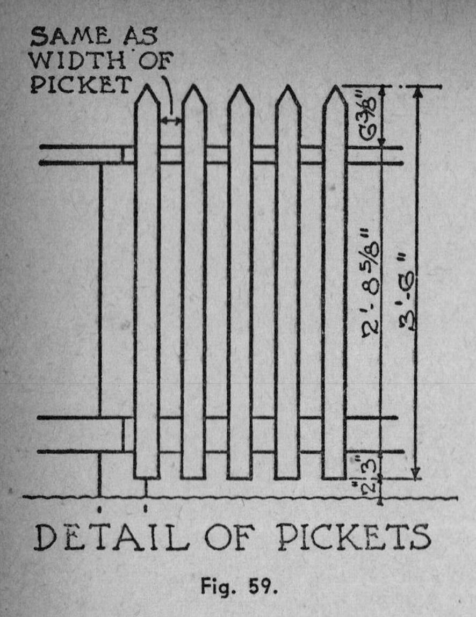

Fig. 59.

PATTERNS FOR PICKET TOPS

Fig. 60.

the stairway, and worn parts fit in at the inside corners of the risers where they escape further wear.

Worn parts can be shifted still another way on a staircase that turns at landings. Lay the top ends of new runners flush with the wall on the landings. Then, when wear begins to show, re-lay with the top end aligned with the edge of the runner above and trim off the bottom end. This puts the worn parts 2″ or 3″ below the nosings.

JIG ASSURES SQUARE CORNERS WHEN ASSEMBLING PICTURE FRAMES

This jig (fig. 58) will provide perfect corners and a square assembly when you are nailing together the pieces of a picture frame. If the clamp screws are not so long as to interfere, then the jig also can be used to cut saw kerfs for the slip tongues.

To build it, you will need two 6″ C-clamps, a piece of ¾″ plywood about 12″ wide and any desired length, and a piece of ⅜″ plywood 8″ square, or the inside size of the smallest frame you are likely to make. After squaring the ⅜″ plywood accurately, screw and glue it to the larger piece, squaring it near one corner to leave a 1″ rabbet each way. Then cut two semicircular holes to admit the ends of the C-clamps, making the straight edges

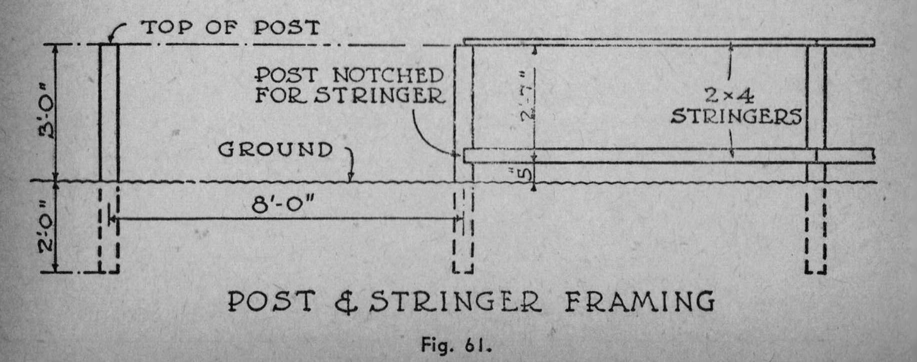

Fig. 61.

parallel with the outside edges of the small piece of plywood.

When you use the jig, place the inside edges of two frame members in the rabbet, adjust until the miters meet, and clamp the pieces in place.

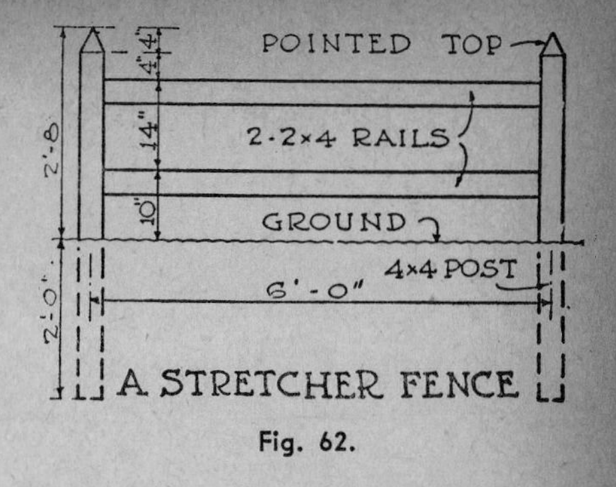

Fig. 62.

USUAL DIMENSIONS AND SPACINGS FOR PICKET AND STRETCHER FENCES

There are certain standard dimensions for placing of posts, height of pickets and picket spacing which have come to be accepted standards since they produce a fence of pleasing proportions.

These widely accepted dimensions are illustrated here as a guide to the householder who elects to become his own fence artisan. The dimensions are suggestions only and any one of them may be varied in accordance with individual taste. One dimension, however, the placing of posts, is fairly well established from a good construction standpoint—It is unwise to space posts farther than 8 feet apart, unless stringers are heavier than 2 x 4 stock. (Figs. 59 to 61.)

Stretcher dimensions. After the picket type, a simple two-rail stretcher fence is probably most popular. Ordinary dimensions for a medium height, standard stretcher style are given in figure 62. It is intended that "stock" 4 x 4 posts of five-foot length will be used. Rails may be fitted between posts with large finishing nails—toe-nailed.

SECTION IV

ROOFING, FLASHING, INSULATION AND VENTILATION

Shingles Quantities—Preventing Drip From Gables—Shingle Estimating—The Proper Nails—Shingle Nailing—Never Soak Wood Shingles before Laying—Shingle Exposure—Red Cedar Shingle Grades—Shingling Hips and Ridges—Overroofing with Red Cedar Shingles—Overwalling with Red Cedar Shingles—Staining and Painting Shingles—Moss on Roofs—Roll Roofing—New or Replacement Roll Roofing—Canvas Roofing—How to Paper a Roof—Galvanized Sheets—Precautions with Galvanized Sheets—Zinc Paint—Protect Against Lightning—Stop Leaks in Old Roofs—New Roofs over Old—Roofing Nails—Gutters and Downspouts—Snow Guards—Slate Roof Repair—Repairing Roofs—What's Wrong?—Flashings—Removing Efflorescence—More Flashing Tips—Attic Insulation—Tools for Insulating Attic Floor—Insulating Your Present Home—Where to Place Insulation—Cutting and Measuring—Insulating Walls—Insulating Ceilings—Insulating Attics—Insulating Floors—Ventilation—Attic Ventilation—Exhaust Fan Installation—Safety Control for Exhaust Fans—Estimating Required Fan Capacity—Exchanging Inside and Outside Air for Comfort.

SECTION IV

ROOFING, FLASHING, INSULATION AND VENTILATION

SHINGLE QUANTITIES

When other than standard exposure is used. In computing the number of squares that will be required if shingles are laid with less than the recommended maximum exposure, the following table may be used by dividing the square feet of roof (fig. 2) by the number under each length of exposure:

	No. of Inches Exposed to the Weather							
	4	4½	5	5½	6	6½	7	7½
Sixteen-inch shingles	80	90	100	......	......	......	......	......
Eighteen-inch shingles	70	80	90	100	......	......	......	......
Twenty-four-inch shingles	....	....	......	......	80	90	95	100

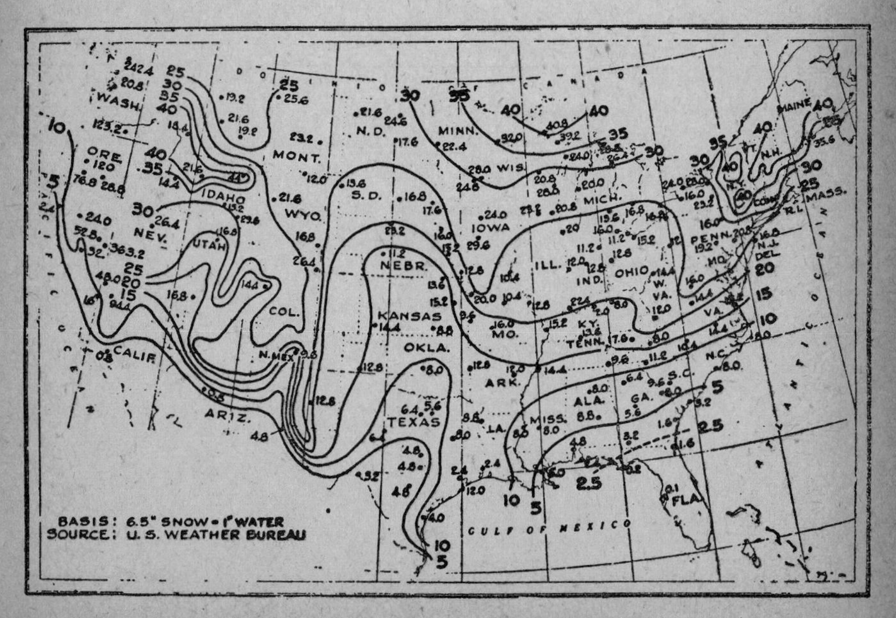

Fig. 1. Snow loads (in pounds per square foot).

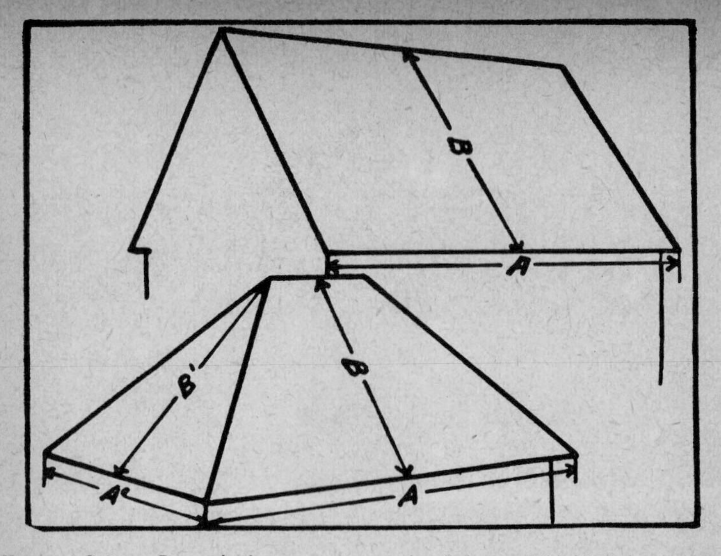

Fig. 2. Upper—A times **B** equals the area of one side of the roof. Multiply by 2 to find whole roof area in square feet. Measure all distances in feet. **Lower**—when **B** and **B**^{1} are equal, the area of any hip roof equals **A** times **B** times 2.

RECOMMENDED MINIMUM ROOF SLOPE AND APPROXIMATE WEIGHTS OF COVERINGS

Type of roofing	Minimum allowable slope per foot, with ordinary lap	Approximate weight per square
	Inches	Pounds
Aluminum	4	30
Asbestos shingles:		
American pattern	4	280
Dutch pattern	5	280
Hexagonal pattern	5	260
Asphalt shingles	4	200
Built-up roofing	½	600
Canvas, 8- to 12-ounce	½	25
Galvanized steel:		
Corrugated	4	100
V-crimp	2½	100
Roll roofing:		
2- to 4-inch lap	4	100
17- to 19-inch lap	1	125
Slate	6	800
Tin:		
Standing seam	3	75
Flat seam	½	75
Wood shingles	6	200

PREVENTING DRIP FROM GABLES

At gables, the shingles should project from 1 to 1½ inches over the end rafters or barge boards and mouldings. A length of 6-inch cedar bevel siding nailed along the edge and parallel with the end rafter, with the thinner edge of the siding inward, can be used to give the shingles a slight tilt away from the edge of the gable. The butts of the shingles which rest on this strip of siding may be cut back to produce a slight slant, so that drainage will be away from the gable edge along the slanted butts. This will prevent drip from the gable and the formation of icicles during cold weather. This simple but practical expedient is illustrated in figure 4.

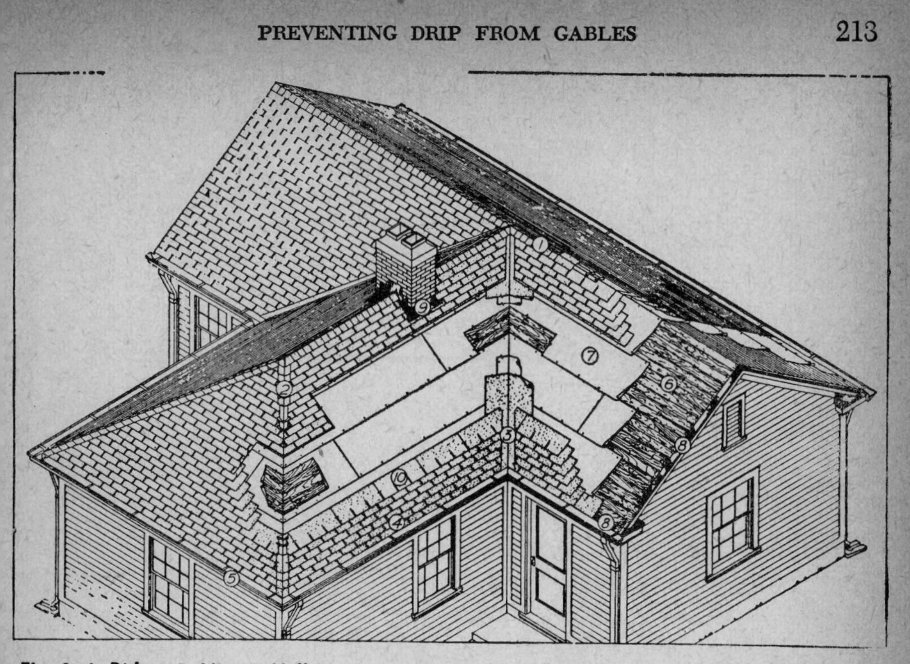

Fig. 3. 1. Ridge. 2. Hip. 3. Valley. 4. Eaves. 5. Eaves trough or gutter. 6. Sheathing boards. 7. Underlay material. 8. Metal edging strips. 9. Metal chimney flashing. 10. Asphalt strip shingles.

Fig. 4. Drip from gables and the formation of icicles can be prevented by this simple expedient.

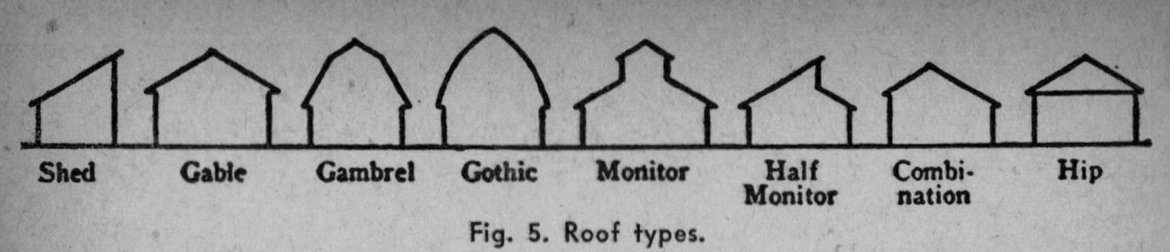

Fig. 5. Roof types.

SHINGLE ESTIMATING

The quantity of material required to shingle the roof or exterior walls of a building depends on several factors, such as (1) the size of the building, (2) the type of roof or design of the outside walls, (3) the exposure of the shingles, and (4) the method of application.

By exposure of shingles is meant the amount of the shingle that remains uncovered and exposed to the weather. This is determined by the steepness of the roof. In column 4 of the table adjoining are listed the various recommended exposures of 16″ shingles for typical roof pitches.

Roof. The area of a roof depends on the size, slope, and type. The usual types of roofs are the shed, gable, hip, gambrel, combination, arch, monitor, and half monitor (fig. 5). The method of estimating is explained here.

It is necessary to make an extra allowance for such items as ridges, hips, valleys, and the double row of starters at the eaves. An addition of

ROOF COVERING CAPACITY OF SIXTEEN-INCH SHINGLES

1 Roof pitch	2 Rise per foot of run	3 Slope of roof	4 Exposure of shingles	5 Coverage for 4-bundle square	6 This factor times the horizontal area to be covered, including the overhang, gives the area of slope
	Inches	Degrees	Inches	Square feet	Secant*
Quarter pitch	6	26	3½	70	1.120
7/24	7	30	4	80	1.157
⅓	8	34	4½	90	1.200
⅜	9	37	5	100	1.250
5/12	10	40	5	100	1.300
11/24	11	42	5	100	1.356
Half pitch	12	45	5	100	1.415
13/24	13	47	5	100	1.473
7/12	14	49	5	100	1.537
⅝	15	51	5	100	1.600
⅔	16	53	5	100	1.667
¾	18	56	5	100	1.800
5/6	20	59	5	100	1.943
⅞	21	60	5	100	2.016
Full pitch	24	63	5	100	2.236

* Also, this factor multiplied by the horizontal run, including overhang, gives length of rafter.

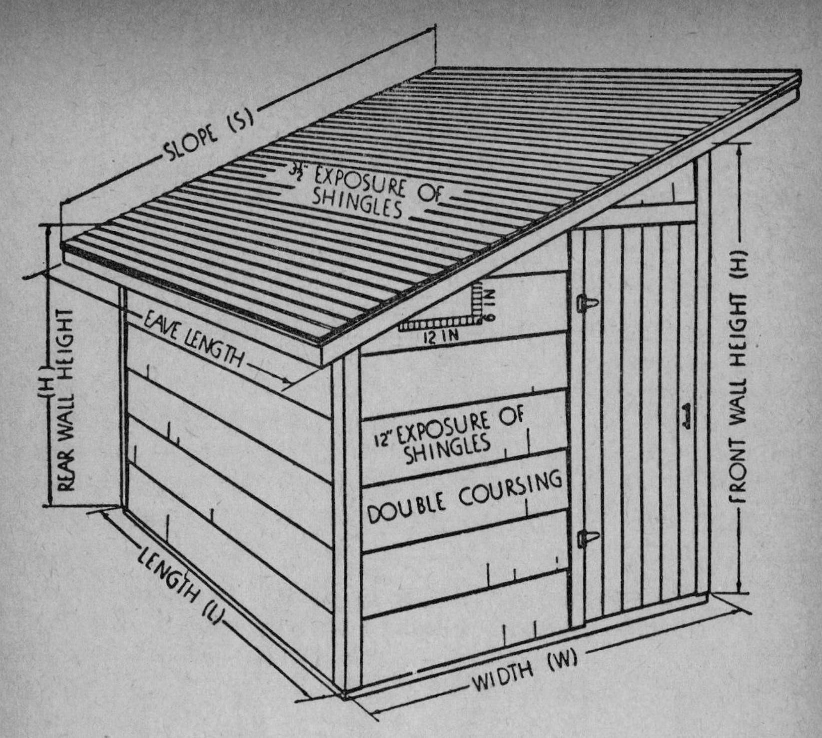

Fig. 6. Shed roof.

one-half square foot should be made for each lineal foot of eaves. For the ridge, hips, and valleys an allowance of one square foot should be added for every lineal foot. Valleys and hips of equal length cancel each other and require few additional shingles as the cut sections from one may be used on the other.

For the shed roof (fig. 6), to compute the area, multiply the eave length (*E*) in feet by the length of the sloping rafter (*S*) in feet and add one-half square foot for each lineal foot of eave.

If length of slope (*S*) is not known, the area of the slope can be obtained by multiplying the area of the floor plan plus the overhang of the roof by the factor found in column 6 of the adjoining table.

Example. If the length of the building is 18 feet, the width 8 feet, the overhang 1 foot on each side, and the rise 6″ per foot, the area would be 20′ x 10′ x 1.12 = 224 square feet. Allowing an extra ½ square foot per lineal foot for the double row at the eaves, we need ½ x 20′ = 10 sq. ft. or a total of 234 sq. ft. area.

The recommended shingle exposure for this slope of roof is 3½″ (column 4). At this exposure, a 4-bundle square of shingles will cover 72 square feet (column 5), so by

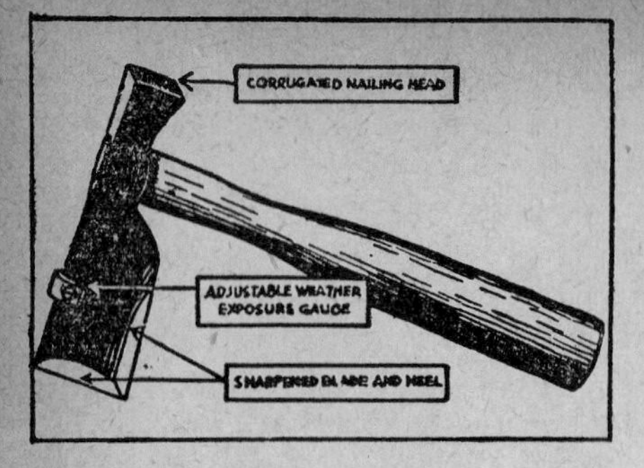

Fig. 7. Professional shingle applicators use a special type of shingling hatchet which is designed to speed application.

dividing the total area by the covering per square $\frac{234}{72} = 3\frac{1}{4}$, or 3 squares and 1 bundle, we get the number of squares needed.

THE PROPER NAILS

For new construction, use three-penny nails (1¼-inch, 14½ gauge) for 16″ and 18″ shingles, and four-penny nails (1½-inch, 14 gauge) for 24″ shingles. For over-roofing, use five-penny nails (1¾-inch, 14 gauge) for 16″ and 18″ shingles, and six-

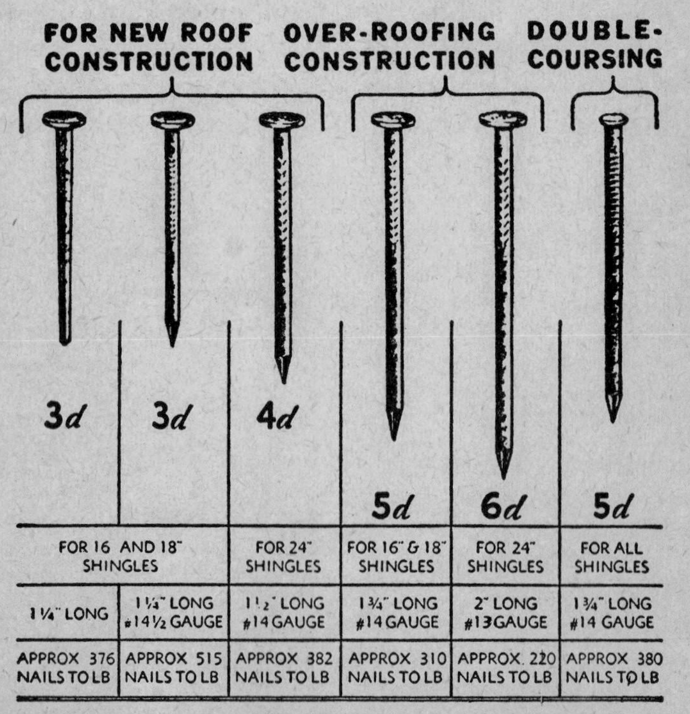

3d	3d	4d	5d	6d	5d
FOR 16 AND 18" SHINGLES		FOR 24" SHINGLES	FOR 16" & 18" SHINGLES	FOR 24" SHINGLES	FOR ALL SHINGLES
1¼" LONG	1¼" LONG #14½ GAUGE	1½" LONG #14 GAUGE	1¾" LONG #14 GAUGE	2" LONG #13 GAUGE	1¾" LONG #14 GAUGE
APPROX 376 NAILS TO LB	APPROX 515 NAILS TO LB	APPROX 382 NAILS TO LB	APPROX 310 NAILS TO LB	APPROX. 220 NAILS TO LB	APPROX 380 NAILS TO LB

SQUARE CUT NAILS OF SAME LENGTH WILL ALSO GIVE SATISFACTORY SERVICE.

STANDARD "BOX" NAILS OF THE SIZES GIVEN WILL PROVE SATISFACTORY IF PROPERLY ZINC COATED OR MADE RUST-RESISTANT.

Fig. 8. Sizes, quantities and use of shingle nails.

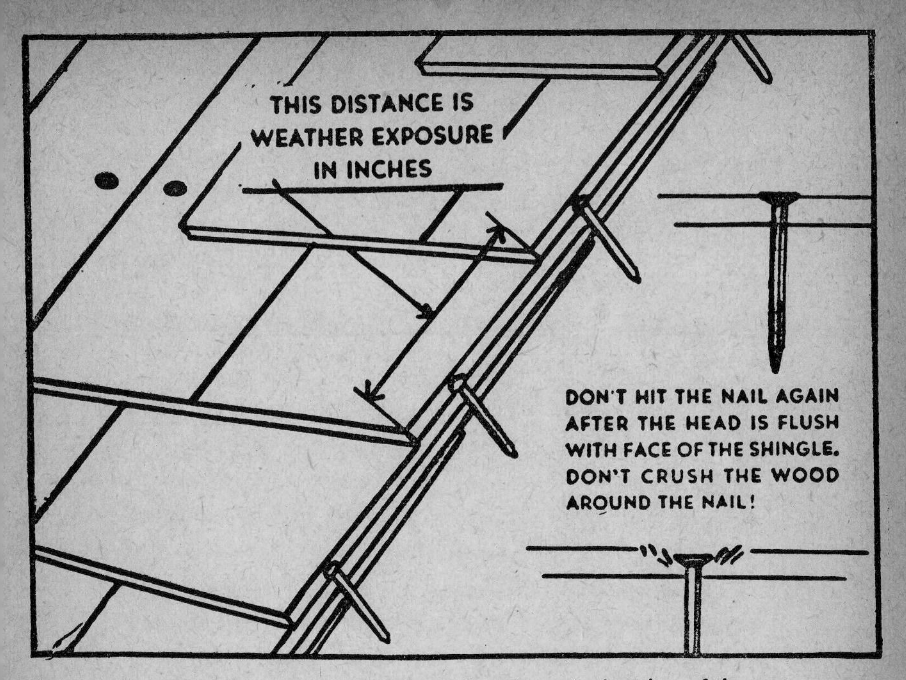

Fig. 9. Nails should never be more than 2 inches above the butt-line of the next course.

penny nails (2-inch, 13 gauge) for 24″ shingles. In double-course wall construction, use five-penny nails (1¾-inch, 14 gauge) for all shingles. (Fig. 8.)

SHINGLE NAILING

Nails should be long enough to penetrate about three-fourths of the thickness of ordinary sheathing, and should be set ½ to ¾ inch from the edge of the shingle and from 1 to 2 inches above the butt line of the covering course, two nails to each shingle (fig. 9). Wide shingles should be split before laying. Nails should be driven flush, but not so hard that the head crushes the wood. Be careful with the last blow. Properly

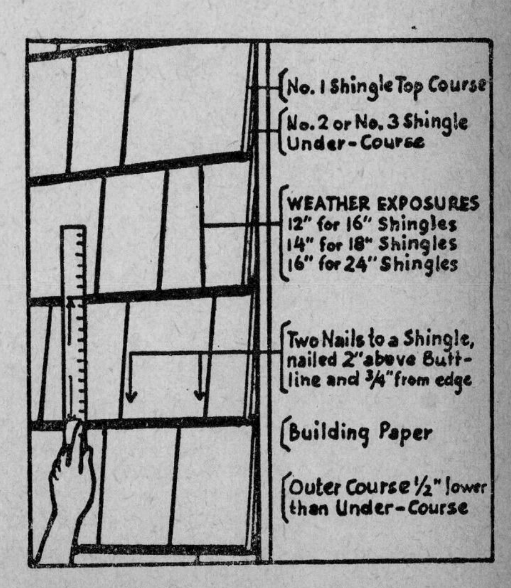

Fig. 10. Double coursing, showing proper spacing of nails in butt nailing.

nailed shingles cannot be blown from a roof.

The wide exposures obtained by double coursing are made possible by so-called "butt nailing," in which 5d small-head, zinc-coated nails are used to hold the butts of the shingles close to the wall. Two nails are used for each shingle, placed approximately ¾″ from each edge and 2″ above the butt, as shown in figure 10.

Fig. 11. Six simple and easy steps that make a perfect over-roofing job. Note in bottom two illustrations that new valley sheets are laid over the old roof.

NEVER SOAK WOOD SHINGLES BEFORE LAYING

When a load of shingles arrives at the yard of the retail dealer and the shingles are placed in storage, they quickly reach a moisture content or "hygroscopic balance" by absorbing moisture from the air, that depends upon prevailing atmospheric conditions in that particular locality.

Shingles should not be wetted before they are laid on a roof, but should be at the average moisture content that the bundles will reach while in ordinary storage in the retail lumberman's yard. Proper attention should, of course, be paid to spacing, so that there will be sufficient room for expansion during rainy weather. A space of ¼ to ⅜ inches between the edges of adjacent shingles will allow for this expansion. The best possible moisture content for the shingles at the time of application is 15%, so that a range of moisture content between 10% and 18%, the average moisture content that shingles reach in storage, will give the best results. When thoroughly wet or green shingles are nailed on a roof, splits and checks may occur, due to the shrinkage stresses between the nails.

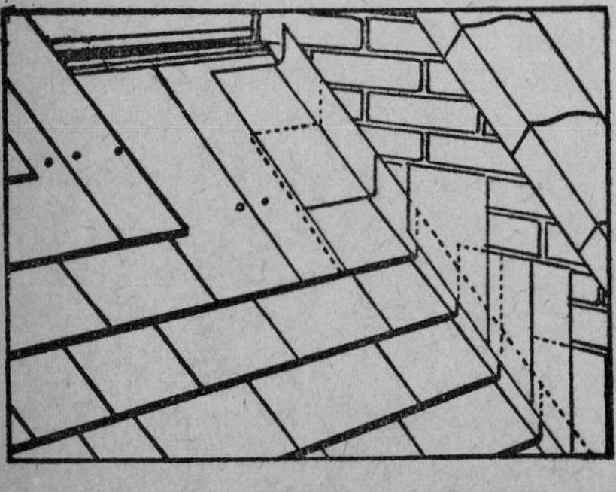

Fig. 12. Flashings and counter flashings are required against brick walls, but for wood walls, flashings in shingle length are completely satisfactory.

SHINGLE EXPOSURE

Roof shingles should be laid with a weather exposure of (*Specify exposure to the weather in inches from the following table.*)

(In general the lowest pitch used in the roof will govern, although certain instances may permit two different weather exposures for separate parts of the same roof.)

Pitch of Roof			Exposure of Shingles in Inches		
Pitch	Rise (in inches)	Run	16	18	24
⅛	3	12			
1/6	4	12	3¾	4¼	5¾
5/24	5	12			
¼	6	12			
⅓	8	12			
½	12	12	5	5½	7½
⅝	15	12			
¾	18	12			

Side wall shingles shall be applied with a weather exposure of (*Specify exposure to the weather in inches from the following table.*)

Length of Shingles (in inches)	Exposure of Shingles (in inches)	
	Single Course	Double Course*
16	6 to 7½	8 to 12
18	6 to 8½	9 to 14
24	8 to 11½	12 to 16

* Assuming exposed course is face or butt-nailed.

Shingles should be doubled at all eaves (*Specify "tripled" where box cornices or narrow eaves occur*) and at foundation line. Butts of the shingles in the first course on roofs shall project 1½″ from the first sheathing board. Roof shingles shall be spaced apart not less than ¼″ nor more than ⅜″.

RED CEDAR SHINGLE GRADES

A majority of the shingles made from red cedar are produced by manufacturers who have accepted commercial standards (C.S. 31-38) as their standard of practice in the production and distribution of red cedar shingles. These manufacturers maintain rigid inspection service. Frequent inspection, without warning, is made of their production. They label each bundle produced. These labels clearly state that the shingles have been manufactured in compliance with the U.S. Department of Commerce (Commercial Standards 31-38) and are guaranteed by the manufacturer to meet all the quality requirements of the standard as set up by the government agency. No manufacturer who is unwilling to meet these requirements can use labels of the association or associations that state that shingles so identified have been inspected and guaranteed as to grade. When grades of any manufacturer fall below the recorded standard of the industry, permission to use the label of the association of manufacturers is revoked.

Unlabeled bundles of shingles or those bearing labels of individual manufacturers even when they *imply* that they have been manufactured in accordance with the U.S. Department of Commerce standards (C.S. 31-38) may be of questionable quality. These shingles even though they are labeled and guaranteed by the individual manufacturer to be of standard quality are purchased at considerable unnecessary risk.

Length of shingles. Three different standard lengths of wood shingles are recognized. These standard lengths are 16, 18 and 24 inches. Ten per cent of the shingles in any shipment may be one inch over or under the specified length. For exterior walls and roofs of farm buildings, it is customary to use shingles of 16″ length.

Thickness of shingles. The thickness of shingles at the butts varies with their length, but is the same for all grades of the 16″ length. Shingles 16 inches long must be so thick that five shingles when measured across the butts or thickest portion, when green, will measure two full inches. These are known as 16″-5/2 shingles. Five butts of 18-inch shingles measure 2 inches or 2¼ inches. These are known as 18″-5/2 or 18″-5/2¼ shingles. The longest commercial shingles are 24 inches in length and the thickness at the butt is one-half inch—four such shingles will measure two full inches. These are known as 24″-4/2 shingles.

Since 16-inch shingles are packed with 20 courses on each side of the band sticks, a bundle of 16-inch shingles must, therefore, measure 8 inches in thickness when green. If measured after seasoning has occurred, an allowance of ¼ inch per bundle is made for shrinkage. In No. 3 grade only, an additional allowance of ¼ inch is made for variations in sawing.

The following grades of 16″-5/2 red cedar shingles are recognized by the U.S. Department of Commerce (Commercial Standards 31-38):

No. 1 shingles. No. 1 red cedar shingles represent the best grade that is manufactured. These shingles are intended primarily for roof construction, where the shingles should lie flat and tight and give complete protection from rain water driven by high winds. (See fig. 13.)

No. 1 shingles must be 100% edge or vertical grain, 100% clear, and 100% heartwood. None of these shingles should be wider than 14″ and none narrower than 3″. There should be 20 courses of shingles at each end of the bundle. Not more than 10% of the combined width of the shingles laid side by side (running inches) in any shipment may be less than 4″ in width.

No. 2 shingles. Shingles of No. 2 grade must be clear or free from blemishes for three-fourths of their length as measured from the butts. A maximum width of only one inch of sapwood is permissible in the first ten inches. Mixed vertical and flat grains are allowed. No shingles shall be wider than 14″ and none narrower than 3″. Not more than 20% of the running inches in any shipment may be less than 4 inches.

No. 3 shingles. No. 3 shingles must be 8″ clear or better and may contain sapwood. No shingles shall be wider than 14″ and none narrower than 2½″ and not more than 30% of the running inches in any shipment may be less than 4″ wide. Knot holes up to 3″ in diameter are permitted in the upper half.

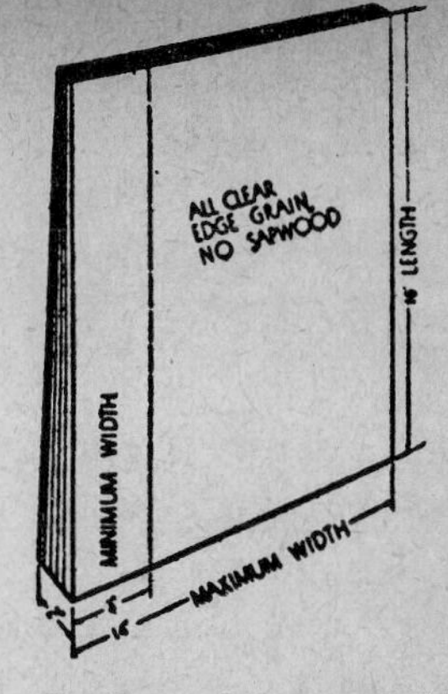

Fig. 13. Thickness of five 16-inch shingles measures 2 inches.

Selection of shingles. It will pay to use only the best grade of shingles. Only No. 1 grade red cedar shingles should be used for permanent roof construction and the best wall construction. The No. 2 grade of shingles should be used only on temporary roofs or for undercoursing, and for side walls. The No. 3 shingles should be used only on outside walls as undercoursing under No. 1 or 2.

SHINGLING HIPS AND RIDGES

Good tight hips and ridges are necessary to avoid air infiltration and prevent leakage from rain. A good type of construction is the modified "Boston" hip or ridge. In constructing this type of hip,

Fig. 14. A Boston hip.

shingles of approximately the same size, six or more inches wide, should be sorted out. Two lines are marked on the shingles on the roof, five inches back from the center line of the ridge or hip, one on each side. The first shingle in the hip should be sawed across the butt to conform with the shingles at the eave line. It should then be nailed in place with one edge extending along the line previously marked on the roof. After the shingle is nailed, the edge of shingle projecting above the center line of the hip should be beveled or cut back. (Fig. 14.) The shingle on the opposite side of the hip should now be applied and the projecting edge cut back. The next two shingles are applied in reverse order. The starter course and end course of a hip should be doubled. Ridges may be constructed similarly.

OVERROOFING WITH RED CEDAR SHINGLES

It is wasteful and unnecessary to remove old shingles. These should be left in place and covered with new shingles. The result is double insulation against heat transmission, operating in both summer and winter, with a consequent saving of fuel during cold weather that often reaches such proportions that in a few years the price of the new roof has been absorbed. The reduced heat transmission in summer adds vastly to home comfort. The double roof, moreover, is considerably stronger, so that a heavier snow load can be carried.

Overroofing has the further advantages of saving the labor of removing old shingles, avoiding litter and dirt, and retaining protection for building contents while the work is in progress, so that reroofing may be done at any season.

The method of reshingling described has been demonstrated and proved to be practical. New red cedar shingles will give fully as good service when applied over old shingles as on new roof decks.

In preparing an old wood-shingle surface to receive a new covering, all curled, badly warped, and loose shingles should be nailed flat and secure, and all protruding nails should be driven down.

THE FIRST STEP consists in cutting back the first course of the old shingles at the eaves. This may be done with a hatchet.

THE SECOND STEP consists merely in replacing the shingles that were removed with a strip of lumber 3 or 4 inches wide, nailed flush with the eave line.

THE THIRD STEP is to cut back the old shingles from the gable edges for a distance of 2 or 3 inches.

THE FOURTH STEP involves nailing a narrow strip of lumber, approximately as wide as the shingles that were removed, along the gable edge. This can be done as shingling progresses.

THE FIFTH STEP is to place a strip or strips of lumber in each valley to separate old metal from new and to make the valley level with the old shingle surface. Renew all other flashings. Remove old ridge and replace with B or C grade beveled siding, thin edge down.

THE SIXTH AND FINAL STEP is the application of new shingles over the old, using 5d or 6d hot-dipped, zinc-coated box or special overroofing nails, and the final application of new combs or ridges.

A much finer and workmanlike job can be produced by applying new 1″ x 6″ or 1″ x 8″ strips over the old shingles, nailing them solidly to the rafters with eight-penny nails. These strips should be wide enough to cover the edges of two rows of the old shingles in order to bring them to an even surface for the new shingles.

Another method of preparing old shingles for reroofing is as follows: The ends of the bottom course of the old roof are cut off or driven up so that the butts are flush with the fascia board. They are then hidden by nailing a piece of blind stop on to the fascia board, even with the top of the old shingles. On the gable ends the old shingles are cut off even with the bargeboard, and similar treatment with blind stop used or, if there was a moulding on the sides, this is removed and replaced, even with the top of the old shingles, after cutting them back.

Shingles can be quickly applied over roll roofing composition shingles by first laying horizontal furring strips, 1″ x 4″, spaced the same distance center to center as the exposure of the new shingles. It may be necessary to remove some of the metal flashings when reroofing with red cedar shingles so as to provide a smooth deck, as any unevenness may cause breaks and waste. Metal under the shingles may permit accumulation of condensed moisture beneath them, causing a "weeping" roof and hastening decay of the roof deck and rafters.

OVERWALLING WITH RED CEDAR SHINGLES

Just as old roofs can be covered with new wood shingles, so old side walls can be re-sided with new red cedar shingles.

Infiltration of air through the side walls often results in unsatisfactory shelter for the family. Cold, drafty structures take their toll in increased heating costs. Buildings that lack tight construction are often cold in winter and hot in summer. Such buildings may be greatly improved by overwalling the sides with red cedar shingles. Double coursing old walls improves the appearance of the building and insulates to a high degree against heat losses. Double coursing and wide spacing give a clapboard effect that is popular today.

To begin an overwall of wood shingles, run a line around the building with a spirit level. This will insure the proper running and spacing of all courses above and below the starting line. If old casings around windows and doors are thinner than the new walls, molding strips should be nailed flush with the edges of the old casings, to which the shingles should be joined. New flashings should be applied over window and door heads, and, on the exposed sides of the building, vertical flashing should be used between the casing and walls.

Overwalling on wood walls. On old wood walls of all types, whether bevel siding, novelty siding, or rustic, the shingles can be applied directly as on new sheathing. Building paper should be used as with new work. Various combinations of single and double coursing can be used to advantage in giving new lines to an old building.

Often the paint on the old wood siding or boards must be burned or scraped before repainting. Under these conditions it may prove economical to cover the old lumber side walls with red cedar shingles.

Overwalling over stucco. The application of shingles to old, cracked, leaky, and unsightly stucco walls is a simple matter. Nailing strips should be attached with nails long enough to penetrate the stucco and the underlying sheathing. These nailing strips of 1″ x 4″ or 1″ x 6″ boards should have a center to center spacing equal to the exposure of the new side wall shingles. To these the shingles may be nailed directly as on new sheathing.

Stucco often can be easily and inexpensively removed and this is desirable if the material is loose and does not provide the proper support for the nails used in shingling. New paper can then be applied to the walls and the shingling can proceed as in new construction.

Overwalling over brick. Brick walls that are troublesome because of water absorption and infiltration through the brick may be easily covered with red cedar shingles. Vertical furring strips should be fastened to the window frames and to the walls through the use of anchors or special nails made for this purpose driven between the bricks.

To these furring strips nailing or shingle strips should be attached for the nailing of the outer shingled wall. The horizontal nailing strips should have a center to center spacing equal to the exposure of the shingles.

STAINING AND PAINTING SHINGLES

The main reason for staining or painting red cedar shingles on roof or outside walls is to improve appearance. Red cedar shingles withstand the effect of exposure remarkably well and will last as long without stain or paint as with most of them.

Where appearance demands it, staining red cedar shingle roofs is recommended because of the economy of application and because

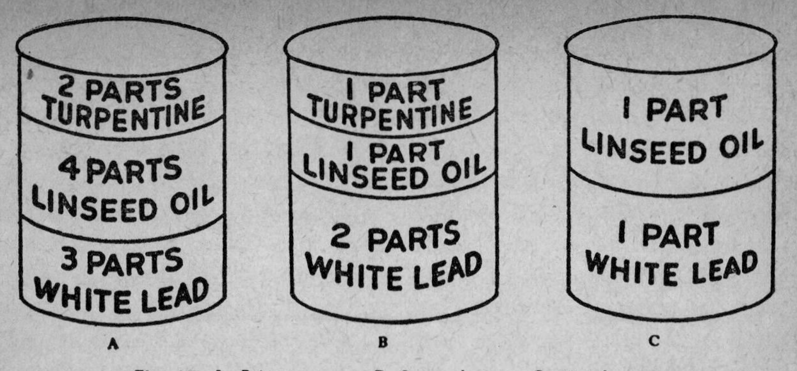

Fig. 15. **A.** Primary coat; **B.** Second coat; **C.** Finish coat.

staining causes no unequal stresses in the wood fiber, and no moisture pockets at the joints of the shingles.

A good shingle stain should be quite thin so that it may be applied evenly and quickly. Prepared shingle stains are supplied by stain and paint manufacturers at low cost. Red and brown colors have the best lasting qualities; blues and greens the least. Some shingle stains contain preservative materials such as coal-tar creosote; others contain none.

A simple formula for mixing shingle stain consists of one part turpentine, two parts boiled linseed oil, and coloring material.

Window and door casings, sashes, cornices, and other trim should be well protected from the elements with three coats of lead and oil paint.

Paste white lead and linseed oil, the principal paint ingredients, may be purchased in quantity, usually at a saving in cost, and kept in readiness for painting at odd times. These basic paint materials can be used for many kinds of painting by mixing in turpentine and tinting material.

In mixing paint, pour a quantity of soft white lead into a clean, dry, water-tight receptacle; thin it by adding the right amount of turpentine, linseed oil, and tinting material; and stir thoroughly (fig. 15).

Common sense dictates extreme care in the selection of ready-mixed paints. Scores of reliable manufacturers of mixed paints produce paints that can be used with safety and assurance. Most of them show the formula on the label.

More than half the cost of painting a building is for labor. Low-grade paint usually has less coverage. It may crack and peel away from the wood. Moisture then gets behind the paint film through the cracks, causing the paint to blister, and necessitating its removal, which is often costly, before a new coat of paint can be applied.

Always bear in mind that the priming coat on new wood is the foundation of the paint film. Brush the paint carefully into the wood and lay it on in an even film. When priming soft woods like red cedar, enough linseed oil should be added in the primer so that laps between stretches are not noticeable. Such laps are caused by oil soaking into the soft, porous wood, leaving the pigment on the surface.

The dipping method of painting or staining shingles is preferred. Shingles should be dipped to cover about two-thirds of their length and the surface should be thoroughly colored. Dipping should be done well in advance of laying so the shingles will be thoroughly dry as handling shingles wet with stain is sometimes hard on the workman. Some persons are seriously affected by contact with the solvents used in shingle stains. Red cedar shingles may be purchased already stained.

Painting flashings. Copper flashing does not require painting. Other flashing material will last longer if protected with paint. The most satisfactory way to prepare galvanized sheet metal for painting is to allow it to "weather" for a few months. If it is desired to paint without delay, wash the surface thoroughly with vinegar, dry, and paint. Tin, if used, should be painted before it is applied. A good flashing paint may be mixed as follows: 1 part dryer, 1 part turpentine, 10 parts linseed oil, 12 parts red lead. An aluminum paint may be used when metallic appearance is desired or when heat reflecting properties are important.

MOSS ON ROOFS

Control of moss on roofs can be accomplished very readily by spraying the roof with a 10 per cent solution of zinc chloride during dry

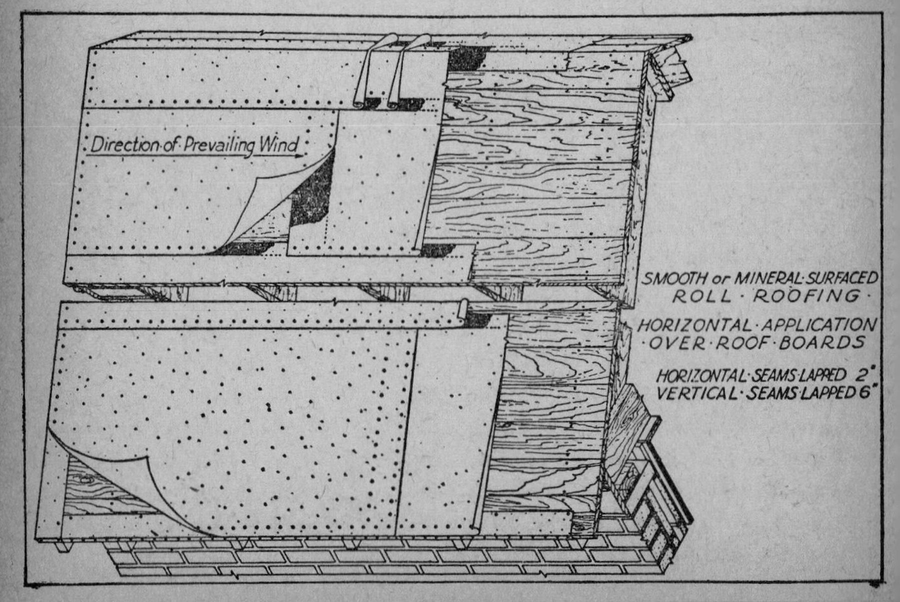

Fig. 16.

weather. The moss absorbs the zinc chloride and is killed.

Spraying the roof with any standard strength of bordeaux or sprinkling dry bordeaux powder on slopes at the ridge kills moss.

A ridge roll of copper or galvanized sheet metal may discourage the growth of moss. There is evidence that this growth cannot get started in the presence of zinc or copper. On long slopes, however, the effect of the metal at the ridge may not extend the full length of the slope. When hips are present, galvanized hip shingles may help to extend the metallic influence to the lower parts of the roof.

AVERAGE SIZES AND WEIGHTS OF ROLL ROOFINGS

Material	Width	Area per roll	Weight per roll
	Inches	Square Feet	Pounds
15-pound asphalt or tarred felt	32 and 36	432	60
30-pound asphalt or tarred felt	32 and 36	216	60
Slater's felt	36	500	32
Sheathing felt	36	500	35
Red rosin-sized sheathing paper	36	500	20, 25, 30, and 40
Roll roofing:			
Talc both sides	36	108	45 to 65
Mineral surfaced	36	108	55 to 90

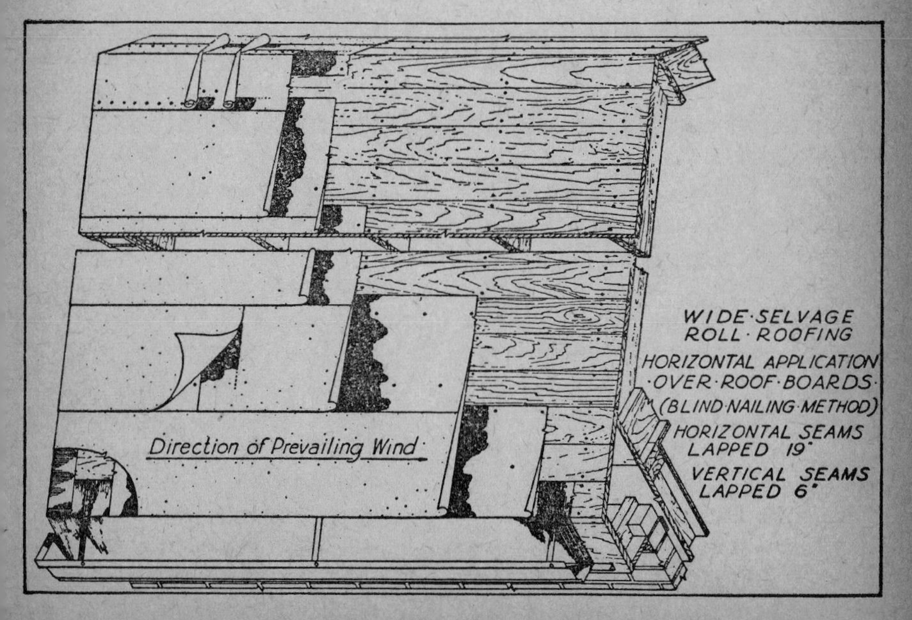

Fig. 17.

ROLL ROOFING

Figures 16 to 21, inclusive, illustrate methods of applying asphalt-prepared roll roofing and shingles, also recommended practices for the construction of valleys and flashings, and finishing hips and ridges. Only the shingles used most commonly are illustrated. In general, the purpose has been to show a variety of satisfactory practices rather than to indicate that a particular method must be used with a particular type of shingle. For example, some illustrations show a metal drip edge at the eaves, while others use wood shingles for this purpose. Either is considered satisfactory. Some illustrations show the use of underlay materials, and in others they are omitted.

NEW OR REPLACEMENT ROLL ROOFING

Base course should be 15-lb. felt. Apply it by nailing through the concealed or unsurfaced portion of each strip, then apply hot asphalt on the preceding selvage surface.

Reroofing is applied over existing roofing under normal conditions. In such cases, the first layer of 15-lb. felt can be omitted, but existing roofing should have buckles cut out and be amply nailed.

This roofing is not recommended on surfaces pitched less than 2½″ per ft.

Repairs. Repairs of "fish mouths" are made by undersurface application of roofing cement to waterproof leaking seams, or by slitting the buckles and patching. Do not apply

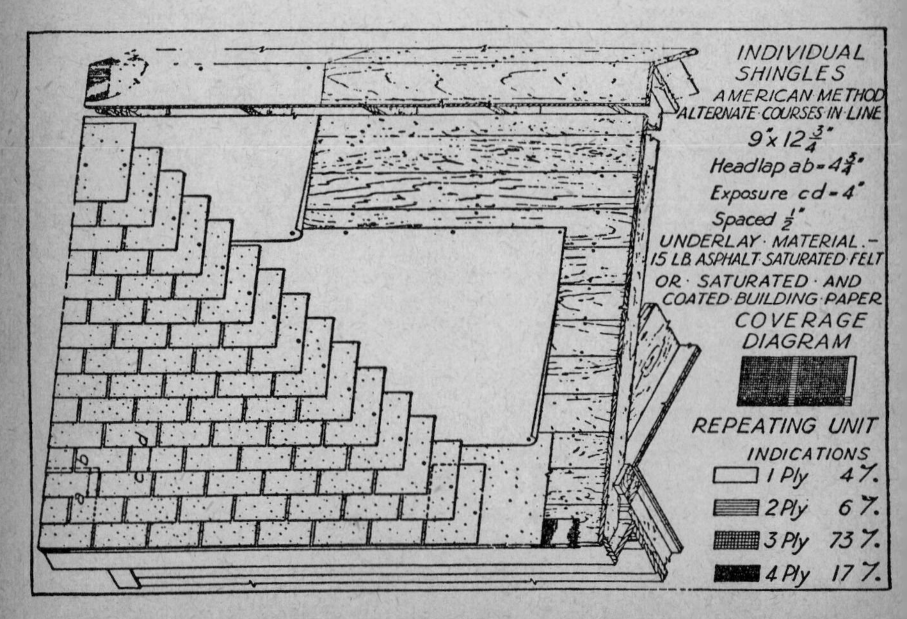

Fig. 18.

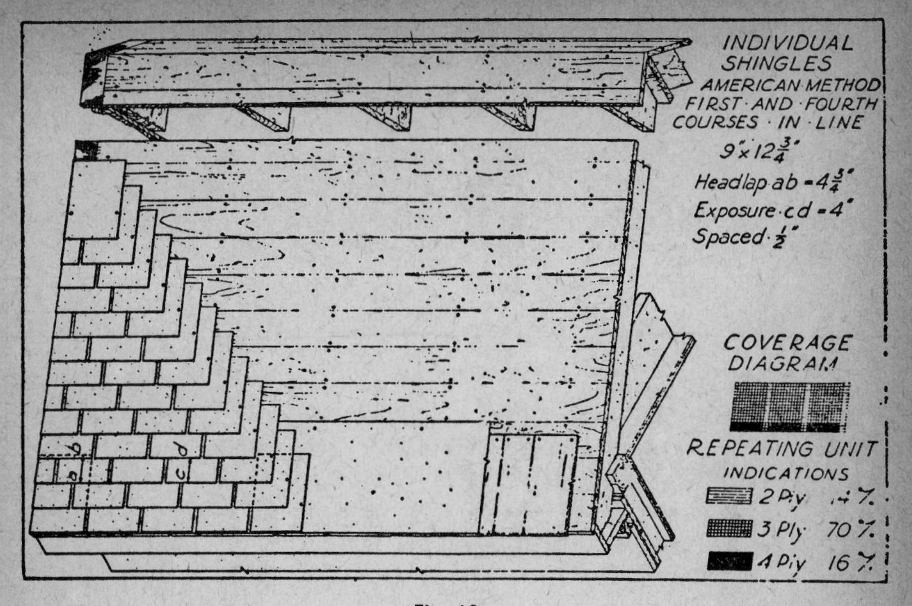
INDIVIDUAL SHINGLES
AMERICAN METHOD
FIRST AND FOURTH COURSES IN LINE
9" x 12 3/4"
Headlap ab = 4 3/4"
Exposure cd = 4"
Spaced 1/2"
COVERAGE DIAGRAM
REPEATING UNIT
INDICATIONS
2 Ply 14 %
3 Ply 70 %
4 Ply 16 %

Fig. 19.

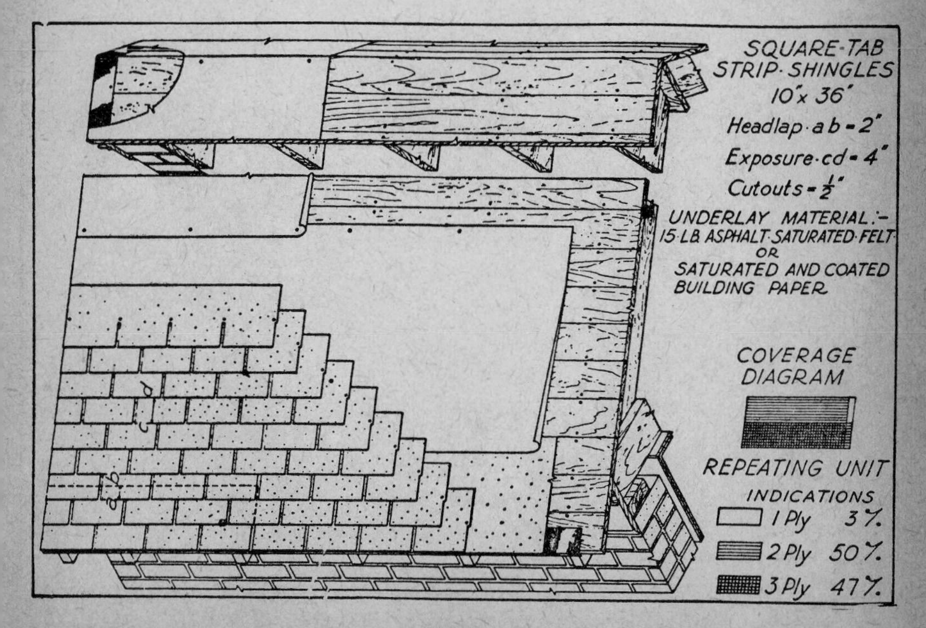
SQUARE TAB STRIP SHINGLES
10" x 36"
Headlap ab = 2"
Exposure cd = 4"
Cutouts = 1/2"
UNDERLAY MATERIAL:-
15 LB. ASPHALT SATURATED FELT
OR
SATURATED AND COATED BUILDING PAPER
COVERAGE DIAGRAM
REPEATING UNIT
INDICATIONS
1 Ply 3 %
2 Ply 50 %
3 Ply 47 %

Fig. 20.

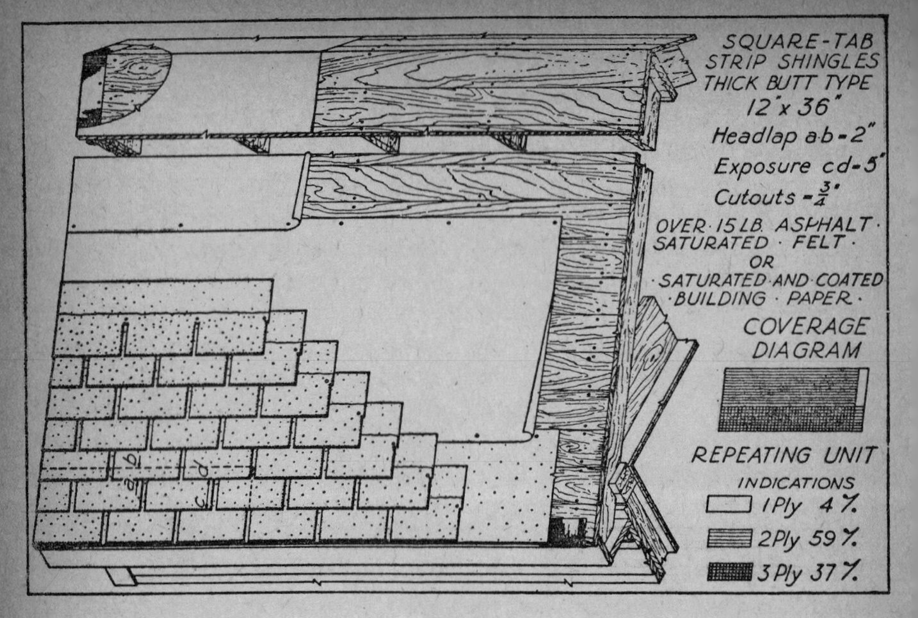
SQUARE-TAB
STRIP SHINGLES
THICK BUTT TYPE
12" x 36"
Headlap a·b - 2"
Exposure cd - 5"
Cutouts - 3/4"
OVER 15 LB. ASPHALT
SATURATED FELT
OR
SATURATED AND COATED
BUILDING PAPER
COVERAGE
DIAGRAM
REPEATING UNIT
INDICATIONS
1 Ply 4%
2 Ply 59%
3 Ply 37%

Fig. 21.

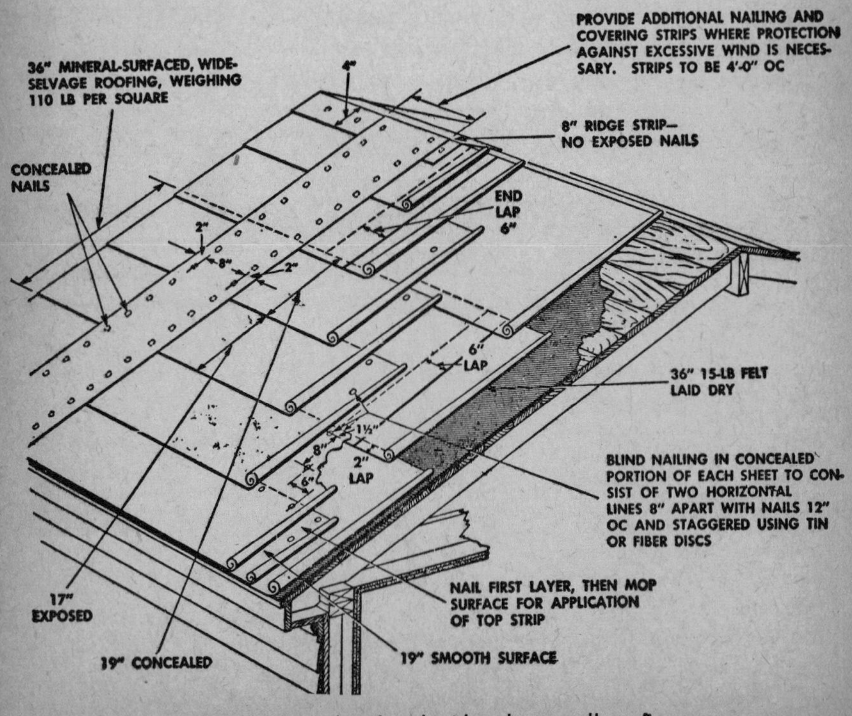
PROVIDE ADDITIONAL NAILING AND COVERING STRIPS WHERE PROTECTION AGAINST EXCESSIVE WIND IS NECESSARY. STRIPS TO BE 4'-0" OC
36" MINERAL-SURFACED, WIDE-SELVAGE ROOFING, WEIGHING 110 LB PER SQUARE
4"
8" RIDGE STRIP—NO EXPOSED NAILS
CONCEALED NAILS
END LAP 6"
2"
8"
2"
6" LAP
36" 15-LB FELT LAID DRY
1½"
8"
2" LAP
6"
BLIND NAILING IN CONCEALED PORTION OF EACH SHEET TO CONSIST OF TWO HORIZONTAL LINES 8" APART WITH NAILS 12" OC AND STAGGERED USING TIN OR FIBER DISCS
NAIL FIRST LAYER, THEN MOP SURFACE FOR APPLICATION OF TOP STRIP
17" EXPOSED
19" CONCEALED
19" SMOOTH SURFACE

Fig. 22. Mineral-surfaced wide-selvage roll roofing.

waterproofing on top of mineral-surfacing, except when other means of repair can not be devised (fig. 22).

Where excessive winds bulge and tear roofing, vertical rows of nails (with tin or fiber discs) can be spaced approximately 4′ 0″ OC with nails 6″ OC and covered in the same manner as shown for the seams.

Where mineral-surface roofing has been applied on relatively flat pitches (approximately ½″ per ft.), final corrective measures consist of an additional 3-ply built-up roof over the existing roof.

CANVAS ROOFING

Canvas roofing has been used for years where a flat roof must be walked upon. It is light in weight, not readily broken under light traffic, long-lived and watertight when kept well painted, and not difficult to lay. It is frequently used along the seacoast and for covering boat decks.

This type of roofing is relatively high in cost but is not expensive considering its durability under the severe service generally imposed upon it.

Canvas, called by manufacturers cotton duck, is made in two general classes—the numbered duck and the ounce duck—the distinction depending upon the method of weaving. Numbered duck is indicated by numbers and ounce duck by ounces. The highest number, 12, is the lightest, weighing 7 ounces per linear yard 22 inches wide, while the lowest number, 00, weighs 20 ounces. The weights of consecutive numbers increase by 1 ounce from No. 12 to No. 00. Ounce ducks weigh from 6

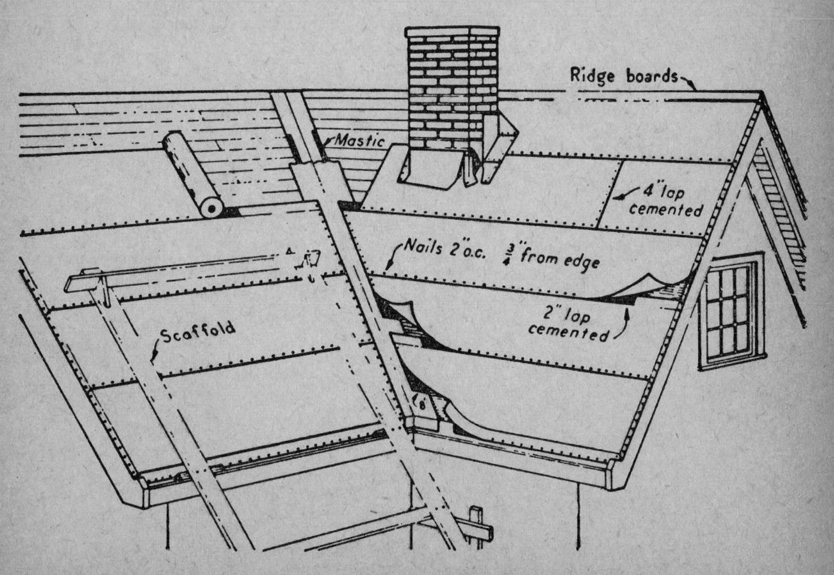

Fig. 23. Common method of applying roll roofing with the strips of roofing running parallel to the eaves of the roof. Scaffolds should be provided as a safety measure.

to 15 ounces per linear yard 28½ inches wide and are made in three grades—army, double filled, and single filled. The last two are not suitable for roofing.

For roofing, the canvas should be unbleached, unsized, closely woven, and not lighter than the 10-ounce grade, although No. 6 and No. 2 are recommended when the roof is to be walked on a great deal. Canvas is available in different widths up to 120 inches, but the 22- and 28½-inch widths of numbered and ounce duck, respectively, are most commonly used for roofing.

The surface upon which the canvas is to be laid should be smooth and tight. It is advisable to use tongue-and-groove flooring 2½ to 4 inches wide. Sheathing 6 to 8 inches wide could be used but is not as good because of greater shrinkage. If the boards cup or warp, the raised edges will make ridges that will wear through the canvas.

In laying a canvas roof the wood sheathing should first be painted with a paint made on the following basis, if a light-colored roof is desired: 100 pounds of white lead in oil heavy paste, 4 gallons of raw linseed oil, 2 gallons of turpentine, and 1 pint of liquid drier. When this paint is thoroughly dry, a heavy coat of the white lead heavy paste should be applied.

The canvas should be placed on the surface and firmly pressed down into the wet paste. A smoother surface is obtained if the canvas is pressed down with rollers. Stretch it slightly and fasten it along the edges with ¾-inch copper tacks or galvanized nails spaced 4 inches apart. The top face should be painted at the edges with heavy paste and the adjacent strip of canvas lapped 1½

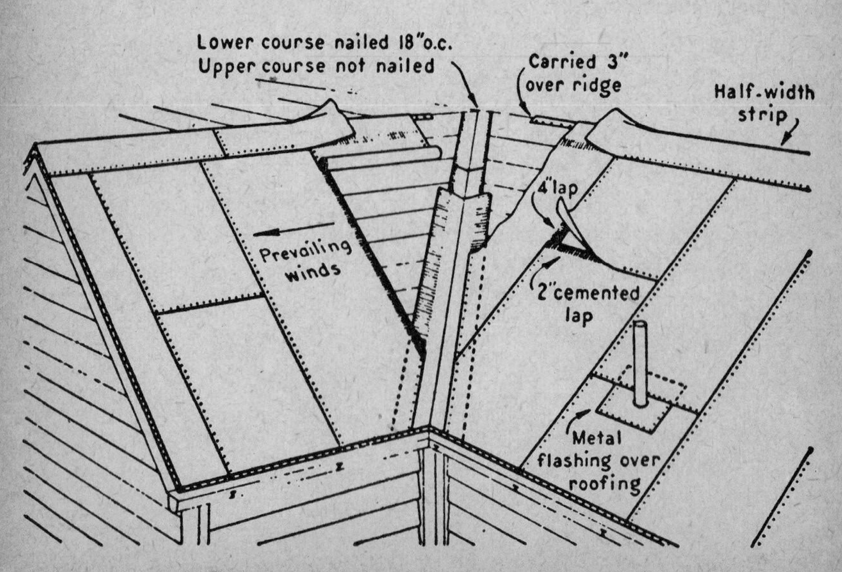

Fig. 24. Roll roofing laid with the roof slope.

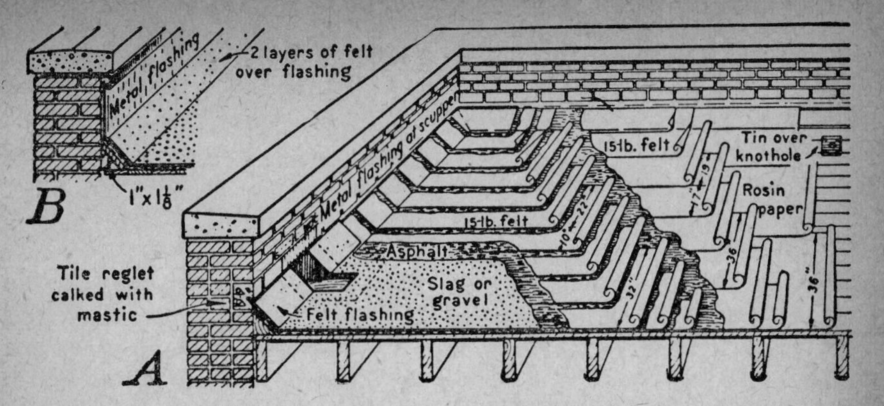

Fig. 25. Details showing method of applying 5-ply built-up roofing for flat roofs. Note the flashing detail in insert **B.** Tar pitch must be used as the cementing material for tarred felt, and asphalt with asphalt felt. As tar is more affected by heat than asphalt, it should not be used on roofs having a steep slope.

inches. The finished joints should be nailed with ¾-inch copper tacks spaced ¾-inch apart. Flashings of canvas are installed in the same manner as flashings of other material.

After the canvas has been laid the exposed surface should receive three coats of paint. The priming coat should be mixed on the following basis: 100 pounds of white lead in oil heavy paste, 3 gallons of raw linseed oil, 2 gallons of turpentine, 1 pint of liquid drier. The second and the finishing coats may be any good paint designed for outside use. The drier may be omitted from the bedding and priming coats if ample time is available for drying—about a week—between coats.

Another method often used in placing the canvas is to stretch it tightly and nail it in place, omitting the paint on both the under side and the sheathing. The canvas is then soaked with water. As soon as the surplus water has disappeared, but while the canvas is still wet, it is painted. The same paints may be used as recommended for the first method of laying, and the priming coat should be worked well into the canvas.

Good results have been obtained by painting the sheathing, wetting the canvas and stretching it on the wet paint, and working in the priming coat when the canvas has partly dried out.

If kept well painted, a canvas roof should last 25 or 30 years.

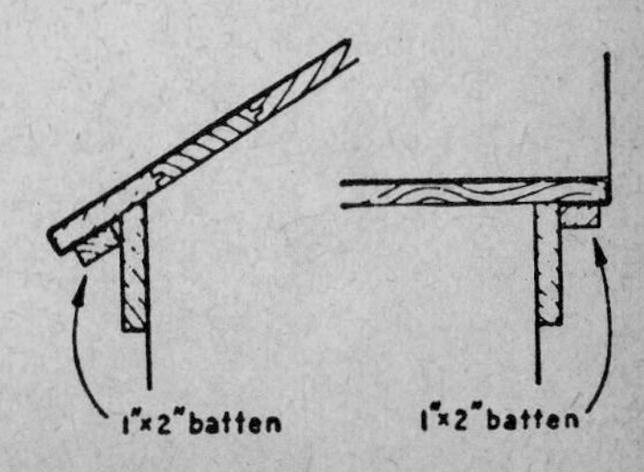

Fig. 26. Battens for holding the edges of roll roofing at eaves.

HOW TO PAPER A ROOF

When a tar-papered roof begins to leak, that's one definite sign it needs immediate repapering. If allowed to go on, leaks will stain ceilings and wallpaper and in time will soften plaster, weaken the clinch, and cause the ceiling to crack, sag, and perhaps fall. Continued dampness also eventually rots the sheathing under the roofing material and may even damage the rafters.

But you don't need to wait until a leak actually occurs to tell that repapering is in order. If the smooth surface looks flaky and fuzzy, the life of the paper has gone and it

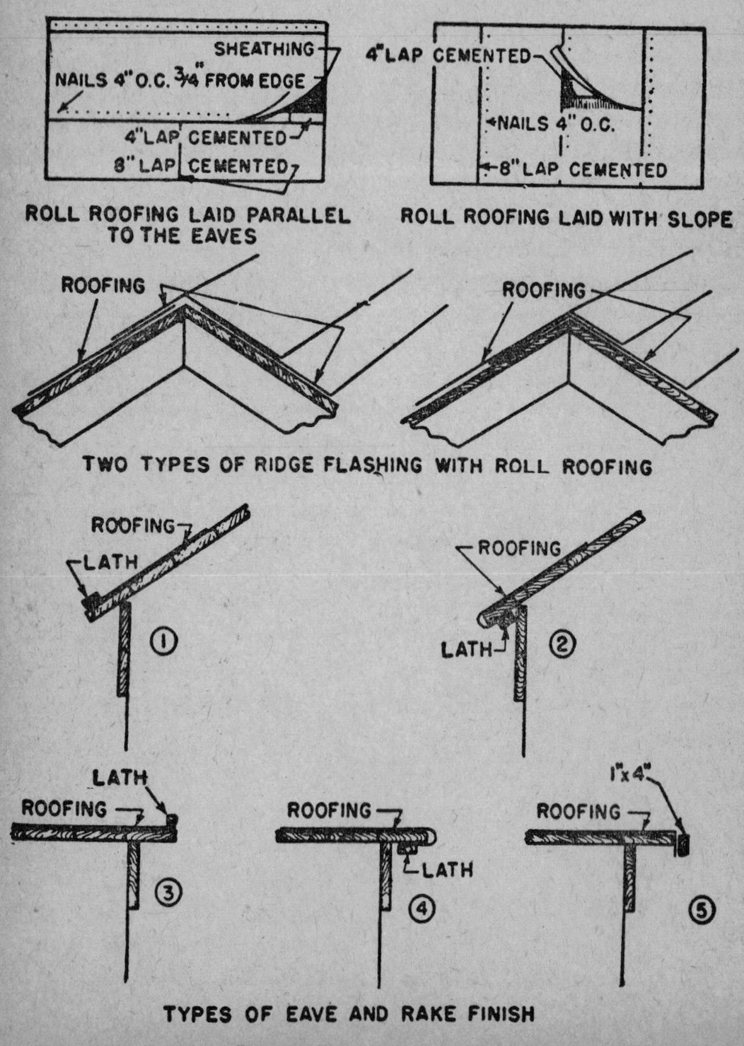

Fig. 27. Types of roof finish.

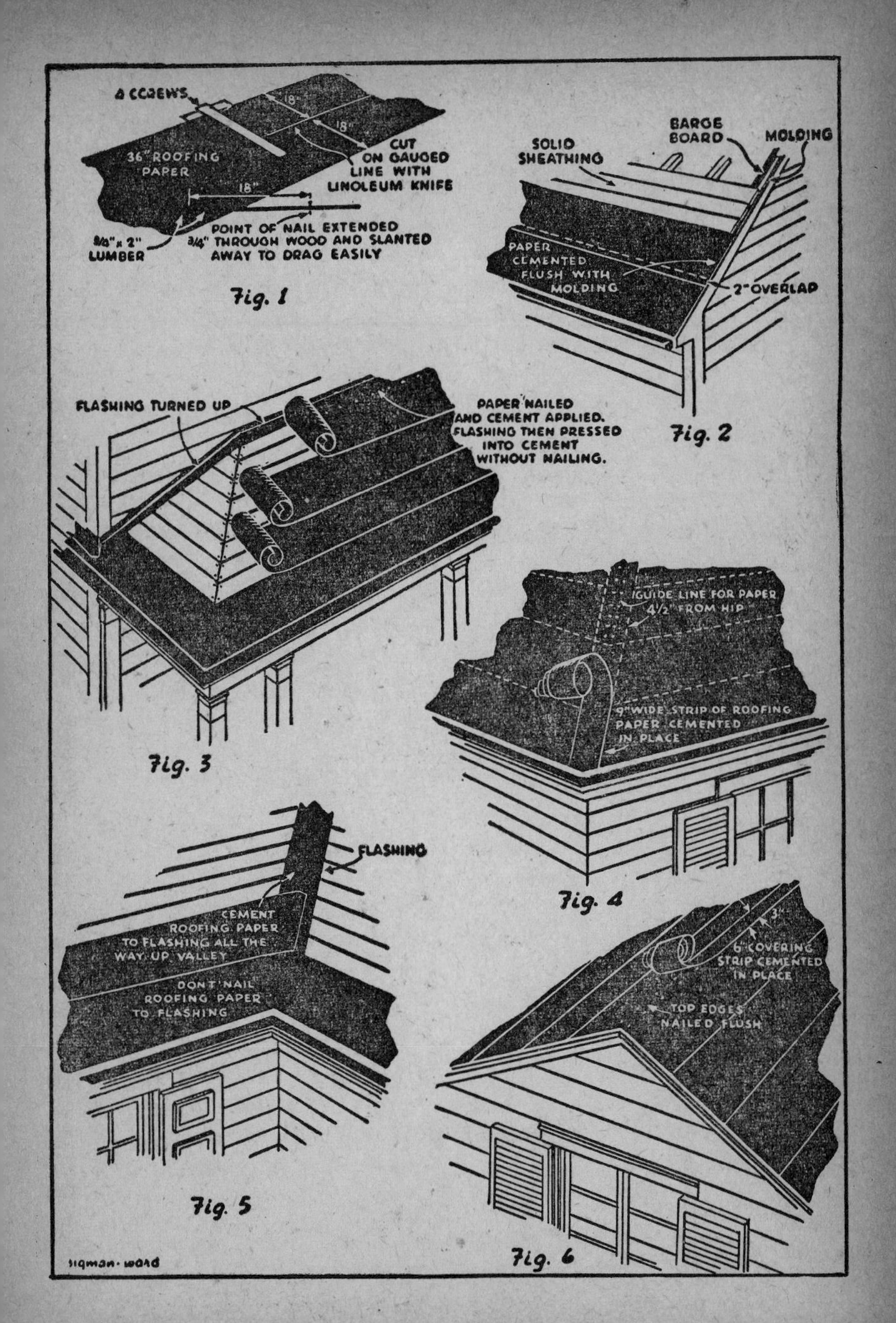

4 SCREWS
18"
18"
36" ROOFING PAPER
CUT ON GAUGED LINE WITH LINOLEUM KNIFE
18"
3/4" x 2" LUMBER
POINT OF NAIL EXTENDED 3/4" THROUGH WOOD AND SLANTED AWAY TO DRAG EASILY
Fig. 1
SOLID SHEATHING
BARGE BOARD
MOLDING
PAPER CEMENTED FLUSH WITH MOLDING
2" OVERLAP
Fig. 2
FLASHING TURNED UP
PAPER NAILED AND CEMENT APPLIED. FLASHING THEN PRESSED INTO CEMENT WITHOUT NAILING.
Fig. 3
GUIDE LINE FOR PAPER 4 1/2" FROM HIP
9" WIDE STRIP OF ROOFING PAPER CEMENTED IN PLACE
Fig. 4
FLASHING
CEMENT ROOFING PAPER TO FLASHING ALL THE WAY UP VALLEY
DON'T NAIL ROOFING PAPER TO FLASHING
Fig. 5
6" COVERING STRIP CEMENTED IN PLACE
TOP EDGES NAILED FLUSH
Fig. 6
sigman-ward

Fig. 28.

should be replaced. This happens earlier than necessary in many cases because of neglect. The third year after a roof has been laid, it should be coated with asphalt, and then recoated each succeeding year.

If the old paper is still solid and fairly smooth, you may repaper over it, but this is not recommended. It is really better to strip off the old paper and take out the old nails first. Many expert roofers prefer to use paper 18″ wide. When the paper gives with the alternate expansion and shrinkage of the wood sheathing to which it is attached, there is a great deal of wrinkling. These wrinkles can't harm the roof, but they are much smaller on 18″ paper than on 36″ width and are less noticeable from the ground. In figure 28, *1* shows a simple method of cutting 36″ paper if the narrower width is not available. The line is gauged with a nail driven in a homemade T-square and is cut with a linoleum knife.

Lay the paper from the lower edge of the roof up, overlapping each piece 2″. Start flush with the bottom and gable edges, as in *2*, and nail (at 6″ intervals) only in the upper margin, which will be covered. (Direct sun heats the paper tremendously, expanding it and causing exposed nails to loosen a little each season.) Cement the paper flush with both edges of the roof, using good roofing cement along a 3″ band, and cement also the overlap of each succeeding piece. Some roofers bend paper over the edges instead of trimming it flush, but in such cases the stiff paper frequently pulls away before the cement can set, the edge of the wood can't be completely coated with paint, and moisture creeps in. Cement itself is a good waterproofer and produces a tight joint when paper is trimmed flush.

When flashing is reached, as at the upper edge of a porch roof (*3*), trim the strip if necessary to required width; then turn up the flashing, nail the paper down, apply cement, and press the flashing onto the cement. Take care not to smear the cement here or at the overlaps, where it will show. Flashing should be sheet copper or lead, but lacking these the roofing paper itself can be used.

At a hip, cut the paper flush and nail it along the hip. Then gauge a line on each side, as indicated in *4*, and cement on a 9″ wide covering strip of paper. No nails and no covering strips are used in valleys (*5*). Instead, the paper is brought up to the center of the valley, trimmed, and fastened to the flashing with a thick coating of cement. If new flashing is needed, apply a 12″ wide strip.

Finishing at the ridge is similar to that at hips, as shown in *6*. Trim the last strip of roofing paper on each side flush with the top, gauge a line on each side 3″ down, and nail within the margin. Then apply cement, and press a 6″ covering strip firmly into it.

Have no qualms about the sticking qualities of good roofing cement. It will hold, if the job is otherwise

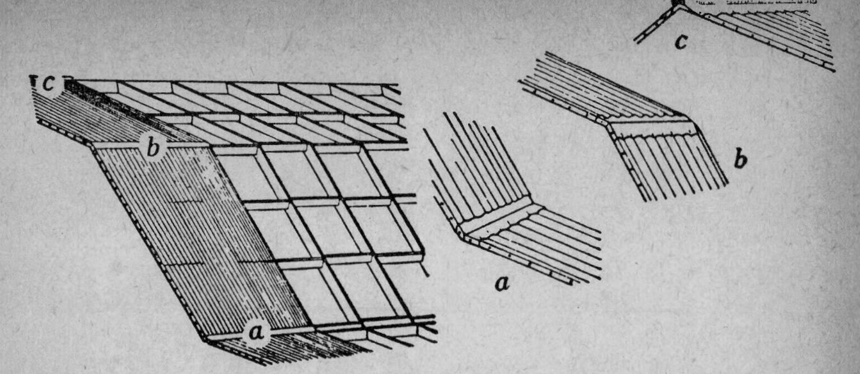

Fig. 29. Corrugated metal roof without sheathing: a, Eaves joint; b, hip; c, ridge cap. 2" x 4" headers are staggered to permit nailing through rafters.

done properly, even in the strongest winds. In using the cement, fasten a 6′ length of the paper at a time, press the paper down, and then do another 6′ length. Complete one piece of paper before starting on the next. Covering strips at the ridge and hips are cemented similarly. Finish one complete side of the ridge first, and then do the other.

GALVANIZED SHEETS

First, and perhaps the most important requirement for success in building with galvanized sheets is a firm, rigid foundation. Unless the sheets are applied on a well braced structure, high wind, ice, or heavy snow may cause bending or swaying and sheets will loosen and leak. If the roof framing sags or is distorted, straighten it up and put in new braces to hold it in shape. In properly constructed roof framing rafters are spaced 2 feet apart, center to center; and roofing sheets, usually 26 to 27½ inches wide, are laid with side laps over rafters so that nails can be driven into the rafters for greater holding power.

Allow ample lap. Sheets should be laid with ample lap, both at the sides and at the ends, and where possible, with the laps facing away from the prevailing winds. The wind should blow over the laps, and not into or under them. Corrugated roofing should be lapped 1½ corrugations at the side and 5 or 6 inches at the end. V-crimp roofing which has two V's at each side, provides better protection against leakage.

Nail to a smooth surface. Because galvanized steel sheets are lighter and stronger than many other types of building materials, a full sheathing or roof deck is unnecessary under them except for buildings where insulation is desired. One-inch by 4 or 6-inch nailing strips nailed to rafters spaced not over 18 inches on center, will give adequate support. Two x four pieces, similarly spaced, are particularly good. If galvanized roofing is laid over old wood shingles or composition roofing, these should be smooth and with no

Fig. 30.

protruding nails which might damage new sheets. Nails of extra length insure adequate holding power.

Valleys, ridges and corners. Sheet metal prepared in ridge rolls to cover the roof ridge (fig. 30), side and end wall flashing, formed gutters and valleys, and corner beads are available from many sheet producers, or they may be formed by bending regular sheets into the proper shapes. One good way to finish corners is to nail down the last sheet and then bend the over-hang around the corner and nail it into place. If sheathing, nailing strips, and roofing is left off from 4 to 6 inches along the roof comb, a waterproof ventilator may be made by running a plain strip of galvanized sheet along the comb which has been bent to fit the slope of the roof. This will extend about 6 inches below the top of the roof comb on either side, and resting on top of the roofing corrugations, will leave openings of about ½ inch through which air can pass along the entire length of the building (fig. 31). Galvanized roofing is not recommended on roofs with a slope less than 3 inches per foot.

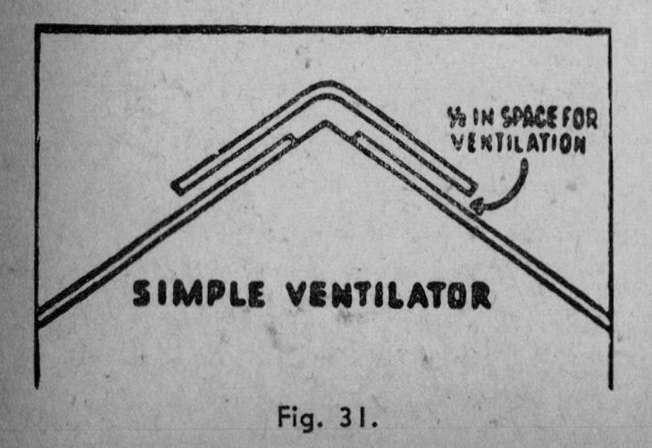

Fig. 31.

How to estimate number of sheets needed for repairs. Sheets are sold by the "square" (100 sq. ft.). First multiply the length of building surface to be covered by its width to get the number of square feet. Divide this by 100 to get the number of "squares" needed. To provide for lap, it is best to increase this amount by 15 to 20%.

After allowance for lap, most sheets cover a 24-inch width. To estimate number of sheets needed, determine number of two-foot widths necessary to cover the area from side to side. Then estimate number of sheets and most desirable lengths required to reach the other way. A gable roof 40 feet long, would require 20 widths of 2 ft. each. If slope of each side is 13 ft., one 8 ft. and one 6 ft. sheet would reach from ridge to eave and leave 10 inches for end lap and 2 inches for overhang. To cover one side of this roof, then, 20 sheets 8 ft. long and 20 sheets 6 ft. long would be needed.

PRECAUTIONS WITH GALVANIZED SHEETS

Both corrugated and V-crimped roofing can be laid over old shingles or old composition roofing, or on nailing strips across the rafters or directly on the rafters; but in the latter case 2 x 4 headers, staggered for easy nailing, should be set in between the rafters (fig. 32). The spacing of these headers should be not over 18″ on center for No. 28 gauge sheets and not over 24″ for No. 26 gauge sheets. In the case of old shingle roofs it is much better to remove the shingles and renail the sheathing, which often is loose.

When nailing strips are used, a secure hold for the nails can be obtained with 1 x 6 hardwood boards or 2 x 4 softwood planks, either of which should be properly spaced according to the gauge of the sheets as indicated above. On the top edge of the rafters, between the nailing strips, fasten 1 x 2 or 2 x 2 pieces to give the sidelaps solid support and also to provide good hold for the side-lap nailing (fig. 33). This is most important.

Lay the sheets properly. Start laying the sheets along drip eaves at end of the building opposite direction of prevailing winds, so that wind and rain will blow over the laps and not under them (fig. 34). If possible, use different lengths of sheets so as to stagger end laps on adjacent rows, as shown, to hold sheets more securely. It is usually more convenient to lay the sheets in complete vertical rows.

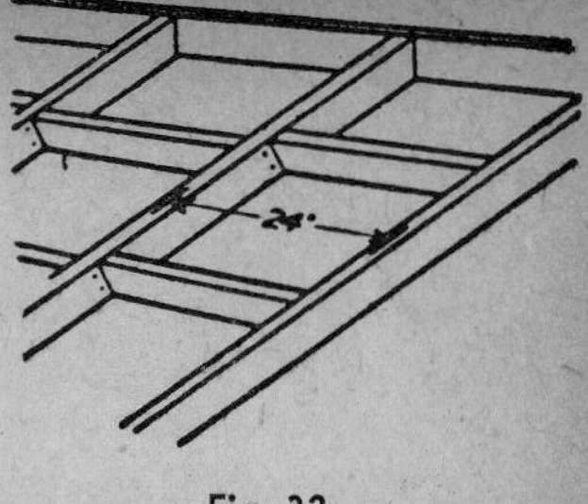

Fig. 32.

The end sheet should be bent over the gable end and nailed to the edge of the roof sheathing or the ends of the nailing strips. A simple way is to bend the edge of the sheet to a right angle, or sharper, before it is put on; with V-crimped sheets, flatten the "V" at one edge, or cut it off before making this bend. At the drip eaves, let the sheets project about 3″.

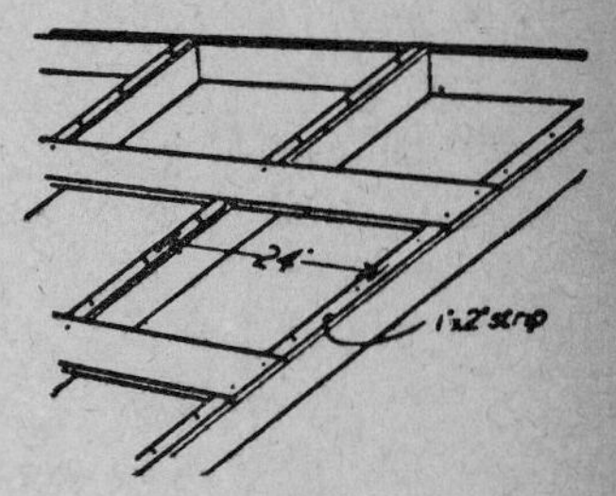

Fig. 33.

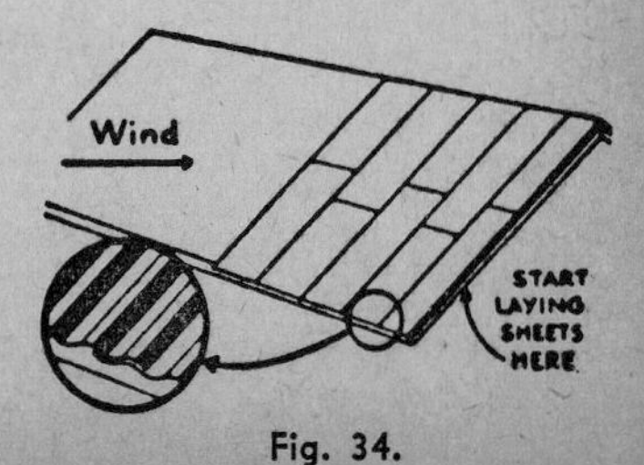

Fig. 34.

The side-lap of 1¼″ corrugated sheets, 26″ wide, should consist of one and one-half corrugations. 2½″ corrugated sheets are made in widths of 27½ and 26″. Use only the 27½″ width, lapped one and one-half corrugations, for roofing; use the 26″ width, lapped one corrugation, for siding. If the 26″ width only is available for roofing, it is desirable to reverse each sheet as laid, so that a side lap of 1½ corrugations is obtained. When so applied the coverage in width per sheets is 22¾″. The side-lap of V-crimped sheets is determined by the number of V-ridges at the sides of the sheet. The end lap on all sheets should be about 6″.

Use special end flashing where the top of a "lean-to" roof adjoins a vertical wall. Sidewall flashing should be used where the gable end of a roof adjoins a vertical wall. The top edge of the flat portion should be fastened to the wall with galvanized roofing nails spaced about two inches apart. Greater security against leakage can be obtained if a thick metallic paint is put between the flat part of the flashing sheet and the wall before nailing.

For finishing the peak of a roof, use 2-ounce coated galvanized ridge roll. Special galvanized forms are made for use at the breaks in gambrel roofs; they fit under the top sheet and over the lower one, and when properly nailed, prevent leakage at the break.

Drive all nails slightly off center on a slant, through the tops of the corrugations.

ZINC PAINT

To lengthen the service life of galvanized roofing and siding and improve its appearance, use metallic zinc paint consisting of approximately 80% metallic zinc dust and 20% zinc oxide. The liquid part of the pigment is usually linseed oil, but it may be made up with soybean oil, or other vehicle.

Metallic zinc paint sticks fast to metal surfaces and effectively prevents rusting. Its tough paint body is sufficiently elastic to adjust itself to the frequent expasion and contraction of metal surfaces, so that it does not crack or peel. It completely obscures even the darkest backgrounds which is important when painting metal surfaces discolored by rust. One gallon will cover from 600 to 800 square feet—often twice as much area per gallon as other types of paint sometimes used on metal surfaces. Metallic zinc paint is now being produced by a large number of reputable paint manufacturers. Most manufacturers supply this paint in the natural color, a soft gray which closely resembles the appearance of a weathered galvanized sheet. However, certain producers can furnish the paint in dark red, green, and possibly other colors.

How to paint galvanized roofing. The usual practice is apply metallic zinc paint as soon as the first sign of rust appears, or when the roofing shows the dark discoloration indicating that rust is imminent. However, the application of this paint to sheets that are relatively new is also recommended because the durability of the sheets is thereby increased. Previous to painting, the whole roof should be put in good physical shape. It is important that the roofing be clean; the usual exposure to the weather keeps roofing fairly clean but if any leaves, dirt or other foreign material has accumulated either on the roofing itself or in the valleys and gutters, it should be completely removed with a broom. If the metal is badly rusted remove the loose rust by wire-brushing.

The roof may have been painted previously with some other kind of paint. In such a case make sure that all loose, crumbly parts of the paint are completely removed by wire-brushing. Any part of the old coat of paint that adheres strongly to the roofing surface will probably not cause trouble.

The best job of painting can be done in warm, dry weather, for the paint will spread better and will dry more readily. Do not apply paint when a shower is imminent or when the roof is damp with dew.

How many coats? Two coats of paint, properly applied, are always better than just one coat. Metallic zinc paint is very opaque and gives excellent coverage; and there may be a temptation to let the job go with just one coat. Ordinarily one coat will be very satisfactory; and from experience in a number of cases a service life of from six to eight years can be expected. However, a two-coat application can be expected to give more than double such service and will likely not cost twice as much as one coat, because the second coat is applied more rapidly and the paint will go further than on the first coat. Moreover, with all equipment at hand and the job under way, preparation and overhead costs will be lower for the second coat than for the first.

If economy is necessary, and the condition of the roof is not too bad, "spot" painting, followed by a single coat, may be acceptable. In this practice those parts of the roof which definitely show rust are given a first coat, and when this dries the whole roof is given a final coat.

General directions for painting. The owner who does his own painting will probably use his own equipment, ladders, scaffolding, etc. The average man has enough mechanical ability to erect the right kind of scaffolding, but special precautions should always be taken to provide one that is safe and strong. On buildings with high roofs of long slopes, long ladders can be laid on the roof and hooked over the ridge to provide good footing for the workman and at the same time prevent damage to the roof. Planks to which cross-pieces are strongly nailed will serve the same purpose. Make sure that the ladders or step-planks are safely and securely anchored; ropes or cables thrown over the ridge and fastened on the other side are a good means of thus obtaining firmness and security.

Cooperative spray paint equipment is available in some localities

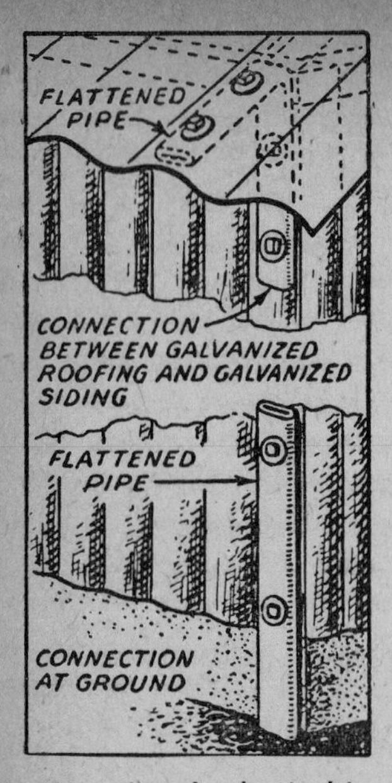

Fig. 35. A section of galvanized iron pipe, flattened, bent as shown, and bolted or riveted to the sheets, forms a satisfactory conductor between metal roofing and siding. Similarly, pipe can be used to connect galvanized siding to the ground.

and when so available can be advantageously used. Metallic zinc paint works satisfactorily in the spray gun although slight thinning with turpentine may sometimes be necessary. The cost of applying paint by this method is generally lower than with brush painting. In applying the metallic zinc paint with a brush, bear in mind that this paint, because of superior opacity and other qualities, should be brushed out thoroughly. A coverage of 600 to 800 square feet per gallon is not at all unusual on warm, dry days.

Take good care of brushes and other painting equipment.

PROTECT AGAINST LIGHTNING

Buildings covered with galvanized metal, correctly installed and properly grounded (connected with the earth by approved lightning conductors), have nearly perfect protection from lightning. It is a relatively simple matter to install adequate grounds for the protection of metal covered buildings from lightning. Most metal roofs on buildings are not properly grounded. The galvanized sheets constituting the roofing or siding of the building must be tightly nailed so that the whole area is in complete and permanent contact. Galvanized roofing should be grounded at diagonally opposite corners of the building. On buildings with large roof areas, the roof may well be grounded at each corner. In any case, the distance between grounds around the building should not be over 100 feet. Grounding conductors should be solidly and permanently connected with the metal roofing itself and should extend into the ground to the depth of permanent moisture—6 to 10 feet.

Grounding cable of copper or steel (at least ⅜ inch diameter) can be attached firmly to roofing with at least two ⅜ inch machine bolts (fig. 35). Bent at right angles an inch below the head, these bolts are extended downward through holes drilled in the ridge of a corrugation and on through the sheathing. When nuts are drawn up, cable is securely held in the valley of the corrugation. Eighteen inches of cable should be in contact with the roof. Cable clamps fasten lower end of cable to a galvanized pipe (1½ inch) or rod (⅝ inch), which has been driven into the ground to the depth of permanent moisture.

Chimneys, cupolas, etc. must be protected by a galvanized rod or pipe extending at least one foot above, and solidly attached to both chimney and roofing. To protect galvanized siding, it should be connected to roofing at all four corners and on large buildings at intervals not greater than 50 feet.

STOP LEAKS IN OLD ROOFS

Leakage seldom occurs in galvanized roofing laid properly. Should leakage occur at the laps, re-drive all nails carefully, but not so hard as to dent the ridge of the sheet. Space nails 6 to 8 inches apart on side laps and 5 to 6 inches apart on end laps. If nails will not hold, use sheet metal screws to draw the sheets together tightly. First punch a small hole through the sheets, and insert the screw which can then be screwed in. (Fig. 36.)

In many cases, use of asbestos wicking, which is readily obtainable from hardware or supply dealers, will be of great benefit. Lay a strip of this between the sheets at the lap; then, when the nails are driven or the screws drawn up, the wicking forms a permanent gasket between sheets which will effectively seal the lap against all moisture. This is especially effective on roofs of low pitch. (Fig. 37.)

Leakage that occurs through old or enlarged nail holes can most readily be stopped by blocking the holes with a good roof caulking compound, which can be purchased in a color to match the roof or made up by mixing metallic zinc dust and linseed oil to a thick putty-like paste; some loose asbestos fibre added to the compound will make it stronger and more durable.

Use the right nail. Galvanized roofing should be applied with special nails made for the purpose. Use only nails having the following characteristics: shank of nail of the threaded or drive screw type which insures maximum holding power;

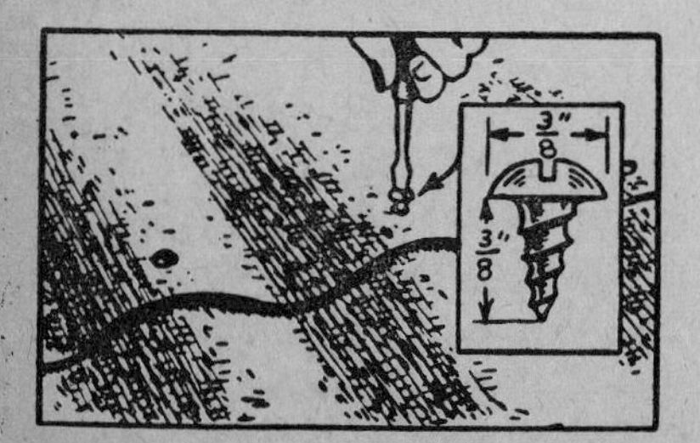

Fig. 36. Use self-tapping sheet metal screws to draw sheets tight together at end laps or other places where a good hold for nails is not provided.

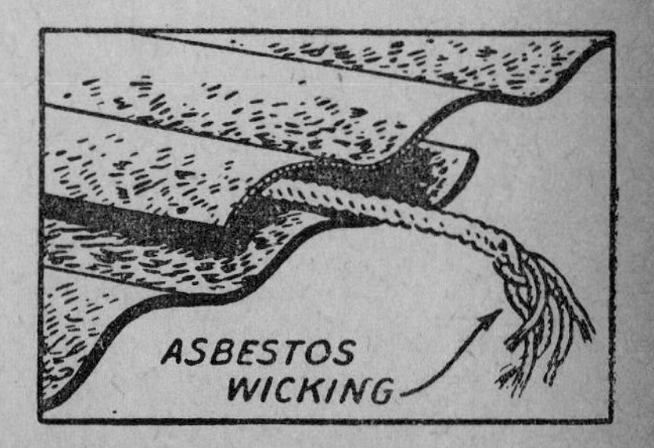

Fig. 37. Nailing or screwing sheets tightly down after a strip of asbestos wicking or other mineral fibre has been laid between will often prevent leakage at laps.

lead under the nail head so that when nail is driven, lead will be forced into the hole around the nail forming a moisture seal; nail heavily zinc-coated for protection against rust; and it should be of proper length to give adequate holding. Nails give greater holding power when driven at a slant and slightly off center of the ridge of the sheet. Never drive nails in the bottom of the corrugations. Ordinary wire nails do not hold well, do not seal holes, and leakage will almost invariably occur. In renailing old roofs, remove loose nails and replace with screw type nails driven at a different angle to penetrate new wood for maximum holding power.

Proper storage. Improper storage of new galvanized sheets may cause permanent damage to the zinc coating and shorten the rust-free service life of the sheets by years. In fact, just one week of poor storage may cause as much deterioration as a full year of use as roofing or siding. Here's what happens. If sheets are left piled flat in the vicinity of the building where they are to be used, and they become wet, electrolysis takes place forming white zinc carbonate which reduces the zinc coating on the sheets and hastens corrosion. For proper storage, place the sheets on end in a dry building separated from the ground by a floor or supporting timbers.

NEW ROOFS OVER OLD

If new roofing can be laid over the old, the work can be done without exposing the interior of the building to the weather, the old roofing will provide additional insulation, and the labor and mess incident to removal will be avoided. Before selecting new covering, however, the roof framing should be examined to determine whether it has sufficient strength to carry the additional weight. Slate, clay tile, and built-up roofing are heavy, and when they are used the rafters may require bracing. When the framing cannot be properly braced it may be necessary to remove the old covering to lessen the load. It is advisable, and in most cases necessary, to remove metal coverings, and if slate or other brittle roofings are selected the old covering should be taken off so as to provide a smooth deck, because any unevenness will cause breakage.

There is a decided advantage in not removing old roll roofing and composition shingles, especially when roofing with rigid shingles or metal, provided the old covering is not puffy or badly wrinkled and the framing will sustain the additional weight. Puffy areas should be slit or cut so that the old roofing may be nailed flat. When the new covering is metal, rosin-sized paper should be laid over the old surface. Old nails at the eaves may have to be removed and new strips of wood fastened under the edges of the sheathing to provide for secure nailing when turning down the edges of the roofing. If the new strip is not provided the additional nails may split the edges of the sheathing and permit the wind to blow under the new covering.

In preparing an old wood-shingle surface for a new covering, all curled, badly warped, and loose shingles should be nailed flat and secure, and all protruding nails should be driven down. Old shingles along the edges of eaves and gables, for a distance of 2 to 4 inches, should be removed to permit the installation of a wooden strip or slat so as to conceal the old shingles at the edges of the roof and provide a firm nailing base. Open valleys should be filled in with wood strips level with the old shingle surface, on top of which a new valley sheet should be laid. A piece of bevel siding, thin edge down, should be nailed along each side of the ridges to provide a substantial nailing base.

The same procedure followed in laying shingles on a new solid-deck roof structure is used in overroofing, even though the original shingles were nailed on lath or strips. That is, no attention need by given the manner in which the nails penetrate the old roof beneath—whether they strike the strips or not—for with the longer nails (fivepenny, 1¾ inches long) that are used, complete penetration and anchorage is obtained.

ROOFING NAILS

Experience has proved the wisdom and economy of using rust-resistant nails. Even low-grade roofing will not give maximum service when lightweight steel nails are used. Only hot-dipped zinc nails, copper, heavily galvanized cut nails, or those of the special type recom-

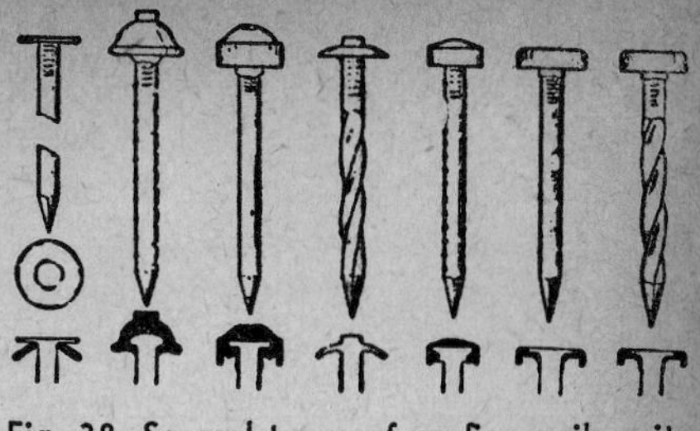

Fig. 38. Several types of roofing nails suitable for zinc-coated roofing. Heavy black sections show location of lead.

mended by the roofing manufacturer should be used. They should be long enough to penetrate about three-fourths the thickness of the sheathing.

GUTTERS AND DOWNSPOUTS

While gutters are not necessary it is advisable to have them to prevent the formation of water holes around the building. If a cistern is used, gutters are imperative. They may be of wood built in as a part of the cornice and lined with metal, or they may be metal troughs hung along the eaves (fig. 39).

In regions of heavy snowfall the outer edge of the gutter should be

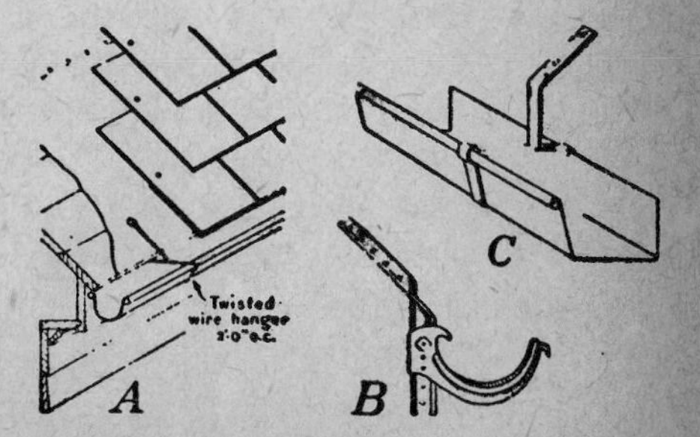

Fig. 39. Hanging eaves trough: **A**, circular section; **B**, adjustable hanger; **C**, rectangular section.

half an inch below the extended slope of the roof to prevent snow banking on the edge of the roof and causing leaks. The hanging gutter is better for such construction.

The expense for maintenance can be considerably reduced if the gutters are built-in and are of first-class material, though the first cost is somewhat greater. Built-in gutters should be wide and shallow with the outer face sloped to prevent being broken by ice forming in the gutter and should be built entirely outside the wall line of the building. Gutters should slope about one-sixteenth inch per foot toward the outlet.

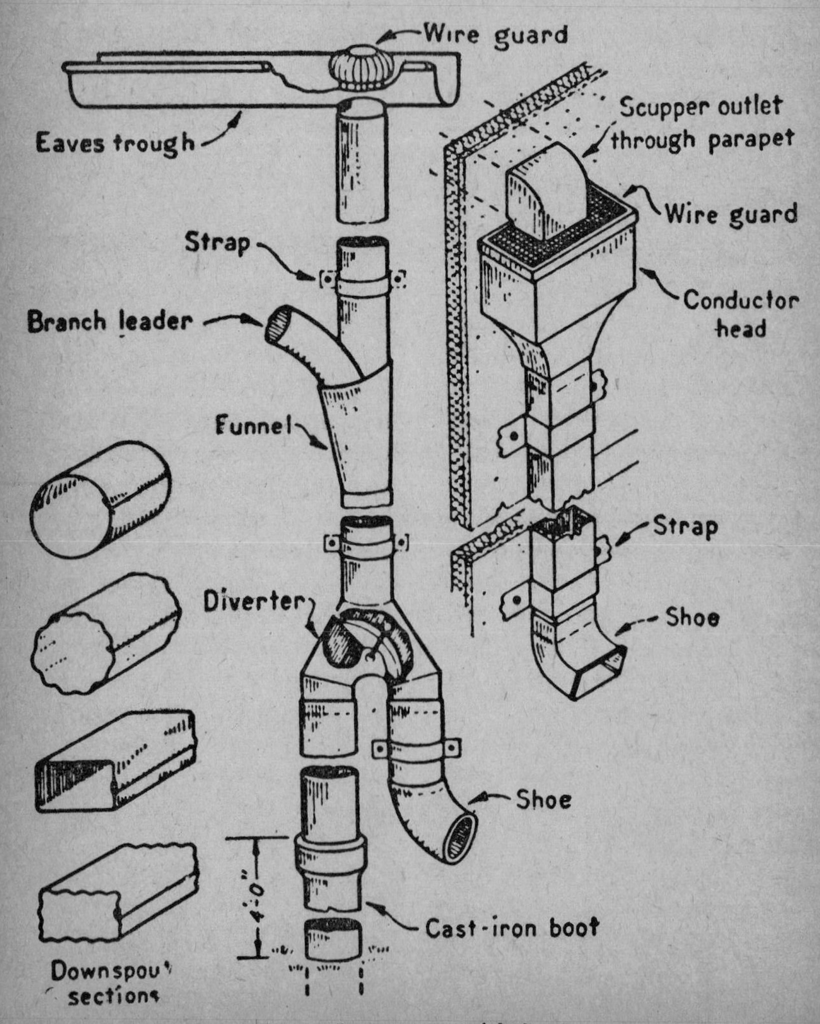

Fig. 40. Downspouts and fittings.

Downspouts (fig. 40) should be large enough to remove the water from the gutters. A common fault is to make the gutter outlet the same size as the downspout. At 18 inches below the gutter a downspout has nearly four times the water-carrying capacity of the inlet at the gutter; therefore an ample entrance to the downspout should be provided. Conductor heads or funnels are readily available from roofing establishments and should be used where branch downspouts converge or at scuppers of flat roofs. Wire baskets or guards should be placed at gutter outlets to prevent leaves and trash collecting in the downspouts.

SIZES OF EAVES, TROUGHS, AND DOWNSPOUTS FOR VARIOUS ROOF AREAS

Roof area (square feet)	Eaves-trough diameter	Down-spout diameter
	Inches	Inches
100–800	4	3
800–1,000	5	3
1,000–1,400	5	4
1,400–2,000	6	4

In cold climates where water will freeze if it should stand in the downspouts, the use of corrugated instead of plain metal will save much trouble and probably prevent the pipe bursting because of expansion.

The lower end of each section of downspout should be fitted inside the next lower section, for if fitted over it water will flow out at the joint. Sometimes the joints are soldered tight, but for general practice this is not advisable, because normally slip joints eliminate the necessity of special provision to take care of expansion and contraction. Downspouts should be soldered to the straps that fasten them to the building. The lower end should be fitted with a shoe, or turn-out, when the water is to be wasted on well-drained ground, with a cast-iron pipe connection or boot when water is to be diverted into a storm sewer, or with a rain switch or diverter for excluding from a cistern the first part of each rain.

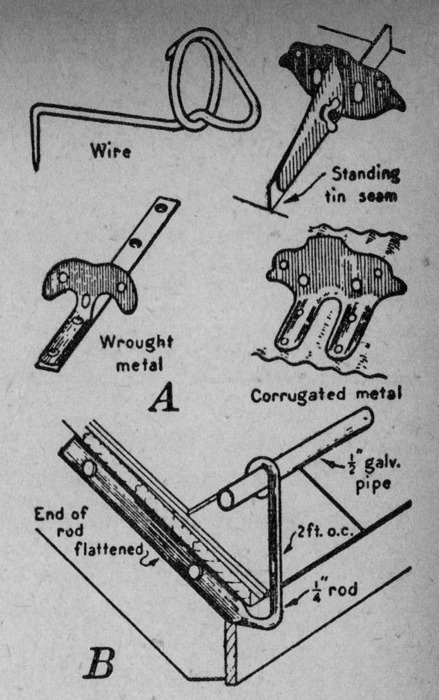

Fig. 41. Snow guards: **A**, Common types installed at time of placing roof covering; **B**, home-made type.

Intense rains occur periodically in certain localities but do no great harm to the contents or surroundings of structures if the gutters overflow for the duration of the storm. For the sake of economy, gutter and downspouts will be ample in size if

Fig. 42. Method of inserting new slate.

large enough to carry off only normal storm water flow.

Sizes of downspouts and half-round gutters are suggested in the above table for general use. Local conditions, of course, may require larger sizes. Downspouts should be placed not more than 40 feet apart in the length of a gutter.

SNOW GUARDS

Snow guards should be used on steep roofs in cold climates to prevent sheets of ice or snow from sliding. Sliding ice will frequently tear off the roof covering, break gutters, or imperil the life of a person walking under the eaves. Several common types of guards, that can be secured to the sheathing so as to project through the joints in the roofing are illustrated in figure 41. The guards should be staggered in three rows near the eaves and 6 to 12 inches apart.

SLATE ROOF REPAIR

The most common repair on slate roofs is the replacement of broken slates. Remove the broken slate and cut the nails with a ripper or hack saw blade. Insert a new slate of the same color and size as the broken one and nail it through the vertical joint of the next course above. (Fig. 42.) Drive the nail about 2 inches below the butt of the slate in the second course above. Force a 3 by 6 inch or larger strip of copper, galvanized iron or painted tin under the course above the nail and bend the strip slightly concave to hold it in place. The strip usually will extend about 2 inches under this course and will cover the nail and extend 2 inches below it.

REPAIRING ROOFS

Periodic inspections should be made to detect breaks, missing shingles, choked gutters, damaged flashings, and also defective mortar joints of chimneys, parapets, coping, and such. At the first appearance of damp spots on ceilings or walls, a careful examination of the roof should be made to determine the cause, and the defect should be promptly repaired. When repairs are delayed, small defects extend rapidly and involve not only the roof covering but also the sheathing, framing, and interior finish.

Many of these defects can be readily repaired by a practical man so as to keep water from the interior and to extend the life of the roof. Large defects or failures should be repaired by men familiar with the work because on many types of roofs an inexperienced man can do more damage than he is likely to repair.

Leaks are sometimes difficult to find, but an examination of the wet spots on a ceiling furnishes a clue to the probable location. If near a chimney or exterior wall the leak is probably caused by defective or narrow flashing, loose mortar joints, or dislodged coping. On flat roofs the trouble may be the result of choked downspouts or an accumulation of water or snow on the roof higher than the flashing. On sloping roofs at valleys and at the junction of dormers with the roof, corroded, loose, or displaced flashing and rotten shingles may be found. Defective and loose flashing is not uncommon around scuttles, cupolas, and plumbing vent pipes. Roofing deteriorates more rapidly on a south than on a north exposure, which is especially noticeable when wood or composition shingles are used. The south slope of a roof should be watched closely for leaks.

Wet spots under plain roof areas are generally caused by holes in the covering. Frequently the drip may occur much lower down the slope than the hole. Where attics are unsealed and roofing strips have been used holes can be detected from the inside by light shining through. If a straw is stuck through the hole it can be located from the outside. Sometimes gutters are so arranged that when choked they overflow into the house, or ice accumulating on the eaves will form a ridge that backs up melting snow under shingles. Leaky downspouts permit water to splash against the wall and the wind-driven water may find its way through a defect into the interior.

WHAT'S WRONG?

Seven errors in building a roof are shown in the three drawings in

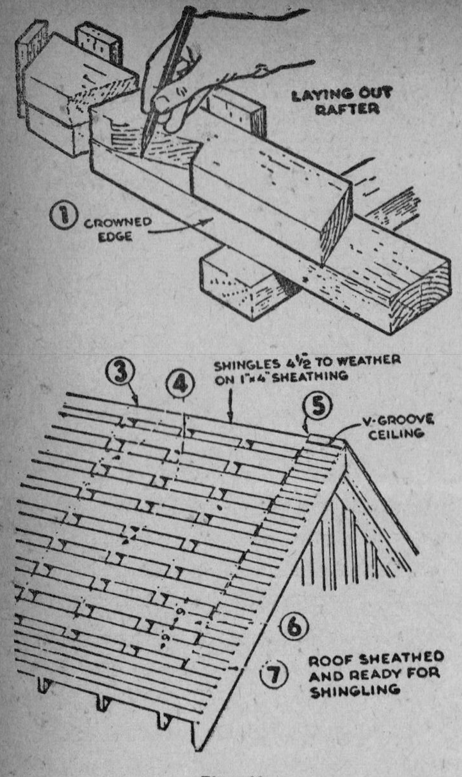

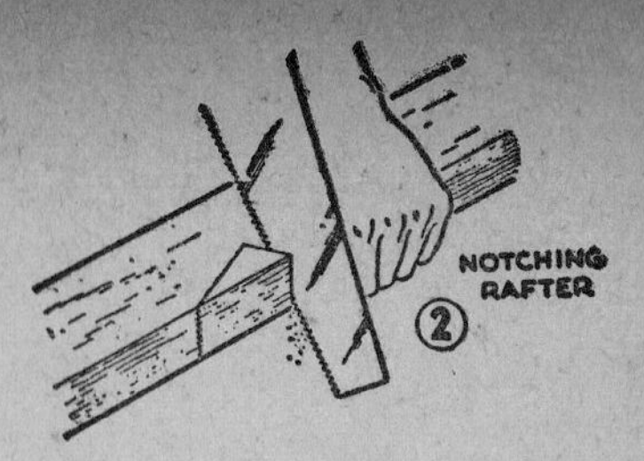

Fig. 43.

figure 43—one each in the drawings above and five in the bottom one. The points at which to look for errors are numbered. When you have decided on what you consider wrong, see the answers below.

Answers.

1. Since rafters are laid crowned edge up, the piece being marked for notching should be turned over.

2. Make the rip cuts first so the waste will help support the saw.

3. A filler strip must be nailed at each side of the ridge to provide solid nailing for rip-rap or other trim.

4. Joints should be staggered with no more than two together.

5. About half the ceiling boards should extend to the second rafter for more support for the barge board.

6. Spacing on 4½″ centers permits uniform shingle nailing and extends shingle life.

7. The shingle molding is missing.

Fig. 44. Wire mesh placed over gutters will prevent leaves and other debris collecting in the gutters and causing rust, rot or sags. The wire is held in place by turning the edges down over the edges of the gutters.

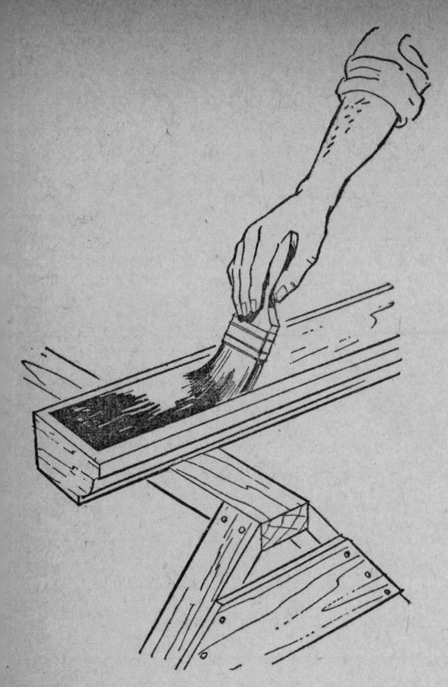

Fig. 45. The life of wood gutters can be increased by coating the inside of the gutter with roofing compound or lining the inside with non-corrosive metal. If metal is used, be sure that all joints are soldered to prevent moisture seeping through to the wood.

Fig. 46. Diagrammatic map of the United States showing the northern limits of damage by subterranean termites (**A-A**) and north limits of nonsubterranean or dry-wood termites (**B-B**).

FLASHINGS

Ridges and hips. The beveled copper ridge covering of the type illustrated in figure 49 must be made slightly larger than the wood supports or difficulty will be experienced in springing the metal in place. A copper drive screw is recommended for attaching the copper, after which the hemmed edge is malleted to 45° covering the nails.

The flanges of the copper ridge roll must be made to fit tight against the slate. The copper drive screws are used to fasten the metal with a 24″ spacing.

The intersection of the slate at the ridge line is flashed with 8 ft. lengths of inverted V-shaped concealed flashings covered by the top courses of slate.

A separate piece of concealed copper flashing, formed in an inverted V-shape, is laid in with each course of slate on hips, and occasionally on ridges, as shown. On hips, lugs are turned on the high side to prevent the copper from slipping below the slate.

Vents. The copper vent-pipe flashing is turned under the slate or the shingle at the top and passes over the slate or shingle at the bottom (fig. 50). The sheet has a ½″ edge folded over on both sides of the vent, to prevent water from driving under the slate. The copper cap is slit every ¾″, turned down in the pipe 2″ and soldered. Special pipe fittings provided with a space to receive base flashing are frequently used, and where the pipe terminates

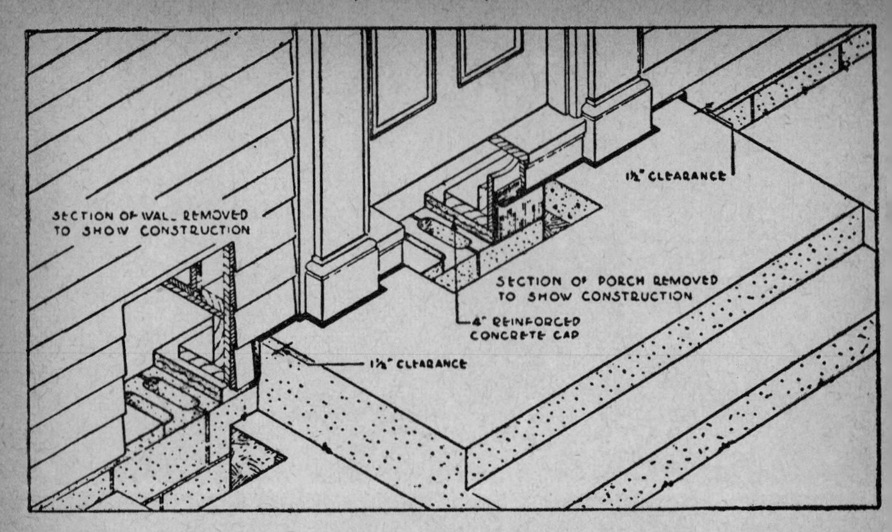

Fig. 47. Special protection at porch against hidden termite attack by the use of a metal apron to isolate the entrance platform and soil or fill from the building. Note the projection of the apron at the top and ends of the porch slab. This is essential. The reinforced poured concrete cap on the masonry foundation wall prevents hidden access through the wall back of the apron or beyond the porch.

without a thread a threadless cap may be used. In another method shown, a flat piece of copper cut to a radius is neatly soldered to the cap flashing tube.

Intersections. Figure 51 shows method of flashing at a change of slope in slate or shingle roofs. The copper on the upper side extends to just short of the nailing line and is

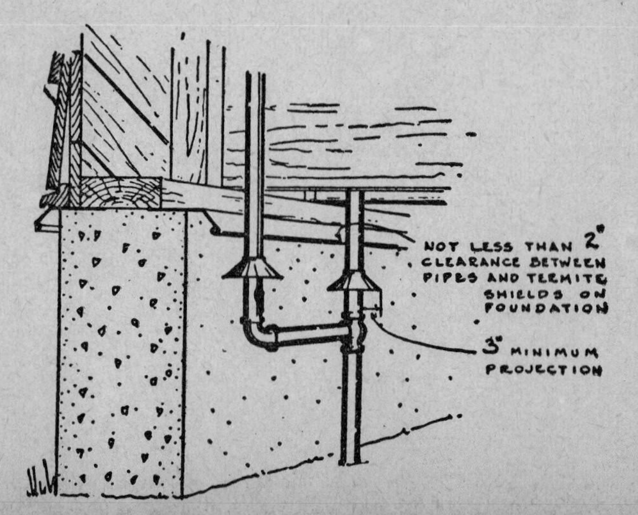

Fig. 48. Termite shields around pipes and at top of foundation wall.

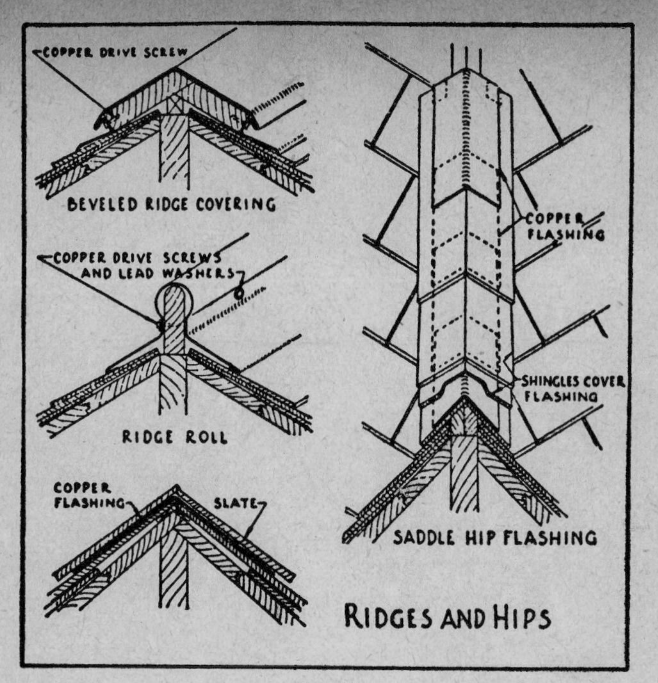
COPPER DRIVE SCREW
BEVELED RIDGE COVERING
COPPER DRIVE SCREWS AND LEAD WASHERS
RIDGE ROLL
COPPER FLASHING
SLATE
COPPER FLASHING
SHINGLES COVER FLASHING
SADDLE HIP FLASHING
RIDGES AND HIPS

Fig. 49.

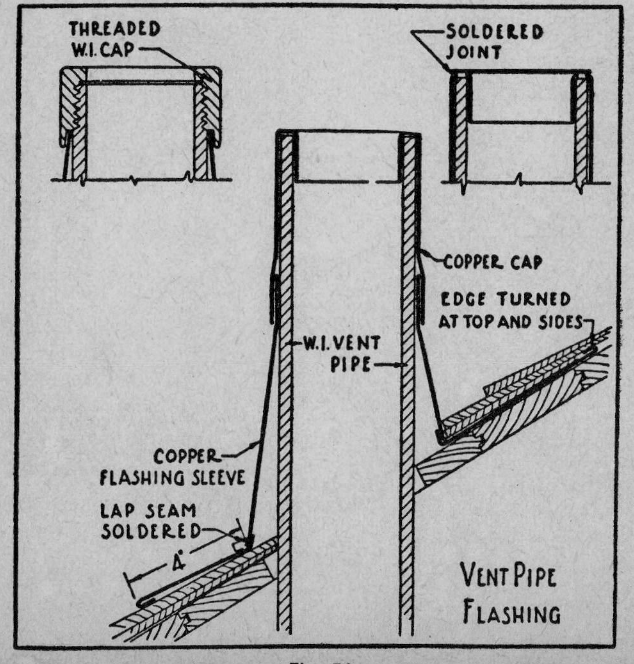
THREADED W.I. CAP
SOLDERED JOINT
COPPER CAP
EDGE TURNED AT TOP AND SIDES
W.I. VENT PIPE
COPPER FLASHING SLEEVE
LAP SEAM SOLDERED
4"
VENT PIPE FLASHING

Fig. 50.

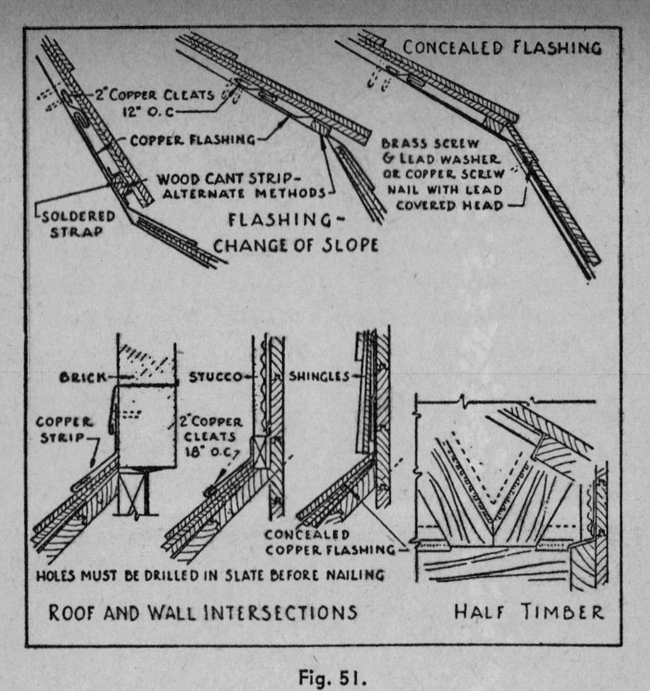

Fig. 51.

cleated. On the lower slope it extends 4″ to cover the nail holes. A cant strip, held with soldered straps, raises the butts of the last course on the upper slope to permit proper laying of the shingles. The exposed end is screwed down with copper alloy screws through washers, if extended down so far that its own rigidity is not enough to keep the sheet tight.

If a closed joint is desired, concealed flashing is used. On the upper slope the construction is the same as described above. On the lower slope the copper is carried down between the shingles.

Windows. Window heads and sills are flashed as shown in figure 54. The sill flashing for a dormer shown at *A* is put in position before the frame is set. Water bar at *B* and copper flashing at *C* in both sketches are also inserted before window frames are set. Flashing at window head is set on top of window frame before the slate or shingle work is started. Flashing, as at *D* behind stucco should be carried up not more than one inch so as not to break the keying between the stucco and its base. A termite barrier shield for frame construction is shown. In some instances this serves as a damp-proof course as well. Detail of anchor bolt *E* is shown in enlarged sketch at bottom.

Doorways. Doorways are flashed with copper, as shown in figure 55. In sections *XX* and *YY* the cornice cover is nailed back above the water line into the brick joints or wood framing, to prevent the copper from becoming detached. Where the cap flashing is not walled in as the brickwork progresses, it is possible to make the cap flashing on each side of the pediment in one piece as shown at bottom in section *X′-X′*.

The beveled exposed part of the wash of the pediments over each pilaster should be covered with copper for protection. At the outer edge the base flashing or roofing should be fastened over an edge strip, several varieties of which are shown.

REMOVING EFFLORESCENCE

With watertight walls and good flashing (fig. 56) installations, efflorescence which appears on the walls soon after the building is erected, or repaired, will quite often disappear after several rains. If not, water applied with a stiff scrubbing brush will frequently do the job. If either

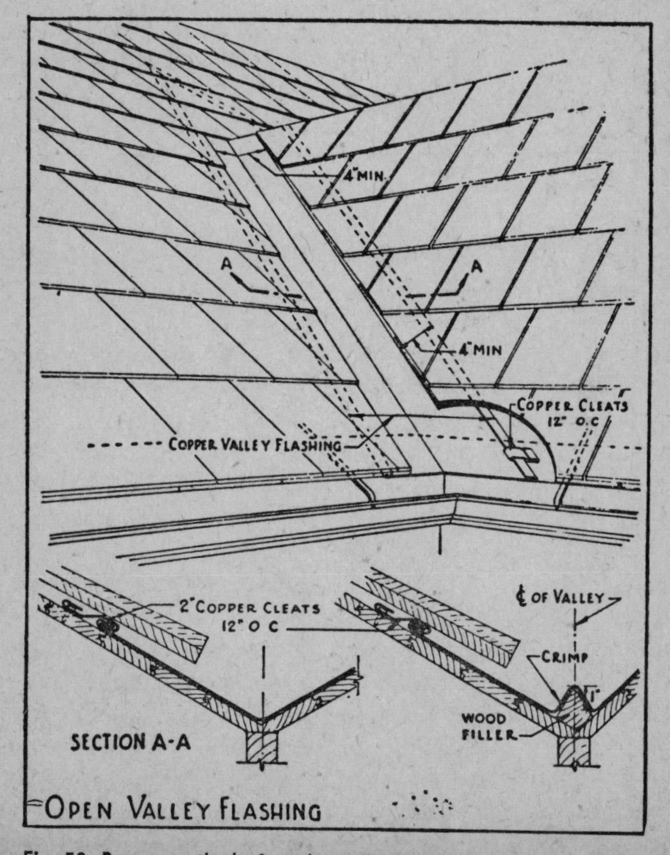

Fig. 52. Proper method of applying flashing to an open roof valley.

of the above two procedures does not completely remove the efflorescence, the wall should be wetted, then scrubbed with water containing not more than one part of muriatic (hydrochloric) acid to nine parts water. Immediately thereafter, the wall should be thoroughly rinsed with plain water. It is very important to water rinse the wall *both* before and after acid washing. All frames, trim, sills or other installations adjacent to the masonry should be carefully protected against contact with the acid solution. The workman should protect his skin from contact with the acid solution and wear rubber gloves. It is also sometimes desirable to give the surface a final washing with water containing approximately 5% of household ammonia.

Efflorescence in masonry construction is evidence of the use of materials containing soluble salts along with design and workmanship which permit excess water to enter the wall. It can be prevented by the

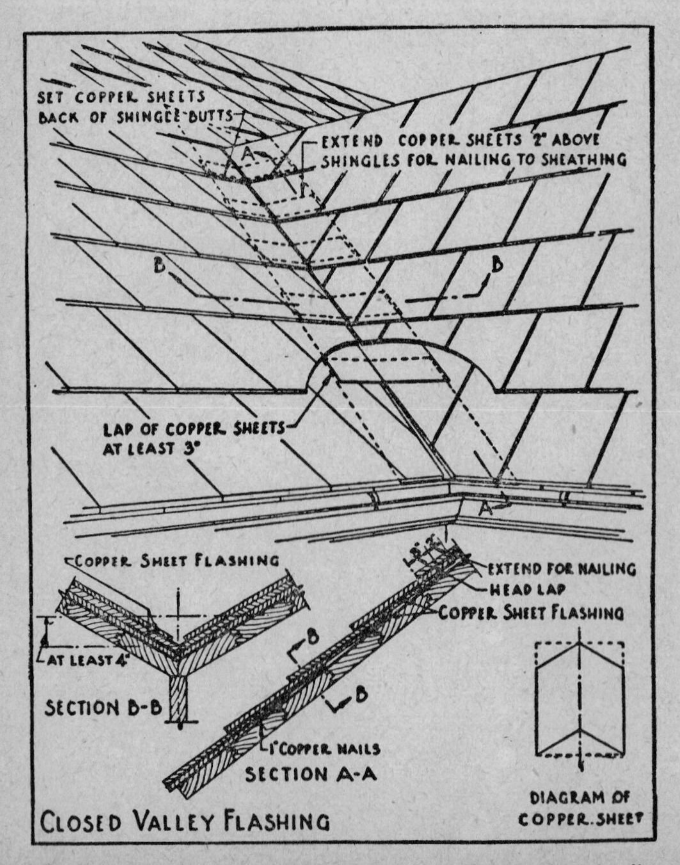

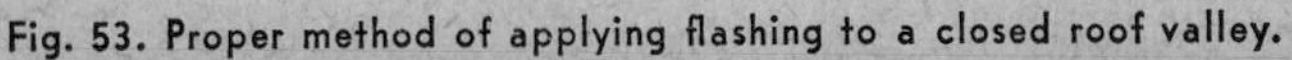
Fig. 53. Proper method of applying flashing to a closed roof valley.

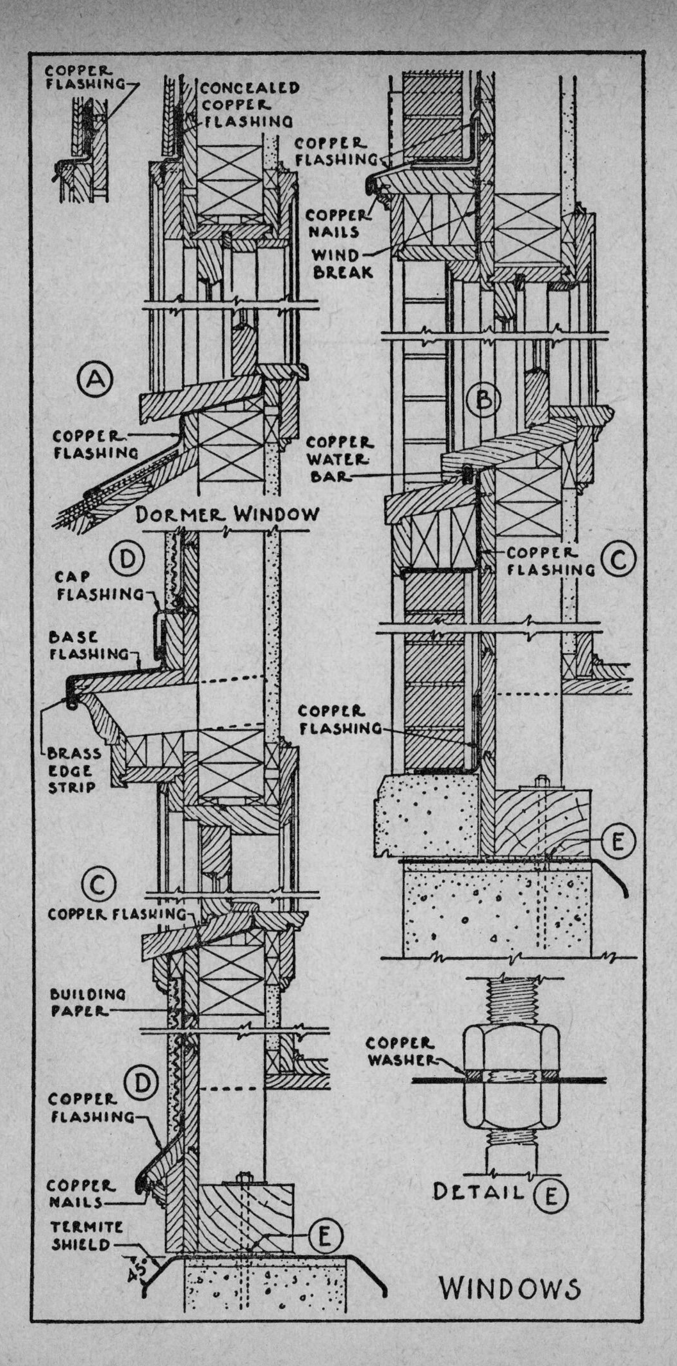
COPPER FLASHING
CONCEALED COPPER FLASHING
COPPER FLASHING
COPPER NAILS
WIND BREAK
A
B
COPPER FLASHING
COPPER WATER BAR
DORMER WINDOW
D
CAP FLASHING
BASE FLASHING
COPPER FLASHING
C
BRASS EDGE STRIP
COPPER FLASHING
E
C
COPPER FLASHING
BUILDING PAPER
COPPER WASHER
D
COPPER FLASHING
COPPER NAILS
DETAIL E
TERMITE SHIELD
E
45°
WINDOWS

Fig. 54.

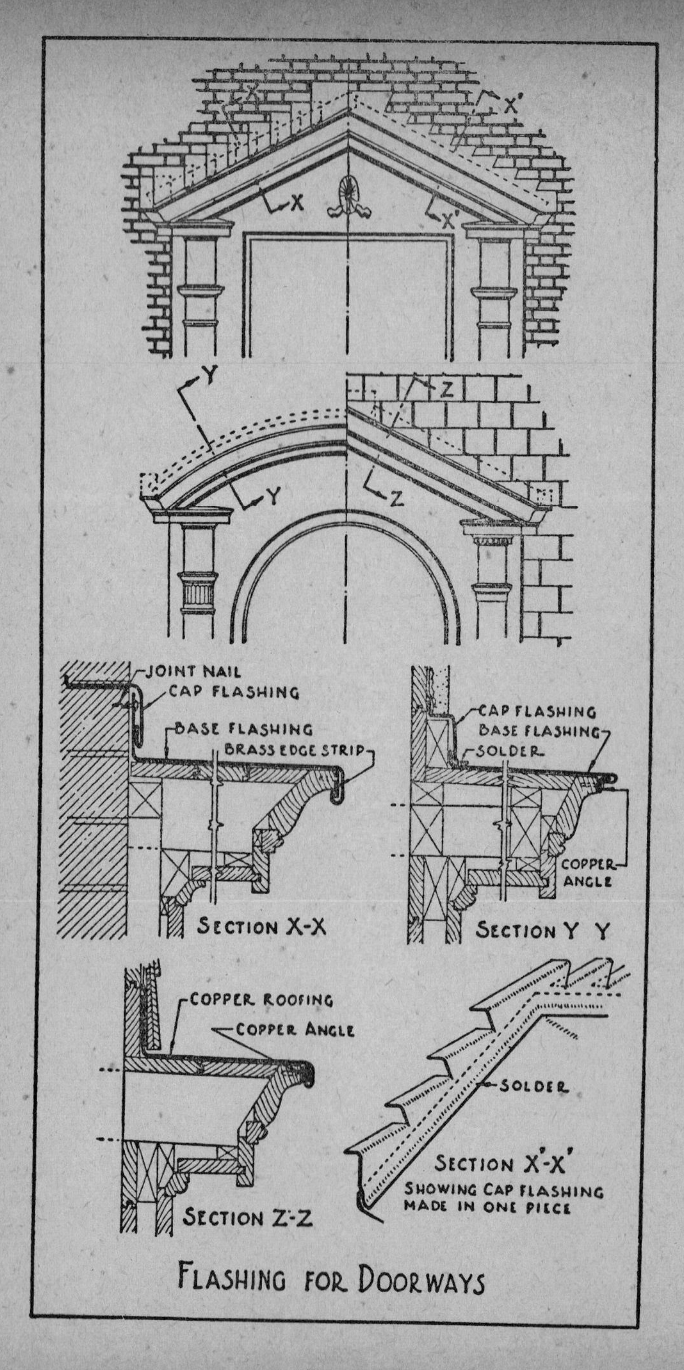
X
X'
X
X'
Y
Z
Y
Z
JOINT NAIL
CAP FLASHING
BASE FLASHING
BRASS EDGE STRIP
SECTION X-X
CAP FLASHING
BASE FLASHING
SOLDER
COPPER ANGLE
SECTION Y Y
COPPER ROOFING
COPPER ANGLE
SECTION Z-Z
SOLDER
SECTION X'-X'
SHOWING CAP FLASHING
MADE IN ONE PIECE
FLASHING FOR DOORWAYS

Fig. 55.

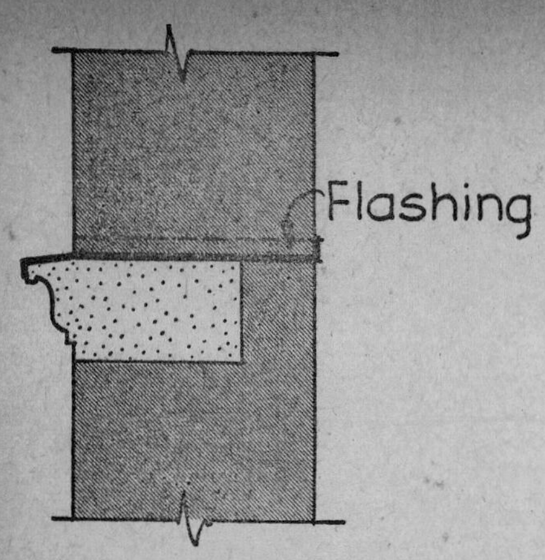

Fig. 56. Non-corrosive metal flashing should be used in masonry walls in all joints directly above projections. If flashing is not installed at these points, there is a good chance of moisture penetrating the masonry at this point.

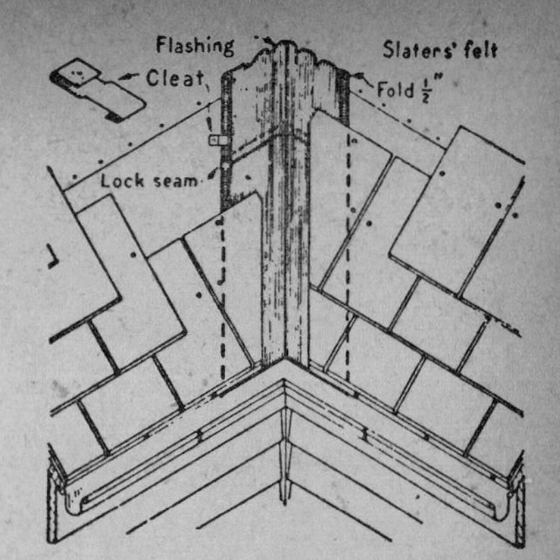

Fig. 57. Open valleys flashed with metal. The figure shows a slate roof.

use of suitable materials, proper design and good workmanship.

MORE FLASHING TIPS

Cross seams should be locked and soldered to form one continuous strip for open valleys. Proper methods of fastening the metal to the sheathing with cleats is shown in figure 57. Closed valleys where slate or asbestos shingles are used may be flashed with a continuous metal strip under the shingles (fig. 58, *A*) or by building in short pieces of metal as the shingles are laid (fig. 58, *B*). Where nail holes of slate or asbestos shingles come over the metal,

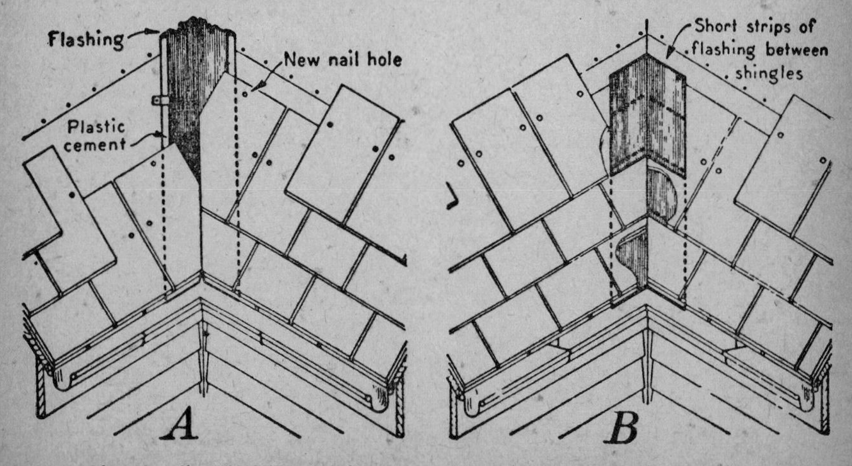

Fig. 58. Closed valley flashings: **A,** long sheets under shingles; **B,** short pieces intermembered with shingles.

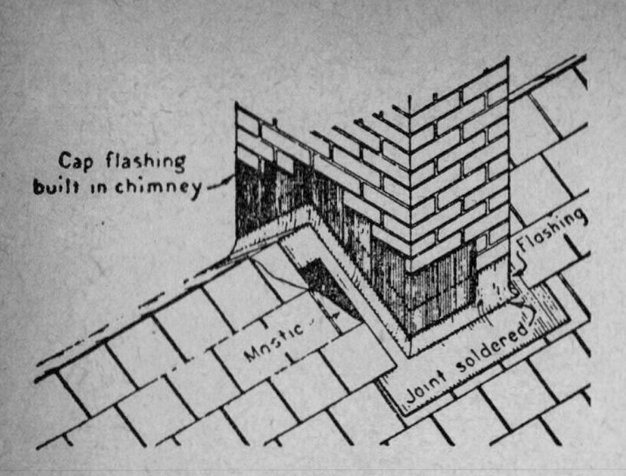

Fig. 59. The cap flashing for a chimney is built into the joints when the masonry is laid and is folded down at least 4 inches over the base flashing that is installed when the roofing is placed.

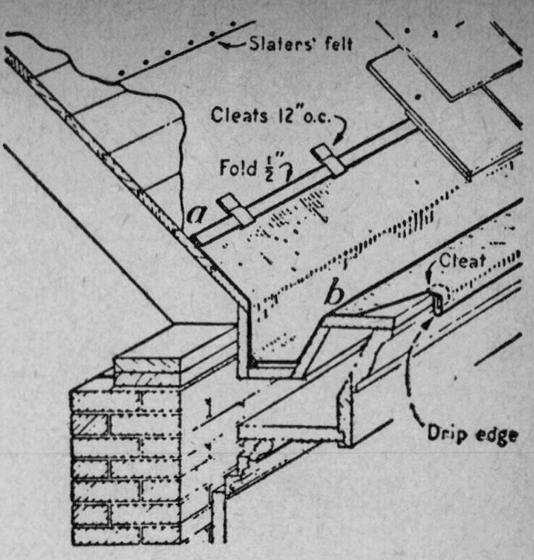

Fig. 60. Built-in gutter.

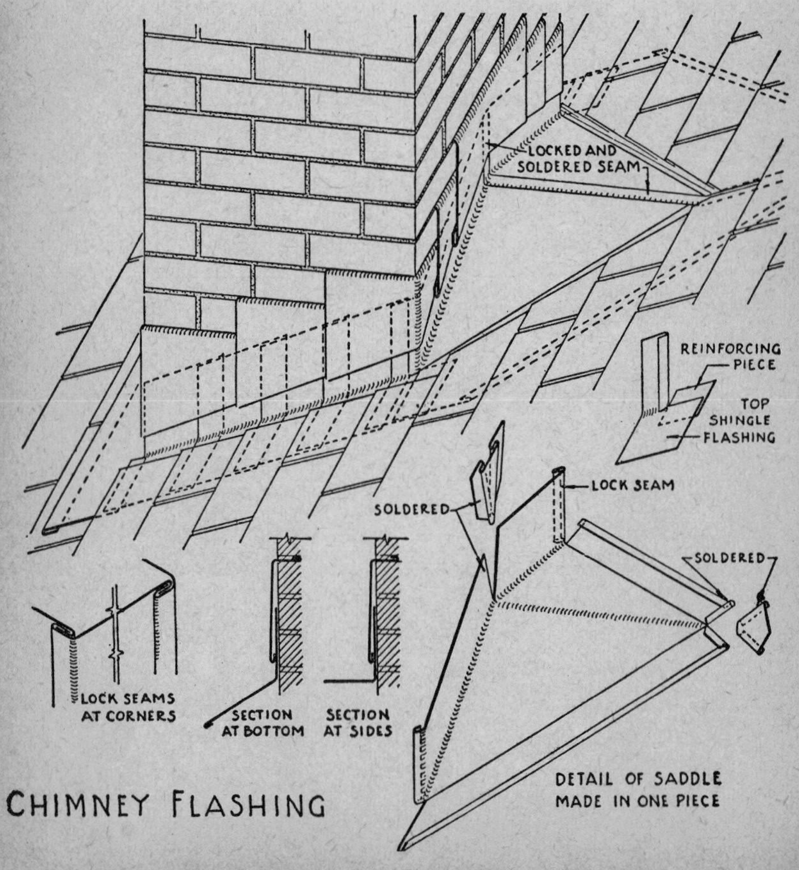

Fig. 61. Details of saddle for flashing chimney.

new holes should be provided in each slate so it can be secured by two nails located outside the metal. It is good practice to embed in plastic cement the edges of slate and other coverings that lap the flashing.

When flashing extends up vertical surfaces it must be counterflashed with cap flashing. The cap flashing should not be fastened rigidly to the base flashing. In masonry walls a groove half an inch high and about

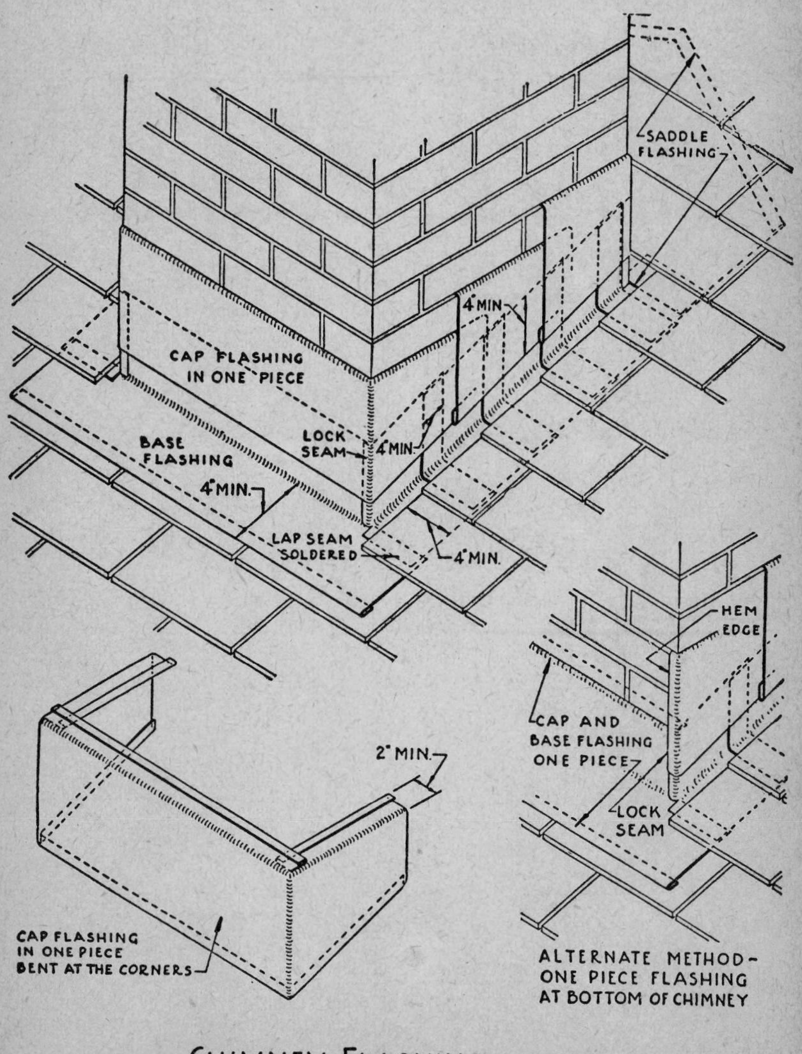

Fig. 62. Base and cap copper flashing for chimney.

1½ inches deep, into which the cap flashing is folded, wedged, and calked, is provided 6 inches or more above the roof level. In brick walls the cap flashing may be built into the joints, or a reglet tile may be used, and in concrete walls the groove may be formed at the time of pouring the concrete. The method of flashing at a chimney located on the ridge is shown in figure 59. A cricket, or saddle, should be provided behind a chimney located on a slope, to divert water coming from the upper part of the roof and to prevent ice forming behind the chimney. Plumbing vent stacks should be flashed so as to permit the pipe to settle or expand without causing leaks.

ATTIC INSULATION

Heat rises. Therefore, attic insulation is of the greatest importance. Properly installed, attic insulation can reduce fuel bills by 33 1/3%. It is also a barrier against summer's sun, keeping upper rooms as much as 10° cooler. Fortunately, the attic insulation job is the easiest and most economical to perform. Under normal conditions, you can do the job yourself *in less than a day.*

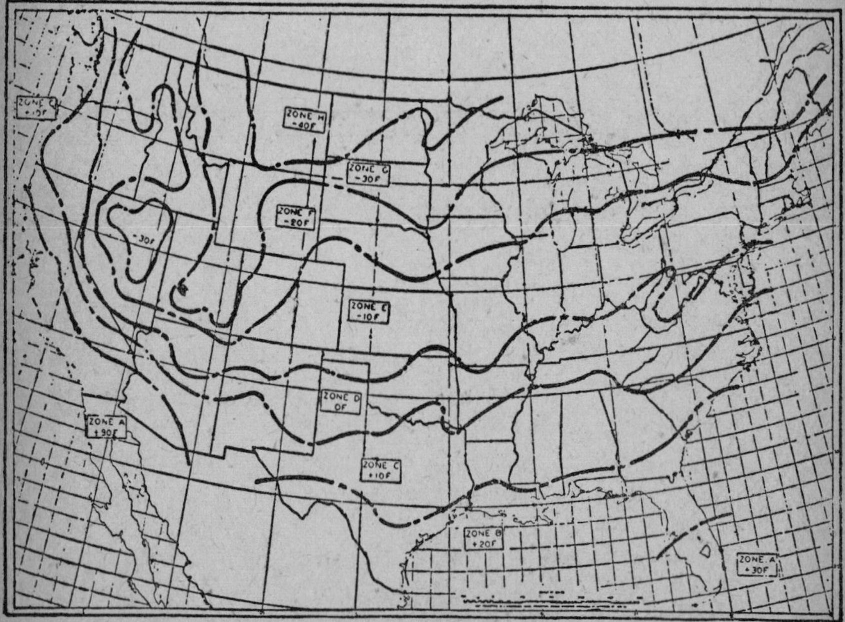

From Heating Ventilating Air Conditioning Guide 1947 Chap. 14

Fig. 63. Average minimum temperatures of the United States by zones, for use in designing the insulation requirements of houses.

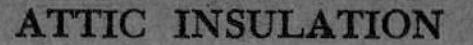

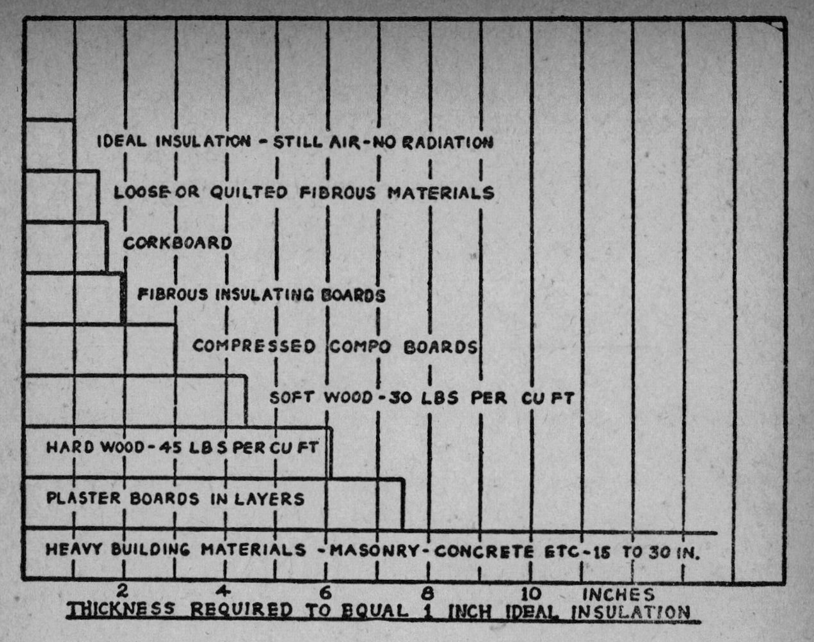

Fig. 64. Thicknesses of various materials having equivalent heat-insulating values.

APPROXIMATE FUEL SAVINGS IN DWELLING HOUSES

[Expressed in percentage of fuel which would have been required for similar house without insulation or weather stripping]

	Saving
	Per cent
No insulation, weather stripped	15 to 20
Same, with double (storm) windows	25 to 30
½-inch insulation, not weather stripped	20 to 30
½-inch insulation, weather stripped	About 40
½-inch insulation, with double windows	About 50
1-inch insulation, not weather stripped	30 to 40
1-inch insulation, weather stripped	About 50
1-inch insulation, with double windows	About 60

[Expressed in percentage of fuel which would have been required for similar house without insulation, but with weather stripping]

	Per cent
With double windows, no insulation	10 to 15
½-inch insulation only	25 to 35
½-inch insulation, with double windows	40 to 45
1-inch insulation only	35 to 45
1-inch insulation with double windows	50 to 55

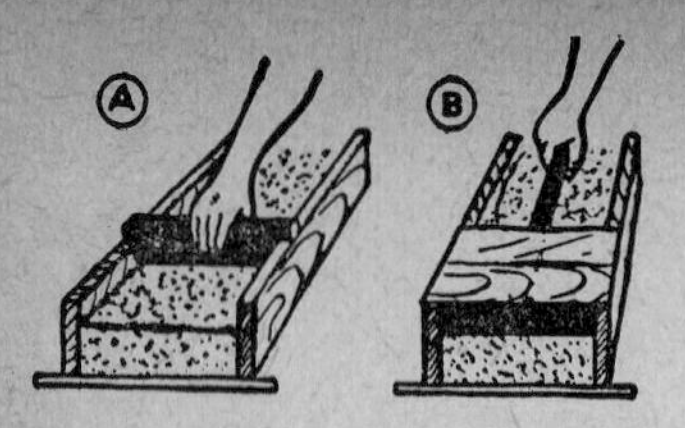

Fig. 65. Tools for attic floor insulation.

TOOLS FOR INSULATING ATTIC FLOOR

Figure 65 shows the only tools necessary for loose fill insulation of the attic. For an unfloored attic, a small hand rake cut to proper depth is used (*A*, fig. 65). The two extended "ears" which ride the top of the joists will give a uniform insulation coverage. In floored attics, the rake is made without "ears" and has a hand knob (*B*). Floor boards are taken up at convenient intervals. Insulation is then poured in the space and worked under the flooring to the proper depth by running the rake over it. The rake is held flush to the underside of the boards.

Fig. 66

INSULATING YOUR PRESENT HOUSE

One of the simplest and most satisfactory ways to insulate your present home is to use the type of blanket insulation which comes in com-

Fig. 67

Fig. 68

pressed rolls, ready to be expanded, cut to fit, and nailed or stapled in place. This material is easily handled by the home handyman, and is one of the most efficient methods of home insulation. Besides its protection against heat loss, it also provides a vapor barrier.

This roll insulation comes in various widths to fit varying spacing of joists, studs, or rafters. For a standard 14½″ space, order 16″ rolls; for 18½″ space, order 20″ rolls; for 22½″ space, 24″ rolls.

WHERE TO PLACE INSULATION

If your attic has no floor, the place to put this roll insulation is between the joists, as shown in fig. 66.

One roll of Double Thick insulation insulates 100 square feet; 8 rolls, or 800 square feet, will insulate the attic floor of the average 6-room house. To determine the amount of roll insulation required for your attic floor, simply multiply the length of the attic by the width to get the number of square feet of floor space. Then divide by 100 to get the number of rolls of insulation you will require.

If your attic is floored, or if you intend to make it into living space later, it is better to insulate the sloping roof and gable ends (fig. 67). Usually this area is 1½ times the area of the floor; the average 6-room house requires about 12 rolls.

If your attic has been made into rooms, with floor, side walls and ceiling, this same insulation can be installed in the sloping roof and attic room ceiling as shown in fig. 68. This requires access to the space above the ceilings and to the space behind the wall. The insulation blanket is then expanded to installed length, fastened at one end to the floor plate, and fed up between the sloping wall and the roof boards to the ceiling area.

In any installation, be sure to provide louvers or other ventilation.

CUTTING AND MEASURING

The only tools needed to install roll insulation are a pair of long shears to cut the material to required length, a hammer or stapler, to fasten the material in place. 1¼″ blue plasterboard nails are recommended if the ends are to be nailed. ½″ staples are recommended for the ends, and ¼″ staples for the flanges. Fiber strips for fastening the ends are included in each roll.

Take the measurements as indicated in fig. 69A and add 6 inches to allow for end fastening. The blankets may be expanded fully before installing or expanded during installation. Where the work area is readily accessible, it is probably easier to expand it during installation. Where special widths are required to fit narrow spaces, the material can be rolled up and cut with a saw (fig. 69B).

INSULATING WALLS

1. Fasten the blanket at the top with fiber strip (fig. 70A).
2. Hold strip on other end (fig. 70B).

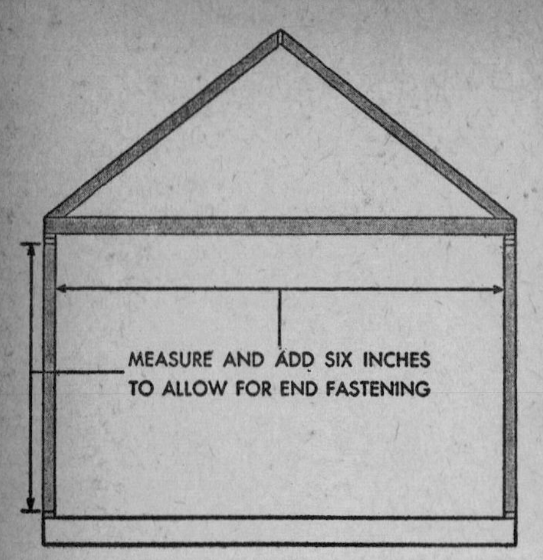

Fig. 69A

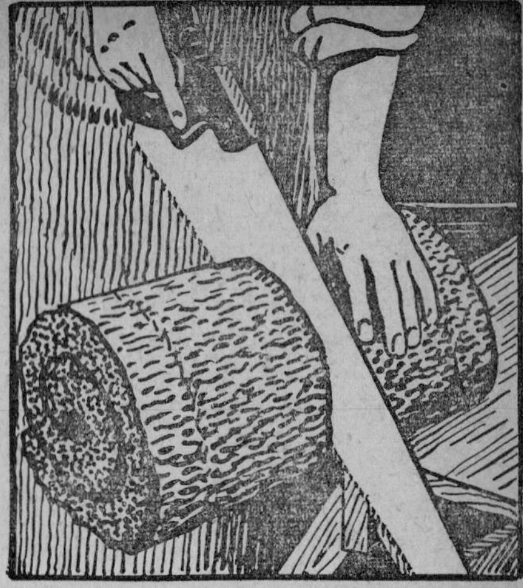

Fig. 69B

3. Pull blanket tight. Cut off any excess length and fasten at bottom using fiber strip, as in fig. 70C.

4. Then fasten the flanges (fig. 70D).

INSULATING CEILINGS

From Above

1. Run the blanket over bridging (fig. 71), keeping it 1″ from wiring.

From Below

1. Attach blanket end near eave. Expand to partition head and attach, or run blanket all the way across to other eave and fasten (fig. 72). Always face cover sheet down.

2. Staple flanges near fold to keep blanket tight. If necessary, use occasional fiber strips opposite each other.

3. For convenience, two lengths of blanket may be used and joined at a partition.

Fig. 70A Fig. 70B Fig. 70C Fig. 70D

Fig. 71

Fig. 72

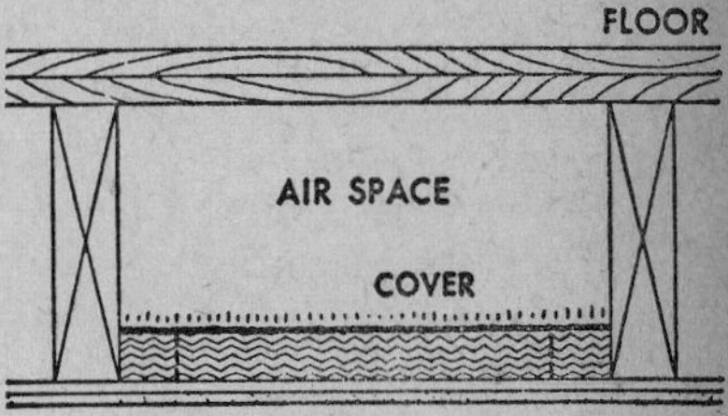

FLOOR

AIR SPACE

COVER

Fig. 74

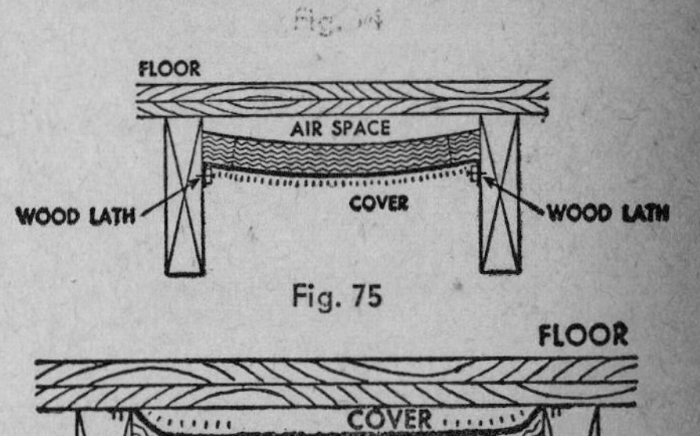

Fig. 75

FLOOR

COVER

ASPHALT BACKER BOARD

Fig. 76

INSULATING ATTICS

1. Follow the instructions for installing blanket insulation in ceilings from below.

2. Use props to hold blanket in place while stapling flanges (fig. 73).

INSULATING FLOORS

Blanket insulation may be placed over cold or unexcavated sections of the building to good advantage.

Fig. 74 shows the installation over cold sections of the building.

Over unexcavated areas, the insulation maybe installed from below when the floors are already in place, as in fig. 75, or from above, before the flooring is laid, as in fig. 76.

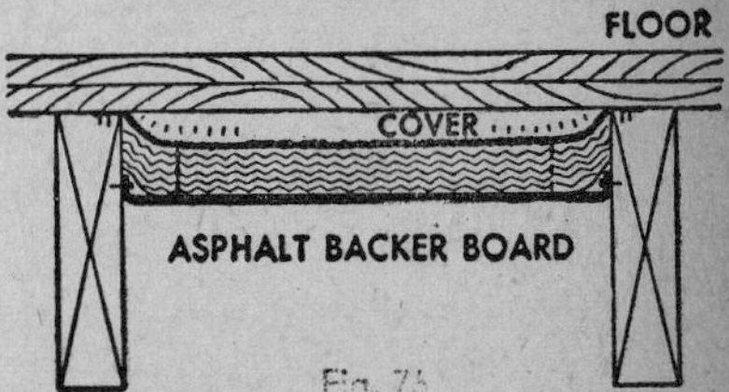

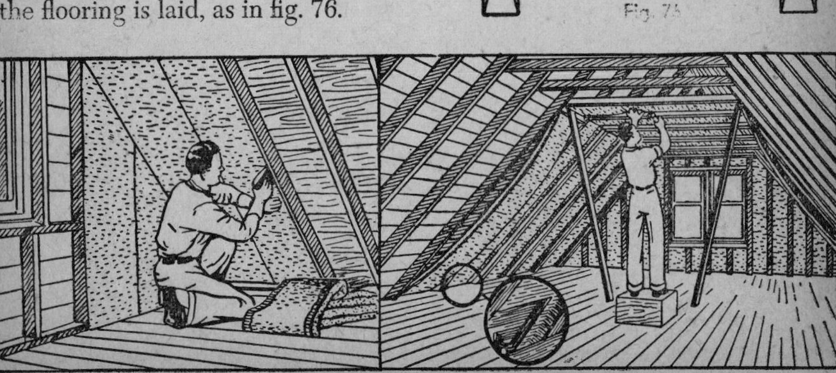

Fig. 73

Fig. 77

Fig. 78

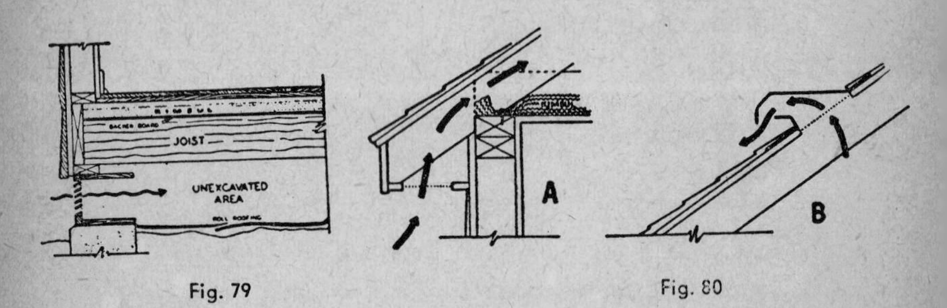

Fig. 79

Fig. 80

VENTILATION

The spaces between any insulation and the roof should always be ventilated with air from outdoors to carry off excessive heat in hot weather and to ventilate out excessive water vapor in very cold weather. Unexcavated spaces should always be ventilated.

1. Louvers in both gable ends ventilate the space between insulation and roof as in figs. 77 and 78.

2. Louvers ventilate a space between floor and ground as in fig. 79. Add a layer of roll roofing if the ground is damp.

3. Screened openings in eaves (fig. 80) (A) allow air to enter above the insulation and leave through the roof vents (B).

ATTIC VENTILATION

A widely practicable means of improving comfort conditions in summer is the use of an attic ventilating fan, an extension of the very old practice of ventilating for cooling by simply opening windows. The equipment usually consists of a fan, from 1½ to 4 or 5 feet in diameter depending on the size of the house, installed in a window, door or other opening in the attic to exhaust the air out of the house. Open doors, and sometimes grills installed for the purpose, permit passage of air from other parts of the house to the attic. A usual practice is to start the fan during the early hours of the eve-

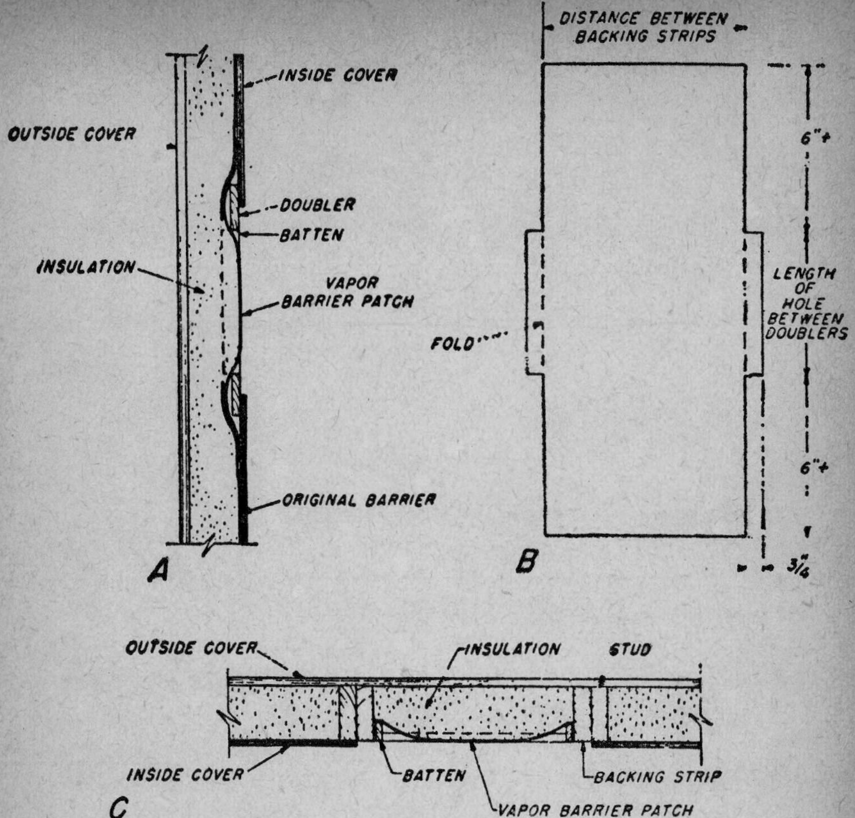
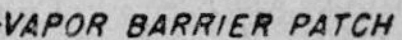

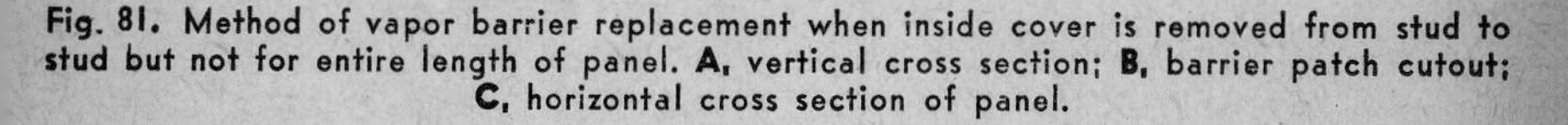

Fig. 81. Method of vapor barrier replacement when inside cover is removed from stud to stud but not for entire length of panel. **A**, vertical cross section; **B**, barrier patch cutout; **C**, horizontal cross section of panel.

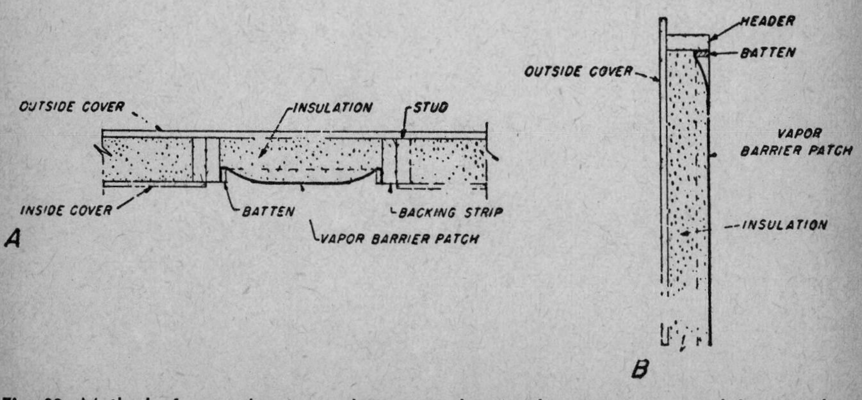

Fig. 82. Method of vapor barrier replacement when inside cover is removed from stud to stud entire length of panel. **A**, horizontal cross section; **B**, vertical cross section of panel.

ning and so take advantage of the temperature drop which usually accompanies nightfall. With the fan operated only at night and the house closed during the day, the house may be kept cooler than the average temperature out-of-doors. Manufacturers of fans designed for this purpose recommend sufficient fan capacity for one air change in the house in from 2 to 5 minutes. This will result in a breeze through any open window or door. Lesser capacities would also be of some benefit. A small ventilating fan in the kitchen to expel heat and vapor in-

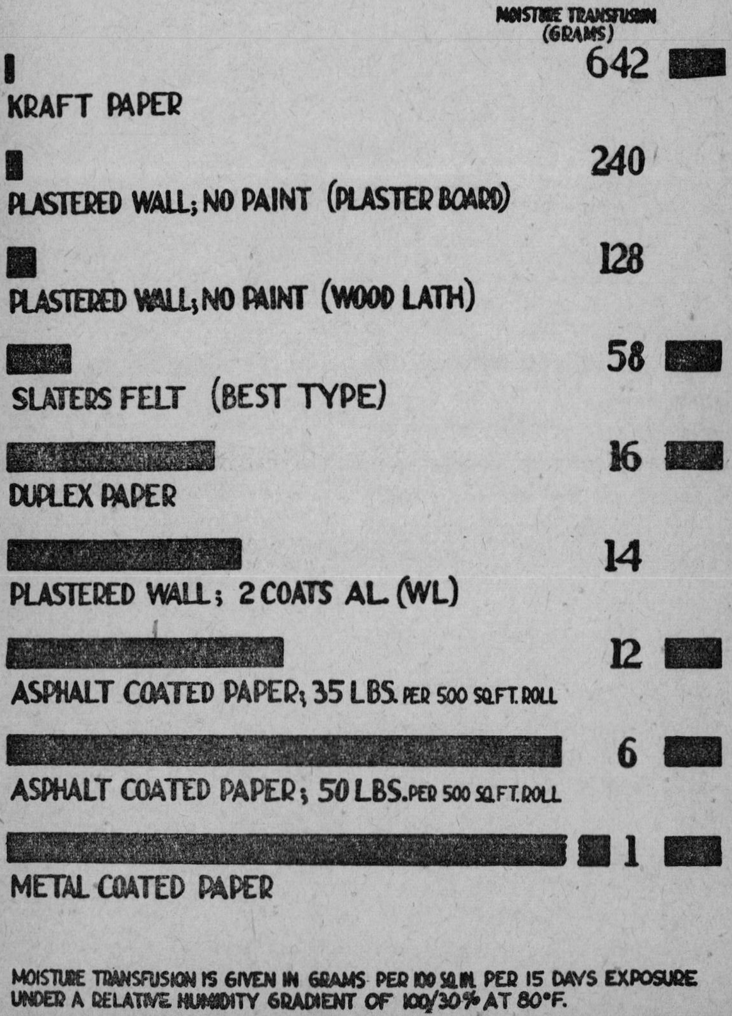

	MOISTURE TRANSFUSION (GRAMS)
KRAFT PAPER	642
PLASTERED WALL; NO PAINT (PLASTER BOARD)	240
PLASTERED WALL; NO PAINT (WOOD LATH)	128
SLATERS FELT (BEST TYPE)	58
DUPLEX PAPER	16
PLASTERED WALL; 2 COATS AL. (WL)	14
ASPHALT COATED PAPER; 35 LBS. PER 500 SQ.FT. ROLL	12
ASPHALT COATED PAPER; 50 LBS. PER 500 SQ.FT. ROLL	6
METAL COATED PAPER	1

MOISTURE TRANSFUSION IS GIVEN IN GRAMS PER 100 SQ.IN. PER 15 DAYS EXPOSURE UNDER A RELATIVE HUMIDITY GRADIENT OF 100/30% AT 80°F.

Fig. 83. Relative efficiency of various materials as moisture barriers in walls.

Fig. 84. A small portable vacuum cleaner with the bag detached provides an easy method of distributing loose fill insulation in hard-to-get-at areas.

cident to cooking often materially improves comfort conditions in the whole house.

It is important to make all openings through which the air must pass ample in size. Considerable volume of air can be moved at low speed with little power.

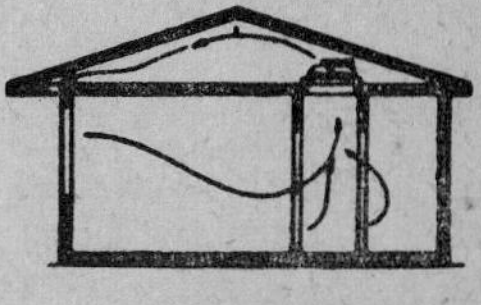

Fig. 85.

EXHAUST FAN INSTALLATION

Figure 85 shows the best location for attic floor exhaust fans in two-story and single-story dwellings. Such installations are ideal where there is limited clearance in the attic, where most of the attic is occupied by rooms, or with flat roofs. Exhaust fans are also useful in recreation and game rooms where occasional ventilation is required.

Figure 86 illustrates the method of framing for an attic floor installation, and figure 87 shows two different types of installation.

Attic and basement stairwell installation. The attic stairwell installation saves valuable attic floor space since the stairway is partially inclosed to form the suction box. The attic door is left open during

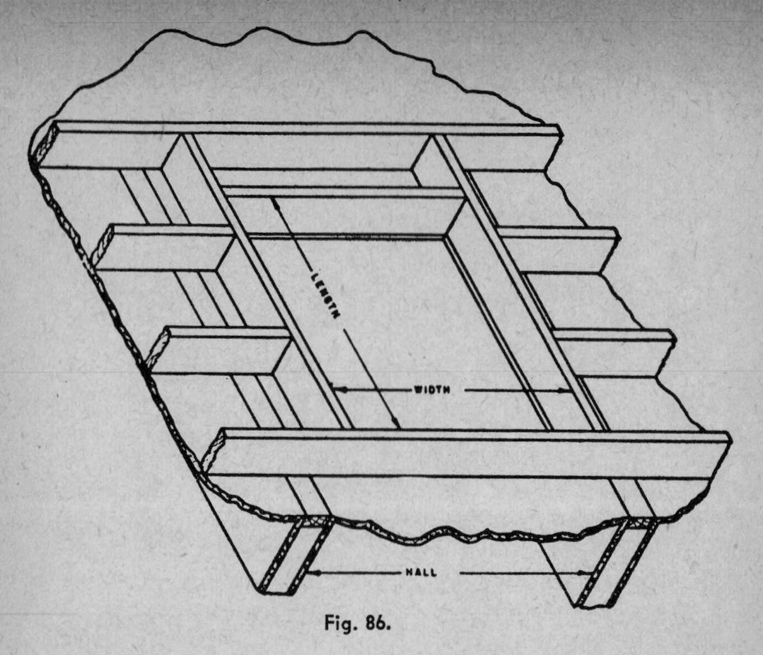

Fig. 86.

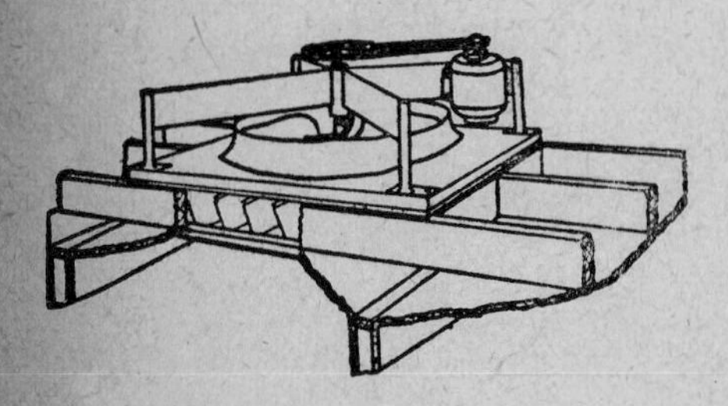

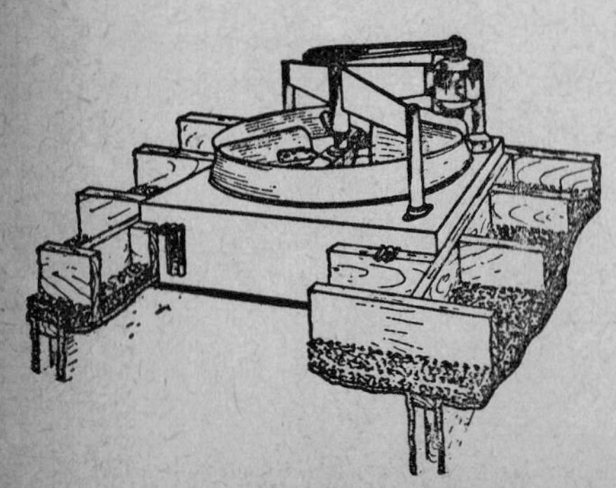

Fig. 87.

the operation of the fan, making a ceiling grille unnecessary. Self-closing doors are recommended with this installation to prevent heat or dust from entering the living space through the door opening.

Where the attic stairway door opens into the central hall, results should be comparable to the ceiling grille installation. If the attic stair door opens into one of the rooms, it may be advisable to arbitrarily increase the fan capacity to offset the unfavorable location of the point of air intake.

Figure 88 shows the installation details of this type application. The bulkhead door may be constructed of wallboard, reinforced with light framing material.

In many sections throughout the Midwest and New England areas

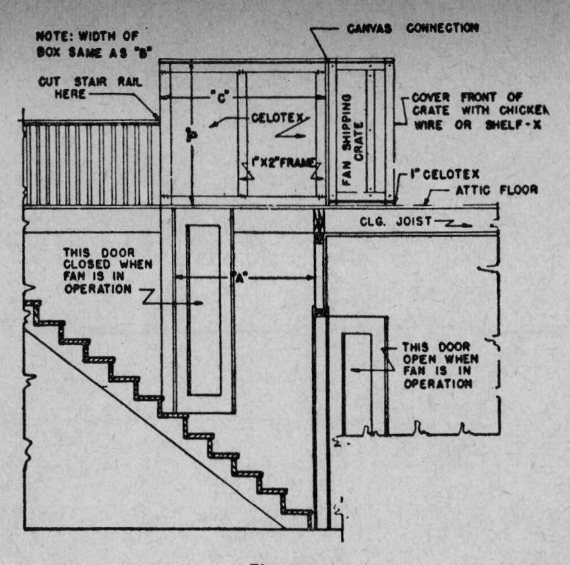

Fig. 88.

where large basements and limited attics prevail, the basement installation is preferred to the attic installation (fig. 89). This application has the following advantages:

1. Cross-sectional air movement is kept at living zone levels.

2. Fan ventilates basement, alleviating dampness.

3. Extremely quiet operation.

The fan may be installed under the stairway to save additional space. Remove risers under stair treads to permit flow of air from the open basement door to the fan. See figure 90 for installation details.

SAFETY CONTROL FOR EXHAUST FANS

Attic exhaust fans in operation become a definite hazard in the event of fire in the house as they increase the draft throughout the entire building. A simple method of automatically switching off the fan in such an event is illustrated in figure 91. The thermal link can be compounded to melt at any particular degree of heat chosen. When it is melted by the heat of the fire, the spring pulls the switch to the "off" position. This arrangement may be varied by substituting a weight for the spring, run over a simple pulley

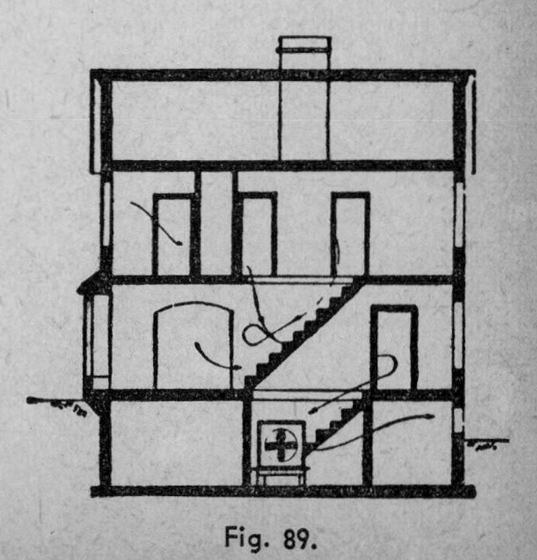

Fig. 89.

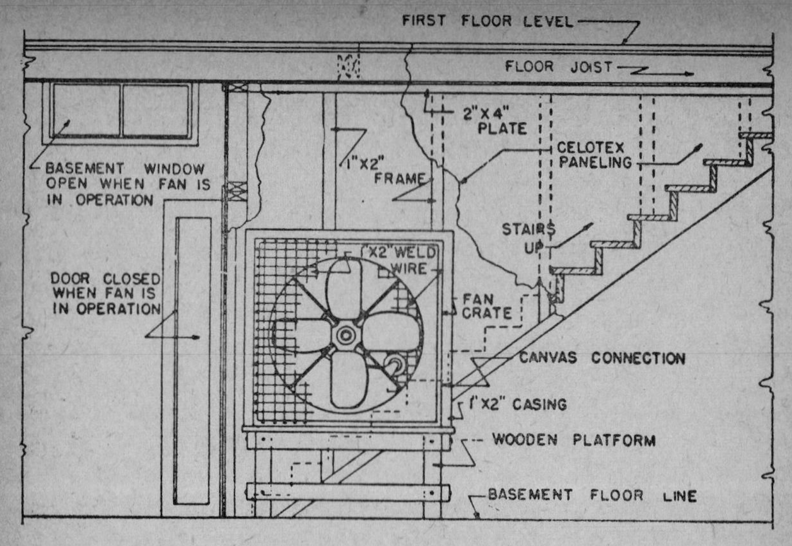

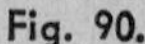
Fig. 90.

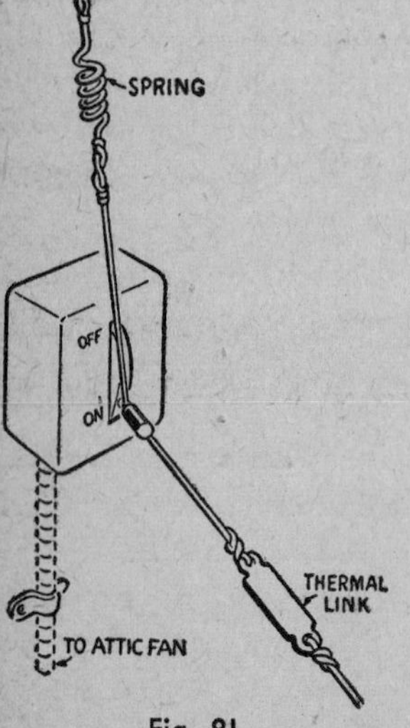

Fig. 91.

if the "off" position is at the top of the switch.

ESTIMATING REQUIRED FAN CAPACITY

Amount. The amount of air to be moved in a room is determined by multiplying the length, by the width, by the height of the room. For example, a room 18 feet long, 12 feet wide and 8 feet high contains 1728 cubic feet of air. Thus, the ability of a fan to move this amount of air must be taken into consideration in selecting the size and design of the fan. Fans are rated according to the cubic feet of air (in volume) they will circulate per minute. This is known as the CFM (cubic feet per minute) rating of a fan. Therefore, it will be necessary to have a fan or fans with a total rated capacity of 1728 CFM circulate the air in this room once every minute. The CFM rating appears on the instruction tag of some fans; on others it is necessary to consult the manufacturer's catalog to learn what the rating is. In warm climates where temperatures often stay extremely warm day and night for ex-

Fig. 92. Kitchen exhaust fans directly over the kitchen range are of great importance in keeping a modern kitchen comfortable in both the winter and summer, as well as in removing excessive moisture from the air in the house

tended periods, greatest comfort results when the air in a room is completely circulated at least every minute. In climates where extremely hot weather occurs less frequently, a three-minute cycle is considered adequate.

Speed. The speed or velocity at which a fan moves air is important. It can be compared with the strength of a breeze. A strong breeze is the result of air moving very rapidly and will produce a cooling effect more quickly than a gentle breeze. Most fans, from the 10-inch size up to the larger models, are equipped with adjustable speed controls so that speed of air motion can be regulated to suit existing conditions. By using a fan with adequate CFM rating, it is possible to regulate the amount and speed of air movement to give the greatest degree of comfort.

EXCHANGING INSIDE AND OUTSIDE AIR FOR COMFORT

Actual temperature reduction of the air temperature in a room, by

Fig. 93. **Left,** room A; **right,** room B.

means of a fan, can take place only when it is cooler outside than it is indoors. After the sun goes down, the outside temperature usually drops rather rapidly. But it takes several hours for it to cool noticeably indoors unless some means are used to force an exchange of hot inside air for cool outside air.

It is recommended in areas where climatic conditions are extremely warm that the air in the home be changed every minute to obtain the desired cooling effect. This is accomplished by having a fan or fans with total capacity in CFM (cubic feet per minute) equal to the cubic volume of the space to be cooled. This may be done by one large fan or two or more smaller fans.

In other areas where climatic conditions are not so severe, the CFM rating of the fan or fans can be equal to one half or one third of the cubic volume of the space to be cooled, thus changing the air every two or three minutes.

The type of house construction will influence the rate of cooling, and hence, to some extent, the size of fan needed for rapid reduction of temperature. For example, an uninsulated frame house will be cooled more quickly than an uninsulated brick house because brick tends to hold heat longer than wood.

The arrangement of windows and doors will determine how fans should be placed for best cooling results. If cross ventilation is possible the problem is different than in a room or suite of rooms without cross ventilation.

To cool a room or several rooms quickly where there is cross ventilation, there must be both an inlet for cool air and an outlet for warm air. Best results will be had when the area of the inlet is two to three times that of the outlet. The outlet should be about one and one-half times the diameter of the fan blades. As an example, in figure 93, the inlet window in room *A* should be opened wider than the outlet window in room *B*. In this illustration the fan is located at a distance about twice the diameter of its blades away from the window. (Thus a 12-inch fan could be placed anywhere within a distance of two feet from the open window to be most effective.) It faces the window squarely so that it forces warm air out of the room in a straight path. Since the inlet and outlet windows are not directly opposite each other, the cool air which enters room *A* and moves in a path across the room and starts up a series of air currents, pushes the warm air on until it is drawn into the low-pressure area back of the fan. The air is then exhausted through the window.

In a room or apartment where all windows are on one side of the building, and doors leading into a main corridor are on the opposite side, it often is impossible to have cross ventilation. This situation requires a slightly different method of using fans.

For best ventilation in a single room, if there are two windows, both are opened the correct distances and the door is closed. A fan is placed

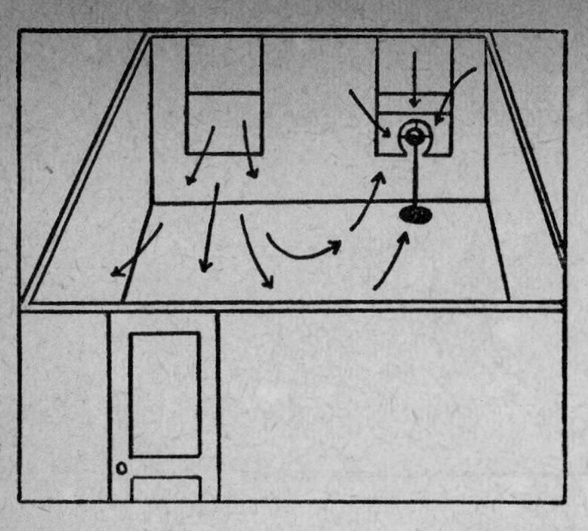

Fig. 94.

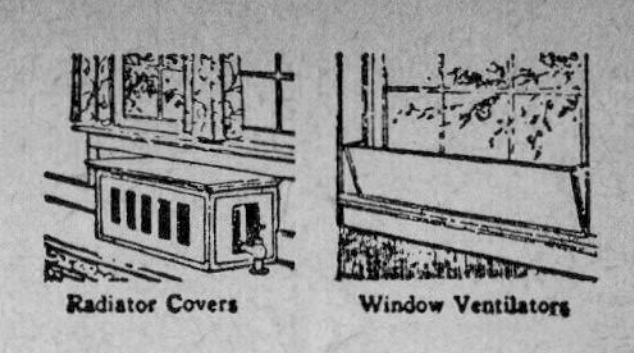

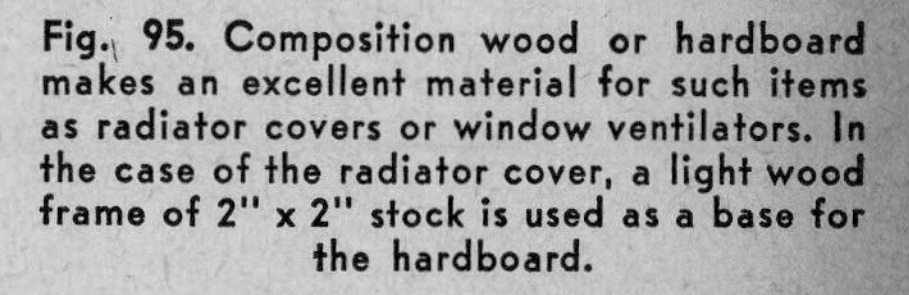

Fig. 95. Composition wood or hardboard makes an excellent material for such items as radiator covers or window ventilators. In the case of the radiator cover, a light wood frame of 2" x 2" stock is used as a base for the hardboard.

facing one of the windows and within two to three feet from it. One window becomes the inlet for cool air and the other is the outlet for warm air. Figure 94 illustrates this situation. If a single room has only one window, this same window must serve as both an inlet and an outlet for the exchange of air. The window should be opened from both top and bottom. The top opening is the inlet. The fan is placed to force air out of the lower part of the window.

An apartment where several adjoining rooms are all located on the same side of a building presents a somewhat similar problem. Effective ventilation may be secured by use of an average-sized fan in each room in one of the ways described above. On the other hand, one extra large fan may be sufficient to cool such an apartment. In this case, one window in a room at one end of the apartment is left open for the outlet. Other windows in this room remain closed. The fan is placed within three feet of the open window, facing it squarely. Windows in the other rooms of the apartment are opened to provide air inlets. Doors between adjoining rooms are left open so the fan may draw in the warm air from all the rooms. Doors leading from each room into a hall are kept closed to permit air to move in the most direct path. Remember, the room in which the fan is placed will be warmest and will stay warm for the longest period, since warm air from the other room or rooms must pass through it.

The direction of an outside breeze should also be taken into consideration when placing a fan for effective cooling. For best advantage, the fan should be pointed in the direction the breeze is blowing so as to take advantage of natural air movement and help in the exchange of inside and outside air.

SECTION V

ELECTRICAL SYSTEMS AND EQUIPMENT AND LIGHTING

Summary of Required Light Fixtures—Things to Remember in Wiring—Measure Your Lighting—Light Reflection—Outlet Requirements—Space Heating by Electricity—Special Outlets—Service Requirements—Circuit Requirements—Summary of Required Outlets—Additional Lighting—Electrical Wiring Tips—Low-Voltage Wiring—Low Voltage Controls Lights—Low-Voltage Control—Switch Control.

SECTION V

ELECTRICAL SYSTEMS AND EQUIPMENT AND LIGHTING

SUMMARY OF REQUIRED LIGHT FIXTURES

For These Places	You'll Need These Light Fixtures	Controlled By These Switches
Front or side porch.	One ceiling or side light on each side of door.	Located inside front door.
Back porch.	One ceiling or side light on each side of door.	Switch inside kitchen door and also at barn.
Lower hall.	One ceiling light to illuminate stairs.	3-way switch inside door and in upper hall.
Upper hall.	One ceiling light at head of stairs.	3-way switch at head of stairs and in lower hall.
Living room.	One ceiling light.	Switch at door.
Dining room.	One center fixture.	Switch at door.
Kitchen.	One center fixture and side wall bracket over sink and range. Light on either side of mirror if men shave in the kitchen.	Switch at door.
Pantry.	One ceiling light.	Switch at door.
Bathroom.	One ceiling light and/or light on each side of mirror.	Switch at door (important).
Bedrooms.	One ceiling light in each bedroom.	Switch at door in each room.
Closets.	One light located over door in each closet.	Pull chain in every light.
Attic.	One ceiling light to illuminate stairs and one for each separate unfinished space.	Switch at top and bottom of stairs.
Basement or work room.	One ceiling light for each 200 square feet or each separate room. One light to be located to illuminate stairway. Light over tubs in laundry.	Switch at top and bottom of stairs.
Garage.	One light over hood of each car.	At door.
Yard light.	Outdoor type, 200-watt, on pole or building, at least 22 feet above ground.	3-way switch, at house and barn.

For These Places	And Don't Forget: Plenty of Outlets	Recommended Lights		Switches	Double Outlets
		Ceiling	Side-wall		
Front or side porch.	One weatherproof outlet for decorative lighting or appliances used on the porch.	1	or 2	1	
Back porch	Outlet if washer is operated here.	1	or 2	1*	
Lower hall.	Outlet for table lamp and vacuum cleaner.	1		2*	1
Upper hall.	Outlet for vacuum cleaner.	1		2*	1

SUMMARY OF REQUIRED LIGHT FIXTURES (CONT.)

For These Places	And Don't Forget: Plenty of Outlets	Recommended Lights		Switches	Double Outlets
		Ceiling	Side-wall		
Living room.	One outlet for each wall space but not greater than 12 feet apart.	1		1	4
Dining room.	Outlet for table appliances and vacuum cleaner.	1		1	2
Kitchen.	Heavy duty outlets for range and water heater. Outlet for refrigerator, outlets for small appliances.	1	2	1	3
Pantry.	Outlet for mixer if used here.	1		1	
Bathroom.	Outlet for electric razor or space heater.	1	2	1	
Bedrooms.	Outlets for dresser lamps, bed lamps and appliances for each room.	1		1	2
Closets.					
Attic.	Outlet suspended from ceiling. Fan, outlets.	1		1	
Basement or work room.	Outlet where needed for iron, washer and ironer; one may be suspended from ceiling if necessary. 220-v heavy-duty outlet for water heater.	1		1*	2
Garage.	Outlet between each two stalls—in front.	1			1 or more
Yard light.		1		2*	

* Three-way switches to control light from two points.

THINGS TO REMEMBER IN WIRING

1. Save steps. Wire lights for all passageways, such as basement steps, stairways and back kitchen doors so that they can be turned off at either end.

2. Try to eliminate dangerous shadows on entrance steps and stairways.

3. Plan sufficient local lighting for close-seeing tasks, such as sewing and reading.

4. Locate kitchen and dining room outlets about 40 inches from the floor.

5. Have a competent electrical inspector check all wiring thoroughly.

MEASURE YOUR LIGHTING

Have your lighting measured by a Home Lighting Specialist. Below is the minimum amount of footcandles you should have for household tasks.

Specific Visual Tasks	*Footcandles Current Recommended Practice*
READING	
Prolonged periods (small type)	40
Casual periods (larger type)	20

Specific Visual Tasks	*Footcandles Current Recommended Practice*
SEWING	
On dark goods, fine needlework	100 or more
Average sewing—prolonged	40
Average sewing—periodic	20
WRITING	20
STUDY	40
GAME PLAYING	
Cards	10
Table Tennis	40
KITCHEN COUNTERS, RANGE, SINK	40
DRESSING-TABLE, DRESSER MIRROR	20
BATHROOM MIRROR	40
LAUNDRY TUBS, IRONER, IRONING BOARD	40
WORKBENCH	40
GENERAL LIGHTING	
Entrance Hall, Stairways, Landings	5
Living-room, Library, Sunroom	5
Dining-room	5
Kitchen	10
Bed- and Bathrooms	5

LIGHT REFLECTION

Color	*Approximate Percent Reflection*
White	85%
Ivory	75%
Pink	65%
Yellow	65%
Apricot	50%
Tan	60%
Medium Gray	60%
Light Blue	60%
Light Green	55%
Dark Brown	10%
Dark Blue	5%
Olive Green	10%

OUTLET REQUIREMENTS

Living Room (Also Library, Den, and Sunroom)

LIGHTING OUTLETS. One ceiling outlet, wall switch controlled. Rooms of a length more than twice the width to have two ceiling outlets. The ceiling outlets may be omitted provided wall, cove, or valance lighting outlets, wall switch controlled, are substituted.

Balanced illumination in a room is the ultimate purpose of lighting. Fixed lighting equipment forms an essential part of provisions for balanced illumination. Although often omitted in former years, recent developments in fixtures and fluorescent lighting indicate a return to former practices. This makes it advisable to provide outlets (ceiling, wall, cove, valance, etc.), with proper switch controls, even though installation of fixtures is not immediately contemplated. The installation of outlets for picture illumination and bookcase lighting is recommended.

CONVENIENCE OUTLETS. Convenience outlets placed so that no point along the floor line in any usable wall space, unbroken by a doorway, is more than 6 feet from an outlet in that space. Wall spaces less than 3 feet in length at the floor line are not considered usable. Two or more outlets to be wall switch controlled. Install one convenience outlet flush in mantel shelf, where construction permits.

It is recommended that at one of the switch locations a convenience outlet be provided for the use of vacuum cleaners, and other portable appliances. Outlets for the use of clocks, radios, decorative lighting, etc., in bookcases and other suitable locations are recommended.

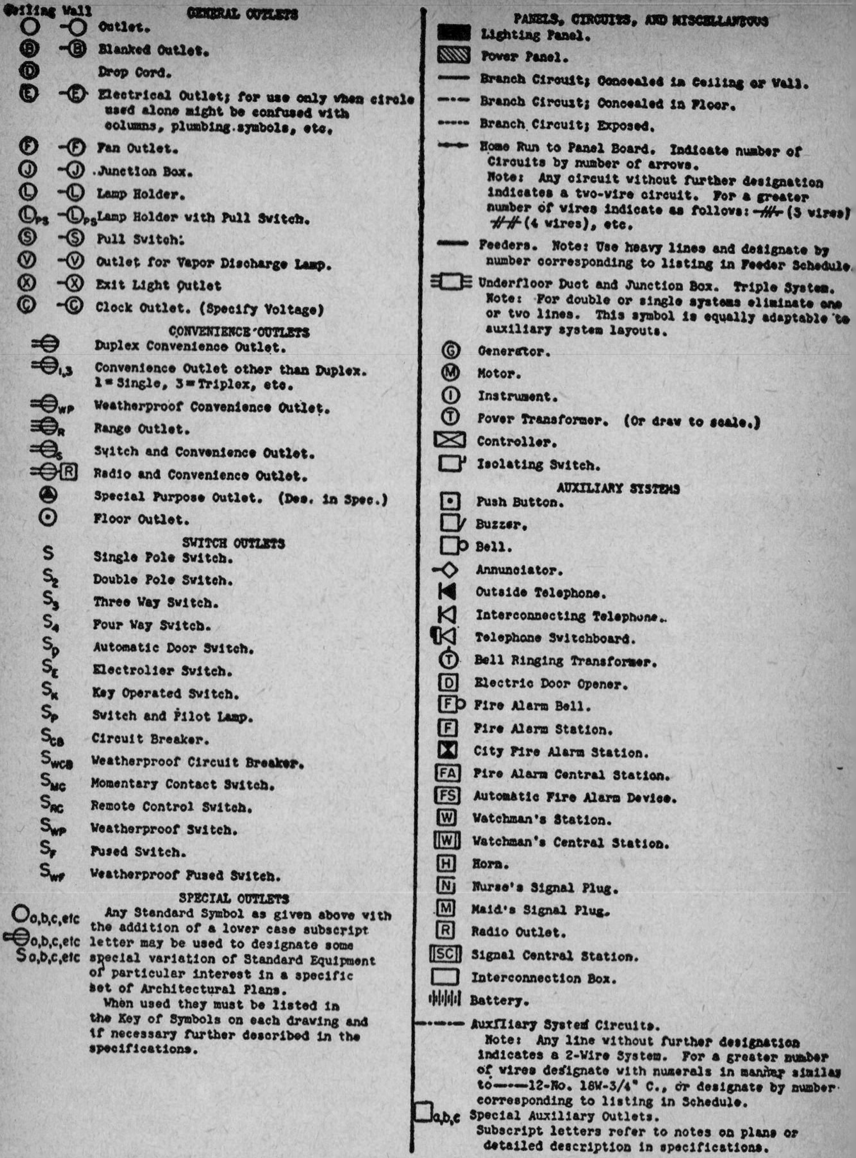

Ceiling Wall

GENERAL OUTLETS

- Outlet.
- Blanked Outlet.
- Drop Cord.
- Electrical Outlet; for use only when circle used alone might be confused with columns, plumbing symbols, etc.
- Fan Outlet.
- Junction Box.
- Lamp Holder.
- Lamp Holder with Pull Switch.
- Pull Switch.
- Outlet for Vapor Discharge Lamp.
- Exit Light Outlet
- Clock Outlet. (Specify Voltage)

CONVENIENCE OUTLETS

- Duplex Convenience Outlet.
- 1,3 Convenience Outlet other than Duplex. 1 = Single, 3 = Triplex, etc.
- WP Weatherproof Convenience Outlet.
- R Range Outlet.
- S Switch and Convenience Outlet.
- R Radio and Convenience Outlet.
- Special Purpose Outlet. (Des. in Spec.)
- Floor Outlet.

SWITCH OUTLETS

- S Single Pole Switch.
- S_2 Double Pole Switch.
- S_3 Three Way Switch.
- S_4 Four Way Switch.
- S_D Automatic Door Switch.
- S_E Electrolier Switch.
- S_K Key Operated Switch.
- S_P Switch and Pilot Lamp.
- S_{CB} Circuit Breaker.
- S_{WCB} Weatherproof Circuit Breaker.
- S_{MC} Momentary Contact Switch.
- S_{RC} Remote Control Switch.
- S_{WP} Weatherproof Switch.
- S_F Fused Switch.
- S_{WF} Weatherproof Fused Switch.

SPECIAL OUTLETS

$O_{a,b,c,etc}$ $S_{a,b,c,etc}$ Any Standard Symbol as given above with the addition of a lower case subscript letter may be used to designate some special variation of Standard Equipment of particular interest in a specific set of Architectural Plans.

When used they must be listed in the Key of Symbols on each drawing and if necessary further described in the specifications.

PANELS, CIRCUITS, AND MISCELLANEOUS

- Lighting Panel.
- Power Panel.
- Branch Circuit; Concealed in Ceiling or Wall.
- Branch Circuit; Concealed in Floor.
- Branch Circuit; Exposed.
- Home Run to Panel Board. Indicate number of Circuits by number of arrows.
  Note: Any circuit without further designation indicates a two-wire circuit. For a greater number of wires indicate as follows: (3 wires) (4 wires), etc.
- Feeders. Note: Use heavy lines and designate by number corresponding to listing in Feeder Schedule.
- Underfloor Duct and Junction Box. Triple System.
  Note: For double or single systems eliminate one or two lines. This symbol is equally adaptable to auxiliary system layouts.
- G Generator.
- M Motor.
- I Instrument.
- T Power Transformer. (Or draw to scale.)
- Controller.
- Isolating Switch.

AUXILIARY SYSTEMS

- Push Button.
- Buzzer.
- Bell.
- Annunciator.
- Outside Telephone.
- Interconnecting Telephone.
- Telephone Switchboard.
- T Bell Ringing Transformer.
- D Electric Door Opener.
- FD Fire Alarm Bell.
- F Fire Alarm Station.
- City Fire Alarm Station.
- FA Fire Alarm Central Station.
- FS Automatic Fire Alarm Device.
- W Watchman's Station.
- W Watchman's Central Station.
- H Horn.
- N Nurse's Signal Plug.
- M Maid's Signal Plug.
- R Radio Outlet.
- SC Signal Central Station.
- Interconnection Box.
- Battery.
- Auxiliary System Circuits.
  Note: Any line without further designation indicates a 2-Wire System. For a greater number of wires designate with numerals in manner similar to ——12-No. 18W-3/4" C., or designate by number corresponding to listing in Schedule.
- a,b,c Special Auxiliary Outlets.
  Subscript letters refer to notes on plans or detailed description in specifications.

Fig. 1. Graphical electrical symbols for plans and diagrams.

Dining Room (Also Dinette and Breakfast Room)

LIGHTING OUTLETS. One ceiling outlet, wall switch controlled.

Additional outlets may be desired for decorative or subdued type of lighting. Cove and valance lighting are of this type. Any such additional

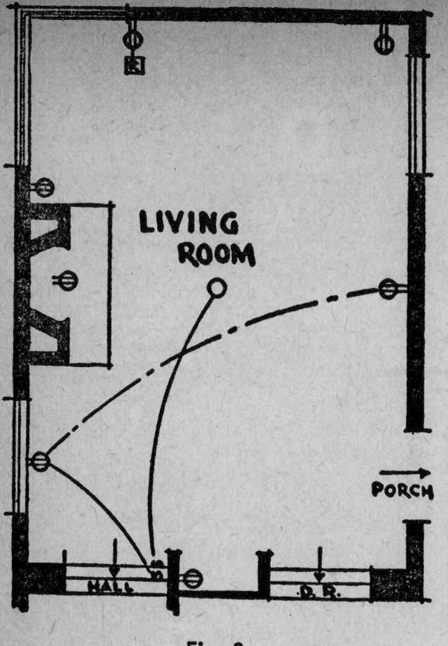

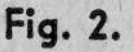
Fig. 2.

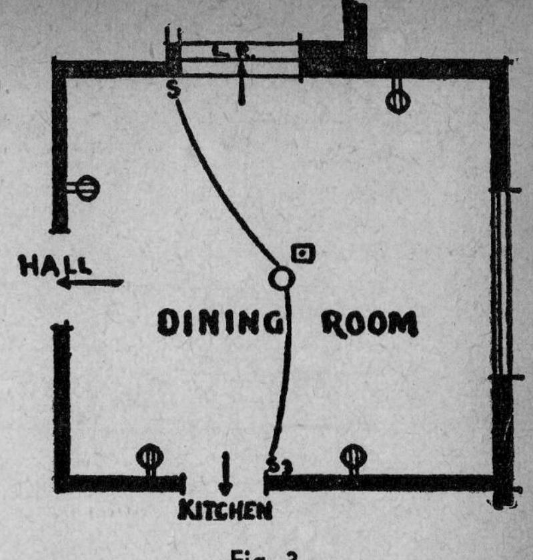

Fig. 3.

outlets that are installed should be switch controlled at a convenient location.

Convenience Outlets. Convenience outlets placed so that no point along the floor line in any usable wall space unbroken by a doorway is more than 10 feet from an outlet in that space. Wall spaces less than 3 feet in length at the floor line are not considered usable. In dinettes, breakfast rooms, or other small dining areas, one of these outlets to be adjacent to the table and slightly above table height.

In dining rooms place one of the required outlets at a location on the wall as near the hostess' chair as possible.

Kitchen (Also Kitchenette and Pantry)

Lighting Outlets One ceiling outlet for general illumination, wall switch controlled. One ceiling or wall outlet at sink, switch controlled.

Additional local illumination at work areas for food preparation, cooking, serving, etc., is recommended. It is suggested that outlets be considered for inside lighting of cabinets.

Convenience Outlets. One outlet for every 4 linear feet frontage of kitchen work surface; outlets located for greatest convenience. By kitchen work surface is meant all of the work area, approximately 36 inches above floor, exclusive of (a) the cooking range surface, and (b) the sink surface. If areas are divided by space, at least one outlet shall be provided at each such area. In addition to the aforementioned requirement, one outlet shall be provided at the refrigerator location. All outlets, with the exception of that provided for the refrigerator, should be located approximately 44 inches above the floor line.

An additional outlet is desirable for any space in the kitchen which

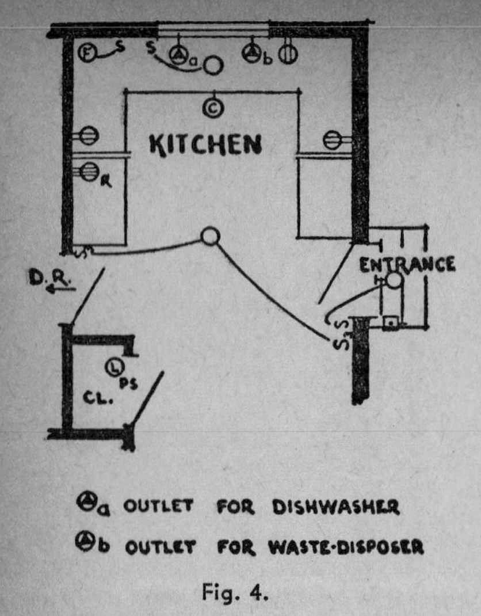

Fig. 4.

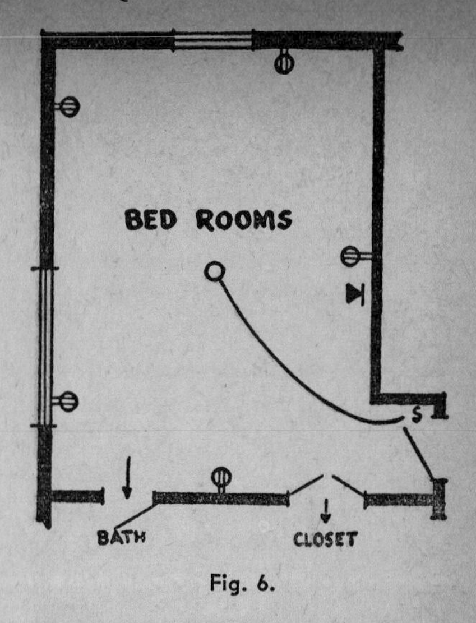

Fig. 6.

might be used for ironing purposes. Such an outlet should be located approximately 48 inches above the finished floor line.

Special Purpose Outlets. One outlet for each of the following pieces of equipment:

Range
Clock (Recessed receptacle)
Kitchen Ventilating Fan
Dishwasher—Waste Disposal Unit

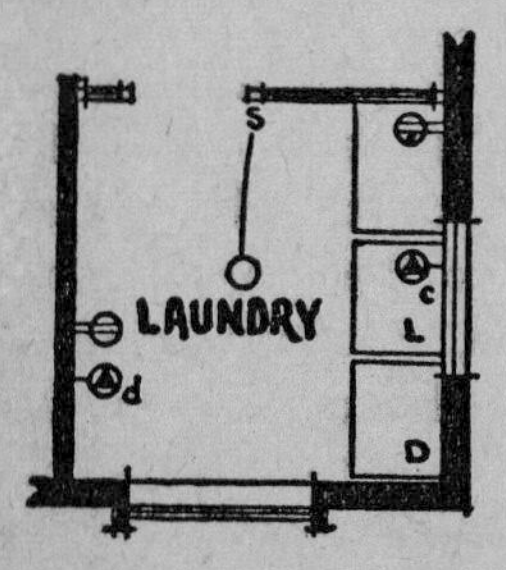

Ⓐc OUTLET FOR WASHER
Ⓐd OUTLET FOR HAND IRON OR IRONER

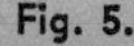
Fig. 5.

The installation of additional special purpose outlets should be given serious consideration. The trend toward using many more labor- and time-saving devices in the kitchen is obvious. Providing outlets for towel drying cabinet, home freeze units, etc., is recommended. The clock outlet should be placed high on the wall, 6 to 7 feet, and in a location easily visible from all parts of the kitchen.

Laundry

Lighting Outlets. One ceiling outlet or wall outlet at laundry tubs or washing center, and one ceiling outlet or wall outlet at ironing center. Provide wall switch control for one of these outlets; remaining outlets may be equipped with pull-chain controlled fixture.

Additional lighting outlets may be required if the laundry area is large.

Special Purpose Outlets. One outlet for each of the following pieces of equipment:

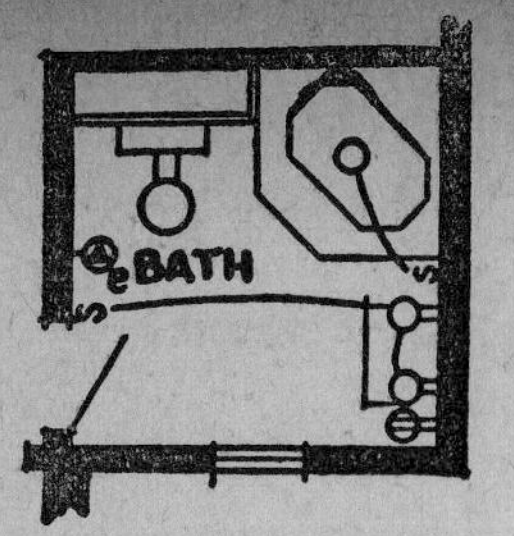

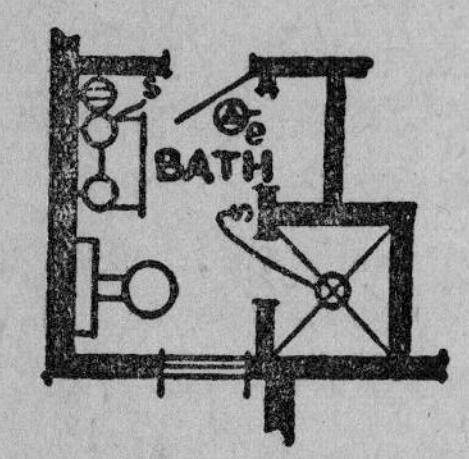

Fig. 7.

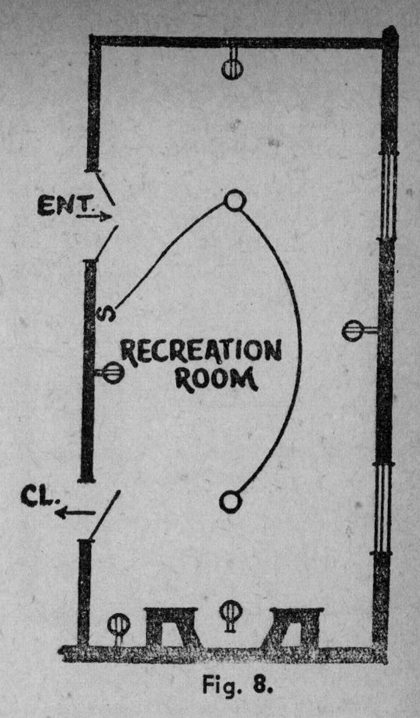

Fig. 8.

Washer
Hand iron or ironer

Bedrooms

LIGHTING OUTLETS. One ceiling outlet, wall switch controlled.

Additional outlets for decorative lighting and illumination at mirrors is suggested. Master switch control, in the master bedroom, is suggested for selected interior and exterior light.

CONVENIENCE OUTLETS. Convenience outlets placed so that no point along the floor line in any usable wall space, unbroken by a doorway, is more than 6 feet from an outlet in that space. Wall spaces less than 3 feet in length at the floor line are not considered usable.

It is recommended that at one of the switch locations a receptacle outlet be provided for the use of vacuum cleaners and other portable appliances.

SPECIAL PURPOSE OUTLETS. The installation of one heavy-duty special purpose outlet in each bedroom for the connection of portable space heaters is recommended, particularly for warmer climates in which a small amount of local heat is sufficient. Such outlets may also be used for operating individual air cooling equipment during hot weather.

Bathrooms (Also Lavatories)

LIGHTING OUTLETS. One outlet at each side of the mirror, wall switch controlled. One ceiling outlet in completely enclosed shower compartments, controlled by a switch outside the compartment. Bathrooms having an area of 60 square feet or greater shall be equipped with a wall switch controlled ceiling outlet.

CONVENIENCE OUTLETS. One convenience outlet near the mirror and at a height of 3 to 4 feet above the floor line.

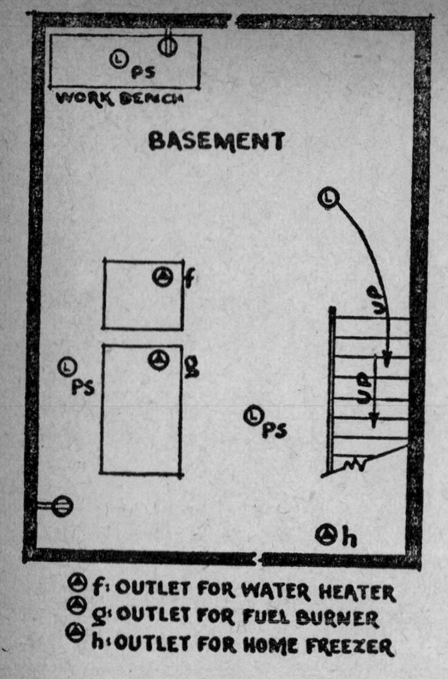

Fig. 9.

The provision of outlets for the connection of various health devices, such as sun lamps, is recommended. It also is recommended that a switch controlled night light be installed.

Special Purpose Outlets. It is recommended that each bathroom be equipped with an outlet for the connection of a built-in wall type space heater.

Recreation Room

Lighting Outlets. One ceiling outlet, wall switch controlled, for each 150 square feet of floor area. The ceiling outlets may be omitted provided wall, cove, or valance lighting outlets, wall switch controlled, are substituted.

Convenience Outlets. Convenience outlets placed so that no point along the floor line in any usable wall space, unbroken by a doorway, is more than 10 feet from an outlet in that space. Wall spaces less than 3 feet in length at the floor line are not considered usable. Install one convenience outlet flush in mantel shelf, where construction permits.

It is recommended that at one of the switch locations a receptacle outlet be provided for the use of vacuum cleaners and other portable appliances. Outlets for the use of clocks, radios, motion picture projectors, decorative lighting, etc., in bookcases and other suitable locations are recommended.

Basement (Also Utility Space)

Lighting Outlets. One outlet for each enclosed space, one for local illumination of work bench and one for furnace location, each pull-chain or switch controlled. Sufficient additional outlets to provide at least one for each 150 square feet of open space, pull-chain or switch controlled. If the utility space is a portion of the first floor of the residence, at least one ceiling outlet shall be wall switch controlled.

A light at the head and foot of basement stairway (multiple switch controlled) should be provided, and it may be included as one of those required above for the open spaces. Wall switches, near doors, for lights in enclosed spaces, or door type switches, are recommended in place of pull-chain control.

Convenience Outlets. One outlet at work bench location and one at furnace location.

If one of the outlets required above will adequately serve both locations, one may be omitted. The outlet at the work bench location is intended to serve the many power driven tools now available. The outlet at the furnace is intended to serve cleaning and maintenance tools used in connection with the heating plant.

Special Purpose Outlets. One for electrical equipment used in connection with furnace operation.

The installation of an outlet, multiple switch controlled from desirable locations throughout the house, is recommended for the connection of a summer cooling fan. Such a fan may, as an alternative, be installed in the attic.

Accessible Attics

Lighting Outlets. One outlet for general illumination, wall switch controlled. One outlet for each enclosed space, switch or pull-chain controlled.

The installation of a pilot light in connection with the switch controlling the attic light is suggested for consideration.

Convenience Outlets. One outlet for general use.

A convenience outlet in the attic is desirable for providing additional illumination in dark corners, and also for use of a vacuum sweeper and its accessories in cleaning.

Special Purpose Outlets. The installation of an outlet, multiple switch controlled from desirable points throughout the house, is recommended in connection with the use of a summer cooling fan.

Garage

Lighting Outlets. One interior outlet, wall switch controlled, for a one- or two-car garage; and sufficient additional wall switched outlets to provide one for each additional two-car storage area. If garage is detached from residence, provide one exterior outlet, multiple switch controlled from garage and residence.

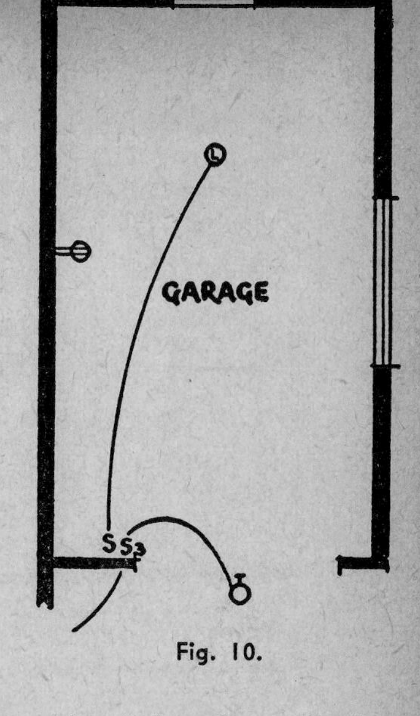

Fig. 10.

Where garage is attached to the residence, an exterior lighting out-

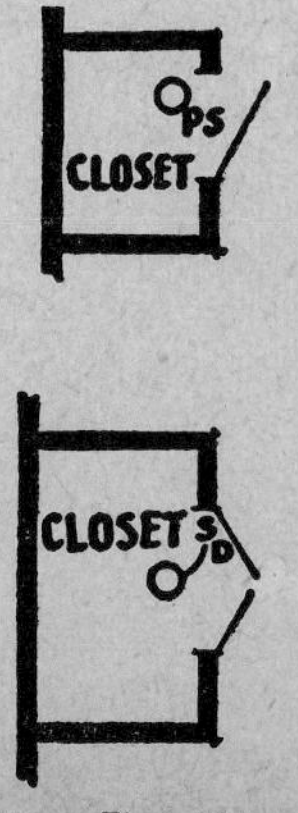

Fig. 11.

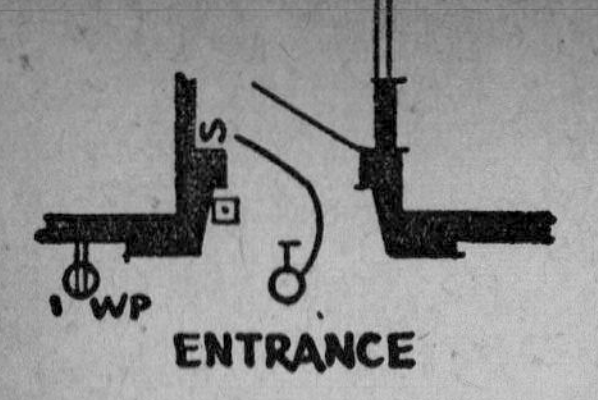

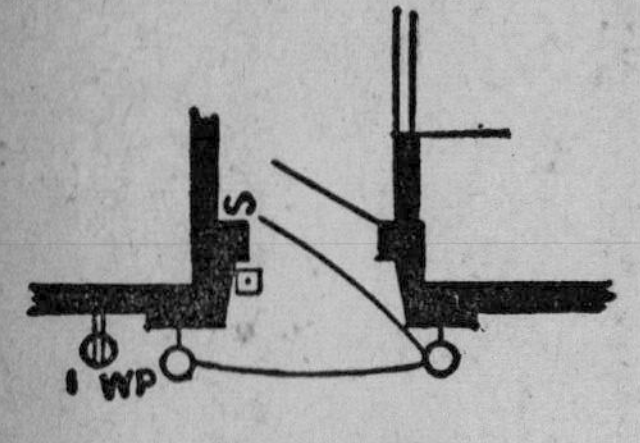

Fig. 12.

let, wall switch controlled, is recommended.

Convenience Outlets. One outlet for a one- or two-car garage; and sufficient additional outlets to provide one for each additional two-car storage area.

Outlet to be located approximately 48 inches above the floor. If a work bench is to be used in the garage, it is recommended that both a lighting outlet and convenience receptacle outlet be installed at the chosen location.

Closets

Lighting Outlets. An outlet for lighting in every closet 3 feet or more deep or having a floor area of 10 square feet or more except where shelving would make any light source ineffective.

Closet lighting outlets should be located at the lock side of the door and at a height sufficient (7 feet or more) to prevent the fixture being used as a clothes hook. The installation of wall switches near the closet door, or door type switches, is recommended in place of the pull-chain control.

Exterior Entrances (Front and Trade Entrances)

Lighting Outlets. One ceiling outlet or one or two wall outlets as architecture dictates, wall switch controlled.

The principal lighting requirements at entrances are illumination of the steps leading to the entrance and of the faces of people at the door. Where a single wall outlet is desired, located at lock side of the doorway, an outlet on each side of door is preferable where architecture permits. Additional outlets are desirable to provide lighting for those cases in which the entrance light does not fully illuminate all the steps. Terraced steps, or broken flights of steps represent such cases, and may be taken care of by the installation of outlets to provide post or mushroom type of lighting. Three-way switch control from inside and outside of door is convenient and should be considered.

Convenience Outlets. Single weatherproof outlet at front entrance, located approximately 18 inches above grade line.

It is recommended that this outlet be controlled by a wall switch inside the door. The outlet is for outdoor decorative lighting and for appliances that may be used outside. Additional outlets along the exterior of the house, about 18 inches above grade, located to serve decorative garden treatments are recommended; such outlets should be switch controlled.

Covered Porches

LIGHTING OUTLETS. One outlet for each 150 square feet of porch area, wall switch controlled. Where an exterior entrance enters on a covered porch, the lighting outlets as required for the "Exterior Entrance" (see above) may be considered as satisfying one of the lighting outlets required for "Covered Porches."

CONVENIENCE OUTLETS. One outlet for each 15 linear feet of house wall bordering porch.

Convenience outlets are necessary for the covered porch not only to provide for decorative lighting, but also for lamps, fans, etc., when screened and used as part of the living quarters. It is recommended that all such outlets be controlled by a wall switch inside the door.

Terraces and Patios

LIGHTING OUTLETS. The installation of an outlet on the building wall or on a post, centrally located in the area, is recommended for the purpose of providing fixed general illumination. Such outlets should be wall switch controlled just inside house door opening onto area.

CONVENIENCE OUTLETS. Single weatherproof outlet located approximately 18 inches above floor line, for each 15 linear feet of house wall bordering terrace or patio.

Spaces such as these are generally used as outdoor living rooms. Therefore, consider similar—though reduced—electrical requirements as for living room.

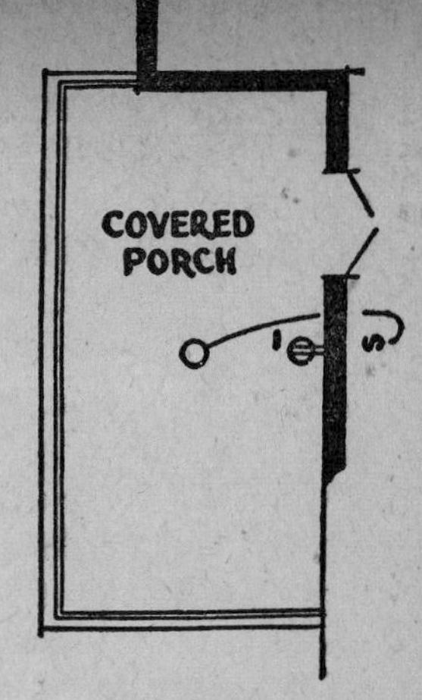

Fig. 13.

SPACE HEATING BY ELECTRICITY

Although electricity is much more efficient as a heating medium than fuels such as coal, oil, gas, liquefied petroleum and wood, its original energy cost for such purpose is often prohibitive. Where rates are low enough to justify its use and where no other suitable means of heating are available, electrical heating devices are, in general, satisfactory. Electrical efficiency is about 98 percent, producing 3413 Btu's per hour for each kilowatt of energy consumed. Often, when electricity is used for heating it has been found economical to provide more thermal insulation in the floor, walls and roof of a building than would ordinarily be provided for other means of heating, as an offset against the higher cost of the energy. While the over-insulation reduces the cost of electricity, it also reduces the cost of other fuel in proportion. The same number of Btu's are required in any case, the variables being the cost of fuel and efficiency of utilization, outside of operating labor and maintenance expense.

Wall-mounted and portable heaters used in dwellings of ordinary construction for supplementary purposes may be sized on a rule of thumb basis, by allowing one watt of power for each cubic foot of volume in the room for each 20° that it is desired to increase the temperature. For example, a room 8′ wide by 10′ long and 8′ high contains 640 cu. ft. If the outside temperature is 32° F. and it is desired to maintain a temperature of 72° F. in the room, the wattage of the heater should be, approximately:

$$\frac{640 \times 72 - 32}{20} = 1280 \text{ watts}$$

If a larger heater is used a thermostat should be provided to turn off the heater at 72° F., otherwise the room will get too hot, unless properly controlled manually. For each hour of operation the current consumption would be 1.28 kilowatt-hours.

Electrical heating may be accomplished by means of strips, pads, coils, blankets, tapestries, conductive rubber blocks, radiant ray lamps and heat cables designed to be installed in ceiling, wall or floor panels. Electric heat is distributed by conduction, convection and radiation just as heat from any other source is distributed.

Heated panels are formed by embedding electric heating conductors in plaster or concrete. These conductors are available in various lengths and wattages. They are suitably covered for protection. One installation, made on the basis of 1.5 watts per cubic feet for large rooms and 2 watts per cubic feet for small rooms, with a conductor temperature of from 160 to 170° F. uses somewhat less than 1.5 kw.-hrs. per cubic foot of space per year. These figures are not offered as conclusive, but merely illustrative. Cables may be arranged for 115- or 230-volt operation. The radiant heat component of electric panel heating systems permits a lower ambient temperature to maintain the comfort range, as in the case of radiant heating derived from hot water or hot air circulation. Also the same precautions against overheating are necessary. If the plaster becomes too hot it may crack from unequal expansion; and floors, if too hot, are not comfortable to stand on. Limiting values in this respect should be the same as for other radiant heating systems installed in the same material.

Usually heating circuits should be combined into branch circuits of 15, 20 or 30 amperes nominal rating. This load is in addition to the calculated load for lighting and small appliances, except for small, portable heaters used intermittently for supplementary purposes only.

SPECIAL OUTLETS

With the increasing use of FM radio and television receivers, provision of a ¾-inch non-metallic conduit from the exterior or attic space of the house to one or more wall outlets is becoming increasingly desirable. A blank plate may be provided for each outlet until it is used. Consideration should be given to location of outlets for convenient use, together with a 115-volt convenience outlet, when the room is darkened. Distances between outlets should be as short as practicable.

Telephone Outlets. Outlets may be desirable in the kitchen, hallway, dining room, living room and master bedroom. The local telephone company should be consulted for details of their requirements for raceways and service connections. In general, a ¾-inch metal conduit should be provided from the outlet to accessible basement or attic space. A protector cabinet is often desirable for finished basements.

SERVICE REQUIREMENTS

Service Entrance. The size of service entrance conductors and the rating of service equipment shall not be less than that specified for the floor areas delineated in the tables below. All service shall be 3 wire, 115/230 volt.

Floor Area (Sq. Ft.)	Capacity Service Conductor (Amperes)	Rating of Service Equipment: Circuit Breakers	Rating of Service Equipment: Switch and Fuse — Switch	Switch and Fuse — Fuse	The service capacities provided for in table are sufficient to supply lighting, portable appliances, a range, a water heater, and additional appliances, supplied by individual equipment circuits, having a total rating in watts as follows:
Up to 1,000	60	70	60	60	3,500
To 1,500	65	70	100	70	4,200
To 3,000	85	90	100	90	8,800
To 4,000	100	100	100	100	9,500

The above table provides service sizes adequate for normal lighting and portable appliance loads and for a range and a water heater. In addition it provides for a possible increase by the amounts shown in the last column. If these wattages are to be exceeded, service size should be increased accordingly. If, however, the initial wattages are less than those shown, the service sizes should be at least those given above so that future growth in load may be accommodated.

CIRCUIT REQUIREMENTS

Branch Circuits

1. GENERAL PURPOSE CIRCUITS (15 AMPERE)

General purpose circuits shall supply all lighting outlets throughout the home and all convenience outlets except the convenience outlets in the dining room, breakfast room, kitchen, pantry, and laundry. These shall be provided on the basis of one circuit for not more than each 500 sq. ft. of floor area. Outlets supplied by these circuits shall be divided equally among the circuits.

2. APPLIANCE CIRCUITS (20 AMPERE)

Two 20-ampere circuits for the convenience outlets in the kitchen, pantry, breakfast room, dining room, and laundry in a residence having a floor area of 1,500 square feet or less. The wiring for such circuits to be so installed that outlets supplied from both circuits are available in both the kitchen and the laundry. For residences with a floor area greater than 1,500 square feet one 20-ampere circuit for the convenience outlets in the kitchen, pantry, breakfast room, and dining room; one 20-ampere circuit for the convenience outlets in the laundry; and one 20-ampere circuit supplying convenience outlets in both the kitchen and the laundry.

The number of 20-ampere circuits required are necessary because new appliances are available, of high wattage, and with automatic features that make possible the performance of several household tasks simultaneously. The use of 3-wire circuits for supplying convenience outlets in the locations mentioned is suggested as an economical means for dividing load and offering practical operating advantages.

3. Individual Equipment Circuits

Circuits shall be provided for the following equipment:

Item	*Capacity*
Range (up to 12 Kw)	35A-3W-115/230V
Range (above 12 Kw)	50A-3W-115/230V
Fuel Fired Heating Equipment (if installed)	15A or 20A-115V
Dishwasher-Waste Disposer (if necessary plumbing is installed)	20A-2W-115V

Spare circuit equipment shall be provided for the following appliances:

Item	*Capacity*
Water Heater	Consult local utility
Automatic Washer	20A-2W-115V

Consideration should also be given to the provision of circuits for the following commonly used household devices. The table should not be construed to list all equipment available.

Item	*Circuit*
1. Clothes Dryer	25A 3W 115/230V
2. Summer Cooling Fan	20A 2W 115V (Switched)
3. Air Cooling Unit	25A 2W 230V
4. Home Freeze Unit	20A 2W 115V or 230V
5. Water Pump (where used)	20A 2W 115V or 230V
6. Bathroom Heater	20A 2W 115V or 230V
7. Work Shop or Bench	20A 2W 115V

In some instances one of the circuits recommended may serve two devices which are not liable to be used at the same time, such as a summer cooling fan and a bathroom heater. The majority of appliances for residential use are made for 110- to 120-volt circuits. There is, however, a growing tendency to make fixed appliances for use on 208–220–240-volt circuits. It is recommended that the higher voltage be preferred in those cases where a choice exists.

Feeder Circuits

It is strongly recommended that consideration be given to the installation of branch circuit protective equipment, served by appropriate size feeders, at locations throughout the house, rather than in a single location.

SUMMARY OF REQUIRED OUTLETS

This table is given for quick reference and the requirements are necessarily condensed.

Space	Lighting Outlets	Type of Circuit	Convenience Outlets	Type of Circuit	Special Purpose Outlets	Type of Circuit
Living Room, Library, Den, Sun Room	1 Ceiling outlet, wall switch controlled, 2 outlets where room length exceeds width. Wall, cove or valance outlets may be substituted.	G	No point at wall line more than 6 feet from an outlet; wall spaces 3 feet or more to have outlet; outlet in mantel shelf. Two or more outlets switch controlled.	G		
Dining Room, Dinette, Breakfast Room	1 Ceiling outlet, wall switch controlled.	G	No point at wall line more than 10 feet from an outlet; wall spaces 3 feet or more to have outlet.	A		
Kitchen, Kitchenette, Pantry	1 Ceiling outlet, wall switch controlled; 1 outlet at sink, switch controlled.	G	1 outlet for every 4 linear foot frontage of kitchen work surface. 1 outlet at refrigerator location.	A	1 for range 1 for clock 1 for fan 1 for dishwasher-waste disposal unit.	I G G I
Laundry	1 Ceiling outlet at washing center. 1 Ceiling outlet at ironing center. Wall switch control for one ceiling outlet.	G			1 for washer 1 for hand iron or ironer	A or I A
Bedrooms	1 Overhead outlet, wall switch controlled.	G	No point at wall line more than 6 feet from an outlet. Wall spaces 3 feet or more to have outlet.	G		
Bathrooms, Lavatories	1 Outlet each side mirror, wall switch controlled. 1 Ceiling outlet in shower compartment, wall switch controlled. 1 Ceiling outlet in rooms 60 square feet and over, wall switch controlled.	G	1 near mirror.	G		

(*Continued on next page*)

SUMMARY OF REQUIRED OUTLETS (*cont.*)

Space	Lighting Outlets	Type of Circuit	Convenience Outlets	Type of Circuit	Special Purpose Outlets	Type of Circuit
Recreation Room	1 Ceiling outlet for each 150 square feet of floor area, wall switch controlled. Wall, cove, or valance outlets may be substituted.	G	No point at wall line more than 10 feet from an outlet; wall spaces 3 feet or more to have outlet; outlet in mantel shelf.	G		
Reception Hall	1 Ceiling outlet, wall switch controlled. Wall, cove, or valance outlets may be substituted.	G	No point at wall line more than 10 feet from an outlet; wall spaces 3 feet or more to have outlet.	G		
Halls	1 Outlet for each 15 linear feet, wall switch controlled.	G	1 for each 15 linear feet.	G		
Stairways	1 Outlet on each floor, illuminating head and foot of stairway. Each outlet to have separate switch control at the head and foot of stairway.	G				
Closets	1 Outlet in closets 3 feet or more deep or having a floor area of 10 square feet or more.	G				
Exterior Entrances (Front and Trade)	1 or 2 outlets, wall switch controlled.	G	1 at front entrance	G		
Covered Porches	1 Outlet for each 150 square feet porch floor, wall switch controlled.	G	1 for each 15 linear feet of house wall bordering porch.	G		
Terraces and Patios			1 for each 15 linear feet of house wall bordering porch.	G		

(*Continued on next page*)

Summary of Required Outlets (*cont.*)

Space	Lighting Outlets	Type of Circuit	Convenience Outlets	Type of Circuit	Special Purpose Outlets	Type of Circuit
Basement Utility Space	1 Outlet for each enclosed space, 1 for work bench and 1 for furnace location. Sufficient additional outlets to provide 1 for each 150 square feet of open space.	G	1 at work bench location, 1 at furnace location.	G	1 for electrical equipment used in connection with furnace operation.	I
Accessible Attics	1 Outlet, wall switch controlled. 1 Outlet for each enclosed space.	G	1 for general use.	G		
Garage	1 Interior wall switched outlet for one- or two-car garage, plus 1 for each additional two cars. 1 Outlet for exterior lighting, multiple switch controlled if garage is detached from house.	G	1 for one- or two-car garage, plus 1 for each additional two cars.	G		

G—Outlets supplied by General Purpose Circuits.
A—Outlets supplied by Appliance Circuits.
I—Outlets supplied by Individual Equipment Circuits.

A convenience outlet shall be at least of the duplex type (two or more plug-in positions) except as otherwise specified.

All spaces for which wall switch controls are required, and which have more than one principal entrance, shall be equipped with multiple switch control at the lock side of doors, or the traffic side of arches. If this requirement would result in the placing of switches, controlling the same light, within 10 feet of each other, one of the switch locations may be eliminated.

ADDITIONAL LIGHTING

Additional lighting—where it is needed most—can be obtained through the use of built-in and recessed light fixtures, a few examples of which are shown in the accompanying illustrations, figures 14 to 28. This type of fixture is well suited for bringing light to normally ill-lighted areas such as cupboards, closets and other dark corners, as well as providing more efficient means of lighting walls and ceilings.

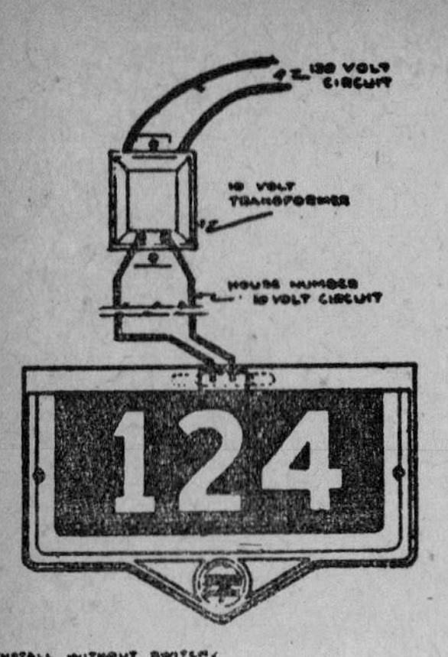

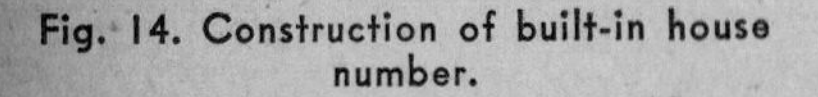

Fig. 14. Construction of built-in house number.

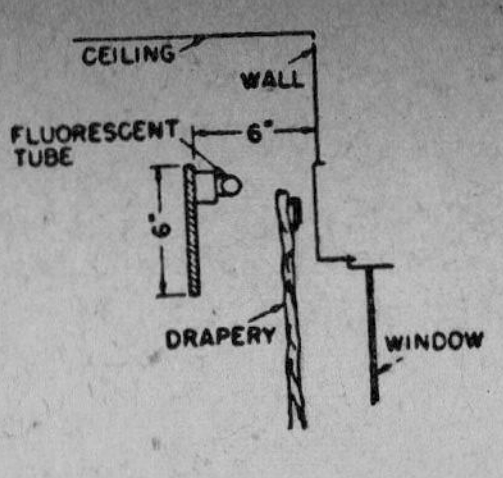

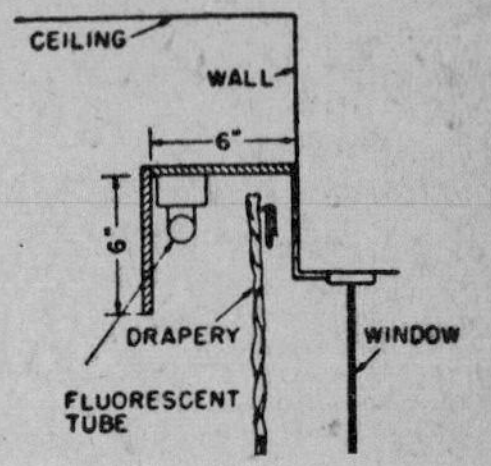

Fig. 15. Window valance detail for fluorescent tube lighting. Upper, open top; lower, closed top.

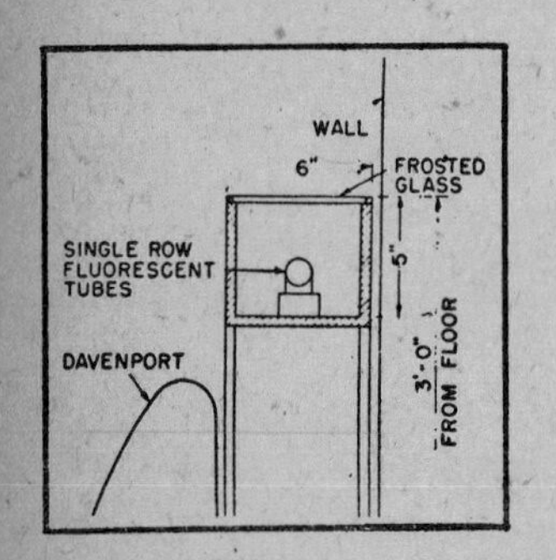

Fig. 16. Soffit lighting over a divan, using frosted glass.

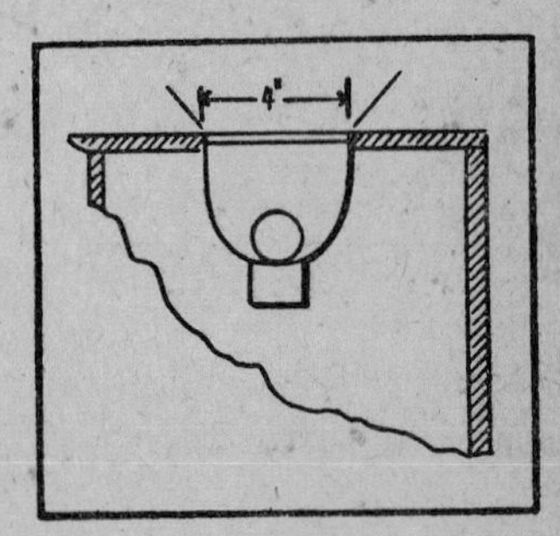

Fig. 17. Method of installing a light and reflector in a mantel to focus light on a picture hanging on the chimney breast.

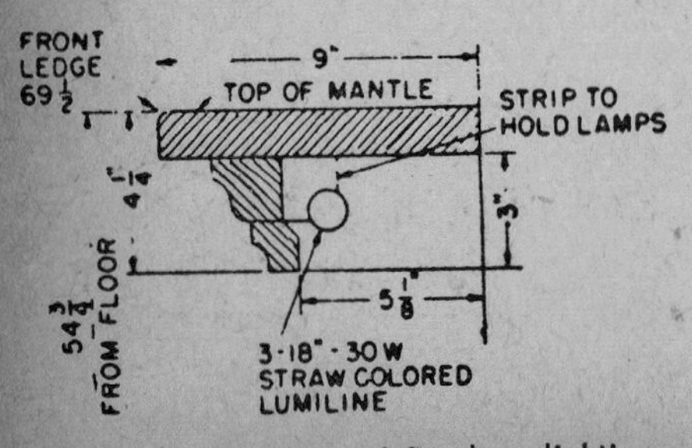

Fig. 18. Cross-section of fireplace lighting.

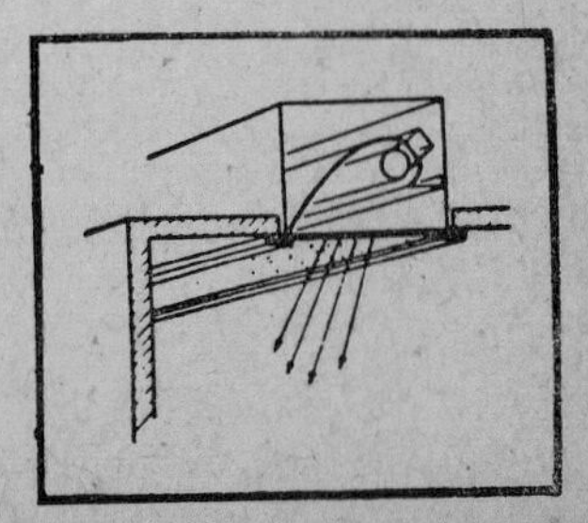

Fig. 19. Construction detail of simple overhead mirror lighting.

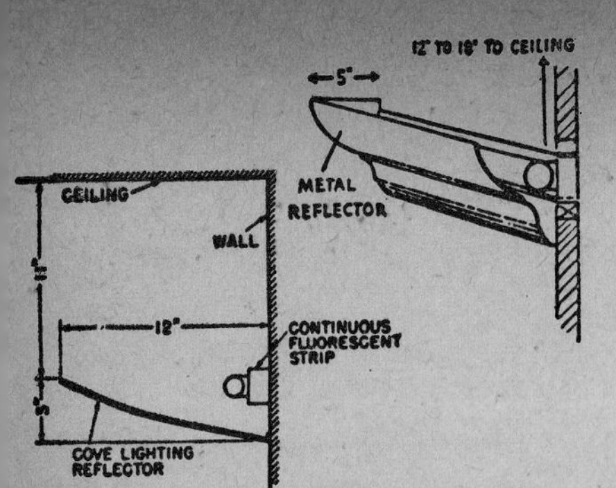

Fig. 20. Method of constructing indirect cove lighting.

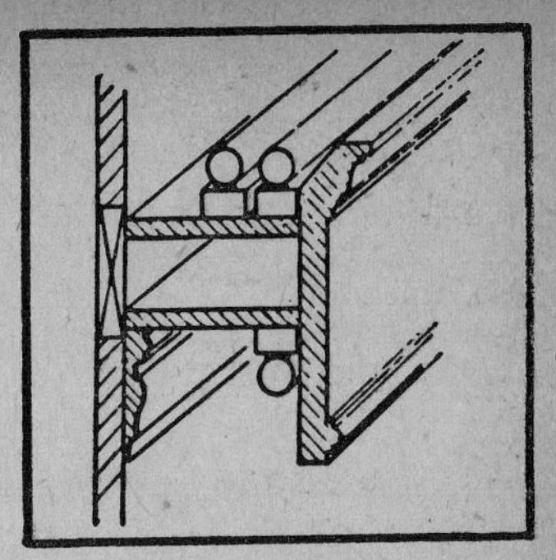

Fig. 21. Combination direct and indirect cove lighting. The row of fluorescent tubes at the top may be single or double.

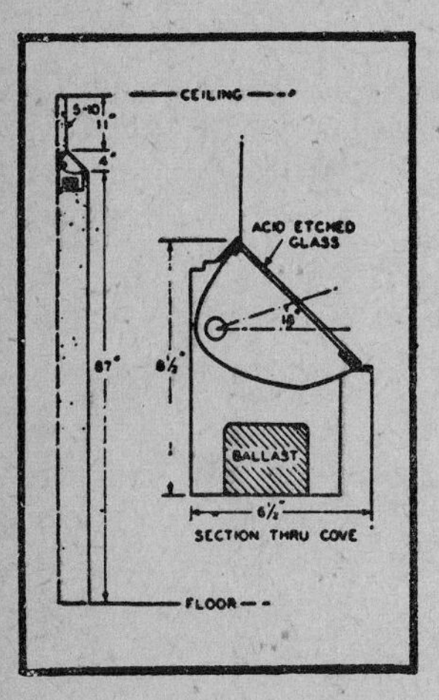

Fig. 22. Construction of a recessed wall cove. The reflectors are polished metal.

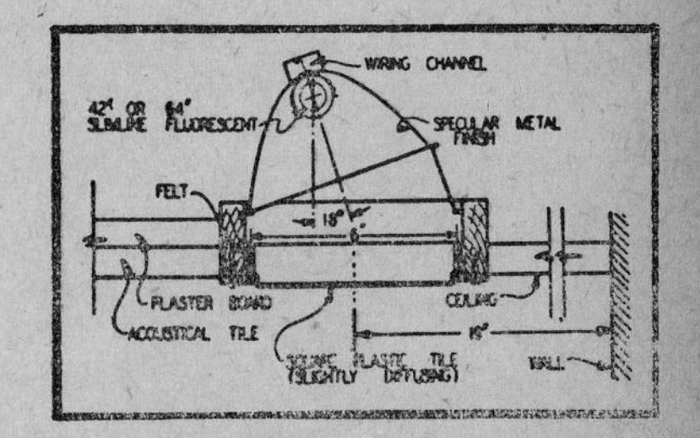

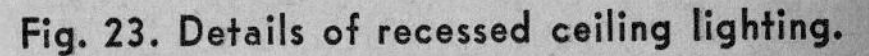

Fig. 23. Details of recessed ceiling lighting.

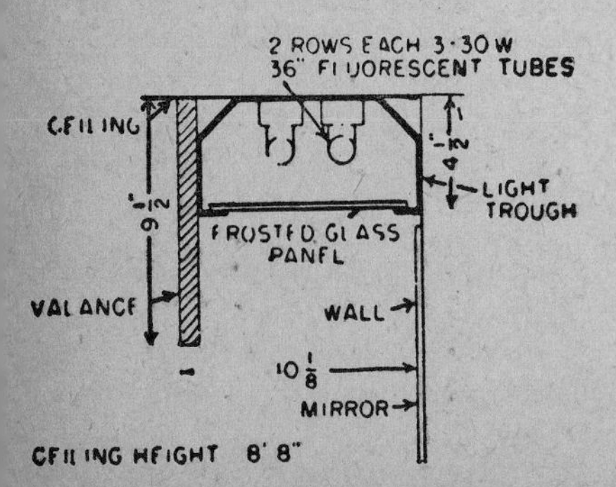

Fig. 24. Recessed bed lighting is easily built in accordance with this diagram.

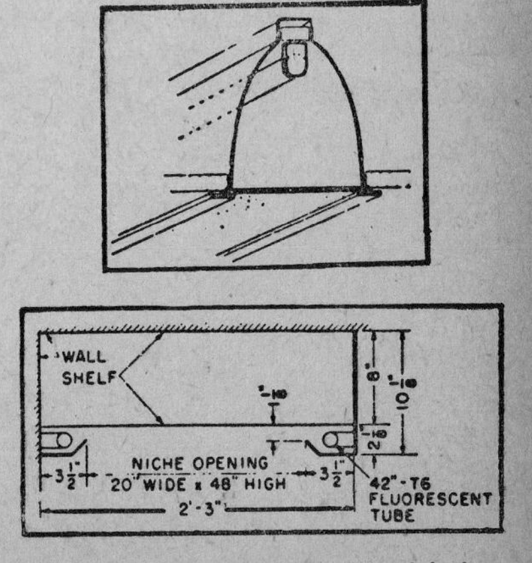

Fig. 25. Several types of cupboard lighting are shown here. They can be adapted to solve almost any cupboard lighting problem.

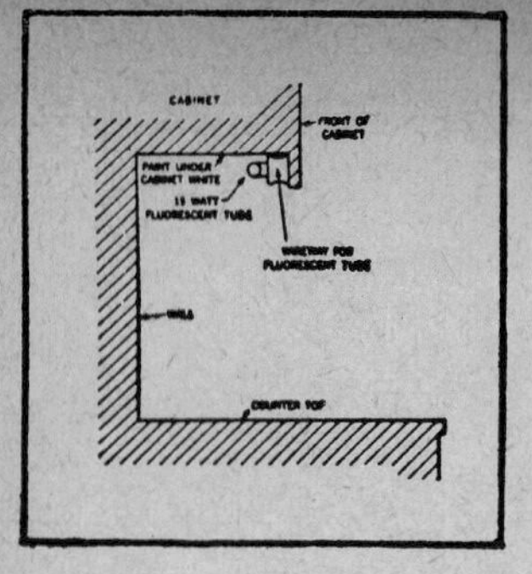

Fig. 26. Detail of lighting for a kitchen counter.

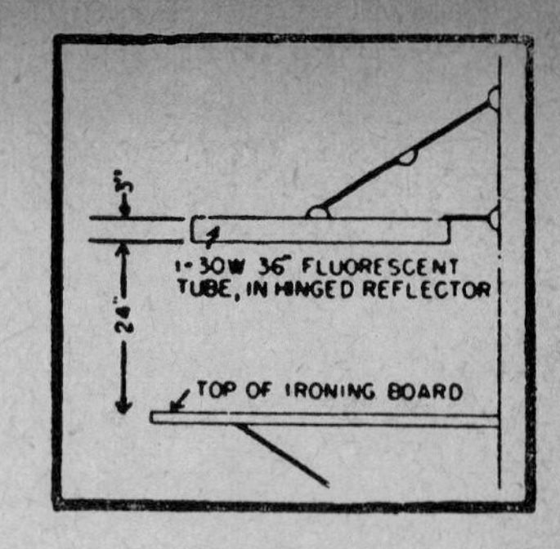

Fig. 28. A foldaway ironing board lamp to go with a foldaway ironing board. This idea is adaptable to many other uses.

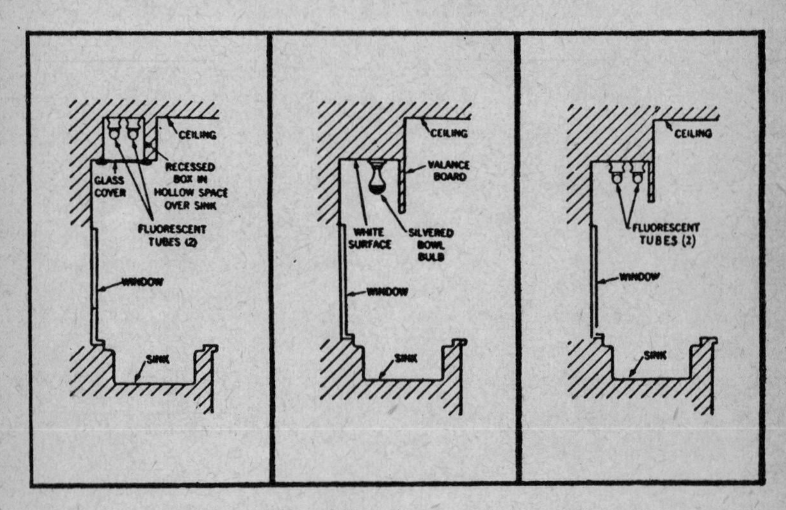

Fig. 27. Three different ways to light a sink.

ELECTRICAL WIRING TIPS

Running Wire. Spooled wire should be unrolled as it is used to avoid kinking and damage. Kinks can be removed by twisting them out by hand and running the wire between a hammer handle and another surface (fig. 29).

Making Bends. To avoid kinking and cutting the cable, the radius of bends should not be less than five times the diameter of the cable (fig. 30).

Cutting Cable. Use a hack saw to cut cable armor. Place saw almost at right angles to strip of armor and cut through one strip. Take care not

Fig. 29.

to cut wire insulation. To remove armor, twist it slightly and pull it off wire (fig. 31).

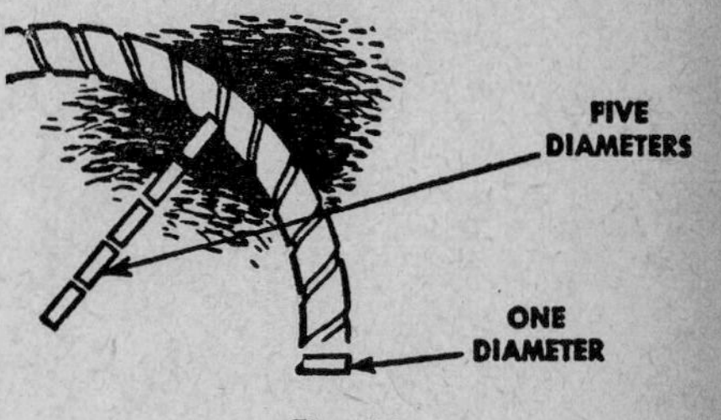

Fig. 30.

Fiber Bushings. Fiber bushings are used under armor at cut to protect wire insulation. To install a bushing:

Pull paper from under wire 2 or 3 inches back of armor and tear it off with a sharp yank (fig. 32, *1*).

Unwrap paper covering on wire (fig. 32, *2*).

Insert bushing under armor (fig. 32, *3*).

Cable Connectors. Connectors are used to hold cable on outlet boxes (fig. 33). To install the connector, first install a fiber bushing. Then, push connector as far as possible over bushing and clamp it to armor back of bushing by tightening set screw. Push male end of connector through a knockout in outlet box and drive locknut tight against box.

Fig. 31.

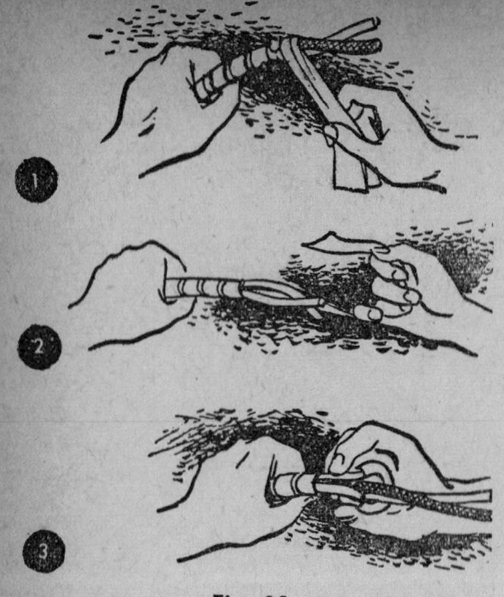

Fig. 32.

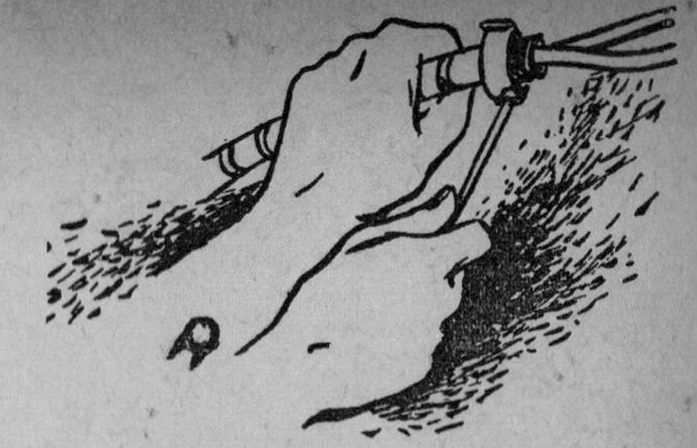

TIGHTEN CABLE CONNECTOR

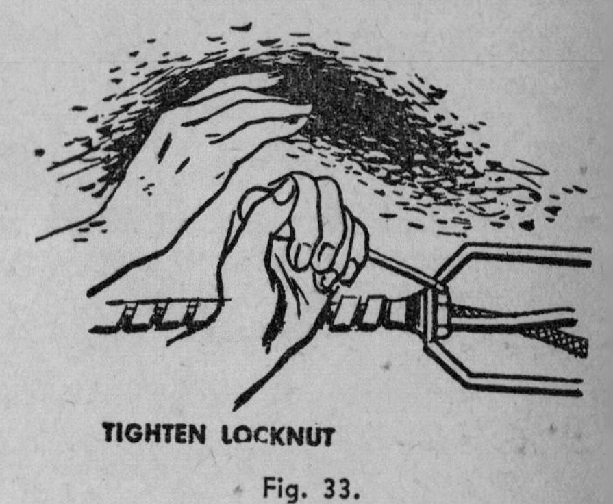

TIGHTEN LOCKNUT

Fig. 33.

Special Connectors. Two-cable and sharp-turn connectors are installed on cables and outlet boxes the same as standard connectors (fig. 34). Some boxes have special built-in clamps. To make the connection, install a fiber bushing, run the cable through the clamp, and tighten clamp on the cable armor.

Conduit Service Entrance. Service wires are run from the pole to the building as shown in figure 35, wire holders (*A*) are installed on the building and the wire is run through the insulator and tied back on itself. An outside conduit is run into the building to the fuse box or circuit breaker. A watertight entrance cap is installed on the conduit. The entrance wire is run through the conduit cap and attached to the service wire.

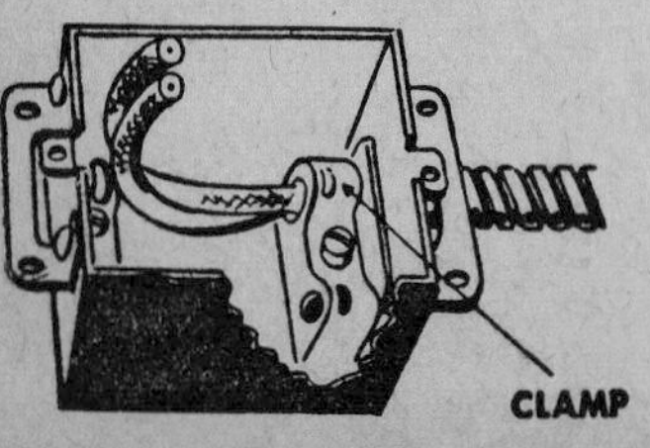

Fig. 34.

LOW-VOLTAGE WIRING

Low-voltage wiring does not require all the safety precautions required for other wiring. Bell wire used is attached to studs with small staples or nails.

A bell-and-buzzer system for small offices can be wired as shown in figure 37.

Two 6-volt dry cells wired in series furnish a 12-volt power source.

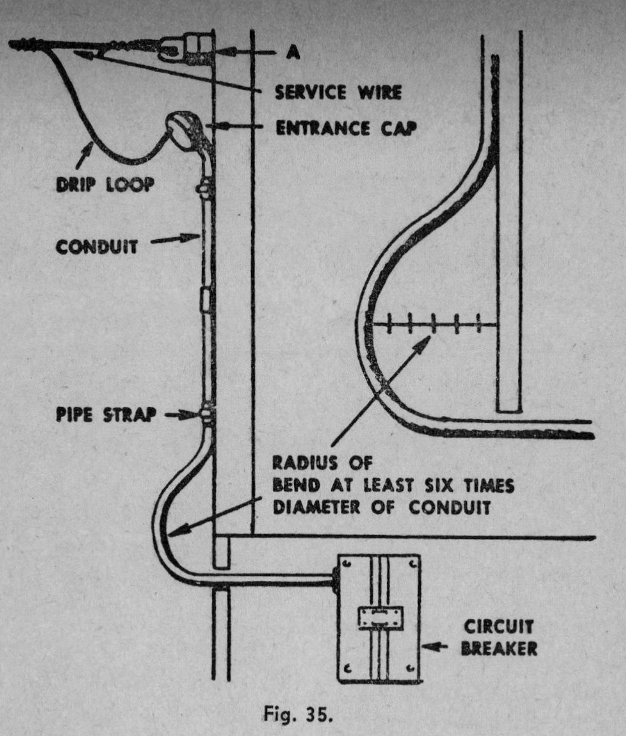

Fig. 35.

In places where the wire lengths are long, bells should be wired as shown in figure 38. It may also be necessary to add one or two more batteries to make the bells ring loud enough.

LOW VOLTAGE CONTROLS LIGHTS

In the conventional home wiring, there's usually only one switch to control each room light—even though the room may have several entrances. A low-voltage control system makes it possible to have one at every door.

The system consists of a magnetic relay at each fixture to control the 115-volt circuit, and one or more S.P.D.T., lever-type switches in a 24-volt control circuit. Because of the low voltage, light-gauge wiring can be used instead of metallic conduits for the control circuits, thus reducing installation costs. Control wires can be run from each relay to as many switches as desired. This arrangement also is adaptable to a master system that will enable you to turn on lights in several different rooms from one control point (fig. 39).

LOW-VOLTAGE CONTROL

Low-voltage control lighting is a method of switching lighting and appliance loads by means of a mag-

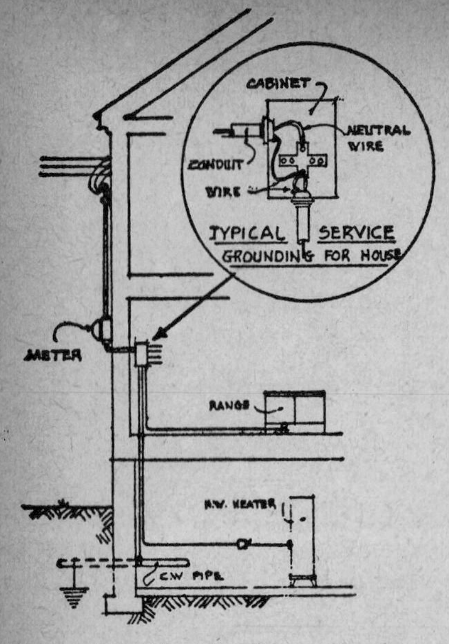

Fig. 36. Typical wiring diagram for the service entrance installation.

netic switch mounted in the conventional outlet box and controlled by any number of small, low-voltage switches located for convenience (fig. 40). The magnetic switch or relay is mounted through a ½-inch knockout in the outlet box (fig. 41) and controlled from paralleled switches by means of a three-wire, low-voltage (24 V) circuit. Since the long switch leads are only for control at low-voltage, the use of expensive three- and four-way switches and large

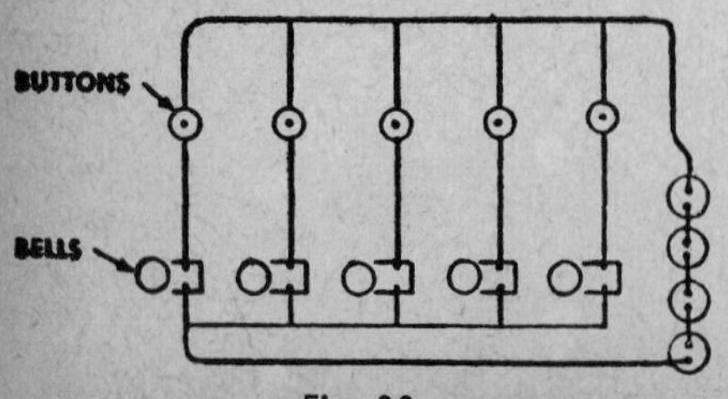

Fig. 38.

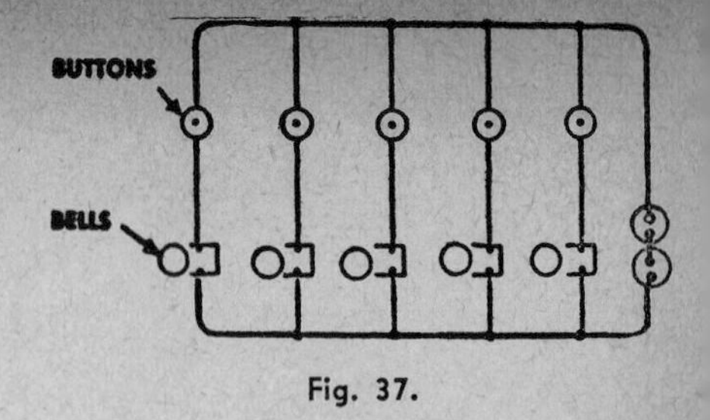

Fig. 37.

quantities of three- and four-conductor cables is avoided. Dangerous, high voltages are thus kept away from all places of possible contact.

SWITCH CONTROL

It is practicable to control one lamp from two or three places. Thus by a duplex or three-point switch and proper wiring, a lamp may be lighted or turned off from either the first or second story at will. By means of two three-point switches and one four-point switch a first-story hall-lamp may be controlled at will from either the first, second or third stories.

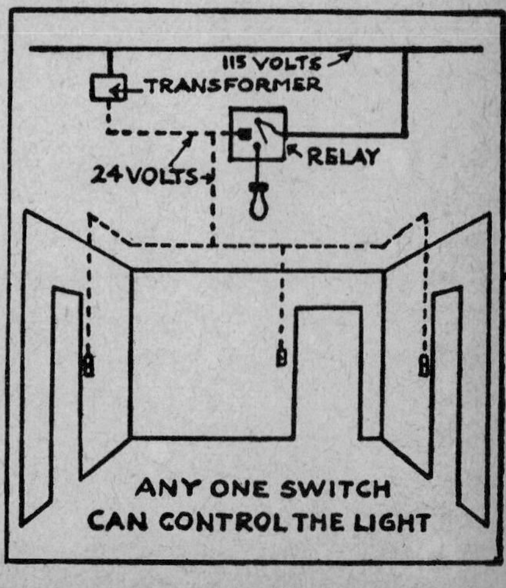

Fig. 39.

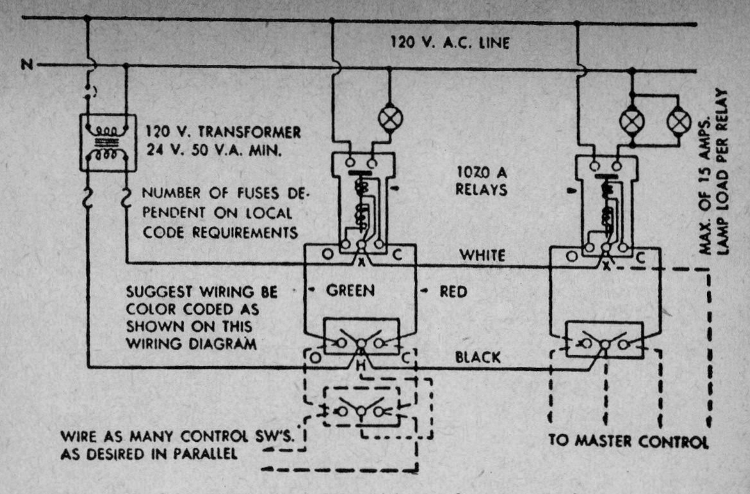

Fig. 40. Basic system of low-voltage control.

Fig. 43 shows the method of control from any number of points, since any number of 4-point snap-switches, such as *B*, *C* and *D*, can be inserted between the 3-point switches *A* and *E* if more points of control are needed. Fig. 44 shows one method of wiring for controlling a hall-light from first and second stories by means of two 3-point switches. With the switches in the position shown the circuit is broken, as there is no connection between the lamps and line *B*. By turning either switch a connection is made with line *B* and the current will flow.

Kinds of Switches. For controlling lamps from one point three kinds of switches are used, namely, snap-switches, flush or push-button switches and knife-switches. When less than eight lamps are controlled by the switch, a flush or push-button switch is commonly used where a neat appearance is desirable, and in places where this is of no importance, a snap-switch is used, as it is the cheaper. Where a circuit of twelve or more lamps is controlled by a switch, a double-pole (d.p.) knife-switch (fig. 45) is commonly used, being generally placed in a cabinet. (*Kidder-Parker Architects' and Builders' Handbook*, published by John Wiley & Sons, Inc., New York, N. Y.)

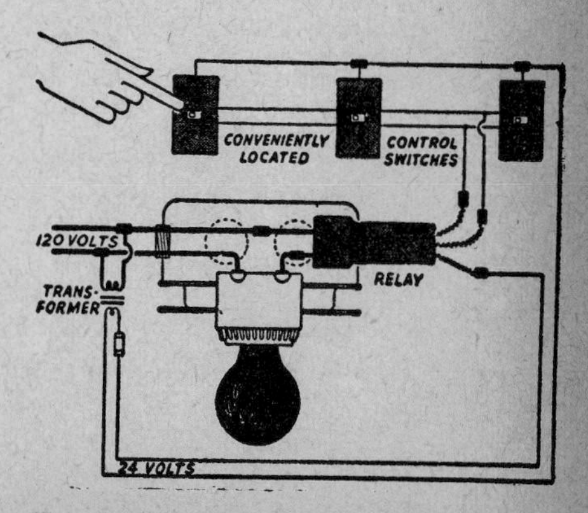

Fig. 41. How remote control relays are installed in knockouts of outlet boxes.

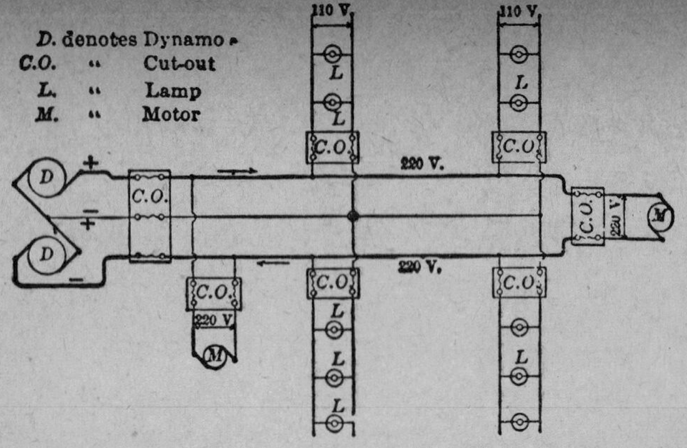

Fig. 42. Example of three-wire system of wiring.

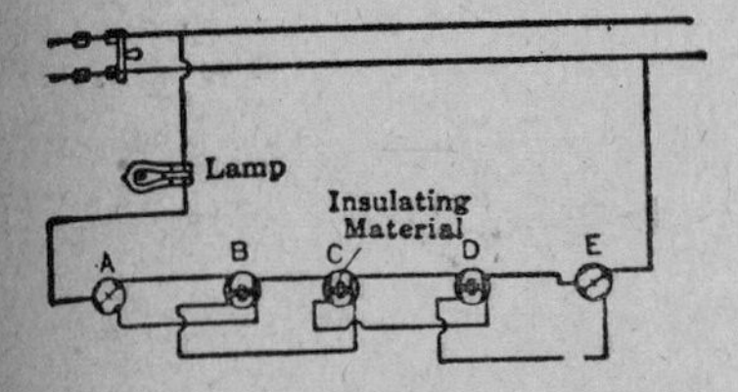

Fig. 43. The lamp may be turned off or on from any of the five points, **A, B, C, D,** or **E.**

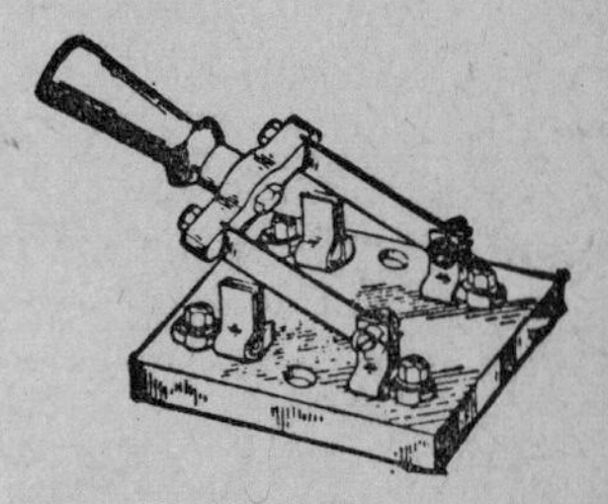

Fig. 45. Common knife-switch.

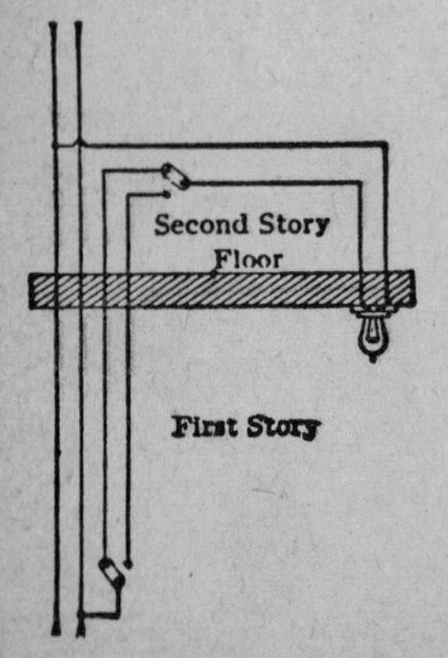

Fig. 44. The lamp may be turned off or on from either the first or second story.

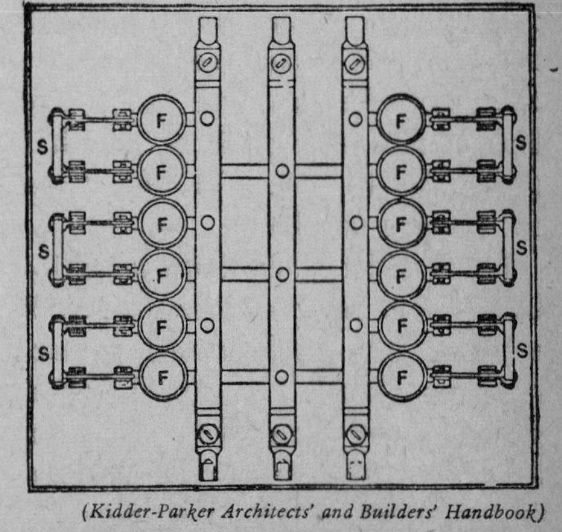

Fig. 46. Cabinet wiring for knife-switch control. **F,** fuse plug; **S,** knife-switch.

SECTION VI

PLUMBING, HEATING FIREPLACES AND CHIMNEYS

Selecting Pipes—Copper and Brass—Cast Iron—Wrought—Cast-Iron Soil Pipe—Water Pipe Sizes—Drainage and Vent Pipes—Fittings—Corrosion and Life of Pipe—Comparison of Pipe Material—Cutting, Threading and Installation of Brass Pipe—Threading Brass Pipe—Threading Nipples and Pipe of Large Diameter—Reaming Brass Pipe—Making Up Joints—Dope—Upside Down Joints—Inserting Fitting in an Existing Line—Deciding Sewer Grade—Jointing Sewer Pipe—Joints and Connections—Opening Joints in Soil Pipe—Simple One-Pipe System—A Two-Pipe System—Insulating Pipe—Recommended Construction Details for Drainage and Vent Systems—Hot Water Tanks—Adjusting Flush Valves for Toilet Tanks—Connecting Range Boilers and Water Backs—Cleaning Clogged Pipes—Thawing Pipes—Stopping Leaks in Pipes and Tanks—Repairing Cracked Laundry Tubs and Garden Hose—Removing Scale from Water Backs and Coils—Saving Hot Water—Garage Drain Trap—Collar Fits Corner Shower—Bathroom Plans—Facts on Bathroom Fixtures—Storage and Accessories—House and Equipment Inspection—Radiators and Convectors—Floor Furnaces—Coal Bin Construction Details—Hand Furnace Operating Hints—Heating and Fireplaces—Metal Chimneys—Avoiding Condensation.

PLUMBING, HEATING, FIREPLACES AND CHIMNEYS

SELECTING PIPES

TABLE A.—INFORMATION ON CAST-IRON SOIL PIPE

Class	Size (inside diameter)	Wall thickness	Hub Inside diameter	Hub Depth	Weight per 5-foot length
	Inches	Inch	Inches	Inches	Pounds
Standard	2	⅛	(1)	(1)	18
Do	3	⅛	(1)	(1)	26
Do	4	⅛	(1)	(1)	35
Do	5	⅛	(1)	(1)	45
Extra heavy	2	¼	3 3/16	2¼	27½
Do	3	¼	4 3/16	2½	47½
Do	4	¼	5 3/16	2¾	65
Do	5	¼	6 3/16	2¾	85

[1] Approximately same as for extra-heavy pipe.

TABLE B.—INFORMATION ON STANDARD-WEIGHT GALVANIZED WROUGHT-IRON AND STEEL PIPES, AND CEMENT-LINED BLACK AND GALVANIZED STEEL PIPES

Nominal size (inside diameter)	Outside diameter	Threads per inch	Nominal weight	
			Galvanized	Cement-lined
	Inches	Number	Pounds	Pounds
⅜ inch	0.675	18	0.57	
½ inch	.840	14	.85	
¾ inch	1.050	14	1.13	1.3
1 inch	1.315	11½	1.68	1.9
1¼ inches	1.660	11½	2.28	2.5
1½ inches	1.900	11½	2.73	3.0
2 inches	2.375	11½	3.68	4.1
2½ inches	2.875	8	5.82	6.6
3 inches	3.500	8	7.62	8.3

COPPER AND BRASS

Seamless copper tubing and seamless copper and brass pipes (iron pipe sizes abbreviated I.P.S.) are meeting with much favor. They have long life and their cost is moderate. It is believed that copper or brass pipe can be used with assurance for conveying all ordinary waters. Although the amount of copper dissolved from pipes in ordinary daily use is extremely minute, it is well, with all kinds of pipe, to waste the so-called "stale" water that has stood long in the pipe. Table C gives information on copper and brass piping.

CAST IRON

Bell and spigot cast-iron pipe, coated with hot coal-tar pitch varnish, is obtainable in various sizes and strengths and is desirable for underground work because of its long life and the ease with which considerable deflection can be made at each joint. Pipes with prepared or foundry-made joints, of which there are several kinds, are desirable for farm use because there is no lead to melt and pour and the time and cost of laying them are reduced. Table D gives information on cast-iron water pipe having the more common types of prepared or bolted joint.

WROUGHT

Within buildings and above ground, soil, waste, and vent pipes may be standard-weight galvanized wrought (either steel or iron) as listed in table B. However, the general practice is to use cast iron for soil stacks and for waste lines larger than 2 inches and to use wrought pipe for waste and vent lines from 1¼ to 2 inches in diameter.

TABLE C.—INFORMATION ON COPPER SERVICE TUBING AND STANDARD-WEIGHT COPPER AND RED-BRASS PIPES (*I.P.S.*)

Kind of pipe	Nominal size	Outside diameter	Wall thickness	Nominal weight per foot
	Inches	Inches	Inch	Pounds
Copper service tubing	⅜	½	0.049	0.27
	½	⅝	.049	.34
	¾	⅞	.065	.64
	1	1⅛	.065	.84
	1¼	1⅜	.065	1.04
	1½	1⅝	.072	1.36
Copper	⅜	0.675	.091	.64
	½	.840	.108	.96
	¾	1.050	.114	1.30
	1	1.315	.127	1.83
	1¼	1.660	.146	2.69
	1½	1.900	.150	3.20
Red brass	⅜	Same as copper.	Same as copper.	.63
	½			.94
	¾			1.27
	1			1.79
	1¼			2.63
	1½			3.13

TABLE D.—INFORMATION ON CAST-IRON PIPE FOR 150 POUNDS WORKING PRESSURE

Type of joint	Nominal size	Outside diameter	Wall thickness	Approximate weight per foot	Laying length
	Inches	Inches	Inch	Pounds	Feet
Bell and spigot prepared for calking	1¼	1.75	0.19	4	5
	2	2.50	.25	6	6
	3	3.66	.31	11½	6
	4	4.80	.34	16½	12 or 16
Tapered, machined male and female ends with lugs and two bolts, nuts, and washers	2	....	.25	6½	6
	3	....	.30	11¼	6
	4	....	.31	16	6
Male and female ends with ring collars, stuffing-box ring gasket, and bolts	2	2.38	.22	6	5
	2½	2.88	.28	8½	5
	3	3.50	.30	11	5
	4	4.80	.34	16	12 or 16

To prevent rust tubercles that impede flow, pipe in the sizes given in table D may be lined with cement at additional costs averaging 10 percent. The first and last listed types of pipe may be obtained in longer laying lengths, the intermediate joints being screwed or welded at the foundry.

CAST-IRON SOIL PIPE

Extra heavy cast-iron soil pipe coated with hot coal-tar pitch varnish and having hub and spigot joints is generally used for soil stacks and all underground lines except the house sewer. The latter is usually vitrified clay or concrete sewer pipe. Standard-weight cast-iron soil pipe is sometimes used, but because of its lightness is more likely to be broken during shipment and handling.

WATER PIPE SIZES

A ½-inch kitchen faucet (inlet 0.53 inch and outlet 0.48 inch) tapped into the side of a barrel of water 2.3 feet from the top, is under a head of 1 pound and discharges, when fully opened, 3 gallons per minute; under a head of 11.5 feet or 5 pounds it discharges 6½ gallons per minute. A reasonable service in an ordinary home requires discharges of not less than 3 gallons per minute for each faucet (or valve) at a sink, washstand, bathtub, water-closet tank, and small shower head, 5 gallons per minute for a sill cock, and 10 gallons per minute for the three usual bathroom fixtures. Seldom are all of these fixtures used at one time. On average days the maximum draft for a family of six may not exceed 10 or 12 gallons per minute, but for short periods fixtures may be used in such combinations as to draw 15 to 20 gallons per minute.

A service pipe should be large enough to deliver the probable maximum draft to the central point of use, usually the bathroom or kitchen sink, and still leave from 1 to 5 pounds pressure on the highest faucet. The problem of how large the service pipe should be can be readily solved by a little study and the use of the diagram below.

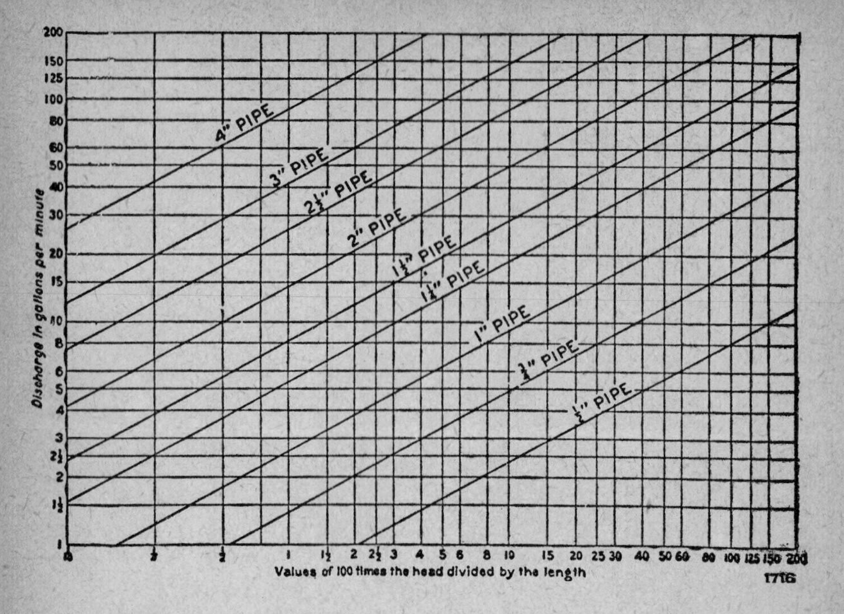

Directions: Measure the head or vertical height in feet from the delivery end of the pipe to the surface of the water in the spring or tank; multiply this head by 100 and divide the product by the actual length of the pipe in feet; find this value on the lower horizontal line of the diagram and follow vertically upward to the inclined line or lines showing pipe sizes; from such intersection follow horizontally to the left to find the discharge in gallons per minute. Example: How much water will be discharged by 128 feet of 1-inch pipe under a head of 32 feet? Solution: Thirty-two multiplied by 100 equals 3,200; 3,200 divided by 128 equals 25; enter the diagram at 25, follow upward to the line marked 1-inch

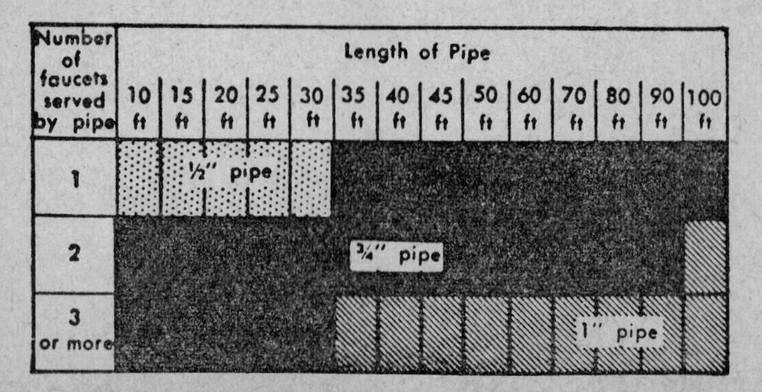

Number of faucets served by pipe
Length of Pipe
10 ft 15 ft 20 ft 25 ft 30 ft 35 ft 40 ft 45 ft 50 ft 60 ft 70 ft 80 ft 90 ft 100 ft
1
2
3 or more
½" pipe
¾" pipe
1" pipe

Fig. 1. Chart for determining proper galvanized pipe sizes.

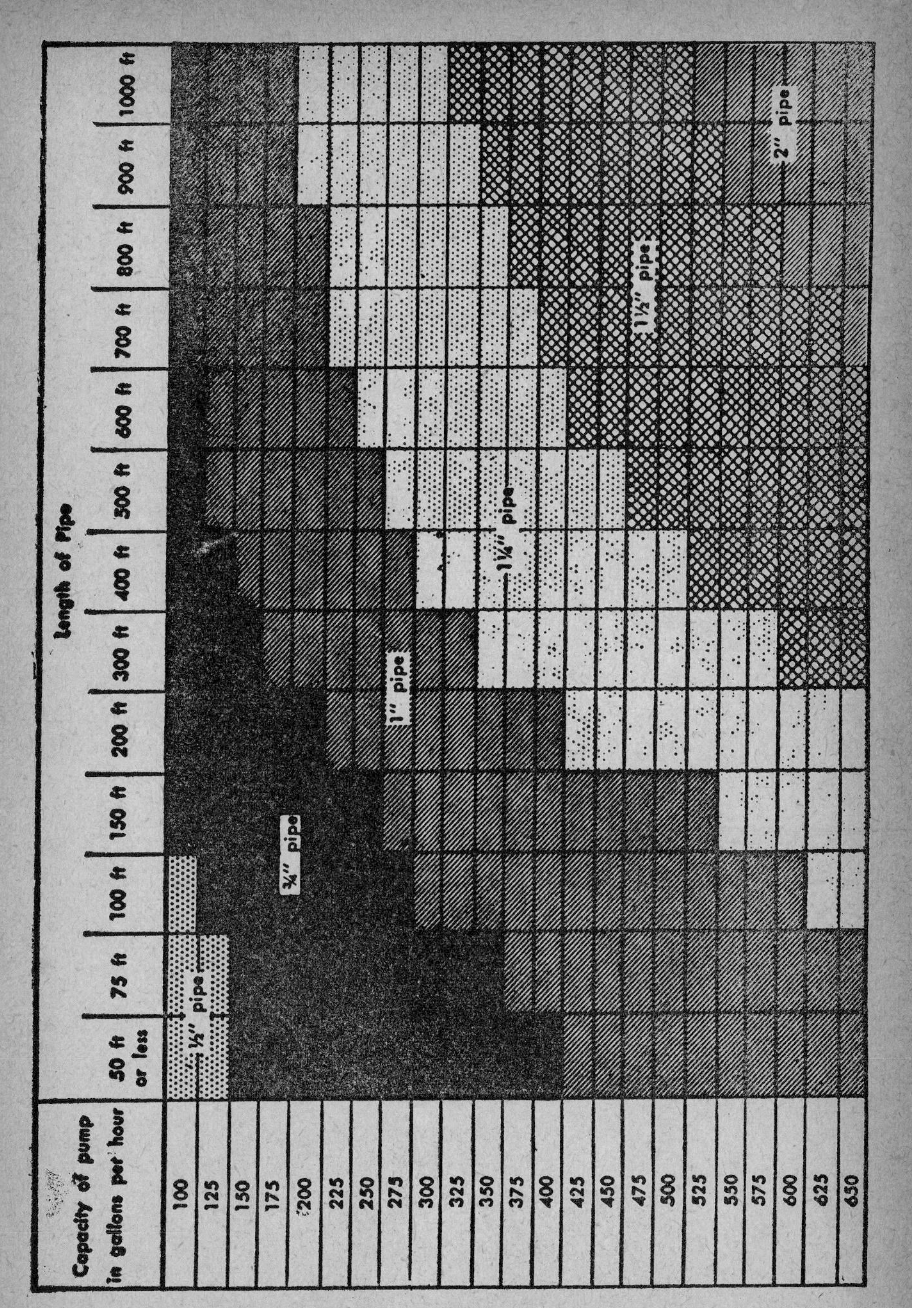

Fig. 2. Chart for determining proper size of galvanized pipe to use depending on pump capacity and length of pipe.

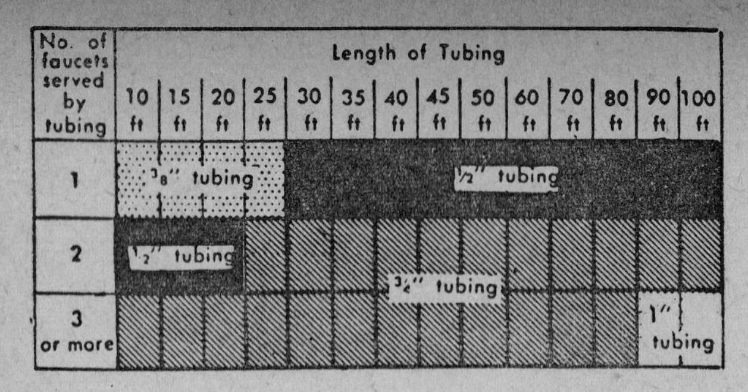

Fig. 3. Chart for determining proper copper tubing sizes.

pipe, and then follow to the left where the discharge is seen to be 15 gallons per minute.

The diagram assumes that all the head is used to overcome friction within the pipe and that the water emerges full bore of the pipe and practically without pressure. Before applying the diagram to find the discharge of a pipe restricted by a faucet at the outlet, several feet should be deducted from the head to allow for friction losses within the faucet. This allowance for an ordinary ½-inch kitchen faucet may vary, as indicated above, from 2.3 feet (1 pound) for a fair flow to 11.5 feet (5 pounds) for a strong flow.

If the flow is from a hydropneumatic tank or street main, the equivalent head is 2.3 feet per pound of gage pressure, plus the vertical height of the tank or main above the faucet, or minus the vertical distance that the tank or main is below the faucet. Elbows and valves retard flow slightly, but this loss of head in fairly direct service lines can usually be disregarded.

Weak flow at faucets is often caused by small or clogged distribution pipes. In general, branches longer than 25 feet or supplying two or more small fixtures should be of ¾-inch pipe. The following table indicates sizes of distribution pipes.

SIZES OF HOUSE DISTRIBUTION PIPES (INCHES)

Class of pressure	Distribution main	Short branch to— Bathroom	Bathtub	Washstand[1]	Closet tank[2]	Kitchen sink	Laundry	Sill cock
High	¾	¾	½	½	½	½	½	½
Medium	¾ or 1	¾	½	½	½	½ or ¾	½ or ¾	¾
Low	1 or 1¼	¾ or 1	½	½	½	¾	¾	¾

[1] Pipe from floor or wall is usually ⅜ or ½ inch, reducing to ¼-inch at faucet tailpiece.
[2] Pipe from floor or wall to ball cock is usually ⅜-inch.

DRAINAGE AND VENT PIPES

Although the requirements of local plumbing codes differ greatly there is a growing tendency toward standardization, and in the absence of code requirement it is believed the following tabulation lists the sizes of soil, waste, flush, and vent pipes that are serviceable and safe in homes.

PIPE AND CONDITIONS

	Size (inches)
House drain; ordinary house, no rain water	4
Soil stack	3
Water-closet bend and branch to soil stack	3 or 4
Water-closet flush, low tank, O.D. tubing	2
Waste; lateral pitched ¼ inch per foot, and including fixture pipe or O.D. tubing to wall or floor:	
Kitchen sink, bathtub, washstand, laundry tub (1, 2, or 3 section) with continuous waste and trap, or combination sink and laundry tub (1 or 2 section) with continuous waste and trap, each fixture	1½
Two washstands	1½
Three washstands or any two of the other fixtures	2
Slop sink, shower stall, floor drain, or kitchen sink waste buried in ground or concrete	2 or 3
Waste stack; usually same size as largest lateral draining into it	1½ or 2
Traps; no smaller than entering waste; minimum seal, 2 inches:	
Vents:	
Extension of soil stack	3
One washstand on a 1¼-inch stack	1¼
Two or three small fixtures on a 1½-inch stack	1½
Up to 6 small fixtures on a 2-inch stack	1½
Water closet (if another is above) with the usual small fixtures	1½ or 2

FITTINGS

Fittings and pipe should be of similar metal—cast iron with cast iron, malleable iron with wrought iron or steel, and brass with brass or copper pipe. Plain galvanized malleable-iron fittings are suitable for low-pressure indoor wrought water pipe, but the stronger banded fittings are generally used for high pressures and also for underground work.

Cast iron drainage fittings avoid abrupt changes of direction. Those for wrought pipe are galvanized or asphalted, and have enlarged ends forming a recess about three-fourths inch deep. They have the same bore as standard pipe (I.P.S.), which, when screwed in, butts against the shoulder, forming a smooth and continuous waterway.

CORROSION AND LIFE OF PIPE

Pipe and fittings are made thicker than is required to sustain water pressure. This is to guard against corrosion and the strains caused by cutting, threading, and joining pipes and by the expansion and contraction of pipe lines. All waters and soils corrode, the action being particularly noticeable at threaded joints in wrought pipe. The results are "red water," reduced capacity, and shortened life. Sometimes the bore is clogged or closed with a rusty coating or deposit long before the pipe wall is destroyed.

Ordinarily, small black wrought pipe in the ground should last 10 to 20 years; galvanized steel, 15 to 30 years; galvanized wrought iron, 20 to 40 years; lead and cast iron, 40 to 75 years. It is, however, not uncommon to find lead and cast-iron pipes sound after 80 to 100 years, and, except for slight external corrosion, cement-lined black wrought pipe has been found in excellent condition after 40 to 60 years in the ground.

COMPARISON OF PIPE MATERIAL

Iron pipe has a rather rough interior which retards the flow of water. Brass and copper pipe, on the other hand, have a smooth interior which allows for a greater flow of water. For this reason, it is possible to use a smaller diameter brass and copper pipe and still obtain the same flow of water as would be had through the larger size iron pipe. The accompanying table shows the sizes of brass and copper pipe to be selected when pipe sizes are shown for iron pipe.

PIPE SIZE COMPARISON

Iron Pipe Nominal Size (inches)	*Corresponding Suitable Sizes for Brass and Copper Pipe (inches)*	
	Hot Water	*Cold Water*
½	⅜	⅜
¾	½	½
1	¾	¾
1¼	1	1
1½	1	1¼
2	1¼	1½
2½	1½	2
3	2	2½

CUTTING, THREADING AND INSTALLATION OF BRASS PIPE

The ever-increasing demand for brass pipe and brass fittings in modern plumbing construction calls for a general knowledge of safe, sure, and quick methods of working the pipe.

The fact, known to plumbers who have had experience with brass installations, and readily manifest to others now acquiring that experience, is that good modern brass pipe can be handled as easily and as quickly as iron or steel pipe.

The operations are very simple. They just require a few different inexpensive tools and a little special information. The special tools can be bought from any reputable plumbers' supply house.

The pipe vises used in brass pipe work may be those commonly used in iron pipe work. It is not necessary to purchase special vises for brass pipe. It is advisable, however, to have a set of friction clamps to protect the pipe from the teeth of the vise. These clamps can be either purchased or made. A set will last a long time.

A home made form is shown in fig. 4. A common steel pipe coupling is sawed in halves. Then each half is lined with a piece of 6 or 8 lb. sheet lead, this being squeezed into the coupling threads by screwing down the clamps and lead pieces tightly over a piece of brass or iron pipe in the vise, then beating the edges of the lead over the iron half-coupling, substantially as shown. The coupling threads penetrate the sheet lead and help to hold it firmly in place. The lead lining thus fits snugly around the pipe, making a large bearing area which holds by friction, not by teeth cutting into the brass.

Fig. 5 illustrates a piece of brass pipe held firmly in a pipe vise by such a clamp. The jaws are screwed tightly on the clamps and the lead holds the pipe by friction. To prevent the pipe from slipping in the clamps, the lead linings may be sprinkled with powdered resin before the pipe is set in them. The resin makes the lead grip the pipe firmly and still does not cut into it.

Factory-made clamps similar to fig. 6 are better. They are stronger and do not spread like the kind shown in fig. 4. They hold firmer and last longer.

Any resin that sticks to the pipe can be dissolved and washed off with a rag moistened with alcohol or gasoline. Alcohol is quicker in action.

Thus in all respects, except the placing of friction clamps in the vise, the operation is the same as in iron pipe work.

THREADING BRASS PIPE

There is no difficulty in the threading of modern brass pipe. Start the thread in the usual way, then pull easily and steadily until the thread is

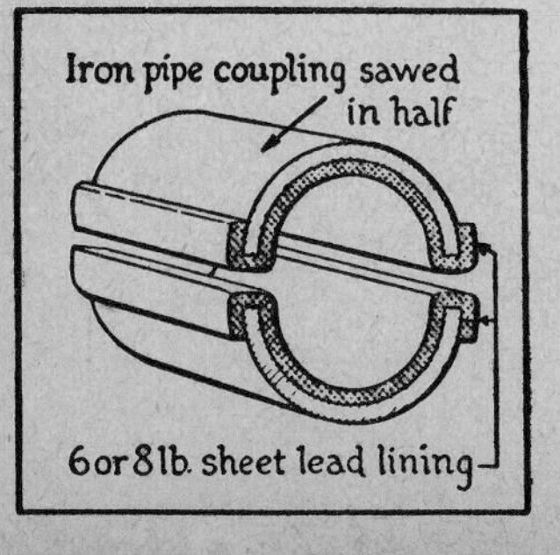

Fig. 4. Friction clamp.

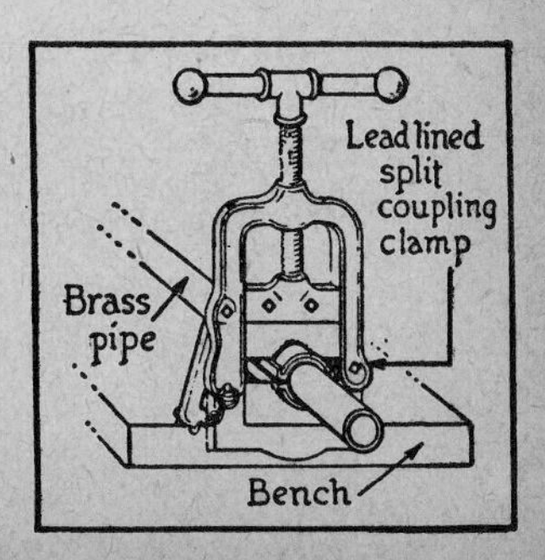

Fig. 5. Friction clamp in use.

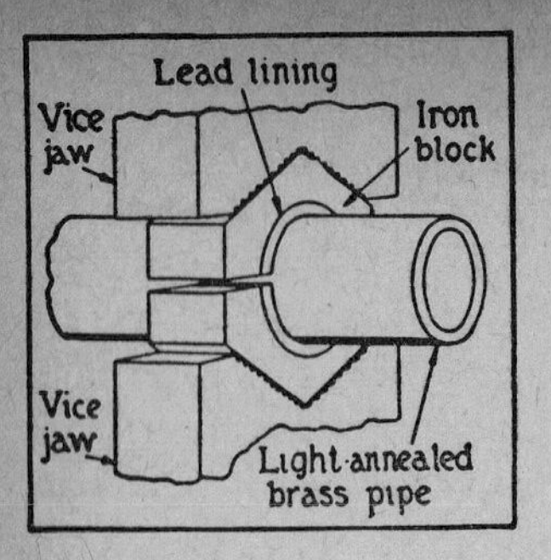

Fig. 6. Detail of friction clamp.

run up full length. Use any desired speed but let it be steady. Don't "jerk" or "yank" at the dies. Just pull steadily and if the dies are in fairly good condition, you will not only get a good, clean-cut thread, but will save energy too. If chips gather, reverse the motion of the stock a little to release them. Then blow them out.

Fix the brass pipe in the vise, using clamps, as shown in figure 7. Do not have the end projecting more than sufficient for easy working, about 6 inches from the face of vise. The less projection the better. It makes the pipe stiffer in resisting the threading strains.

Examine the dies and see that they are set to correct gauge mark so that they will cut the thread standard size, not more, not less, just exactly standard. Remember that the fittings are tapped standard thread, and the thread you cut on the pipe end must match the fitting thread exactly. By cutting an exact-to-standard thread you will have a good tight metal-to-metal screw joint when the thread is screwed up in its fitting. Otherwise the pipe thread will be too tight or too loose for the fitting.

Also blow, or scrape out any chips or dirt that may have been left in the dies from the last threading operation (especially if this was on steel or iron, which is not recommended for dies for brass pipe). Clean, sharp dies should always be used in threading brass pipe, or any other metal. Dies with chipped teeth, or metal chips clogging them, or sand or dirt in them, should not be used. To obtain good, sharp, clean-cut full threads—that is, perfect threads—you must have good, clean, perfect dies.

Knowing that the dies are clean slip the guide over the pipe (this refers to handcut threads at the pipe vise—not machine cut threads).

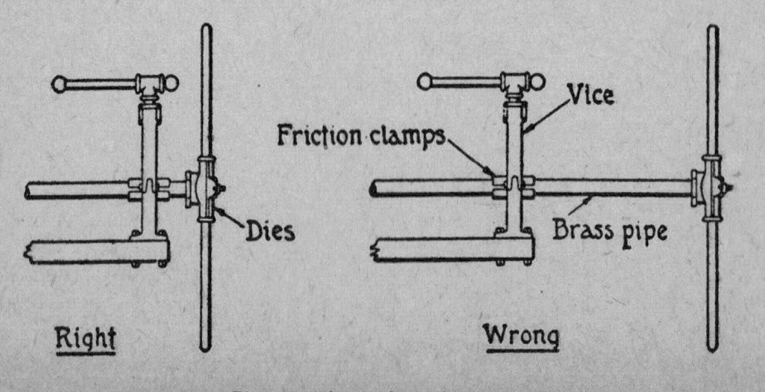

Fig. 7. Threading brass pipe.

Then start the thread. The starting of a thread is the only part of the threading process where it may pay to jerk the dies a little, and then only when the dies are hard to start.

After a few revolutions, if the dies have caught, the die head may be quite hard to revolve with one hand only. Then apply both hands to the handles, and pull slowly at first and the thread will cut along steadily, giving an even resistance to the pull. But if they have not caught, they will quickly strip the thread and ease up the resistance to the pull on the handles. These few pointers combined with a little experience will enable one to properly start a pipe thread by hand.

Lubrication of the die while cutting the thread is most important. It is necessary to keep the die cool and preserve the cutting edges, so that clean smooth threads may be obtained every time. Use plenty of cooling cutting oil. An insufficient quantity, or the improper type of oil may cause "welds" in the die teeth, destroying the pipe threads. Do not jerk the stock when cutting threads, but pull with a steady movement. Reverse the stock occasionally to break the chips. Long chips are apt to scar the threads. After thread is completed clean it with care. The threads in fittings also should be cleaned with care so that no dirt remains in the threads to prevent a satisfactory and perfectly tight metal-to-metal contact.

Perhaps the most important thing in running up the dies is to know when to stop and reverse them. All threads must be the right length. That is to say they must be run long enough to obtain five or more perfect threads to insure a thorough and full metal-to-metal contact when the threads are screwed "home" in their fittings. The pipe should enter the fitting about four threads by hand without a wrench.

To understand this fully refer to figure 8 which illustrates the standard thread, one that is accepted throughout the United States as standard, and used on wrought iron, steel, brass, and copper; steam, gas and water piping. The thread used is the regular American Standards Association Standard B 2.1-1945 pipe thread. This is now the standard thread for the United States, superseding the "Briggs" thread.

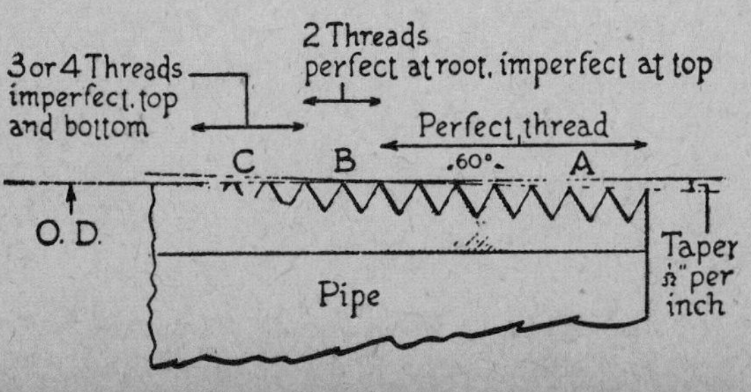

Fig. 8. Standard Pipe thread.

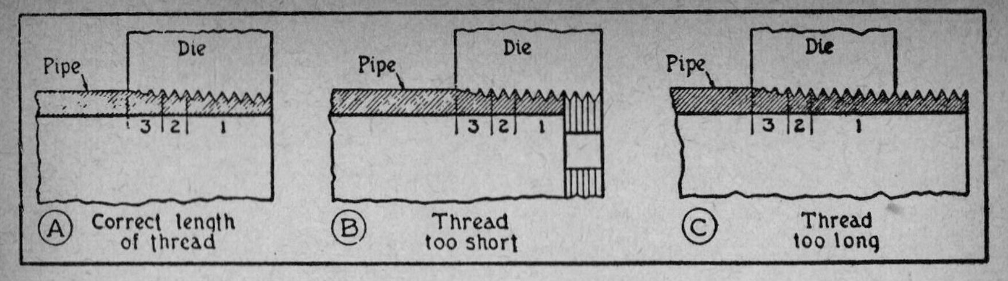

Fig. 9. Correct length of thread.

Note that this thread is composed of three distinctly different parts. The part *A* has all perfect threads. They are perfect top and bottom. At *B* there are two threads perfect at bottom, or root, but imperfect at top. At *C* there are three or four threads imperfect at both top and bottom, but perfect at the sides.

The object in having the threads at *C* not cut down to their roots is to give strength to the pipe here. The two imperfect threads at *B* cannot be otherwise because this is the point where they "die out" at the outer surface of the pipe.

The threads at *A*, however, are all cut well within the body of the metal and consequently are full and perfect at top as well as at the roots. That is the portion of the thread which is depended upon for watertightness of the screwed joints. The portions *B* and *C* are just "tapering off" extensions of the perfect thread and are there only to strengthen the pipe at the fitting.

It may not be necessary on all classes of work to have as many perfect threads as there are shown in figure 8, namely, seven. Four or five usually are quite satisfactory provided the threads in the fittings where these perfect male threads fit in, are also perfect.

The threaded ends of pipe are cut conical, with a taper of ¾-inch to the foot, or 1 in 16 to the axis of the pipe, which is clearly shown in figure 8. This makes the thread enter the fitting easily at first, tightening as it goes in. Incidentally, also, it produces that enormous outward thrust which tends to swell or split the fitting if it is too weak.

Figure 8 and the foregoing reference to it are sufficient to explain just how far up the dies should be run. If the dies are correctly made and properly adjusted, the threading may be stopped when the pipe end is flush with the face of the dies as at *A* in figure 9. This is the correct length for the thread. That is standard.

Some mechanics may feel disposed to save in threading labor by setting the dies a little closer together. This enables them to cut shorter threads as at *B*, figure 9, but this is not good practice.

While these short threads may screw into standard tapped fittings properly, the number of perfect threads is cut down from 4 or 5 to perhaps only 1. That lessens the chance of having the joint water-tight when screwed up as tight with the wrench as the one shown at *A*. But it does not have as much perfect thread contact and therefore cannot be depended on for water-tightness, as much as that in sketch *A*. Threads like that shown at *B* are not considered good practice. Besides they usually require considerable "dope" to make them water-tight.

At *C*, figure 9 is a thread that is too long. Those projecting beyond the dies are useless threads. They have no taper. The tendency is for these non-taper threads to set up tight deep in the fitting before the imperfect threads at Nos. 2 and 3 are screwed up tight. In such a case the non-taper threads may be tight and the others all loose. This is not good practice.

Mechanics are cautioned against making threads either too short or too long, as at *B* and *C*. They should cut threads the full thickness of the die, as in sketch *A*. It is assumed that the die is made right, and of the correct thickness, so that the full length of the standard thread will be obtained when the pipe end is flush with the face of the die or not more than one thread beyond it.

THREADING NIPPLES AND PIPE OF LARGE DIAMETER

Although it is customary to buy ready-made nipples, occasions may arise when it is necessary for a mechanic to make a nipple of special length.

Suitable nipple holders may be used for threading nipples of different lengths. For example, consider the threading of a short nipple. Figure 10 illustrates a nipple holder all ready for threading. The operation of this particular form of holder, which is an excellent one, is as follows:

Place shank part of holder in the vise and hold it tight. Screw the already threaded end of the nipple into the collar as shown. Drive in the wedge lightly with a hammer. Then, using the collar as a guide for the dies, proceed to thread the end of the nipple. When the thread has been run the full length, run back the dies, and the nipple is threaded

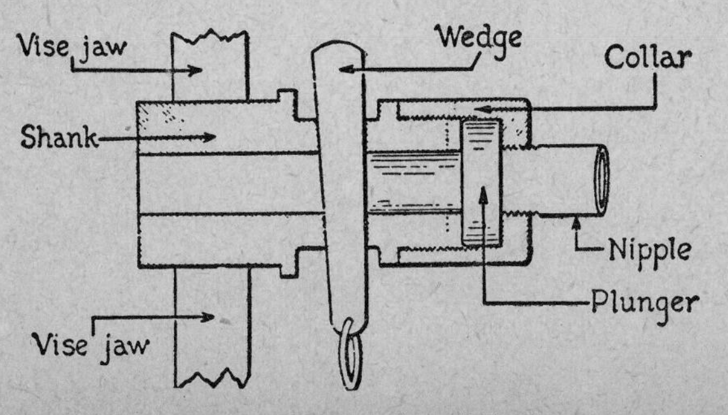

Fig. 10. How to thread nipples.

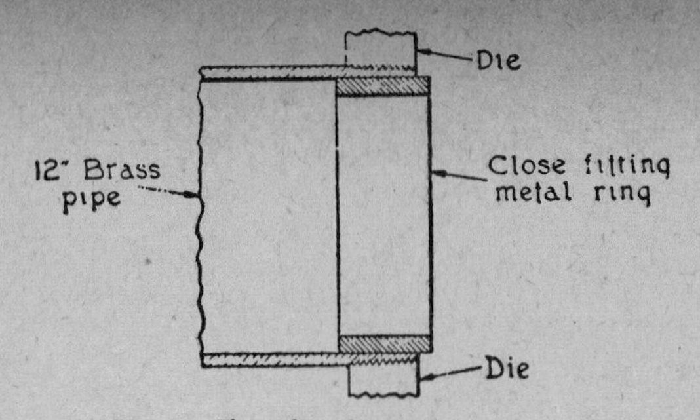

Fig. 11. Threading large diameter pipe.

as easily as if it had been cut on a full length of pipe.

To remove the nipple, drive the wedge back and unscrew the nipple by hand. This can be done because the thread in the collar is a little deeper cut than standard. Consequently the nipple thread fits loosely in it. It is the wedge forcing the face of the plunger against the nipple face that prevents the nipple from turning while being threaded, and from coming out with the dies when their motion is reversed. This is a very simple operation and can be easily performed with the use of a good nipple-holder.

The threading of large diameter pipe is not so simple an operation as is the threading of small pipe. In threading a large size it was found that the pipe became flattened by the inward pressure of the dies, so that at first perfect threads could not be made. However, a solution was found which worked out perfectly. The method employed was simply to fit a metal plug tightly into the end of the pipe where the thread was to be cut (fig. 11). This plug held the end of the pipe in perfect form while the thread was being cut. This practical wrinkle may help others when they encounter the problem of threading large size light-annealed brass pipe in a regular threading machine.

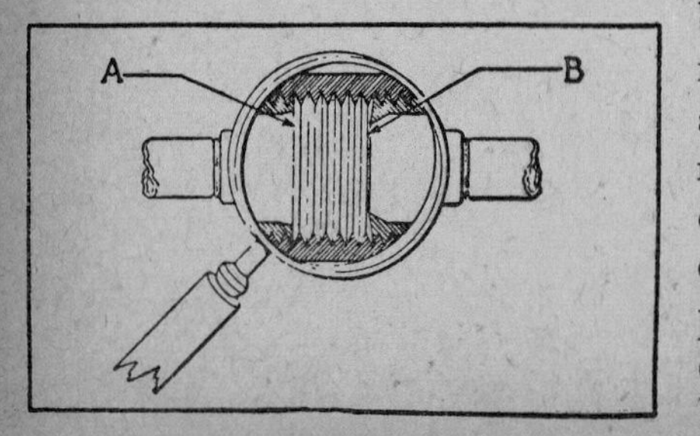

Fig. 12. Avoiding a burr.

REAMING BRASS PIPE

Generally speaking every cut pipe-end should be reamed after it has been threaded so that any burr, no matter how small, even if it is only a ragged sharp edge, will be removed. The object of reaming is to enable the pipe to deliver its full capacity. It is bad practice to install pipes of correct sizes and then reduce the bore at every fitting through burrs made while cutting the pipes. Furthermore large burrs may tend to increase pipe-end corrosion. Every well prepared specification calls for the reaming of every pipe-end to insure the pipes discharging at full capacity.

That reaming is necessary in all water pipe work, whether of wrought iron, steel, or brass, is shown by figure 12 which gives a cut-away view of an ordinary pipe-coupling, magnified. The pipe-end at *A* has a reamed edge with no interior projecting burr to interfere with the flow. But the pipe-end at *B* has a heavy burr, which projects well into the pipe, reducing its bore greatly and thus preventing it from delivering water at its full capacity. It is almost needless to say that this burr should have been reamed out.

A type of tool suitable for reaming pipe-ends and one that is extensively used is shown in figure 13. Its operation is simple. After the pipe-end has been threaded, and before taking the pipe out of the vise, insert the point of this conical reamer in the pipe-end, press it in hard with one hand on the knob, and with the other hand work the handle. With a ratchet type of reamer the operation of the handle is just like that of a pitcher spout pump. In reaming the pipe-ends it is well not to stop the instant the burr, or rough edge, is removed and the exact diameter of the pipe is attained. Just keep on a little longer until the pipe-end is funnel mouthed slightly as in figure 14 and this will increase the carrying capacity of the pipe to its maximum limit. This countersunk reaming is superior to

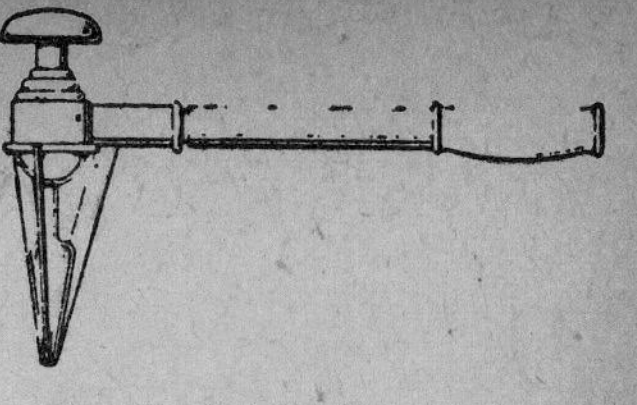

Fig. 13. A tool for reaming.

the clean cut square edge and represents first class reaming.

MAKING UP JOINTS

The method of making up brass pipe screw joints is practically the same as making up wrought-iron and steel pipe screw joints, the only difference being that friction-gripping wrenches are preferable to teeth-gripping wrenches. In screwing up a brass fitting on a pipe, or nipple, in the vise, it is advisable to turn the fitting with a monkey-wrench, which has smooth jaws, rather than with a Stillson wrench, which has teeth in its jaws. The object is to prevent cutting into the bands of the fittings and so reducing their strength. Figure 15 illustrates what is meant. A Stillson wrench is shown in the act of turning a brass elbow or tee at *A*. Note how the teeth cut into the brass bead. This practice is wrong. Brass fittings should never be "chewed into" with such wrenches.

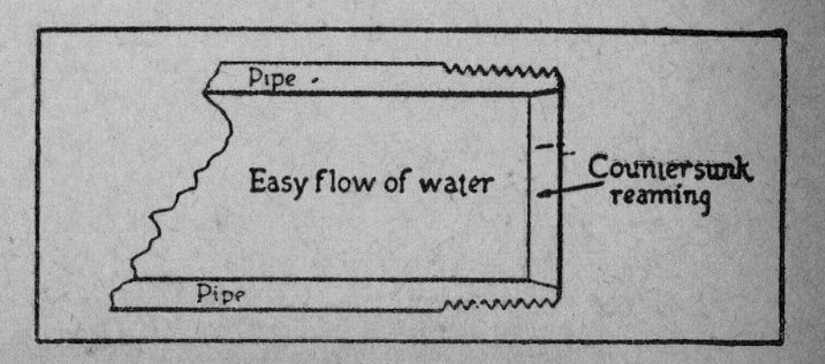

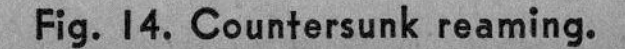

Fig. 14. Countersunk reaming.

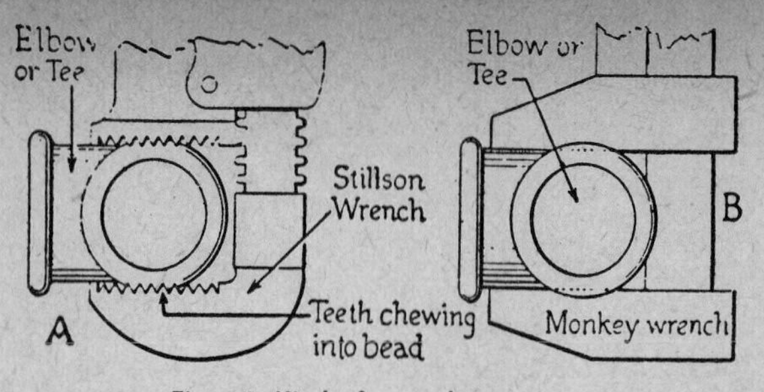

Fig. 15. Kind of wrench to use.

The correct practice is to use a monkey-wrench as shown at *B* in the same figure. The flat smooth jaws are screwed down tight over the body of the fitting. A short piece of pipe can also be used, as previously described. Then the fitting can be screwed up without marring or weakening it in any way.

When an owner, architect or sanitary engineer sees brass pipe fittings or brass pipe marked with wrenches, he immediately brands as incompetent the establishment responsible for such glaringly defective workmanship. If a mechanic desires to hold up his own personal reputation, or the reputation of the concern he works for, he will avoid marring brass pipe and fittings through the use of improper tools. He does not lose time by using proper tools. On the contrary he saves time, because when the water is turned on, the job is found satisfactory.

In screwing a fitting on a pipe held in the vise, the pipe should project as little as possible beyond the vise, the same as mentioned for threading. That is to allow the fitting to be screwed up quite tight without danger of splitting, bending, or twisting the pipe. In screwing up pipes in position on the job the same principles apply. Take, for example, a 6 ft. length of ¾-inch brass pipe with an elbow on one end, the elbow having been screwed on at the vise which is best practice. It is required to screw this up into another elbow, say under the floor.

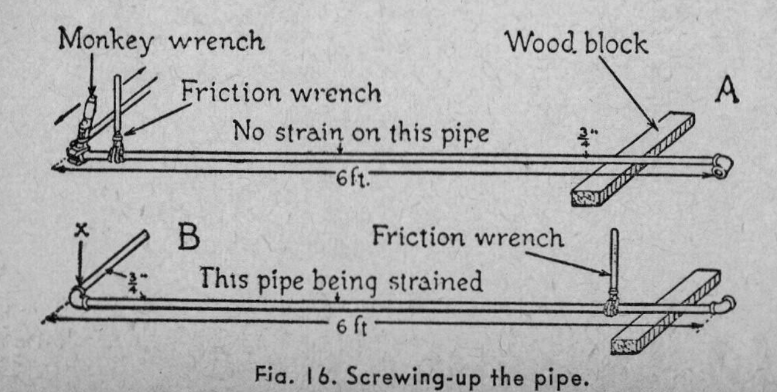

Fig. 16. Screwing-up the pipe.

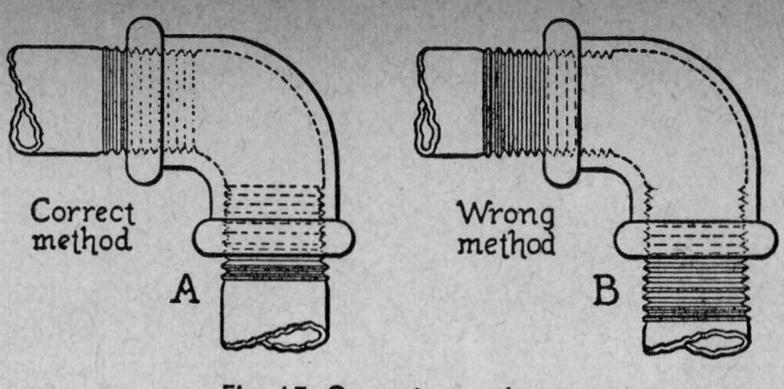

Fig. 17. Correct screwing-up.

The correct procedure is to enter the threaded pipe-end into the elbow by hand, and screw it up by hand as far as it will go. Then apply the friction wrench, say 2 or 3 inches from the fitting to which the pipe is being connected, and set the thread up firm and tight with the wrench, holding the fitting with a monkey-wrench. That is good practice and should produce a strong and permanently water-tight joint without putting unusual strain on the piping anywhere. This method is illustrated in figure 16 (*A*).

At figure 16-*B*, a wrong method is illustrated. It is one which should be avoided. Note that the wrench is about 5 ft. away from the elbow into which the pipe is being screwed. All of that 5 feet of pipe is being subjected to a severe twisting strain. The other pipe is also subjected to excessive strains. It is not a twisting strain but a cross strain which tends to snap the pipe at X where it is cut away at the thread.

In addition to these unnecessary strains being put on the pipe, it is a fact that joints cannot be screwed up as tightly nor as quickly by the method shown at *B* as they can by that shown at *A*. Therefore method *B* should be avoided.

The general principle which is exhibited at *A* in figure 16 should be

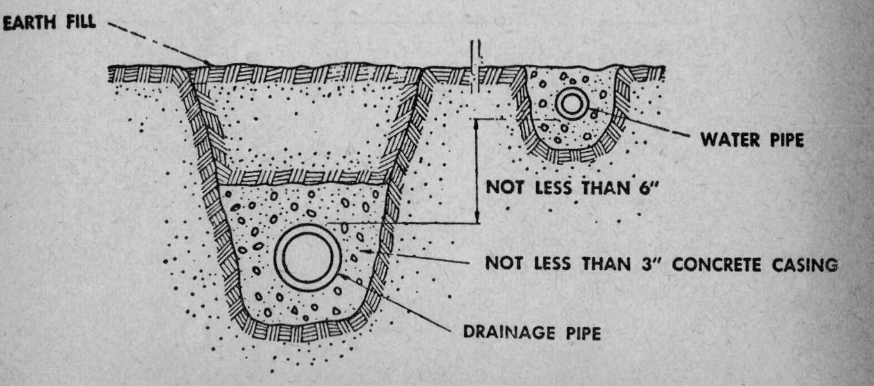

Fig. 18. When it is necessary to run pipes through acid soils or cinder fills, concrete casings are necessary to prevent damage to the pipe.

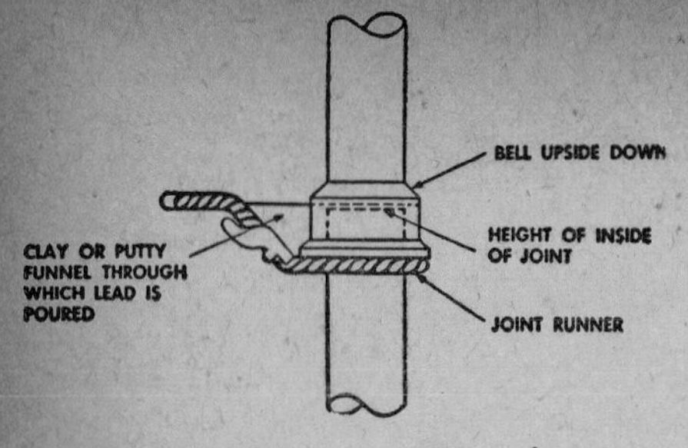

Fig. 19. Using a joint runner to make an upside-down joint.

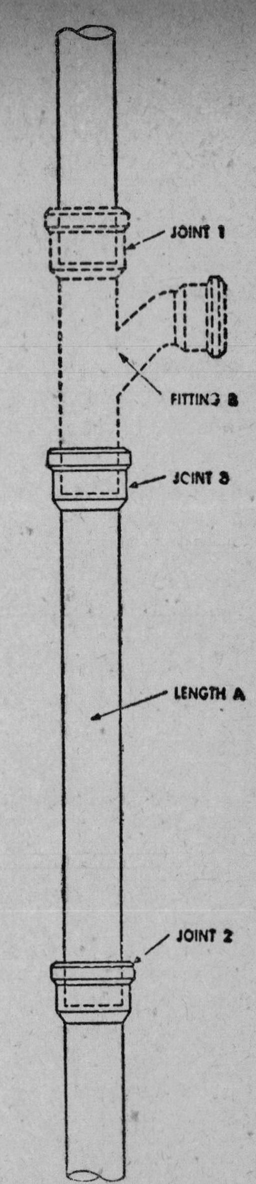

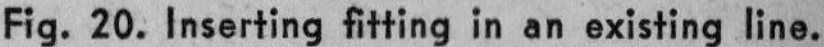

Fig. 20. Inserting fitting in an existing line.

applied throughout a brass pipe job. That is to say, grip the pipe close to the fitting into which it has to be screwed, and hold the fitting tight against the pull of the friction wrench. It is easy. Just work the friction wrench with one hand and hold the fitting with a monkey-wrench in the other hand. This applies to the smaller sizes of pipe.

The larger sizes require the friction wrench to be held with both hands, the helper holding the reverse way with a large wrench on the fitting.

The question has often been asked—"Just how far should a brass pipe thread be run into a brass fitting?"

It should be run in full length of the threaded sections (*A* and *B* fig. 8) which are perfect at the bottom or root so that only the two or three threads imperfect top and bottom extend outside the fitting as at *A* in figure 17.

Exposing of one or two threads is considered good practice. Too many threads being exposed, however, is a bad practice, which usually weakens the pipe at that point, and thus should be avoided.

If all the threads are forced into the fitting so that none show, those two or three imperfect at the root may expand the fitting or, if the fit-

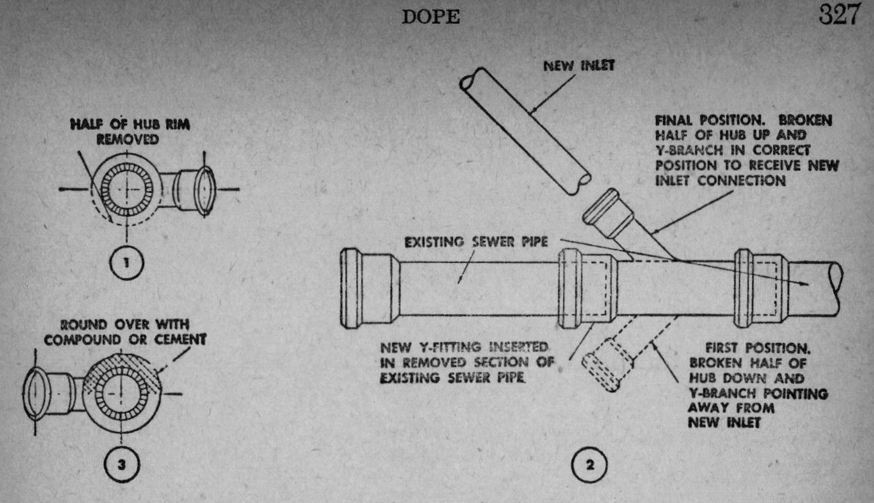

Fig. 21. Additional connections to outside sewer lines can be installed without too much disturbance to the original work as shown above.

ting is heavy, may collapse the pipe and the joint may not be tight or durable. It is known that in method *B*, figure 17, the physical strength of the pipe is greatly reduced at the exposed threads because the metal has been cut away leaving the pipe much thinner at the thread roots.

All pipes on a job have to stand certain strains from expansion and contraction, structural conditions, and otherwise, which may tend to break them at the fittings.

If the fittings are not tapped full enough, threads must be cut deeper than standard. This cuts out too much metal, which weakens the pipe, and is bad practice.

What is wanted is not fittings tapped too small, but accurately tapped fittings which will allow standard male threads to make up full with not more than two threads exposed. Then the best kind of screwed joints result and a maximum pipe-strength remains.

DOPE

Another question that often arises is, "Shall 'dope' be used in making up brass pipe joints, and if so, what should it be?"

The answer is: "Theoretically, no; practically, yes."

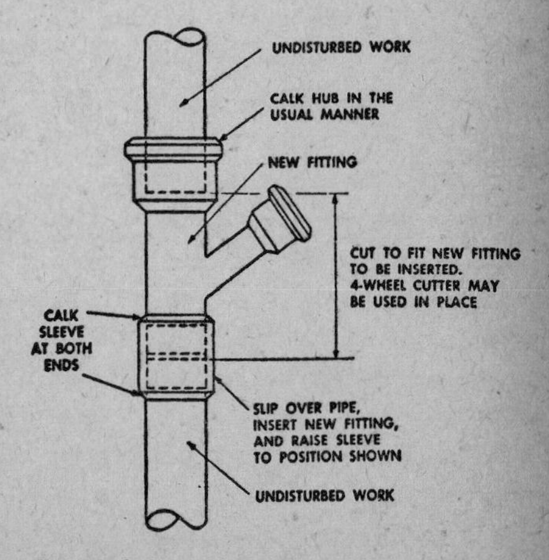

Fig. 22. It is sometimes necessary, especially in remodeling, to install a fitting in a restricted space. This is done by making the joint in the restricted area with a sleeve.

This means that something should be used on the threads when they are being screwed into their fittings, to help make the joints absolutely water-and-gas-tight.

With an absolutely perfect thread on the pipe-end, and an absolutely perfect thread in the fitting, both threads being perfectly clean, and exactly the same in pitch and angle, etc., it is quite possible to screw them together without "dope" and obtain a fine strong water-tight joint. But that calls for a higher degree of perfection than may be expected in practical work, and so the use of "dope" to take care of slight imperfections in both male and female threads becomes necessary.

What that "dope" shall be is very much a matter of opinion, and there is a choice of a variety of satisfactory pipe joint cements now on the market and available to plumbers. These are now extensively used in preference to threads of wicking.

Where prepared cements are not available, red lead mixed to a paste with boiled linseed oil may be used. Litharge and glycerine mixed to a creamy paste is also satisfactory.

The "dope" should be applied to the male thread only, the female thread being left plain, but clean.

Pipe joint cement performs two valuable functions in the screwing up of a joint. It fills small interstices between the threads, if any, making them water-tight. It lubricates the threads so that a joint can be made up tighter with a given pull on the wrench, than is possible in a joint where no lubricant is used.

Several years ago when plumbers were changing over from iron pipes to brass pipes their dies and other tools were not perfectly adapted to brass pipe work, the result frequently being ragged or torn threads. With such imperfect threads it was difficult to make perfectly water-tight joints, without the use of cotton wicking which became chewed inside the threads, filled the comparatively large interstices, and so made the joints water-tight. Conditions, however, are changed now. Modern brass pipe working tools on the market are so improved that there is no excuse for having ragged or torn pipe threads. Consequently wicking is not necessary for present day brass pipe screw thread joints, although it is still used to some extent.

UPSIDE DOWN JOINTS

When making an upside down calked joint in cast iron pipe, the joint runner should be attached as shown in figure 19. To provide a way to pour the lead into the joint, a clay or putty trough is constructed between the end of the joint runner and the pipe. This trough must be high enough to allow the lead to flow to the highest portion of the joint.

INSERTING FITTING IN AN EXISTING LINE

It is often necessary to insert an additional fitting in an existing drain line (fig. 20). The first step is to melt the lead out of the joints *1* and *2*. This can be done by playing a torch on the joints and catching the molten lead as it pours out in a container. This lead can be reused. After the joints have been opened, pipe *A* should be cut to the correct length. The additional fitting (*B*) is then connected to pipe *A* and the assembly fitted into the line. After this has been done, straighten the line up and calk all the joints.

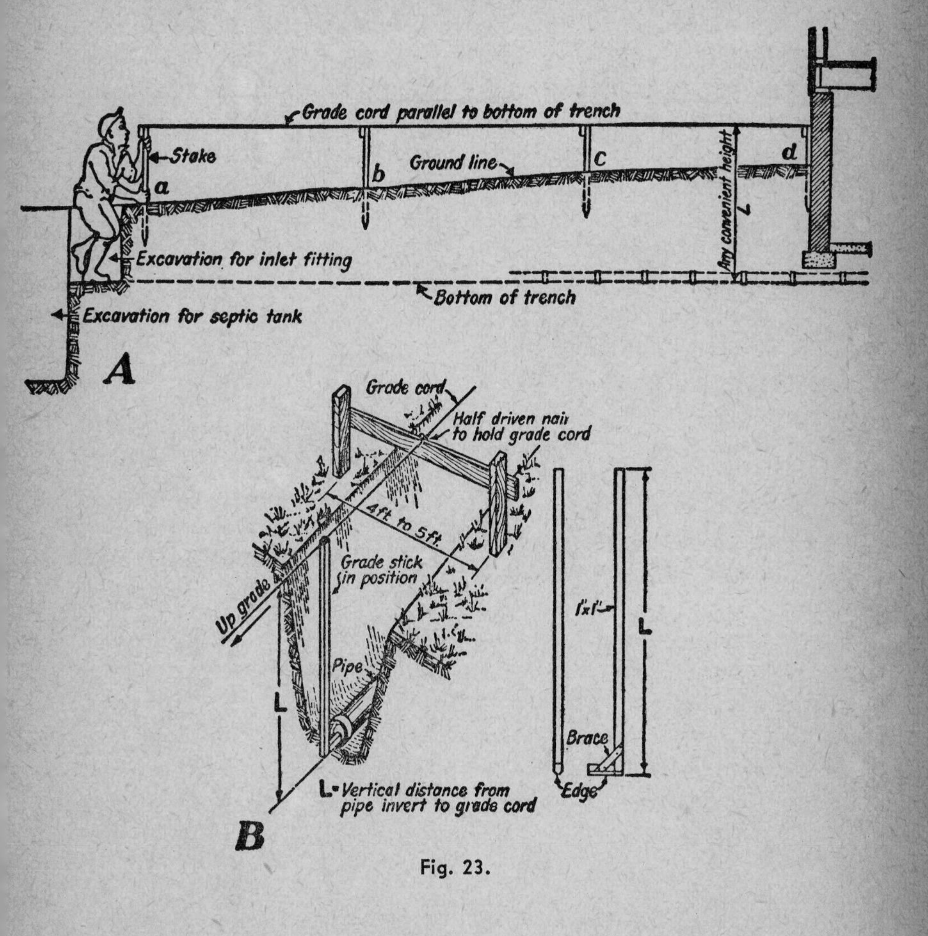

Fig. 23.

DECIDING SEWER GRADE

Figure 23 illustrates the method of establishing the grade necessary for a sewer line. *A*, 2- by 4-inch stakes are set each side of the trench at convenient distances *a*, *b*, *c*, and *d*. Then a board is nailed horizontally on the stakes at *d* at a convenient height above the bottom of the trench, that is, the bottom of the sewer leaving the house. A board is nailed likewise to the stakes at *a* the same height above the inlet to the

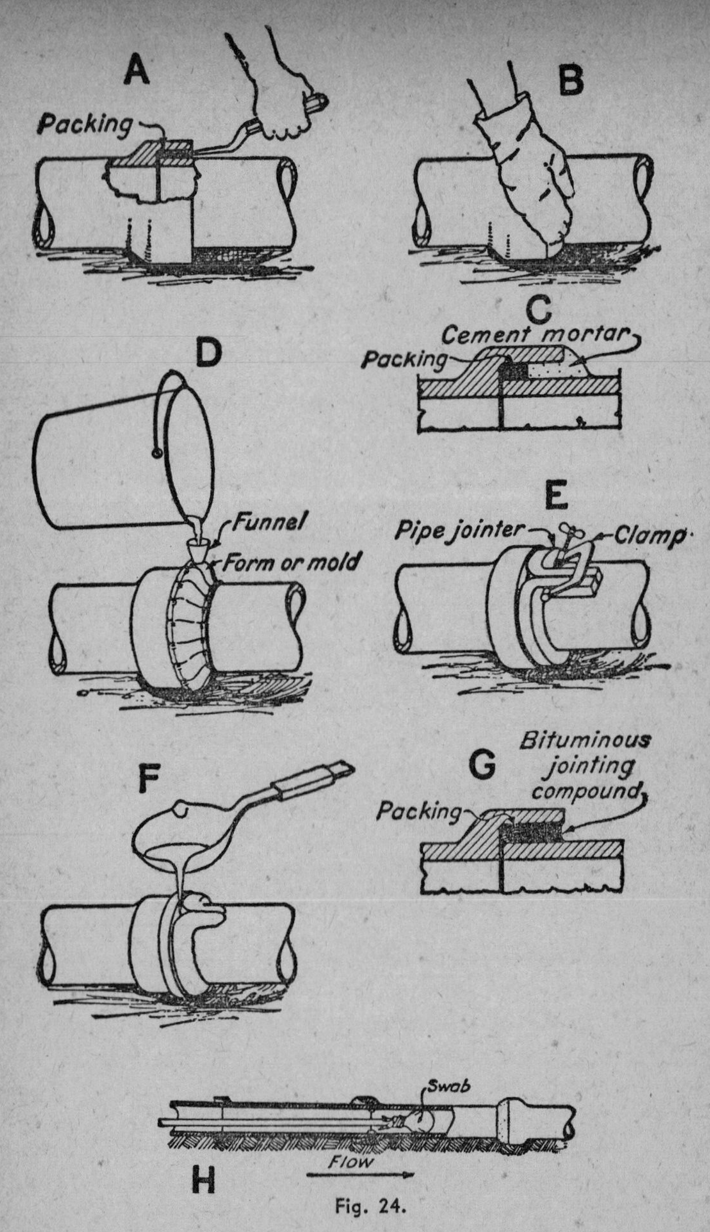

Fig. 24.

tank that *d* is above the bottom of the trench. Similarly, boards are set at *b* and *c* by sighting from *a* to *d* so the tops of the intermediate boards will be in line. *B*, the exact grade of the sewer is obtained by

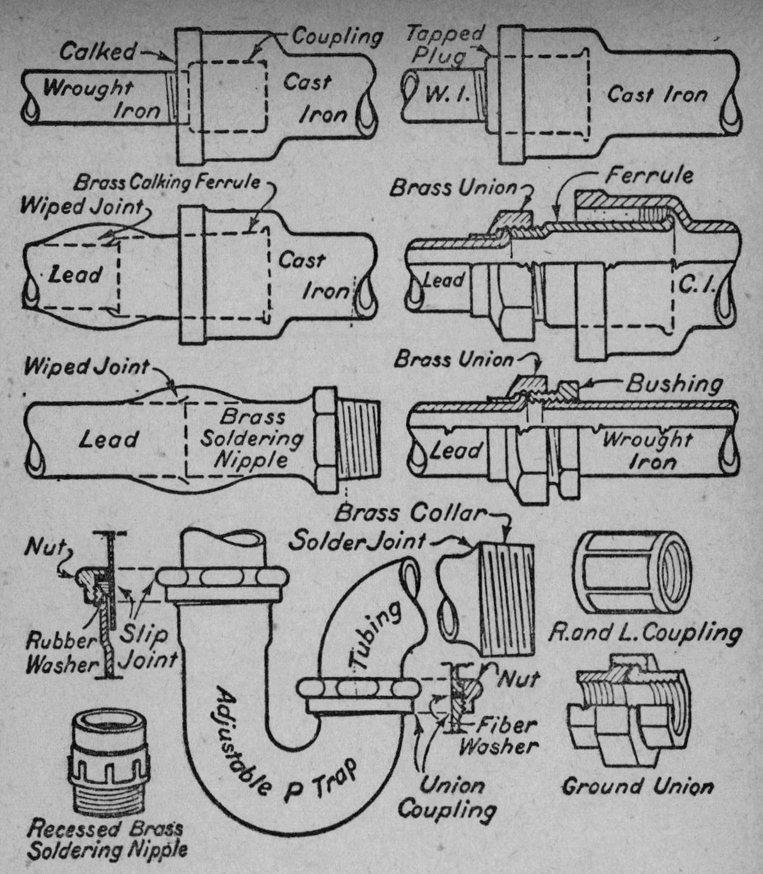

Fig. 25. Methods of joining different kinds of pipe.

measuring from the grade cord with the 1- by 1-inch stick, shown in detail.

The length of the stick must equal the height of the board above the sewer at *d*.

Bituminous, sulfur-sand, lead, and other commercial joint compounds are poured while hot into the joint by means of a ladle and when the work is well done they form a joint that is practically root-proof. They are more expensive than cement mortar.

For molding hot compounds, a clay dike, or funnel, built about 3 inches high around the triangular opening at the top of the jointer greatly aids in the rapid and complete filling of the joint space. A hot joint must be poured continuously, otherwise a seam may develop between successive pourings.

Bituminous compounds make a slightly elastic joint. A joint in 4-inch pipe requires about ⅜ to ½ pound of compound and in 6-inch pipe about 1 to 1½ pounds.

JOINTING SEWER PIPE

The proper method of jointing sewer pipe is shown in figure 24. *A*, Using calking iron to force packing into joint. *B*, Making joint with 1:2 portland cement mortar. Use only enough water to dampen the mix. Recalk after half an hour, to close shrinkage cracks. *C*, The completed joint. Wrap finished joint with cloth and keep dampened, to aid curing. *D*, Joint made by pouring 1:1 portland cement grout of creamy consistency into a form. This type of joint is not feasible unless the metal forms shown are available. *E*, Use of asbestos runner clamped around pipe, for pouring hot joint. *F*, Clay roll used in place of asbestos runner. *G*, A completed bituminous joint. *H*, Use of swab, to remove any joint material forced through to inside of pipe.

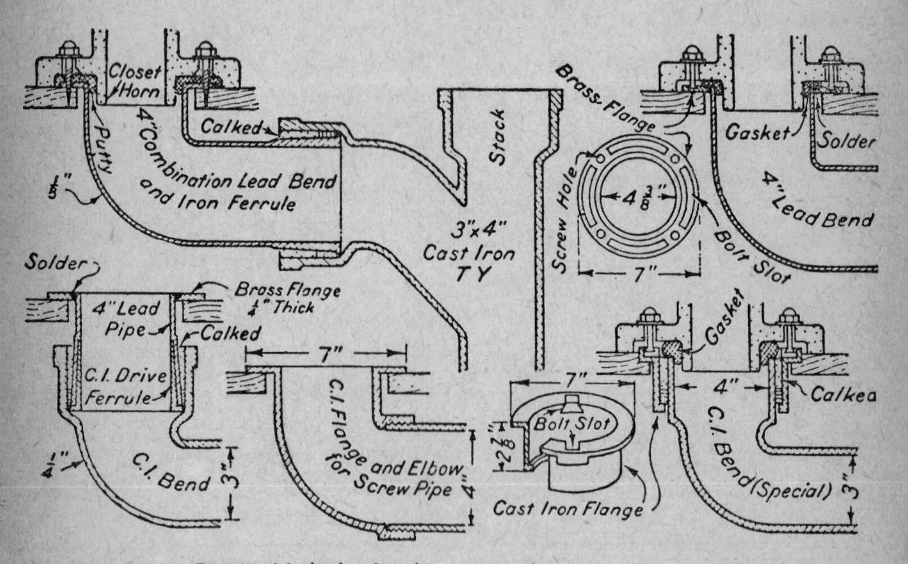

Fig. 26. Methods of making water-closet connections.

JOINTS AND CONNECTIONS

Joints require special care because trouble is likely to occur first in them. Several kinds of prepared joints are shown in figure 25. Making these joints requires clean bearing surfaces and good use of calking tools or a ratchet or monkey wrench.

Wrought, brass, or copper pipe (I.P.S.) is cut with a hack saw or a wheel or knife pipe cutter. Steel dies for cutting threads should be sharp. Lard oil or other suitable lubricant should be applied to the cutting as soon as the die catches, otherwise the thread will be poor and the die may be spoiled.

The application of a lubricant is less necessary on brass-pipe threads and some plumbers use soapy water.

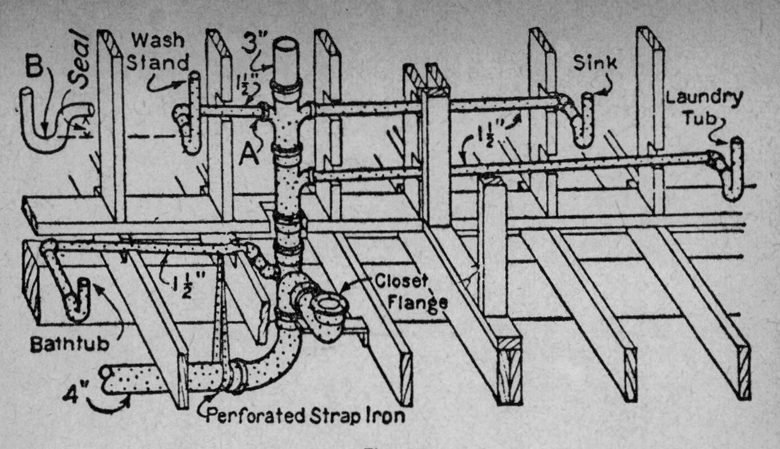

Fig. 27.

OPENING JOINTS IN SOIL PIPES

In remodeling or repairing drainage facilities, it is frequently necessary to insert a Y or remove a section of cast-iron pipe. One practical method of opening a run of soil pipe is to cut through it with a cold chisel just above a convenient joint. Loosen the remaining joints by twisting the pipe. If heat must be applied, use a blowtorch. To remove a long stretch, it is easiest to use the blowtorch on every second joint, the intermediate joints being melted on an open fire.

SIMPLE ONE-PIPE SYSTEM

Figure 27 demonstrates one method of supporting and roughing-in a simple, 1-pipe system—a very economical method for bungalows and cottages with fixtures on one floor and near the soil stack. Note three points: (1) There are no back vents; (2) all small waste pipes enter the stack at or above the side inlet of the "crowfoot" fitting serving the closet branch, thus preventing the water-closet from siphoning the small traps; (3) in no instance is the inside bottom of the waste pipe at the stack (point A) lower than the dip of the trap (point B), thus preventing self-siphonage of the trap; this provision limits the length of the waste; for example if the trap seal is 2 inches and the slope of the waste is one-fourth inch per foot, its length should not exceed 8 feet (2 divided by ¼ equals 8) and less would be better.

A TWO-PIPE SYSTEM

Figure 28 demonstrates a method of supporting and roughing-in a simple 2-pipe system having continuous wastes and vents; the most effective way of venting traps. Drainage pipes are stippled and vent pipes are outlined.

INSULATING PIPE

Vent stacks, running through partition walls often give out unpleas-

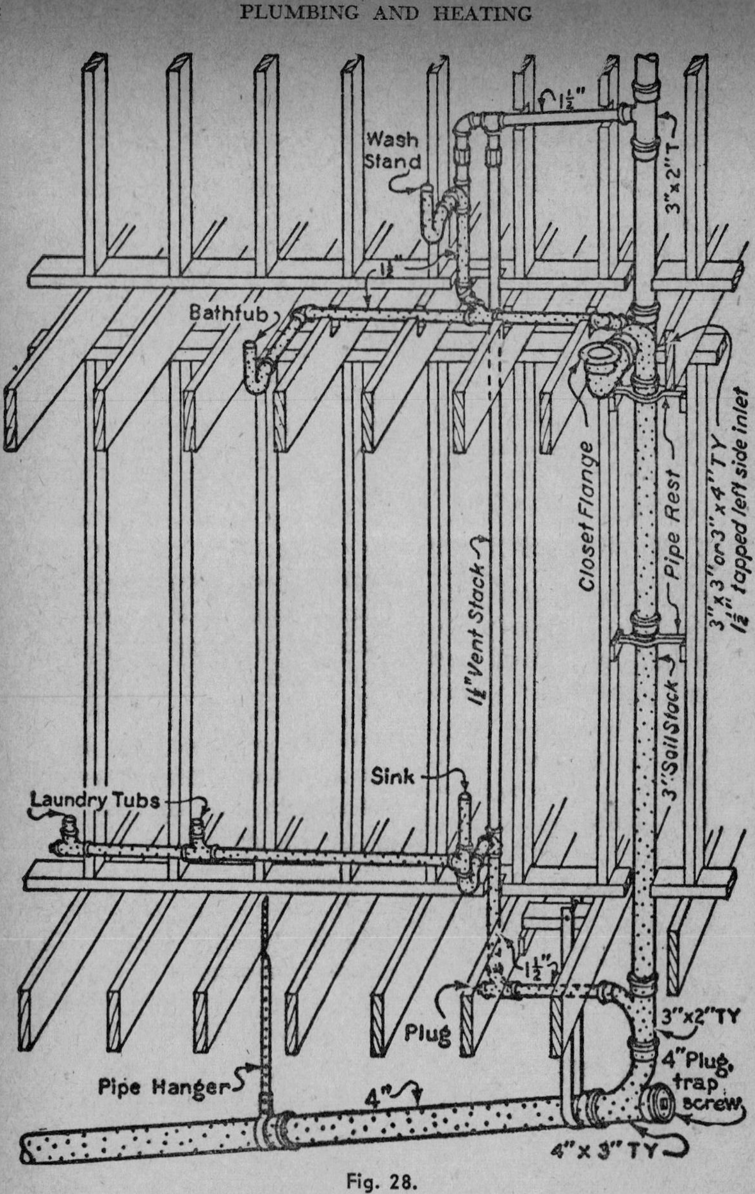

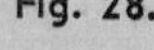
Fig. 28.

ant sounds. These can be eliminated by insulating the lines during the installation of the plumbing system. The pipes can be covered with ordinary pipe insulation or a box can be built around the pipe with two inches or more clearance on all sides of the pipe. The box is then filled with loose fill insulation as illustrated in figure 30.

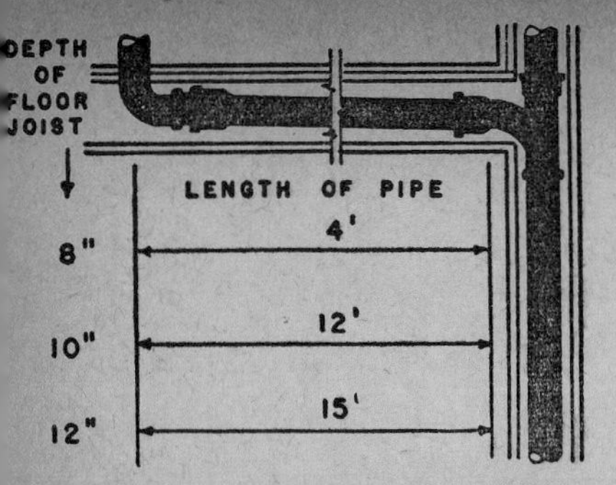

Fig. 29. Joist depth needed for different length of waste pipe sloping ¼ inch per foot.

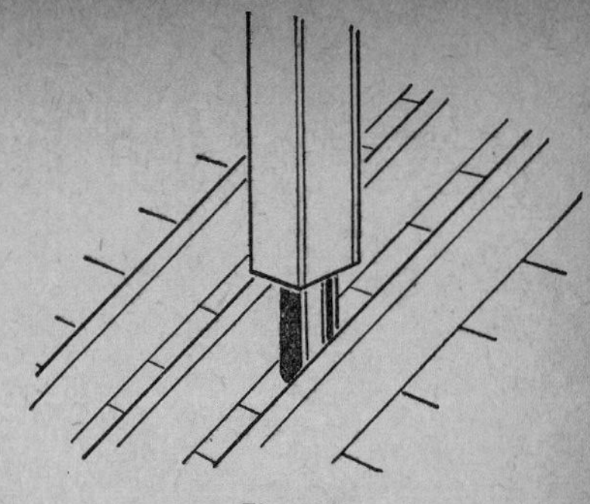

Fig. 30.

Where pipes are liable to freeze they may be covered with a box that will shed water and surrounded with dry shavings, excelsior, sawdust, leaves, chopped straw, charcoal, granulated cork, pea or nut size coke, or mineral wool. Within a building it is more convenient to use a commercial covering of wool felt or hair felt. These coverings come in 3-foot lengths, in sizes to fit different pipes and fittings. They are split on one or both sides to slip over the pipe and are fastened with wires or brass bands. Figure 31 shows two widely used kinds. The wool felt covering for ¾-inch pipe costs about 12 cents per foot. These coverings are sometimes used to deaden sound and to do away with condensation of moisture and drip from exposed overhead pipes. A good homemade covering is a tar-paper lining with a wrapping of felt, the whole jacketed with canvas pasted or wired on and finished with a good water-proof paint.

The insulating material for hot-water pipes and range boilers may be asbestos, magnesia, or plaster of Paris. Cork, hair felt, or wool felt lined with asbestos paper are effective.

RECOMMENDED CONSTRUCTION DETAILS FOR DRAINAGE AND VENT SYSTEMS

Figures 33 to 41 represent details of construction applied to small dwelling houses. The layouts by no means show all the variations that may be made with the more elaborate systems composed of two or more bathroom groups and other fixtures, but are sufficient to indicate other variations that might be made to meet different structural condi-

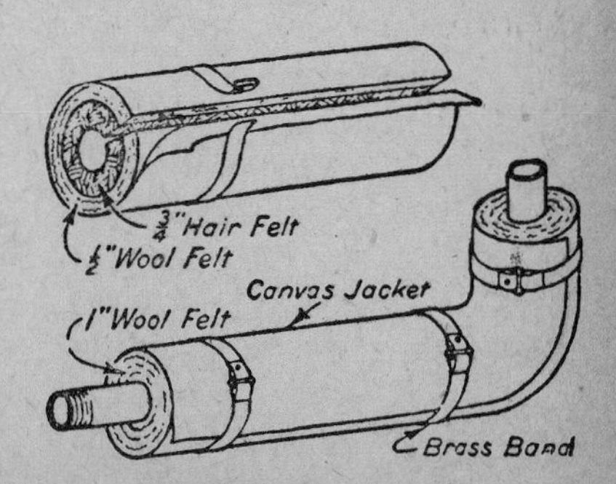

Fig. 31. Two pipe coverings for protecting indoor water pipes from frost.

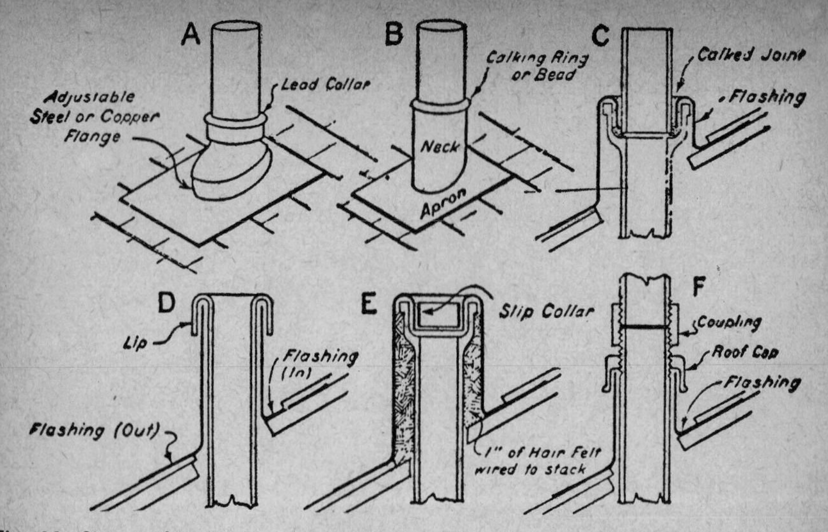

Fig. 32. Six weather-tight roof connections: **A, B,** and **D,** simple commercial products adapted to pitched or flat roofs; **B,** 1-piece all-lead flange; **D,** a cast-iron pipe with extended lip covering the top of the flashing; **C,** ordinary cast-iron soil pipe with a flashing bent over and calked into the hub; **E,** a good method of protecting a stack to prevent closure by frost; **F,** a substantial screw-pipe roof connection.

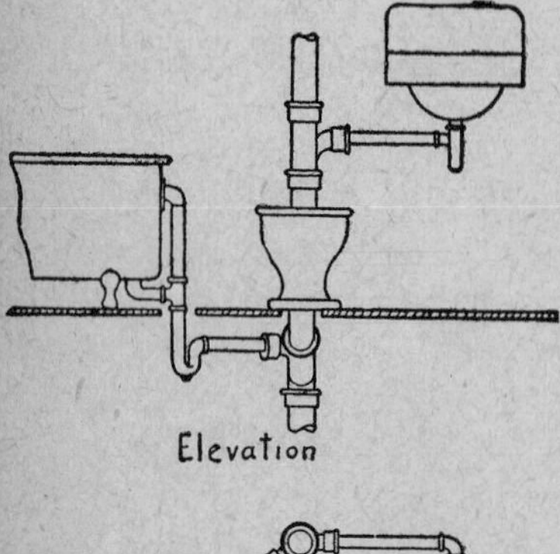

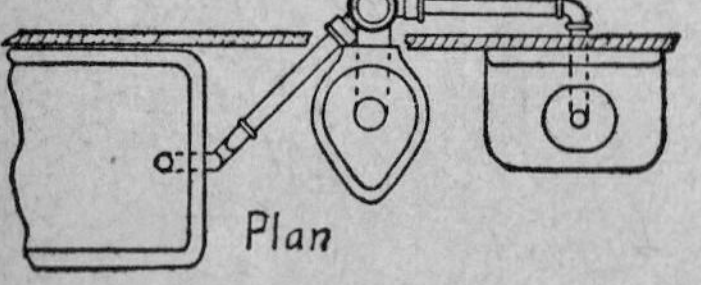

Fig. 33. (Design **A**) Design for a stack vented bathroom group of fixtures (the highest group of fixtures on the stack).

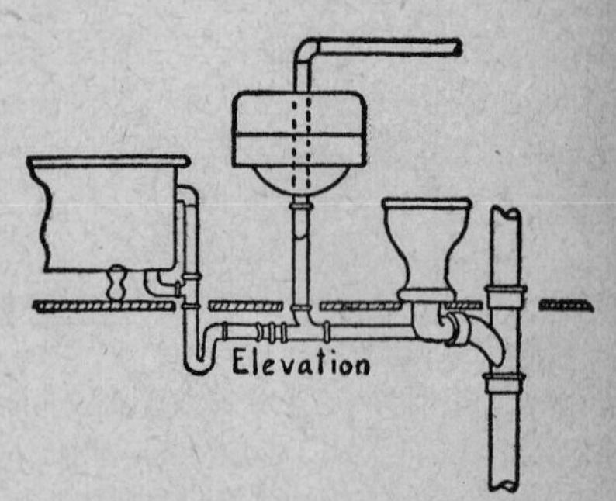

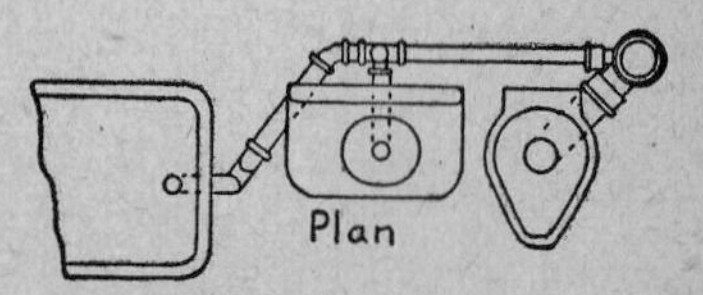

Fig. 34. (Design **B**) Design for stack and group vented fixtures.

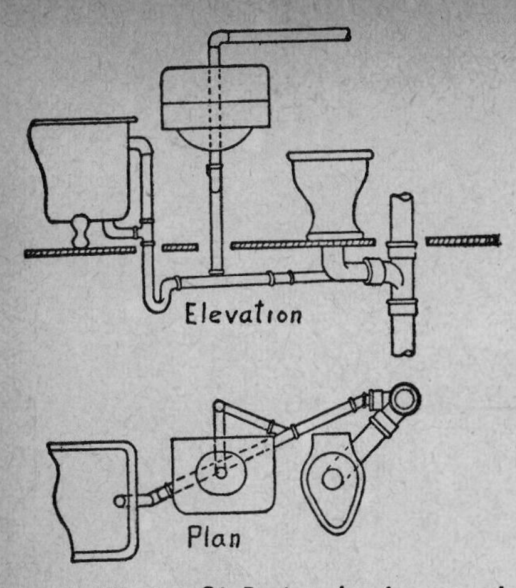

Fig. 35. (Design C) Design showing one alternative arrangement of waste pipes for figure 34.

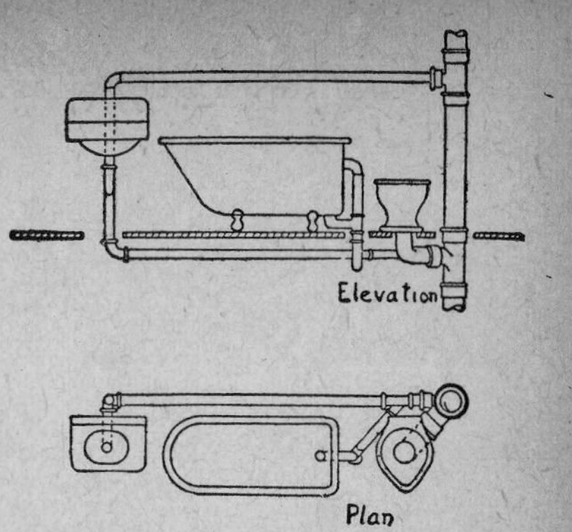

Fig. 36. (Design D) Design for stack-vented and group-vented fixtures.

tions encountered without in any way changing the general results or in any way lessening the efficiency of the system.

The most efficient drainage will be secured with the most direct wastes consistent with the general requirements to protect the trap seals. It follows that an individual vent installed where one is not needed is not only an added expense but may prove a detriment by reducing the velocity of flow and consequently the scour in the waste or soil pipe thus vented. For these reasons preference is given to the plan involving the simplest venting. This, in general, involves a close grouping of fixtures about the stack, assuming that the stack will be located so as to make possible such grouping within the limits of allowable length of unvented wastes. It is recognized that such grouping and arrangement will not always be possible, and alternate plans in the order of preference are given for each type of building represented. The types go from the simplest to the more complex, and, in general, a plan for one type will serve equally well in the same position in a simpler type of building.

The maximum developed length of all horizontal unvented waste branches is limited to 5 feet with slopes of one-fourth to one-half inch per foot. In general, the drawings are shown for wrought-iron construction in waste and vent pipes. Any approved material may be used within the same limits. For the most part dimensions are omitted from the drawings, since the same construction applies to any sized soil stack and required vent and waste pipes.

Design *A* (fig. 33) is suitable for the highest group of fixtures on the soil stack. A kitchen sink, with an independent waste branch connecting to the stack above the water-closet branch, may be added to the group without other change. It will

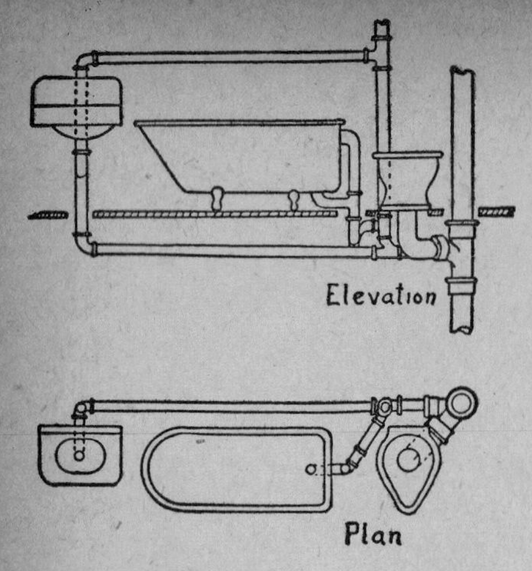

Fig. 37. (Design E) Design for lower floor.

be observed that the design offers great flexibility in the matter of spacing and order of arrangement of fixtures by the selection of the proper "crowfoot" fitting, the principal restriction being the limitation of unvented horizontal waste branches to a maximum developed length of 5

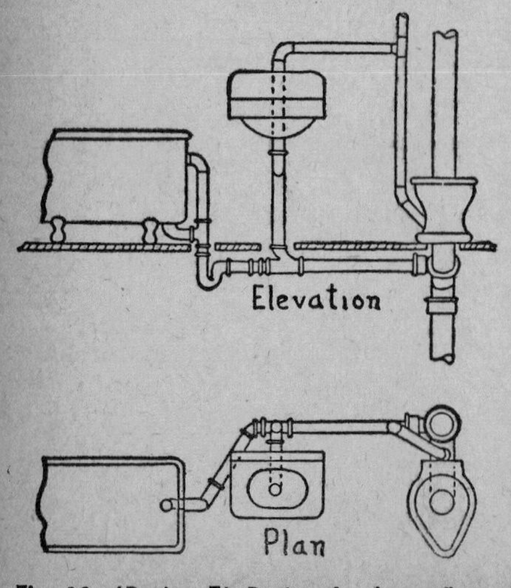

Fig. 38. (Design F) Design for lower-floor bathroom group.

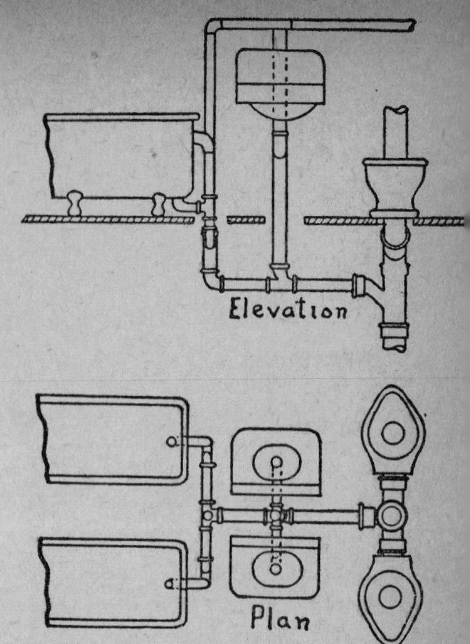

Fig. 39. (Design G) Design for duplex bathroom group.

feet. Still greater flexibility may be secured by a proper location of the stack relative to the desired fixture positions.

Design *B* (fig. 34), design *C* (fig. 35), and design *D* (fig. 36) are alternative layouts recommended for the highest group of fixtures when the desired location of fixtures can not be secured with design *A*. These are not adapted to as many variations in order of arrangement as design *A*, but permit some which can not be secured in design *A*, such as the location of the lavatory on the opposite side of the bathroom from the soil stack. Design *B* will also serve with comparative safety on a lower floor when the possible discharge from above does not exceed one bathroom group plus a kitchen sink

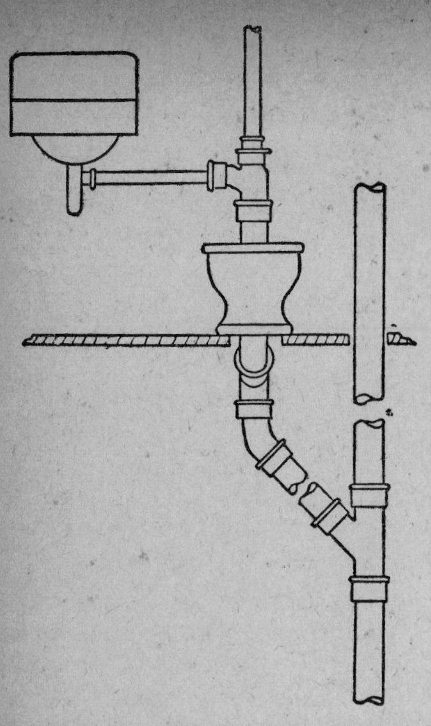

Fig. 40. (Design **H**) Venting for lavatory and water-closet.

or 10½ fixture units. Design *E* (fig. 37) may be used on a lower floor under the same conditions. Design *F* (fig. 38) may be used on a lower floor when the possible discharge from above exceeds 10½ fixture units. Design *G* (fig. 39) represents approved duplex arrangement for the highest group. Two kitchen sinks or two combination fixtures with wastes connecting above the water-closet branches may be added without other changes. Design *H* (fig. 40) shows approved venting of a lavatory and water-closet group on a lower floor.

Figure 41 represents approved forms of venting single fixtures, with wastes connecting independently to the stack to be employed when necessary to vent in any position and approved forms of venting water-closets when connected to the stack near the base and when connected independently to the house drain.

Figures 42 to 44 represent varied types for small dwellings. Many variations of each type might be made without in any way changing the principles or the requirements. In general, a fixture or a group of fixtures may be omitted from a lower floor of any type without changing the requirements in venting for other fixtures on the same floor or floors above.

Types *1* and *3* may use any one of the designs *A* to *E* with variations within the limits for installing fixtures.

Types *2* and *4* may use any one of the same designs for the upper floor, with the basement fixtures vented as

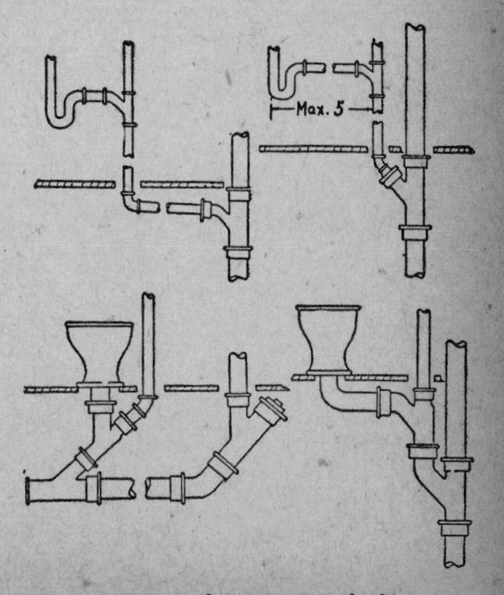

Fig. 41. Forms of venting single fixtures.

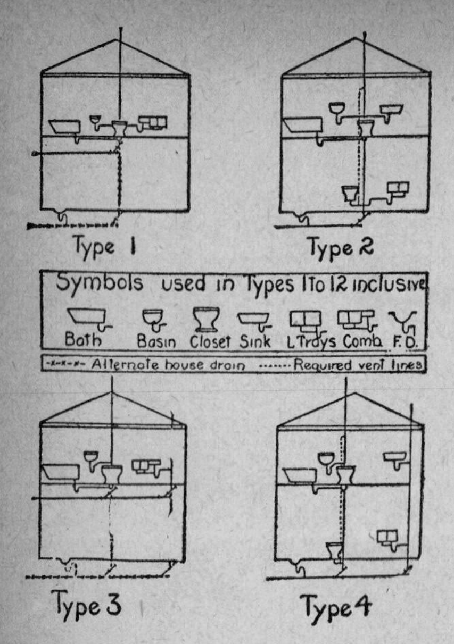

Fig. 42. Types of one-story one-family houses showing required venting.

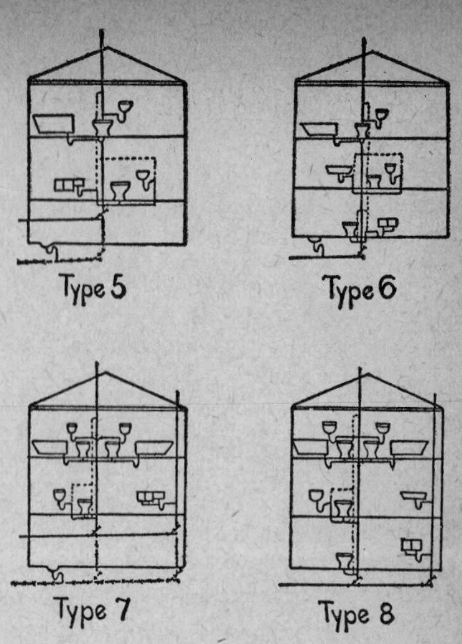

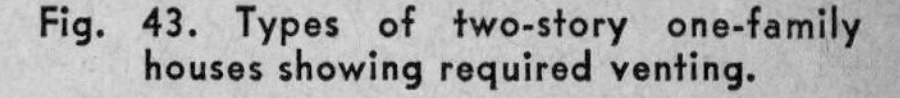
Fig. 43. Types of two-story one-family houses showing required venting.

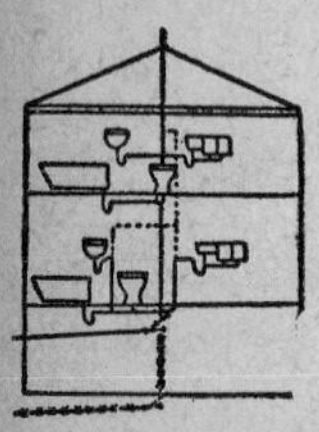

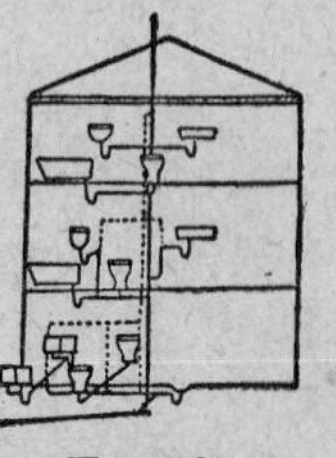

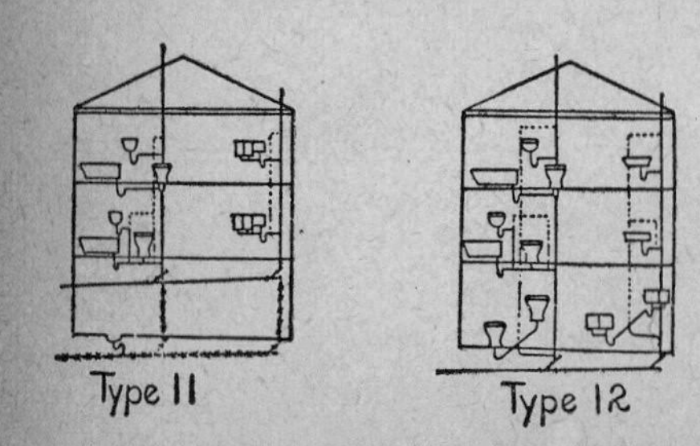

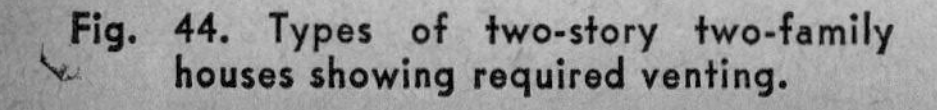
Fig. 44. Types of two-story two-family houses showing required venting.

indicated in any of the approved methods of venting for the position.

Types *5* and *6* may use on the second floor any of the approved designs for the highest floor of a system and designs *B, E,* or *F,* with the sink or combination fixture vented in approved manner as indicated, and the basement fixture in type *6,* vented in approved manner.

Types *7* and *8* may use design *G* (fig. 38) or any equivalent variation for the upper floor within prescribed limits of permitted lengths and design *H* (fig. 40) or an equivalent variation for the first floor with the basement water-closet type *8* vented in an approved manner.

Types *9, 10, 11,* and *12,* two story and two story and basement two-family houses, may use any one of the approved designs for the second or top floor.

Types 9 and *10* may use any of designs *B, E,* or *F* on the first floor with the sink or combination fixture vented in an approved manner as indicated.

Types *11* and *12* may use any designs *B, E,* or *F* on the first floor for the main stack, with fixtures on the waste stack vented in an approved manner.

It is impossible to describe or illustrate all possible variations in design in which the same general characteristics can be maintained. The preceding construction has been described in considerable detail to illustrate the flexibility of the designs given to meet different conditions. It has been pointed out that there is considerable flexibility in the designs themselves. Figures 33 to 41 are limited always by the permitted lengths of wastes and by venting requirements for the position in which the layout is to be installed.

Preference has been given in all illustrations to the simplest form of venting that will be safe for general application because: (1) from the drainage standpoint it will, in general, be more efficient; (2) there is less chance for depreciation in service in the simple system; and (3) the work can generally be installed with a saving in material, labor, and space.

The designs and requirements in venting are given for the 3-inch soil stack. This is not to be interpreted as a requirement for the use of a 3-inch soil stack, but its employment

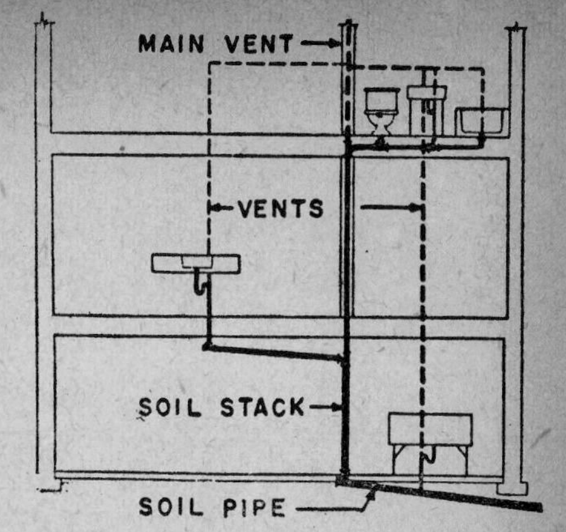

Fig. 45. Diagram of economical waste and vent piping.

in preference to a 4-inch soil stack introduces a saving in material, labor, and space.

The 3-inch soil stack offers distinct advantages over the 4-inch stack in being more readily worked into walls or partitions.

HOT WATER TANKS

When automatic washing appliances such as dishwashers and clothes washers are to be used, the capacity of the hot water storage tank should be increased to take care of this increase in demand. The accompanying table shows the tank

HOT-WATER SUPPLY

No. of Baths	No. of Bedrooms	Tank Capacity Gallons	Total for Automatic Washing, etc.
1 or 2	30	50	1
3 or 4	40	60	1
2 or 3	40	60	2
4 or 5	50	75	2
3	50	75	3
3 or 4	4 or 5	75	100

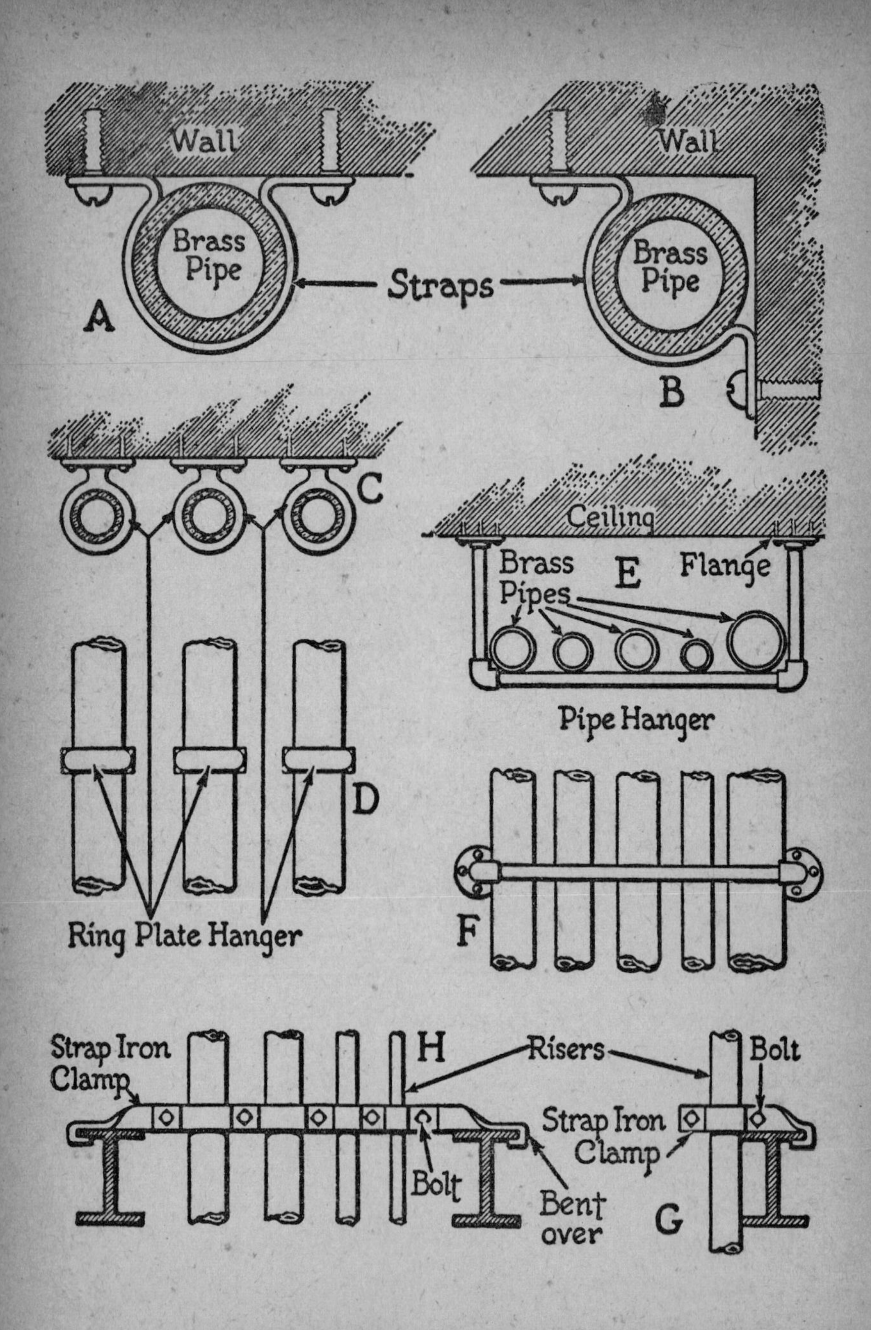

Fig. 46. Types of pipe hangers.

size based on the number of bedrooms and the tank size when automatic washing equipment is to be included.

ADJUSTING FLUSH VALVES FOR TOILET TANKS

Probably no other plumbing in the home needs attention so often as the flush valve on the toilet tank in the bathroom. It is under water and subject to fouling and neglect. The hollow rubber ball gets out of shape and fails to drop squarely into the hollowed seat. The handle and lever fail to work smoothly or the lift wires get out of plumb, causing the ball to remain up when it should drop to its seat.

To repair, stop inflow to the tank by holding up the float of the ball cock or supporting it with a stick. Drain the tank by raising the rubber ball. If the ball is worn, is out of shape, or has lost its elasticity, unscrew the lower lift wire from the ball and replace it with a new one. A 2½-inch rubber ball costs very little and a new one should always be kept in the house. The lift wires should be straight and plumb. The lower lift wire is readily fitted over the center of the valve by means of the adjustable guide holder. By loosening the thumbscrew, the holder is raised, lowered, or rotated about the overflow tube. The horizontal position of the guide is fixed exactly over the center of the valve by loosening the lock nut and turning the guide screw. These adjustments are very important. The upper lift wire should loop into the lever armhole nearest to a vertical from the center of the valve. A tank should empty within 10 seconds. Owing to lengthening of the rubber ball and insufficient rise from its seat, the time may be longer than 10 seconds and the flush correspondingly weak. This may be overcome by shortening the loop in the upper lift wire. A drop or two of lubricating oil on the lever mechanism makes it work more smoothly.

CONNECTING RANGE BOILERS AND WATER BACKS

The four principal methods of connecting range boilers and water backs are shown in figure 49. Arrows

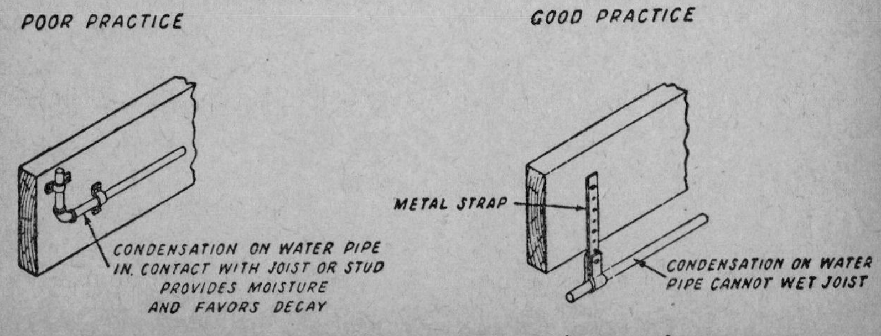

Fig. 47. Good and poor practice with water pipes.

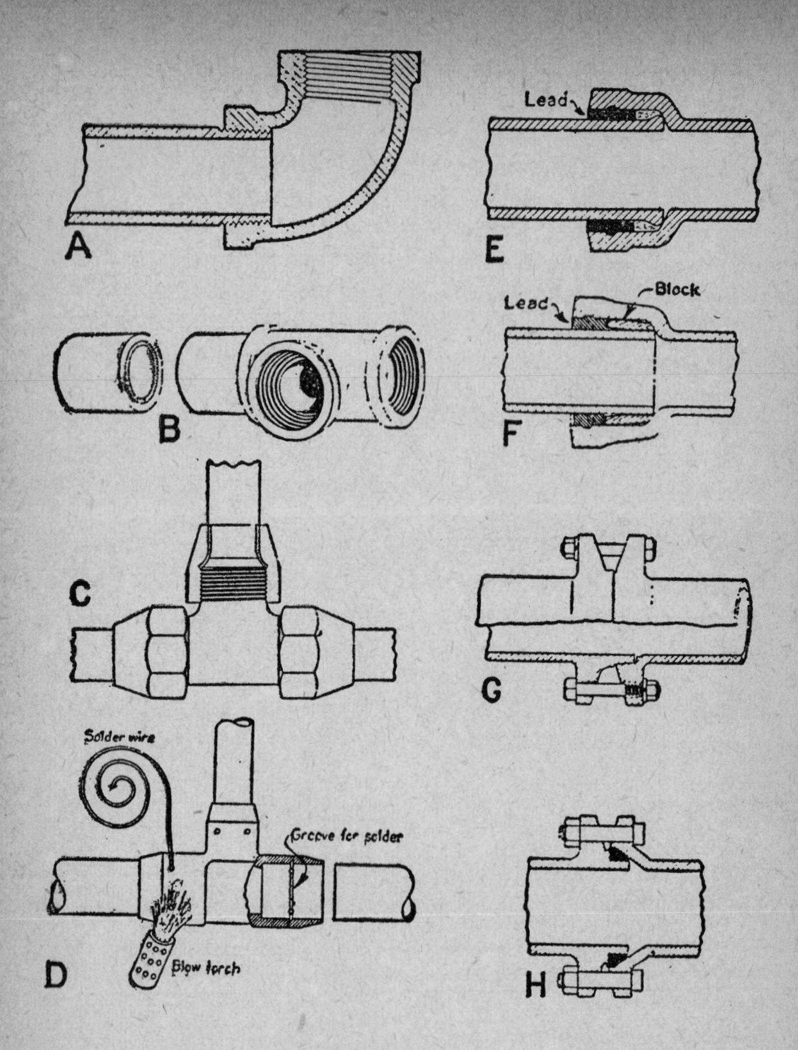

Fig. 48. Water pipes and typical joints: A, standard wrought pipe and elbow; B, cement-lined wrought pipe and lead-lined T-branch; C, copper service tubing and union T-branch; D, copper tubing and threadless T-branch with sweat-solder joints; E, common bell and spigot cast-iron pipe; F, bell and spigot pipe prepared for top calking in the trench; G, cast-iron pipe and machined bolted joint; H, cast-iron pipe and bolted joint with rubber-ring gasket.

show the direction in which the water moves. A, Standard tappings; short, direct connections; excellent for either water back or gas heater; has ample space in which sediment may settle below the line of circulation; occasionally a pail of water should be drawn off at the drain cock. B, Cold-water circulation pipe from bottom of boiler. C, A common method where the height of the boiler stand does not permit the straight connection shown in A and B. D, Connection just above the boiler; often used with a gas heater because small quantities of hot water can be drawn in a minute or two after lighting the gas. This connection is not so satisfactory as A, B, or C because circulation and equalization of temperature are not so good.

CLEANING CLOGGED PIPES

Rust and dirt in water pipes are more or less successfully removed as follows:

1. Tie a piece of small, stout cord to each end of a 2-foot length of small chain. Each piece of cord should be a little longer than the length of pipe to be cleaned. Attach the free end of one of the cords to a stiff steel wire and push the wire and cord through the pipe. By means of the cords pull the chain back and forth through the pipe, and then thoroughly flush the pipe with clean water under strong pressure. Long lines may be opened at intervals and cleaned section by section.

2. Use a swab or wire brush attached to a small steel or brass rod.

3. Flush with a powerful hand pump.

4. Fill the pipe with diluted muriatic acid and allow it to stand in the pipe long enough for the acid to act. If the treatment is unsuccessful it should be repeated. A mixture of 1

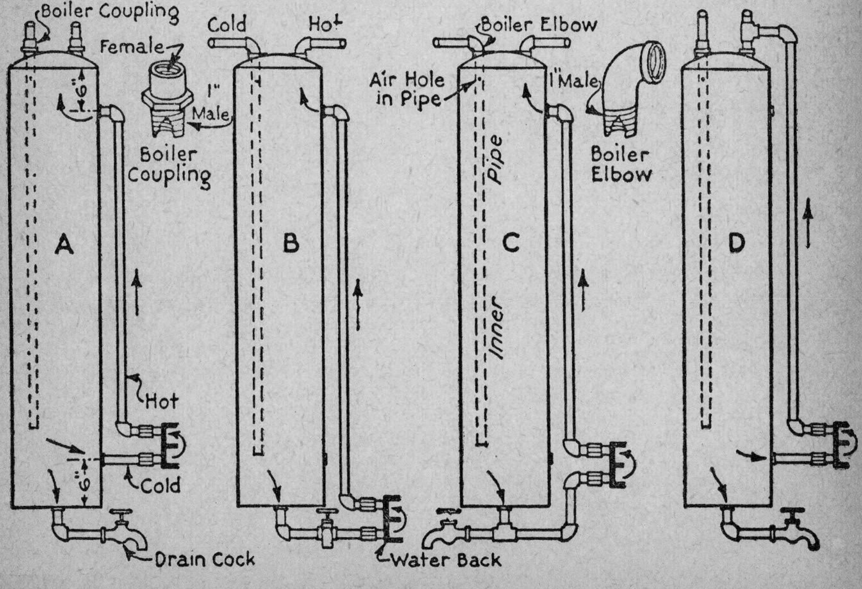

Fig. 49

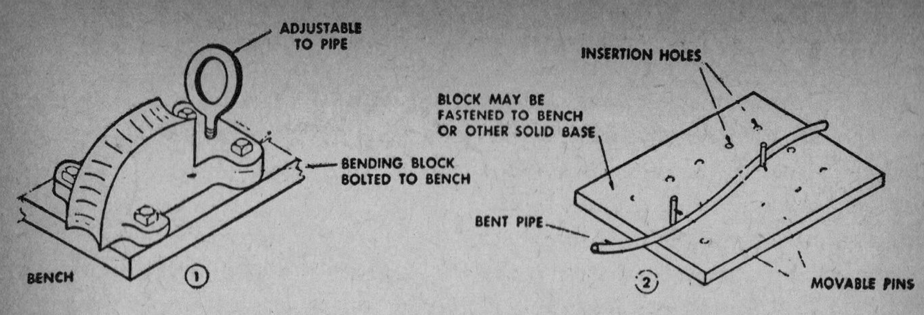

Fig. 50. Two types of pipe bending devices. The block with movable pins can be constructed out of heavy metal with metal pins or bolts.

part of acid and 7 parts of water allowed to stand overnight in 1,000 feet of badly rusted 1-inch pipe has given good results. After the acid treatment the pipe should be flushed thoroughly with clean water to remove as fully as possible all dirt, rust, and traces of acid.

When new piping is put in, abrupt turns are sometimes made with T-branches instead of elbows. The unused leg of the branch can be closed with a screw plug, permitting easy access to the interior of the pipe.

Caution. When a stop and waste (or valve) on a water service is closed to permit cleaning or repairs, care should be taken to prevent the formation of a vacuum in the high parts of the water piping and the connections to plumbing fixtures; otherwise, siphon action may draw pollution from water closets having water-controlled or seat-operated flush valves and from bathtubs, washbasins, laundry tubs, or other fixtures in which the spout (discharge end of the water line) is lower than the fixture rim, or worse, below the fixture overflow. Vacuum and siphon action may be destroyed by opening the highest connected faucet or an air cock in the top of the water line or by equipping the system with suitable automatic vacuum breakers.

All waste pipes and traps are subject to fouling. Dirt collects in the bottom and grease adheres to the sides. The usual way of clearing ordinary fixture traps is to unscrew the clean-out plug, and wash out the obstructing matter or pull it out with a wire bent to form a hook. Small obstructions are often forced down or drawn up by the use of a simple rubber force cup, sometimes called "the plumber's friend." The fixture is partly filled with water and the force cup placed over the fixture outlet. The wood handle of the cup is then worked rapidly down and up, causing alternate expulsion of the water from beneath the cup and suction upward through the waste pipe and trap. If a trap and the waste pipe from it are clogged with grease, hair, or lint, it is best to open or disconnect the trap and dig out the greasy matter with either a stick or wire.

A variety of inexpensive flexible-coil wire augers and sewer rods are available for removing obstructions —mainly newspapers, rags, toilet articles, grease, garbage, or other solids—from traps, drains, and sewers. The growth of roots in sewers and drains causes much trouble that better workmanship in making the joints would have avoided. Augers and rods come in various sizes and lengths. Stock length for clean-out augers for closet bowls are 3, 6, and 9 feet. Placing a few sheets of toilet paper in the bowl and then flushing usually indicates whether the obstruction has been dislodged.

Flexible coil steel waste-pipe cleaners commonly come in diameters of 3/16, ¼, ⅜, ½, and ⅝ inch and in lengths of 6, 9, 15, 25, 50, and 100 feet. The small sizes are useful in sink, lavatory, and bathtub traps and waste pipes.

Flat-steel sewer rods, equipped with either an oval or a revolving spear point and an automatic grip handle, come in stock lengths of 25, 50, 75, and 100 feet, in widths of ¼ to 1½ inches, and in thicknesses of 1/16 and ⅛ inch. A rod ⅛-inch thick is desirable for ordinary sewer-cleaning purposes. Round wooden sewer rods in 3- or 4-foot lengths with hook couplings, wire sewer

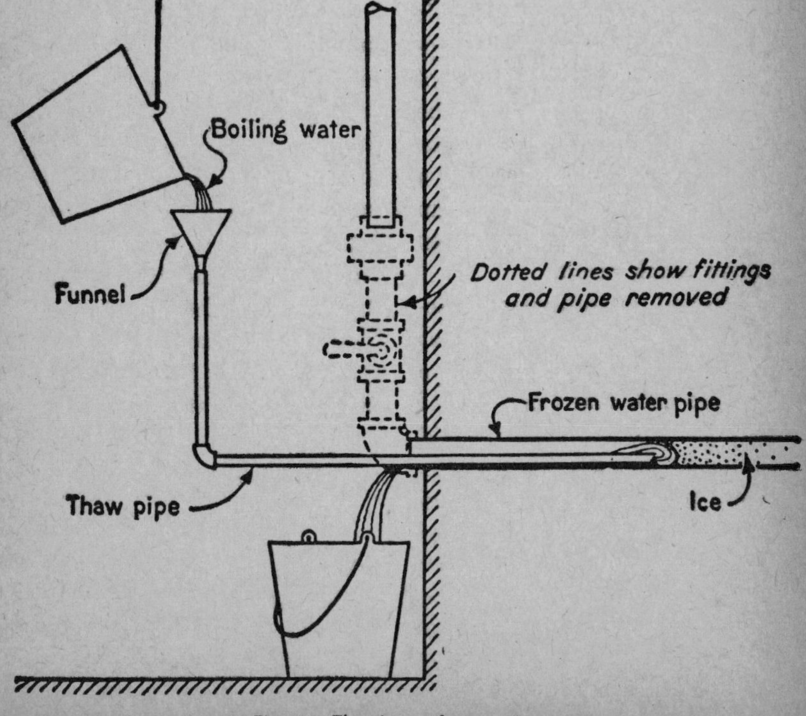

Fig. 51. Thawing a frozen pipe.

brushes, gouges, scrapers, root cutters, and other devices are on the market or can be made for cleaning clogged drain and sewer pipes.

THAWING PIPES

The middle of a frozen pipe should never be thawed first, because expansion of the water confined by ice on both sides may burst the pipe. When thawing a water pipe, work toward the supply, opening a faucet to show when the flow starts. When thawing a waste or sewer pipe, work upward from the lower end to permit the water to drain away.

It is simple and effective to thaw a frozen pipe with boiling water, hot cloths, or heat from an electric lamp, heater, or special electrical apparatus. Because of the danger of shock, however, electricity should be used only by experienced workers. Where there is no danger of fire a torch or burning newspaper run back and forth along the frozen pipes gives quick results.

Underground or otherwise inaccessible pipes may be thawed as follows: Open the frozen water pipe on the house end. Insert one end of a small pipe or tube. With the aid of a funnel at the other end of the small pipe pour boiling water into it and push it forward as the ice melts. A piece of rubber tubing may be used to connect the funnel to the thaw pipe. Hold the funnel higher than the frozen pipe, so that the hot water has head and forces the cooled water back to the opening, where it may be caught in a pail. The head may be increased and the funnel may be used more conveniently if an elbow and a piece of vertical pipe are added to the outer end of the thaw pipe, as shown in figure 51. Add more thaw pipe at the outer end until a passage is made through the ice. Withdraw the thaw pipe quickly after the flow starts. Do not stop the flow until the thaw pipe is fully removed and the frozen pipe is cleared of ice.

A small force pump is often used instead of a funnel and is much to be preferred for opening a long piece of pipe. If available, a jet of steam may be used instead of hot water; as it is hotter, the thawing is more rapid.

Frozen traps and waste pipes are sometimes thawed by pouring in caustic soda or lye, obtainable at grocery stores. Chemicals of this character should be labeled "Poison" and should be kept where children cannot get them. To prevent freezing, the water in the traps of a vacant house should be removed during cold weather, and the traps filled with kerosene, crude glycerin, or a very strong brine made of common salt and water.

STOPPING LEAKS IN PIPES AND TANKS

A small leak in a water pipe can be stopped in an emergency as follows: Place a flat rubber or leather gasket over the leak and hammer a piece of sheet metal to fit over the gasket; secure both to the pipe with a clamp obtainable at hardware or 5-and-10-cent stores. A small leak under low pressure is sometimes stopped by shutting off the water and then embedding the pipe in richly mixed portland cement mortar or concrete. Broken sewer pipe can be repaired in like manner, and a wrapping of wire netting embedded in the mortar or concrete increases its strength. It is better, however, to re-lay the sewer and make all joints watertight and root-proof. A small hole in cast-iron pipe may be tapped for a screw plug.

Where a leaky screw joint cannot be tightened with a pipe wrench, the leak is sometimes stopped with a blunt chisel or calking tool and hammer. Sometimes a crack or hole is cleaned out and then plugged and calked with lead or a commercial iron cement mixed to the consistency of stiff putty. Sometimes a pipe band, a clamp with two bolts or a split sleeve is employed to hold a thin coating of iron cement or a gasket over a leak. If the leak is at a screw joint, the band is usually coated inside with one-eighth of an inch of iron cement and then slipped over the pipe. Keeping the bolt farthest from the coupling or fitting a little tighter than the other, tighten both bolts. During the tightening, the band should be driven with a hammer snugly against the coupling or fitting.

In addition to these methods and devices, there are several kinds of good, inexpensive, ready-made pipe and joint repairers obtainable from manufacturers and dealers.

A corroded and leaky spot in a steel tank or range boiler can be closed with an inexpensive repair bolt or plug available at dealers. A home-made repairer consists of a 3/16-inch by 3-inch toggle bolt and a flat rubber gasket, brass washer, and nut. The link of the bolt, after being passed through the hole, takes an upright position, and screwing up the nut forces the gasket tightly against the outside of the boiler. A small hole must be reamed or enlarged with a round file to a diameter that will admit the toggle bolt. The metal beneath the gasket should be firm and clean. A little candlewick packing may be wrapped around the bolt to prevent leakage along the bolt.

Sometimes a hole is closed by driving in a tapered steel pin to turn the metal inward, forming a surface that can be tapped for an ordinary screw plug. A hole in the wall of a tank or pipe having considerable thickness can be easily and quickly closed by screwing in a tapered steel tap plug that cuts and threads its way through the wall. These plugs in different sizes are obtainable from dealers, and a monkey wrench is the only tool required to insert them. It is unnecessary to shut off or drain the water from the tank or pipe.

A small leak at a seam or rivet can often be closed by merely rubbing a cold chisel along the beveled edge of the joint. Do not attempt to calk a seam unless the plates have considerable thickness and the rivets are closely spaced and are close to the calking edge, and then use extreme caution. Run a regular calking tool or blunt chisel along the beveled edge, tapping the tool very lightly with a light hammer to force the edge of the upper plate against and into the lower plate.

REPAIRING CRACKED LAUNDRY TUBS AND GARDEN HOSE

Cracks in slate, soapstone, or cement laundry tubs are made watertight with a mixture of litharge and glycerin or a specially prepared commercial cement. The litharge and glycerin are mixed and stirred to form a smooth heavy paste free from lumps. The crack should be cleaned out to remove all grease and dirt, and the paste should be worked into the crack with a case knife. A paste of portland cement and water or of white of egg and fresh lump lime has been used sucessfully for this purpose. A break in garden hose can be quickly repaired or two pieces of hose can be joined with an inexpensive iron or brass hose mender or splicer. Cut off the defective piece of hose, insert the mender in the good ends, and wire or clamp the hose. Menders come to slip inside ½-, ¾-, or 1-inch hose.

REMOVING SCALE FROM WATER BACKS AND COILS

Hard water causes a limy deposit, or scale, on the inside of water backs and heating coils, which retards the circulation and heating of the water and, by closure of the bore, may prove dangerous. Continued neglect, moreover, makes removal increasingly difficult.

The water back or coil should be removed from the fire box. At the union or other joints nearest the fire box disconnect all pipes and unscrew them from the water back. If there is a clamp that holds the fire-brick lining against the oven, loosen it and remove side and end linings. Lift out the water back. Soft scale or sludge may be removed by pounding the water back with a mallet or hammer and then flushing with a strong jet of water. A long gouge or chisel is used on surfaces that can be reached. Sometimes the water back is heated in a blacksmith's forge and then pounded, but unless carefully done this treatment may break it.

Waters of varying chemical make-up cause scale differing in composition and hardness. Ordinary limestone (calcium carbonate) scale, if not too thick, may readily be removed with muriatic acid. Gypsum (calcium sulphate) scale is hard and resistant and with other materials in their more compact forms is little affected by muriatic acid. The water back should be laid on the ground or floor and filled with a strong solution of the acid in water. The strength of the solution should vary with the amount of deposit, the ordinary mixture being 1 part of acid and 5 to 7 parts of water. If the deposit is very thick, the acid needs little dilution. Commercial muriatic acid comes in bottles that should be LABELED "MURIATIC ACID—POISON" AND, LIKE THE CHEMICALS PREVIOUSLY MENTIONED, SHOULD BE KEPT WHERE CHILDREN

CANNOT GET IT. Heating the water back hastens the action of the acid. At the end of an hour or two, or sooner if the deposit is dissolved, pour the solution from the water back and flush it thoroughly with hot water to clean out the acid. If all the deposit has not been removed, repeat the operation, making sure that the acid is completely washed out before replacing the water back. It is important to have the water back level when it is replaced; use a spirit level for this purpose.

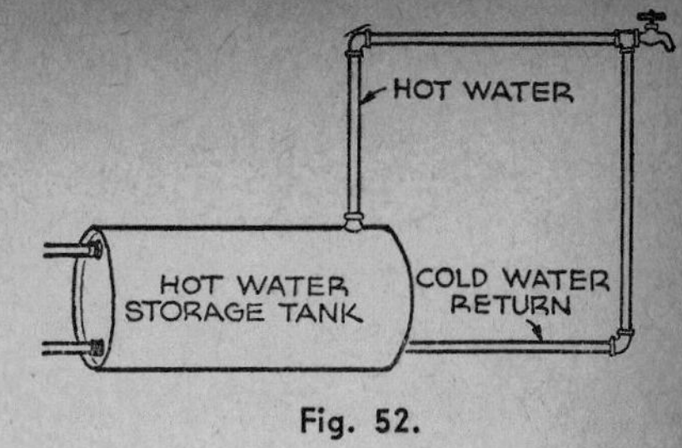

Fig. 52.

Similar methods can be used with copper coils. Place the coil (or heater) on two sticks over a large bowl. With the aid of a lead funnel pour the acid solution down through the coil. Dip from the bowl and continue to circulate the solution through the coil until the deposit is dissolved. The coil should then be thoroughly washed out with hot water.

The hot-water flow pipe close to a water back or coil frequently becomes thickly covered with scale. If the pipe is brass, it may be disconnected and treated with acid and then washed out with hot water. If it is of galvanized iron and in bad condition, it will probably be more satisfactory to replace it.

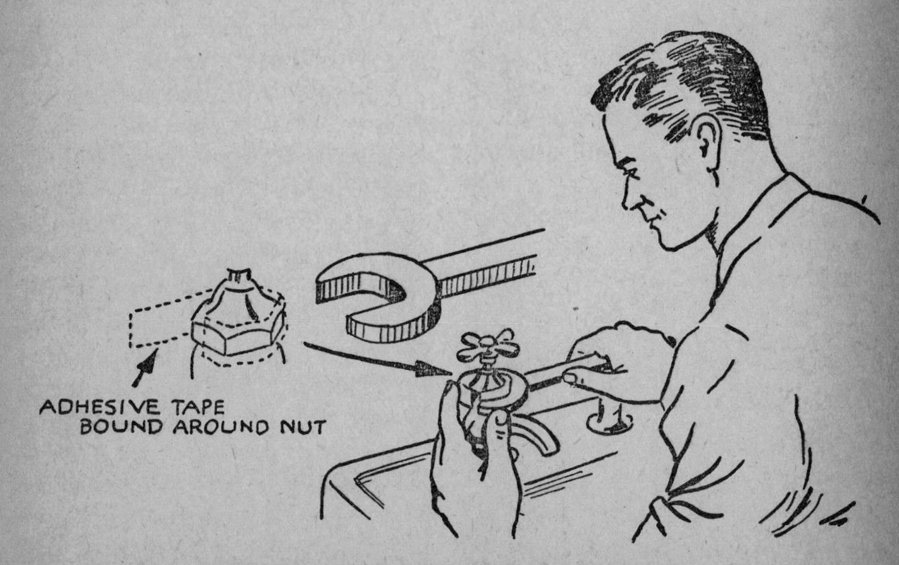

Fig. 53. When you must use a wrench on a plated plumbing fixture, wrap a strip of adhesive tape around the polished metal to avoid scratching the surface. Also tape other points that are liable to be accidentally scratched by slipping tools.

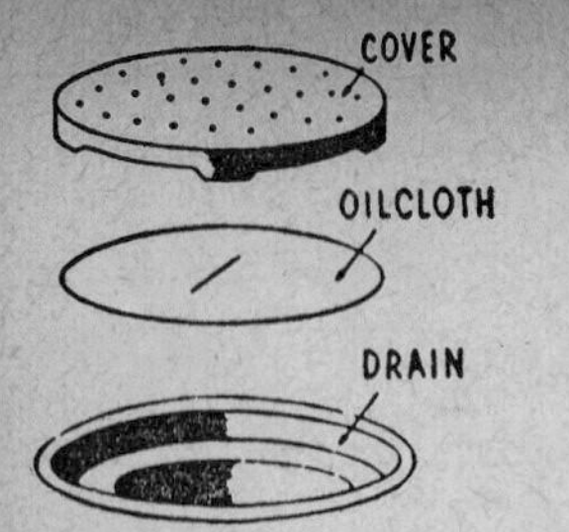

Fig. 54.

SAVING HOT WATER

It is often necessary to let water run out of a hot water tap for a considerable length of time before it runs hot. This wastes both fuel and water. By running a return line back to the hot water storage tank from a point near the faucet outlet as shown in fig. 52, this waste is avoided. To make the system doubly efficient, insulate the hot water lines.

GARAGE DRAIN TRAP

Provide a blanket for the water that sometimes freezes up the drain trap in front of the garage. First, lift out the perforated cover of the trap with a screw-driver. Then cut a piece of oilcloth to fit down into the round depression, make a slit in the center, and put back the cover with the oilcloth under it. In winter, the oilcloth prevents the drain from cooling off so quickly and freezing the water there. When it rains or water from melting snow goes through the holes in the cover, the slit opens sufficiently to enable it to drain through and run off as illustrated in figure 54.

COLLAR FITS CORNER SHOWER

Corner shower stalls shaped like the one in fig. 55 call for a head projecting from the back corner. A common split collar can be used to finish off such an installation if it is bent near the pivot joint so that the halves form a 90-deg. angle. To compensate for the decrease in size of the hole as the result of bending, an oversize collar must be used, for instance a ¾″ collar on ½″ pipe.

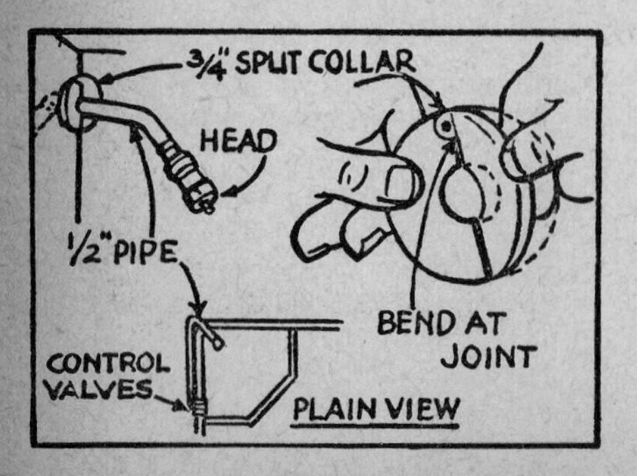

Fig. 55.

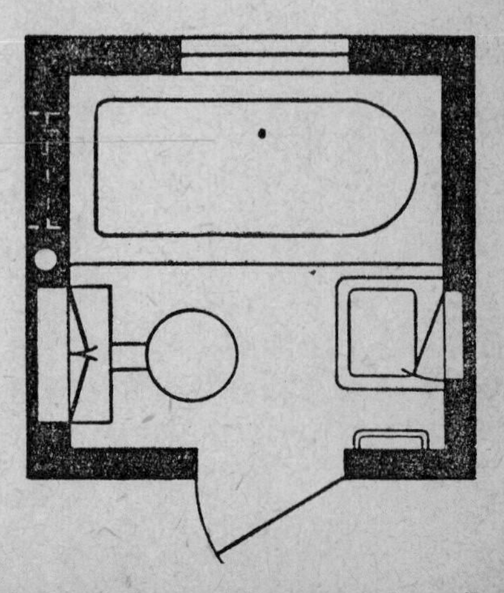

Fig. 56. Bathroom 5 feet square is smallest room that will take an average size tub.

Fig. 57. Bathroom, 5 by 6½ feet, has space for door to open into room.

Fig. 58. With shower only, 5 by 6½ foot bath has space for lavatory with counters.

BATHROOM PLANS

Small bathroom. The smallest bathroom you can build and use an average size tub is 5 feet square (fig. 56). The lavatory in this room can extend from the wall only 15 inches, the water closet only 27 inches. This provides the minimum space needed between front of lavatory and water closet, but not enough in front of the tub for easy cleaning.

In a room as small as this, there is space for storage cabinets under the lavatory and in the studs of the wall above the water closet and lavatory. With steam or hot-water heat, you will need to use a guarded wall-hung radiator.

The door opens out of the room and the window is over the tub. This is not a good or a safe place for a window, but sometimes it is the only possible location. Over a tub, casement windows with cranks are easier to open than double-hung windows.

This is strictly a one-person bathroom. If there are children or others who need help in the bathroom, plan a bigger room.

By making the bathroom slightly larger, 5 by 6½ feet, the door can open into the room (fig. 57).

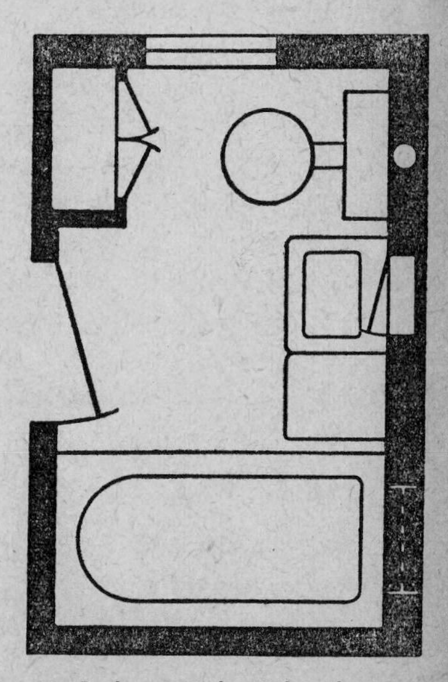

Fig. 59. Bathroom 5 by 8 feet has fixtures along one wall—an economical arrangement. There is space for a floor-to-ceiling cabinet and a movable cabinet next to lavatory.

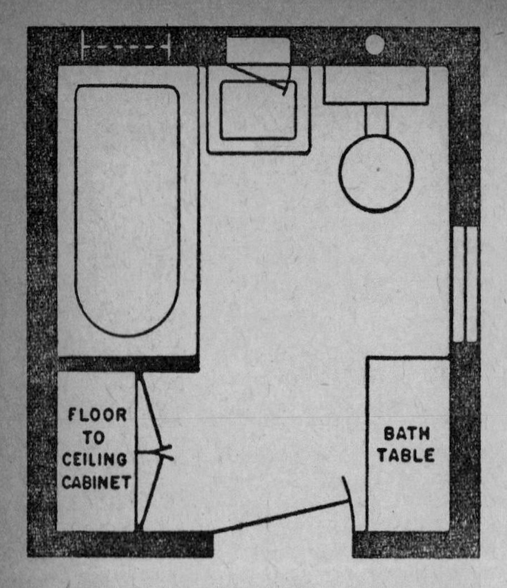

Fig. 60. Bathroom 7 by 8 feet has plenty of space for dressing and for baby bath table.

Figure 58 shows another bathroom 5 by 6½ feet. With a shower stall instead of the tub, there is space along the 5-foot wall for a built-in lavatory with counters and storage cabinets underneath. Two casement windows over the counters allow plenty of daylight at the mirror.

Large bathroom. Figure 59 shows how you might arrange a bathroom that is 5 by 8 feet. Here the door is centered in the long wall. To allow the door to open, the lavatory cannot extend more than 18 inches from the wall. The tub fits into one end of the room.

Behind the door there is space for a floor-to-ceiling cabinet 12 inches deep and 24 inches wide. Next to the lavatory is room for a movable storage cabinet or a built-in counter. Either of these can be made at home.

If your bathroom can be as large as 7 by 8 feet, you can arrange the fixtures in a number of ways. Also the extra floor space makes it possible to use the bathroom as a dressing room. In figure 60, all fixtures are placed along the 7-foot wall across from the door, an economical arrangement.

In a room this size, there is space for a baby bath table to the right of the door. If the table is on casters, it can be wheeled to the lavatory at bath time. To the left of the door is a floor-to-ceiling cabinet for towels and bath supplies. The tub has been recessed by building a wall between the tub and cabinet.

Heating and lighting. Let warmth and safety be your guides in planning heat for your bathroom. Remember to plan a place for your radiator, heater, or register. If you have steam or hot-water heat, you can save space by using a radiator recessed under the window.

If you use an electric heater, get a wall panel or built-in heater. Avoid using portable heaters. Place heater where towels, curtains, or clothing will not catch fire from it, and make sure it is shielded so there is no danger of anyone getting burned. Electric heaters must be properly grounded for safety. Gas heater should be vented.

In the large bathroom you'll need an overhead light as well as light at the mirror. For a small room a light over the mirror or brackets at the sides will be enough. For side brackets, about 5½ feet from floor to center of bulb is the right height. Place fixtures so light shines on sides of face instead of in the mirror.

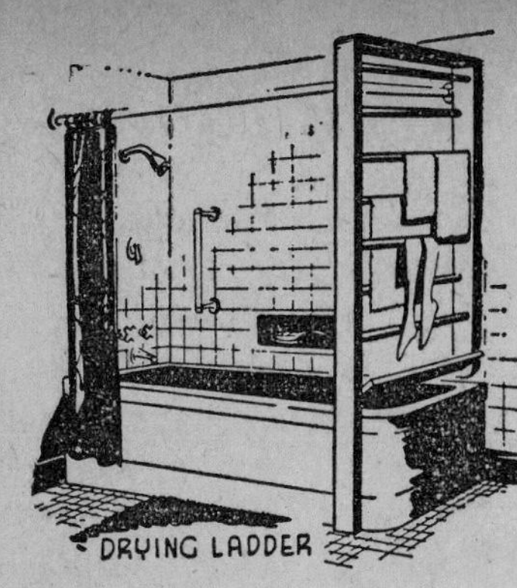

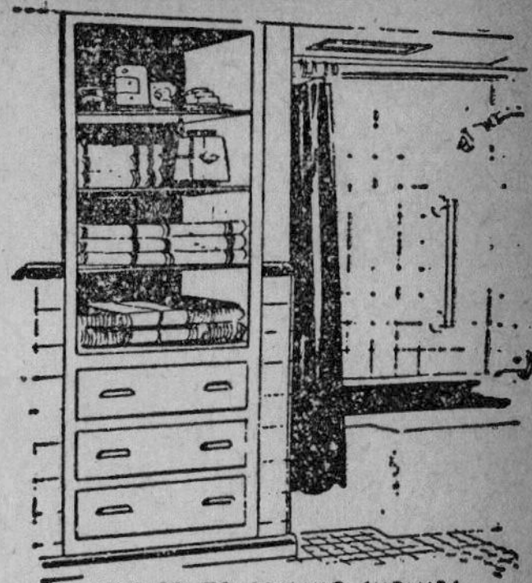

Fig. 61. Eye-catching bathrooms.

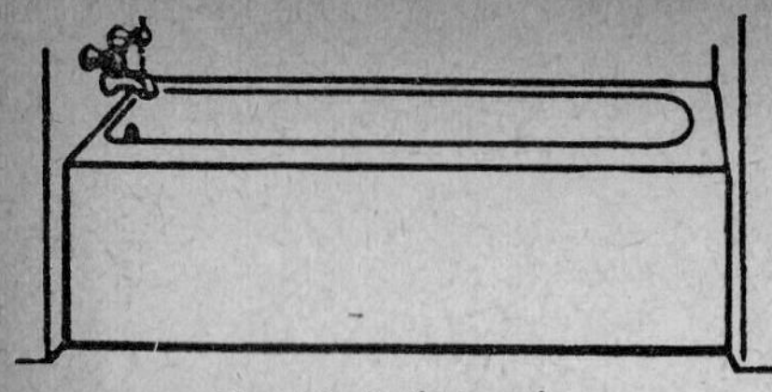

Fig. 62. Built-in tub.

For safety use wall switches rather than pull chains. In the bathroom it is usually possible to touch both water and metal while using electric equipment or switching on lights. There is great danger of shock if wiring or cord is defective, or equipment is not properly grounded. So, try to locate switches and convenience outlets out of reach of anyone in the tub and away from pipes or other metal objects.

FACTS ON BATHROOM FIXTURES

The kind of fixtures you buy will depend on how much you have to spend, and on how large a room you are planning. Cost of fixtures varies with size, style, fittings, and materials used. Average size fixtures are usually satisfactory. The smallest size may be inconvenient; the largest, especially the tub, may take too much water.

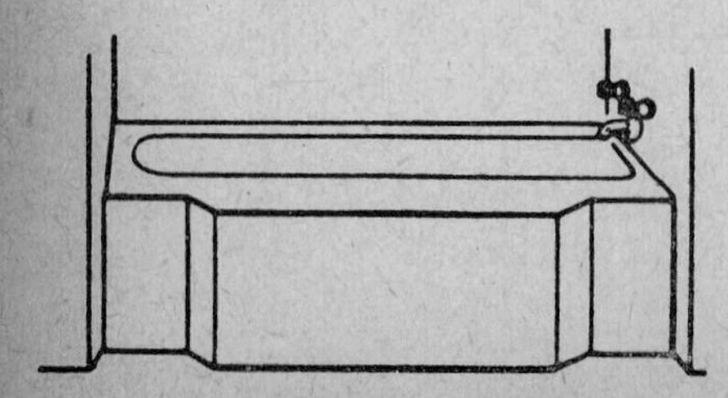

Fig. 63. Built-in tub, wide rim.

Fixtures may be made of vitreous china, enameled iron, or enameled steel. Vitreous china fixtures, the most expensive type, do not stain easily and are very resistent to both acids and alkalies. Water-closet bowls are all made of this material, and it is especially desirable for lavatories that receive much use. Enameled iron or enameled steel fixtures may have an acid-resisting finish. Enameled steel fixtures are cheaper than enameled iron.

You will want to consider whether fixtures are easy to clean and keep in working order, and safe to use. A water closet with a one-piece tank and bowl, for instance, is easier to clean and neater than the two-piece type with exposed pipes. Seats of plastic or plastic finish wear longer than those of painted wood.

With faucets that mix hot and cold water you can regulate the temperature. Metal and most plastic faucet handles are less likely to break than porcelain ones.

Think about safety when you buy a bathtub. There is less danger of slipping in a flat-bottomed tub.

Bathtubs. Built-in tub without wide rim is 30 inches in width, with wide rim 36 inches; and 4½, 5 (most common length), 5½ or 6 feet long. Fits into less space than tub on legs. No exposed pipes (figs. 62 and 63).

Built-in corner tub may be 4½, 5 (most common length), or 5½ feet long and 30 inches wide.

If there is no outside apron, enclose built-in tub with tile, linoleum,

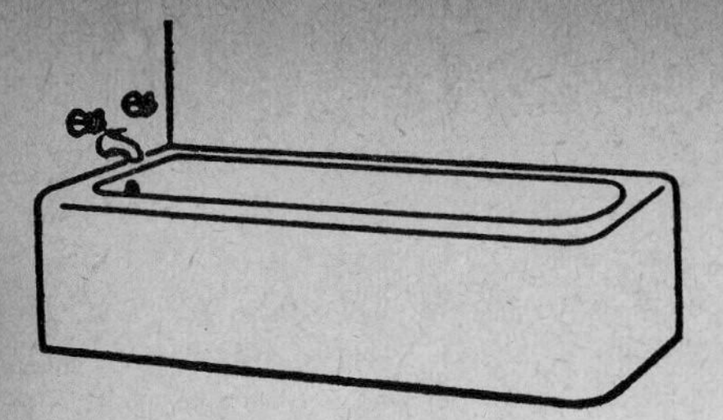

Fig. 64. Corner tub.

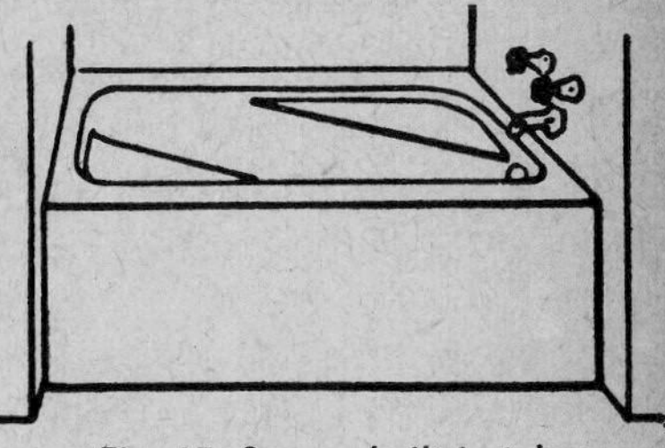

Fig. 65. Corner tub, no apron.

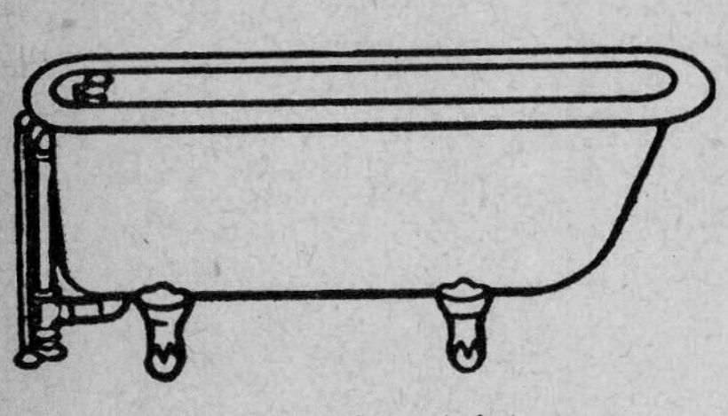

Fig. 66. Tub with legs.

Fig. 67. Square built-in tub.

or other water-resistant material (fig. 64 and 65).

Tub with legs may be 26 or 30 inches wide and 5 feet long. Costs less than other models. May be difficult to step into because of height from floor. Tub is hard to clean around—both underneath tub and around pipes (fig. 66).

Square built-in tub may be 42 by 31 inches, 46 by 48, 48 by 49, or 48 by 51 inches. Back of tub is hard to reach for cleaning (fig. 67).

Lavatories. Regardless of the type of lavatory you choose, it is important to have it at a height that is right for most members of your family. You can place a wall-hung lavatory at whatever height is best. A lavatory with fixed legs or on a pedestal is usually 31 inches high. Lavatories with adjustable legs can

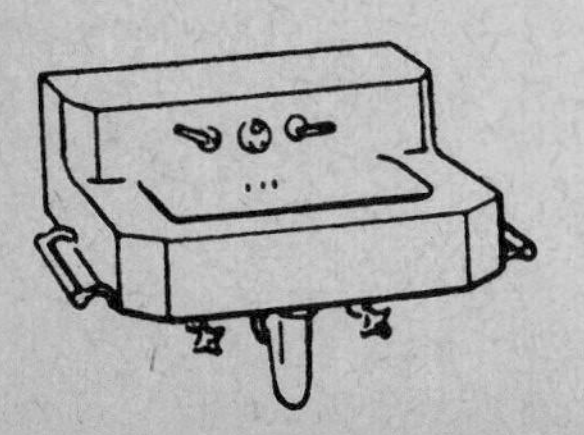

Fig. 68. Wall-hung lavatory with shelf back is easy to clean, moderate in cost.

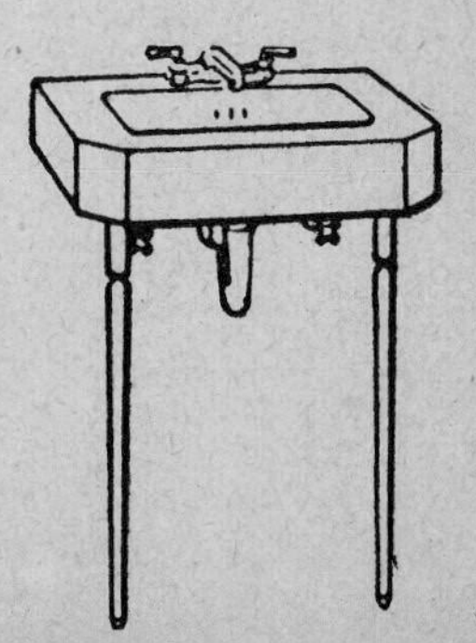

Fig. 69. Lavatory on legs looks modern, but legs add to cost and work of cleaning.

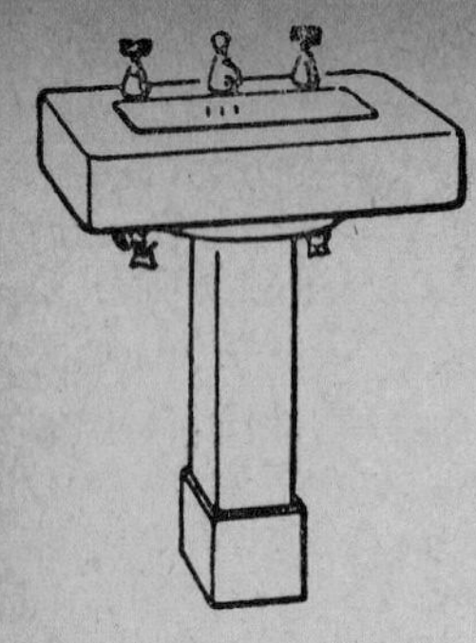

Fig. 70. Lavatory on pedestal is more expensive, has more surface to clean.

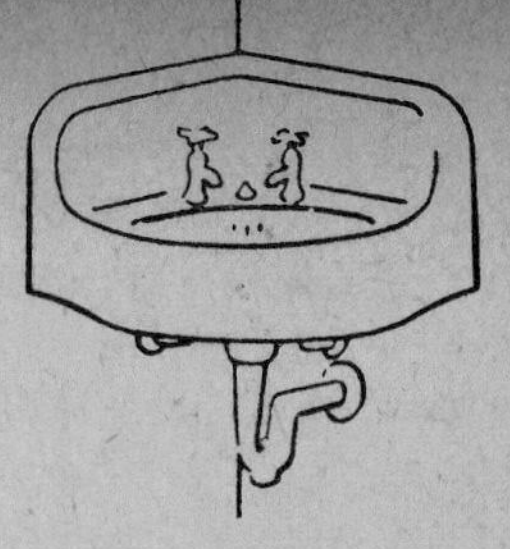

Fig. 71. Wall-hung lavatory to fit into corner. For use under special conditions, such as when space is limited.

be set at any height up to 36 inches, which is a more comfortable height for the average person. You can adjust the height of a ready-made cabinet under the lavatory by building up the toe space.

For the small children, plan to provide a movable step stool (figs. 68 to 73).

Showers. You may want to include a shower in your bathroom. A stall shower (fig. 74) is usually cheaper than a tub. However, if you already have a tub you can add a shower head. Mount high enough to suit the tallest member of your family. If the head is on a ball joint, the direction of the spray can be adjusted (figs. 75 to 77).

STORAGE AND ACCESSORIES

Cabinets over lavatory. Plan cabinets over the lavatory for storing tooth paste, shaving lotion, and other toilet articles. Or if you prefer, have fixed mirrors over the lavatory with cabinets on each side. For medicines,

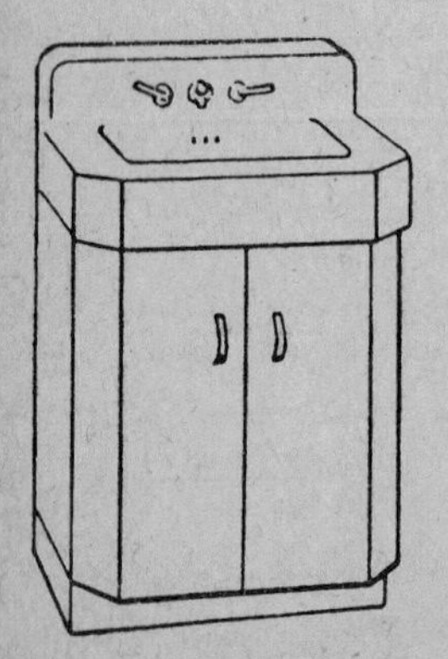

Fig. 72. Lavatory on cabinet base. Provides storage space; is good choice for a small room.

Fig. 73. Flat-rim basin, can be built into counter covered with water-resistant material. Cabinet can be built any length desired. Gives good storage space, handy surface on which to lay articles used at lavatory.

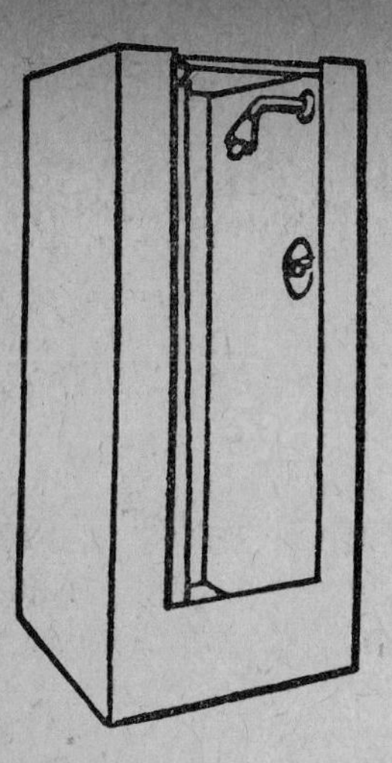

Fig. 74. Ready-built shower stall. Make sure water-tight construction is used in base of shower. Use floor in shower that will not get slippery when wet.

Fig. 75. Rainhead shower has wide face plate. Gives best distribution of water.

Fig. 76. Circular spray has holes around outer edge of plate only, so takes less water than rainhead shower.

Fig. 77. Economy shower head has fine spray, small water spread. It uses least water of any shower head but is often objectionable because of small flow of water.

you'll need a cabinet that can be locked and that is out of the children's reach.

Usual height for cabinets over the lavatory is 62 inches from floor to center of cabinet. However, you may find that some other height is more convenient for your family.

Ready-made cabinets are of the wall-hung or recessed types. They come in varying sizes. The recessed cabinet most commonly used is 14 inches wide because it fits between the studs. If you want a wider cabinet the studs will have to be cut and a simple box framing made.

It is easy to keep jars and bottles in order and within reach if you have plenty of shelf space. To figure how much shelf space you will need over the lavatory, line up the bottles and jars and tubes you will keep there. Measure the line, then divide by the number of shelves you plan to have. This will give you just about the width of the cabinet you need. You won't want a cabinet less than 14 inches wide, however, for next year you may have more articles to store there.

To make the best use of the space in the cabinets, plan shelves that are adjustable. This allows for flexibility in spacing of shelves to meet your own special needs.

Glass makes good shelving for the cabinets because it cleans easily. If you have wood shelves, cover them with linoleum or paint to protect them from dampness and toilet preparations.

A low-set cabinet for the children's use is generally placed so the center is from 30 to 36 inches from the floor. Installed low enough, this cabinet gives the children a place to keep their own toilet articles. Later, when the children outgrow the cabinet, you can use it to store shoe polish and brushes or other supplies.

Towel cabinets. Plan for storage of towels in your bathroom unless you live in a humid area. Even in a small room, you can set a towel cabinet in the wall over the closet tank if the soil stack or vent pipe is not in the way. If the wall has 6-inch studs, the cabinet can set back in the wall 5 inches, and stand out from the wall even with the front of the tank. Build the cabinet to the ceiling for extra storage space. Place the cabinet at least 12 inches above the tank or install a removable bottom shelf in the cabinet so you can make repairs in the tank.

Towels can be kept in a cabinet under the lavatory if there is no other place and if moisture does not condense on the pipes. You can build this type of cabinet or buy one ready-made. A floor-to-ceiling cabinet provides room for many more bathroom supplies.

If you have ample space, plan shelves at least 18 inches deep. Make them adjustable in height to get the best use from your storage space. Put shellac, varnish, enamel, or wax on shelves, trays, drawers. The finish makes them easy to clean, and also protects them from bathroom dampness.

Utility cabinets. Plan to store cleaning supplies in the bathroom. A cabinet under the lavatory may be used for this. A utility cabinet can be set between the studs in the wall at the end of the tub. It can be 3¾ or 5 inches deep, depending on the size of the studs. Slots at the top and bottom will give ventilation. Besides the cleaning supplies, there should be room in the cabinet for articles such as hot-water bottles. Do not plan for this cabinet if there is to be a shower at the other end of the tub.

Small accessories.

TOWEL RODS. Plan enough rods so there is towel space for each member of the family, and an extra rod for guest towels. If possible, allow about 21 inches of rod space for each person.

Place children's towel rods low enough for them to reach. There are inexpensive rods which fasten to the side of a lavatory. This height is convenient for the children.

Are you short on wall space? Install rods on the door. Or if there is no shower, you can place towel rods above the tub.

SOAP DISHES. You'll need a soap dish at the tub and one at the lavatory. Be sure the soap dishes drain well and hold even small pieces of soap. In some bathroom fixtures the soap dish comes already built in. There are others on the market in metal and tile that set in the wall.

TOOTH-BRUSH HOLDERS. Plan a place near the lavatory to keep tooth brushes. The cabinet above the lavatory is a good place if it is ventilated.

PAPER HOLDER. Set the center of the toilet-paper holder about 23 inches from the floor, within easy reach. If it goes on the side wall, place holder even with the front of the water closet. Holders come in two types. One type is fastened on the wall, and the other is set in the wall.

GRAB BARS. Grab bars installed by the bathtub and shower help protect your family from falls. Make sure they are firmly anchored and will hold securely.

Two grab bars may be used together for a tub and shower combination. A long vertical bar for support at the shower is placed about 18 inches from the shower end of the tub. The center of a horizontal bar is placed about one-third of the length of the tub from the faucets. You can get a horizontal grab bar combined with a soap dish that is set in the wall. This comes in metal or in tile.

CLOTHES HOOKS. A nonrusting hook on the door or wall is needed for hanging bathrobes and other clothing. For safety, place hooks above or below eye level.

RAZOR-BLADE SLOT. Some ready-built cabinets over the lavatory have an opening in the bottom or back so that used razor blades can be dropped between the studs. If you are building your cabinet make the slot ¼ by 1½ inches for this.

Clothes driers. If it is necessary to hang wet clothes in the bathroom, the best place is over the tub where the water can drip and drain away. Here are suggestions for several driers that are handy to use and always ready: Hooks fastened on the wall at each end of set-in tub hold lines stretching over the tub; a line on a reel at the end of the tub; a folding rack installed inside the cabinet door at the end of the tub; a swinging arm rack in a cabinet; a ladder drier at the end of a built-in corner bathtub. Plastic, wood, or metal make good rods for the drier. If you use wood, sandpaper it smooth. Then paint it with waterproof finish so it is easy to clean and will not mildew.

HOUSE AND EQUIPMENT INSPECTION

In checking up on equipment, the following points are important:

Insulation of roofs and walls, especially in localities where winters are severe, can be expected to save substantial sums, while weather-stripping of doors and windows,

Fig. 78. Various ways of installing ventilators in glass block panels to provide light, privacy, ventilation and waterproofness in the bathroom.

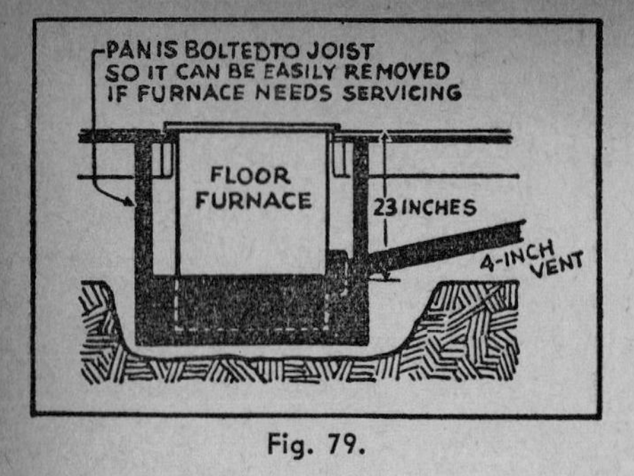

Fig. 79.

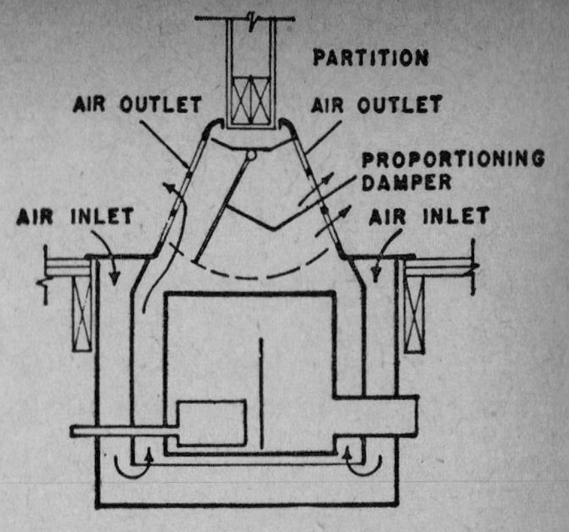

Fig. 81. Section through dual register floor furnace.

where complete insulation is not possible, will also cut heating costs.

The fire pot, smoke pipe, and all metal parts of the furnace should be cleaned at the end of each heating season. Parts which can be reached with a wire brush should be cleaned frequently during the heating season. Heating efficiency will be increased, corrosion will be retarded, by this simple chore.

Poor drafts are costly, inefficient. See that the smoke-pipe connection at the chimney is airtight, otherwise trouble with drafts will result. To test the connection, light a candle and move it slowly around the pipe where it enters the chimney. If there is a leak, the candle flame will be drawn toward it. Asbestos cement can be used to seal most leaks. Cracks in heavy metal parts should be repaired by a mechanic.

If the smoke pipe is lengthy, it should be braced firmly to avoid

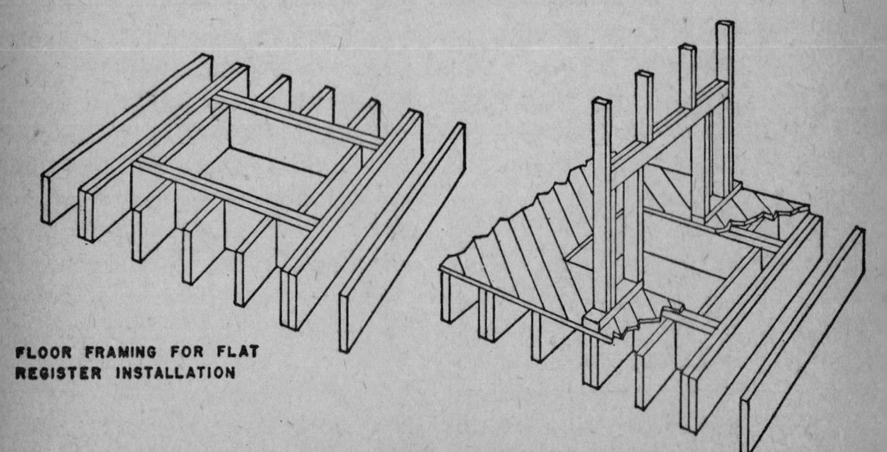

Fig. 80. Typical framing for floor furnaces.

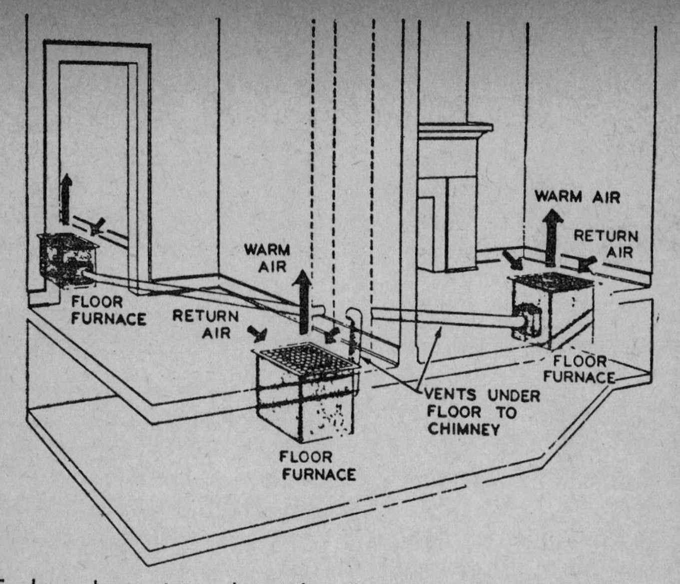

Fig. 82. For larger homes, two and even three floor furnaces can be installed to produce the desired inside temperature.

sagging from the chimney or furnace. A sagging smoke pipe or one with too many elbows retards the rapid flow of heated gases and air through the chimney. These gases are carrying a certain amount of soot and fly ash, and if they are retarded, the soot and ash are deposited in the smoke pipe, particularly at the elbows. Eventually the smoke-pipe opening will be clogged, and poor draft, as well as a fire hazard, will result.

RADIATORS AND CONVECTORS

The heating units used in hot water, steam and vapor systems to transfer the heat from the water or steam into the air in the room are usually the familiar cast iron radiators or convectors. The convector consists of a core or tube through which the steam or hot water is circulated and to which is fastened a series of thin metal fins which are heated from the core and give up their heat to the air as it circulates across them. The core and fins are housed in a cabinet which permits the cool air near the floor to enter the lower portion, then conducts it up across the core and fins to be warmed, and then out through a grille into the room. The convectors may be completely recessed in the walls or enclosed in cabinets located within the rooms.

Radiators are usually installed along outside walls and under windows. They may be recessed in the walls, enclosed in cabinets or stand in the open along the walls. If the radiator is recessed, the wall behind it should be insulated with a minimum of 1″ of rigid insulation or a re-

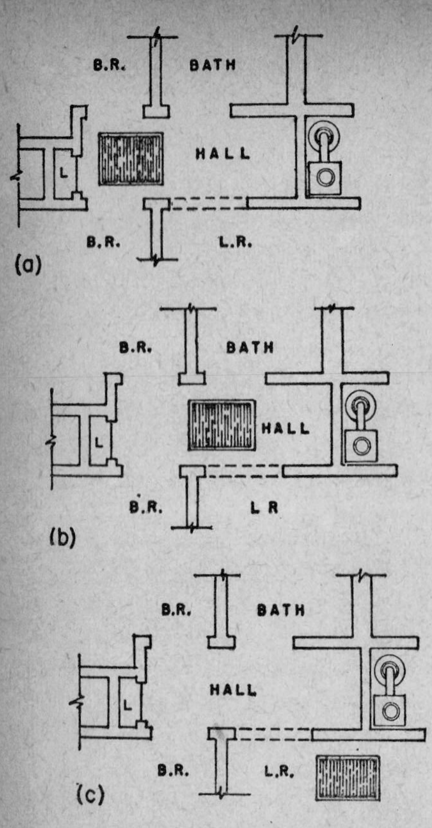

Fig. 83. Successive improvement in floor furnace location to reduce hazard.

flective surface such as aluminum foil. A cabinet or enclosure reduces the output of a radiator and this should be considered when determining the sizes to be used. A shield at the top of the radiator tends to reduce the streaking of the walls above.

FLOOR FURNACES

One or more floor furnaces make a very practical method of heating small homes. These heating units can be fully automatic burning either fuel oil or gas. This type of heating equipment does not require a full basement. Figure 79 shows how a floor furnace, suspended from the first floor, will require only a few cubic feet of excavation of earth under the house. Figure 80 shows one method of framing the opening in the floor for furnace installation. Double headers are installed to support the load. The illustration at the right in figure 80 shows how an opening in the floor can be framed for a furnace that is to have openings on either side of a wall partition. Figure 81 shows this type of heating unit.

While one furnace is sometimes adequate for very small homes, larger size dwellings will require two or even more plants (fig. 82).

In some cases there is a certain hazard in floor furnaces due to the grilles getting hot. It is wise to place them as safely as possible, away from where bare feet, children or drapes may come in contact with them. Figure 83 shows successive improvements (*a* through *c*) in placing a floor furnace. Perhaps safest of all is to use the wall register shown in figure 81.

COAL BIN CONSTRUCTION DETAILS

Square bins are considered in the tables which follow for convenience in estimating intermediate and oblong sizes. The capacities are based on average anthracite occupying 37 cubic feet of space per ton. Labor estimates are based on work by experienced carpenters and masons.

Somewhat more time may be required when building the first bin. Quantities of materials are sufficient for bins eight feet high.

The size and location of the bin should be determined, and 2″ x 4″ blocks fitted between the joists to conform to the outline of the bin. Next place the wallboard to form a dust-tight ceiling by nailing the edges to the underside of these blocks and joists. For vertical bin walls, as shown in fig. 84, plumb down to the floor, and locate the 2″ x 4″ floor plates, which should be fastened to the floor with expansion bolts or an equivalent method.

An alternate wall construction, which eliminates fastening to the floor, is shown in fig. 85. The walls slant about 6″ so that the bin is slightly smaller at the floor than at the ceiling. Use only kiln-dried or well-seasoned 2″ x 4″ lumber for the studding, which should be cut about ⅛″ extra long and driven into place between the ceiling and the floor plates.

The studding should be 2″ x 4″ common lumber spaced not over 24″ apart. Plywood (⅜″) or kiln-dried or well-seasoned tongue-and-groove lumber should be nailed to the outside of the studding. Use large-head galvanized nails for this purpose, as they have much greater holding power than smooth nails. Lattice strips may be used to conceal the seams. Keep the bottom of the plywood about ¼″ above floor level to prevent absorption of water when the floor is wet. The entire bin should be tightly enclosed from floor to ceiling. If the lumber is not kiln-dried or well-seasoned, the bin may be kept tight by means of tar paper tacked to the studding before the boards are nailed in place.

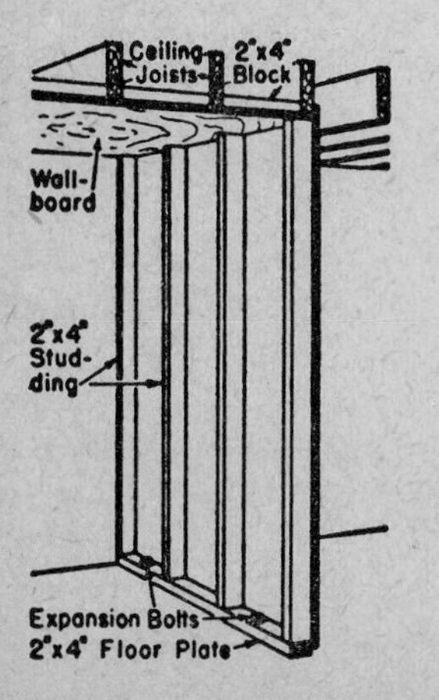

Fig. 84. Vertical wall.

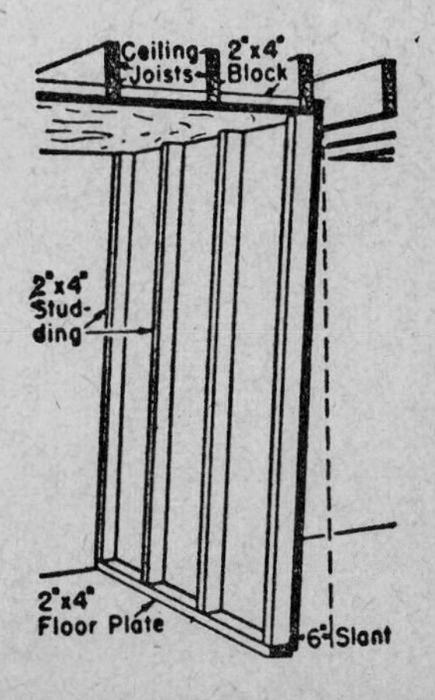

Fig. 85. Slanting wall.

Flat-Bottom Bin for Stoker Firing

BUILT OF PLYWOOD

Capacities and Estimates of Labor and Materials

Rated Capacity:*	2 tons	3 tons	4 tons	5 tons	6 tons
Reserve Capacity:**	¼ ton	¾ ton	1½ tons	2½ tons	3¾ tons
Dimensions, inside length and width (ft.):	4′ x 4′	5′ x 5′	6′ x 6′	7′ x 7′	8′ x 8′
Labor by carpenter (hours):	8	8	8	8	8
Wallboard for ceiling (square feet):	16	25	36	49	64
Plywood, ⅜″ three-ply (square feet):	80	96	114	130	144
Lumber, common (board feet):	70	80	90	110	120

* Rated Capacity means the average tons of anthracite stored six feet deep which will flow to the stoker conveyor.

** Reserve Capacity means the average tons of anthracite which remain in the corners of the bin after normal gravity flow to the stoker conveyor has ceased.

Hopper-Bottom Bin for Stoker Firing

BUILT OF TONGUE-AND-GROOVE

Capacities and Estimates of Labor and Materials

Rated Capacity:*	3¾ tons	4¾ tons	5¾ tons	7½ tons	8¾ tons
Dimensions, inside length and width (ft.):	6′ x 6′	7′ x 7′	8′ x 8′	10′ x 10′	12′ x 12′
Labor by carpenter (hours):	12	12	16	16	16
Wallboard for ceiling (square feet):	36	49	64	100	144
T-and-G Lumber, 1″ x 6″ kiln-dried or well-seasoned (board feet):	175	200	250	350	450
Other lumber, including 2″ x 4″ common (board feet):	225	250	300	400	500

* Rated Capacity means the average tons of anthracite stored six feet deep which will flow to the stoker conveyor.

Sloping-Bottom Bin for Hand Firing

WITH MULTIPLE RECESSED-BIN-OUTLET

Capacities and Estimates of Labor and Materials

Rated Capacity:*	2 tons	3½ tons	5 tons	6½ tons	8 tons	9¾ tons
Reserve Capacity (if sloping bottom is omitted):**	....	1/20 ton	¼ ton	¾ ton	1½ tons	2½ tons
Dimensions, inside length and width (ft.):	4′ x 4′	5′ x 5′	6′ x 6′	7′ x 7′	8′ x 8′	9′ x 9′
Labor by carpenter (hours):	8	8	8	12	12	12
Wallboard for ceiling (square feet):	16	25	36	49	64	81
Plywood, ⅜″ three-ply (square feet):	88	106	124	170	200	232
Lumber, common (board feet):	70	90	100	160	200	250

* Rated Capacity means the average tons of anthracite stored six feet deep which will flow to the outlet by gravity.

** Reserve Capacity means the average tons of anthracite required to replace the sloping bottom. The labor and materials for the sloping bottom have been included only for the three larger sizes of bins shown above.

Sloping-Bottom Bin for Hand Firing

with masonry walls and earth fill

Capacities and Estimates of Labor and Materials

Rated Capacity:*	2¼ tons	3½ tons	5 tons	6¼ tons	7½ tons	9 tons
Reserve Capacity (if sloping bottom is omitted):**	1/20 ton	¼ ton	½ ton	1¼ tons	2 tons	2¾ tons
Dimensions, inside length and width (ft.):	4′ x 4′	5′ x 5′	6′ x 6′	7′ x 7′	8′ x 8′	9′ x 9′
Labor by carpenter and mason (total hours):	8	9	10	13	15	17
Wallboard for ceiling (square feet):	16	25	36	49	64	81
Plywood, ⅜″ three-ply (square feet):	25	25	25	25	25	25
Lumber, kiln-dried or well-seasoned (board feet):	50	50	50	50	50	50
Masonry building units (6″ x 8″ x 16″ size):	54	78	90	102	126	138
Earth or ash fill for sloping bottom (cubic yards):	omit	omit	omit	1⅓	2	3⅓
Portland cement (sacks):	½	¾	1	2½	3	4
Lime (sacks):	½	¾	1	1	1	1
Sand (pounds):	250	350	400	800	1000	1200
Gravel, pea size (pounds):	omit	omit	omit	700	900	1200

* Rated Capacity means the average tons of anthracite stored six feet deep which will flow to the outlet by gravity.

** Reserve Capacity means the average tons of anthracite required to replace the sloping bottom. The labor and materials for the sloping bottom have been included only for the three larger sizes of bins shown above.

Sloping bottoms should be supported by 2″ x 4″ common lumber spaced not over 18″ apart. When tongue-and-groove lumber is used for a sloping bottom, the boards should be laid parallel with the flow of fuel. A protective coating, such as asphalt or tar paint, may be applied.

Insulation should be provided on the walls and top where exposed to freezing temperatures, as under an open porch.

Delivery windows and chutes are available in several types. A metal delivery chute can be built into the wall of the building, with the door opening out. Metal doors are less likely to be damaged when deliveries are made. A typical wood or metal basement window swings inward. The bottom ledge of the window frame should be bevelled to prevent coal from interfering with the closing of the window. A grade-line chute may be used where the basement ceiling is not high enough above the outdoor ground level.

A remote latch-control is a means of opening and closing the delivery window without the necessity for anyone to enter the bin. It consists of a spring-type latch on the delivery window with a chain extending over pulleys and through the wall of the bin. If the window opens in, pulling the chain releases the latch and raises the window to the ceiling. When the chain is released, the window will

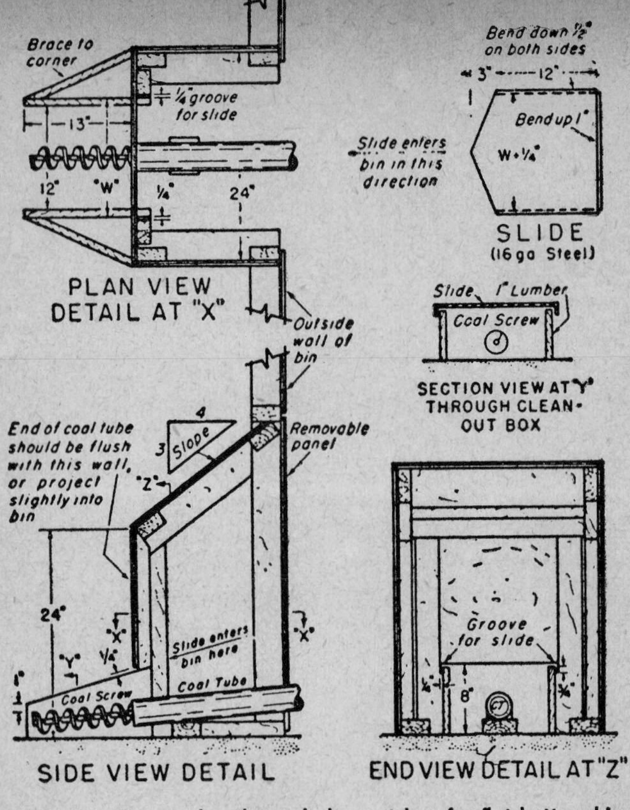

Fig. 86. Recessed outlet and cleanout box for flat-bottom bin.

swing shut and automatically latch. Doors opening out should be equipped with spring-type hinges so that when the chain is pulled to release the latch, the door will swing up against the building wall. By pushing the door shut from outdoors, it will automatically latch.

Screen door hooks and cupboard turns may be used for the access doors, as they are less expensive to buy and install than hinges and cupboard catches.

A small inspection window permits the user to determine how much fuel is left in the bin. When installed in the wall, it should be at eye level. If placed in an inner access door, it should be below the top section. If daylight does not enter the bin through a delivery window, a shielded electric light may be provided on the ceiling near the delivery door.

For stoker firing, locating the bin close to the heater results in lower cost of stoker equipment. When designing a house, the relative location of the chimney, heater and bin should be planned for maximum convenience. The points to be considered include delivery of coal to the premises, conveying it to the fire, and finally, the removal of ash from the basement.

A recessed outlet and cleanout box, as shown in fig. 86, permits convenient installation and servicing of the stoker conveyor without removing a large amount of fuel. This arrangement applies to flat-bottom bins or it may be used when a bin for hand firing is converted to stoker firing. The metal slide is inserted only when it is desired to hold up the coal. This design provides for conveying coal from the center of the bottom without an excessive length of exposed screw. With short outlets, the 8″ x 12″ opening around the coal tube should be closed.

The outlet and cleanout box shown in fig. 87 applies only to hopper-bottom bins. The length of the box should correspond to the exposed screw of the stoker selected.

Small and medium-sized bins for stoker firing are usually built with flat bottoms. In most cases it costs less to fill the corners with fuel than to build a hopper bottom. A reserve supply of coal is thereby provided, which does not deteriorate in storage, even for long periods.

HAND FURNACE OPERATING HINTS

The following suggestions are offered for the hand fireman:

a. Select type and size of fuel carefully from those available. No definite rule can be given, as the selection depends on the equipment, the load, and the adaptability of the fireman. Where coal is used, it usually pays to experiment with a few different coals before making final selection. The coal costing the least in dollars per ton may not give least total yearly fuel cost, as more of it may be used. During wartime the

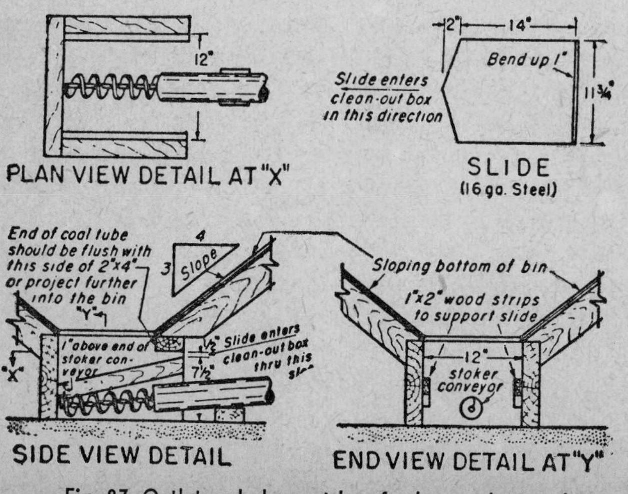

Fig. 87. Outlet and cleanout box for hopper-bottom bin.

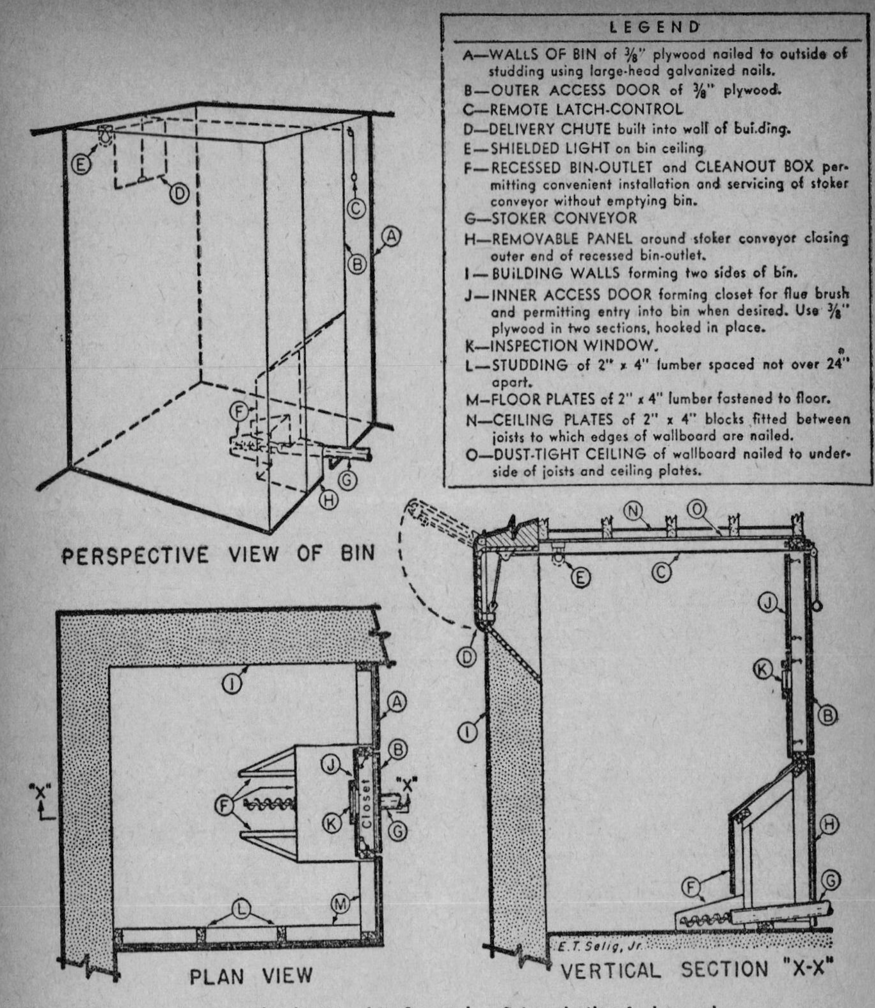

LEGEND
A—WALLS OF BIN of 3/8" plywood nailed to outside of studding using large-head galvanized nails.
B—OUTER ACCESS DOOR of 3/8" plywood.
C—REMOTE LATCH-CONTROL
D—DELIVERY CHUTE built into wall of building.
E—SHIELDED LIGHT on bin ceiling
F—RECESSED BIN-OUTLET and CLEANOUT BOX permitting convenient installation and servicing of stoker conveyor without emptying bin.
G—STOKER CONVEYOR
H—REMOVABLE PANEL around stoker conveyor closing outer end of recessed bin-outlet.
I—BUILDING WALLS forming two sides of bin.
J—INNER ACCESS DOOR forming closet for flue brush and permitting entry into bin when desired. Use 3/8" plywood in two sections, hooked in place.
K—INSPECTION WINDOW.
L—STUDDING of 2" x 4" lumber spaced not over 24" apart.
M—FLOOR PLATES of 2" x 4" lumber fastened to floor.
N—CEILING PLATES of 2" x 4" blocks fitted between joists to which edges of wallboard are nailed.
O—DUST-TIGHT CEILING of wallboard nailed to underside of joists and ceiling plates.
PERSPECTIVE VIEW OF BIN
PLAN VIEW
"X"
Closet
E. T. Selig, Jr.
VERTICAL SECTION "X-X"

Fig. 88. Flat-bottom bin for stoker firing, built of plywood.

exact fuel you would like may not be available.

b. Keep plenty of fuel in the furnace. Avoid thin fuel beds. The amount of fuel that is burned depends on the amount of air permitted to flow through it.

c. Keep air entering ashpit or furnace under control. Air going into the ashpit should be controlled by the ashpit damper. Air entering the furnace for the top of the fire should be controlled by the furnace-door damper. Additional control is obtained from the butterfly damper at the rear of the furnace and, if absolutely necessary, from the check damper. Automatic control based upon the temperature in the house is more satisfactory and efficient than hand control of dampers. Stop all uncontrolled leakage of air into heater, such as around the ashpit and furnace doors. Leaks may be discovered with a lighted match or, better, with a candle flame. Various furnace cements may be used to stop many kinds of leaks; steel wool or even a rag may be used to lessen leakage around grate shaker rod. Badly fitting doors or badly fitting door dampers should either be properly fitted by filing, or they should be replaced.

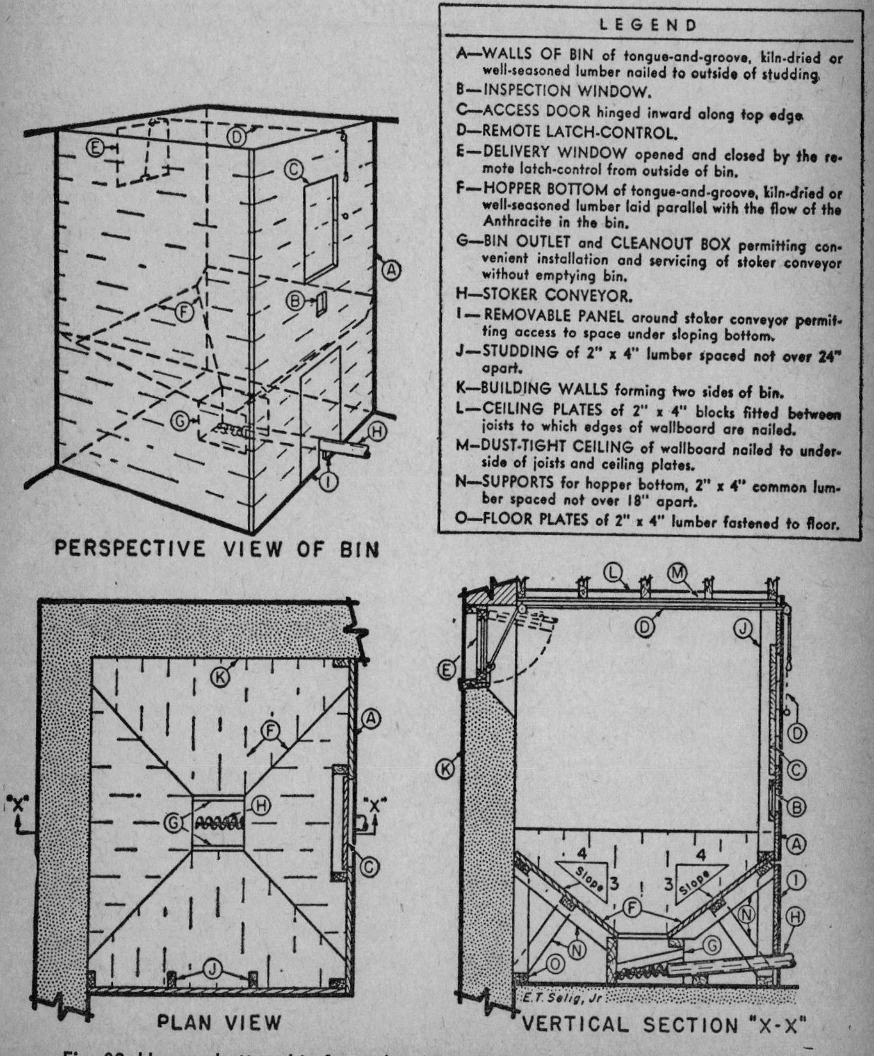

LEGEND
A—WALLS OF BIN of tongue-and-groove, kiln-dried or well-seasoned lumber nailed to outside of studding.
B—INSPECTION WINDOW.
C—ACCESS DOOR hinged inward along top edge.
D—REMOTE LATCH-CONTROL.
E—DELIVERY WINDOW opened and closed by the remote latch-control from outside of bin.
F—HOPPER BOTTOM of tongue-and-groove, kiln-dried or well-seasoned lumber laid parallel with the flow of the Anthracite in the bin.
G—BIN OUTLET and CLEANOUT BOX permitting convenient installation and servicing of stoker conveyor without emptying bin.
H—STOKER CONVEYOR.
I—REMOVABLE PANEL around stoker conveyor permitting access to space under sloping bottom.
J—STUDDING of 2" x 4" lumber spaced not over 24" apart.
K—BUILDING WALLS forming two sides of bin.
L—CEILING PLATES of 2" x 4" blocks fitted between joists to which edges of wallboard are nailed.
M—DUST-TIGHT CEILING of wallboard nailed to underside of joists and ceiling plates.
N—SUPPORTS for hopper bottom, 2" x 4" common lumber spaced not over 18" apart.
O—FLOOR PLATES of 2" x 4" lumber fastened to floor.
PERSPECTIVE VIEW OF BIN
PLAN VIEW
"X"
"X"
VERTICAL SECTION "X-X"
4
Slope
3
E.T. Selig, Jr

Fig. 89. Hopper-bottom bin for stoker firing, built of tongue-and-groove lumber.

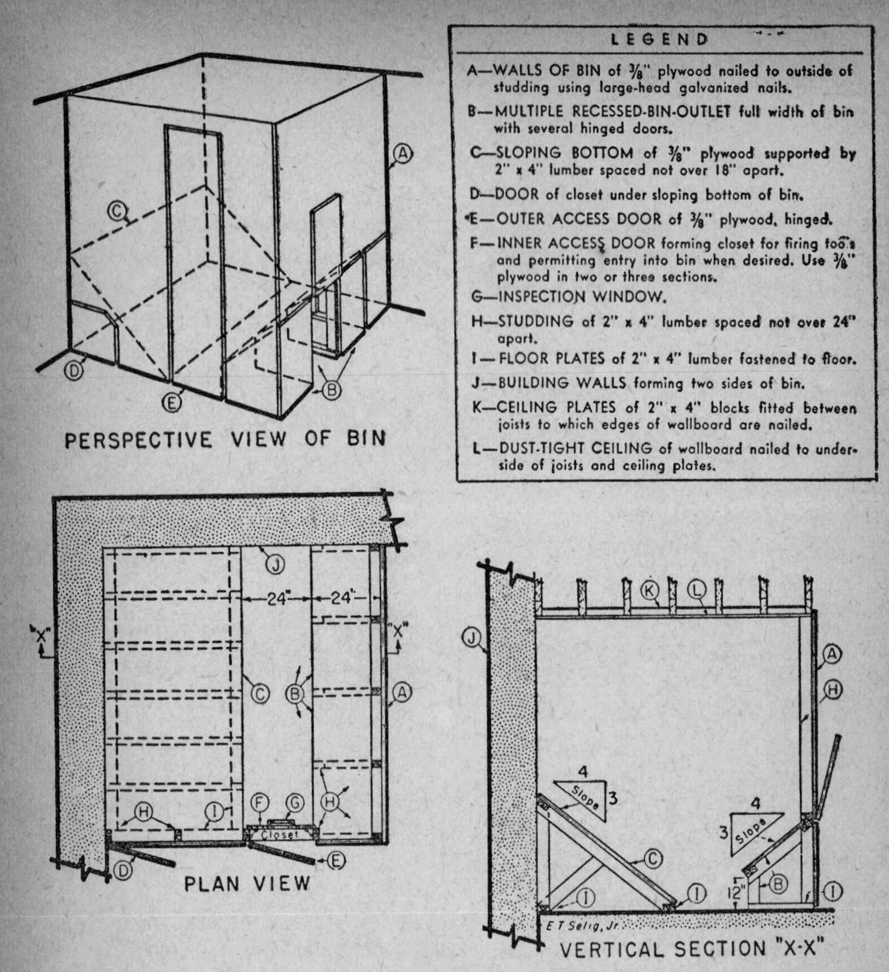

LEGEND
A—WALLS OF BIN of 3/8" plywood nailed to outside of studding using large-head galvanized nails.
B—MULTIPLE RECESSED-BIN-OUTLET full width of bin with several hinged doors.
C—SLOPING BOTTOM of 3/8" plywood supported by 2" x 4" lumber spaced not over 18" apart.
D—DOOR of closet under sloping bottom of bin.
E—OUTER ACCESS DOOR of 3/8" plywood, hinged.
F—INNER ACCESS DOOR forming closet for firing tools and permitting entry into bin when desired. Use 3/8" plywood in two or three sections.
G—INSPECTION WINDOW.
H—STUDDING of 2" x 4" lumber spaced not over 24" apart.
I—FLOOR PLATES of 2" x 4" lumber fastened to floor.
J—BUILDING WALLS forming two sides of bin.
K—CEILING PLATES of 2" x 4" blocks fitted between joists to which edges of wallboard are nailed.
L—DUST-TIGHT CEILING of wallboard nailed to underside of joists and ceiling plates.
PERSPECTIVE VIEW OF BIN
PLAN VIEW
VERTICAL SECTION "X-X"
24"
Closet
Slope
12"
E T Selig, Jr.

Fig. 90. Sloping-bottom bin for hand firing, with multiple recessed-bin-outlet.

d. Before shoveling fresh coal into the furnace, hoe up the fuel bed so that some hot, red fuel will remain on top of the bed after firing. This red fuel ignites unburned gases coming from the fuel bed.

e. Where there is much flaming at the top of the fuel bed, admit some air over the fire through the damper on the firing door. This air is needed to burn the gases at the top of the fuel bed.

f. Shake down the ashes gently and stop when any red particles fall into the ash pit. This usually leaves some ash on the grates, which is desirable to protect them.

g. Do not stir a fire with a poker. This is likely to throw ashes up into the burning part of the fire, where they will melt and form clinkers. If necessary to use the poker do so gently and do not use any deep "lifting-up" strokes.

h. Do not let the ashpit remain full of ashes. There should always be plenty of room over the ashes to permit entering air to reach all parts of the grate. This prevents the grate from heating and softening.

i. Keep the breeching or the furnace pipe to the chimney completely free from both obstruction and air leaks.

j. Keep chimney reasonably clean, free from obstructions and air leaks. This is particularly necessary where there is difficulty in obtaining enough draft. The top of the chimney should be higher than all roof points; this prevents downdrafts when the wind blows.

Automatic fuel-burning equipment should be adjusted by an ex-

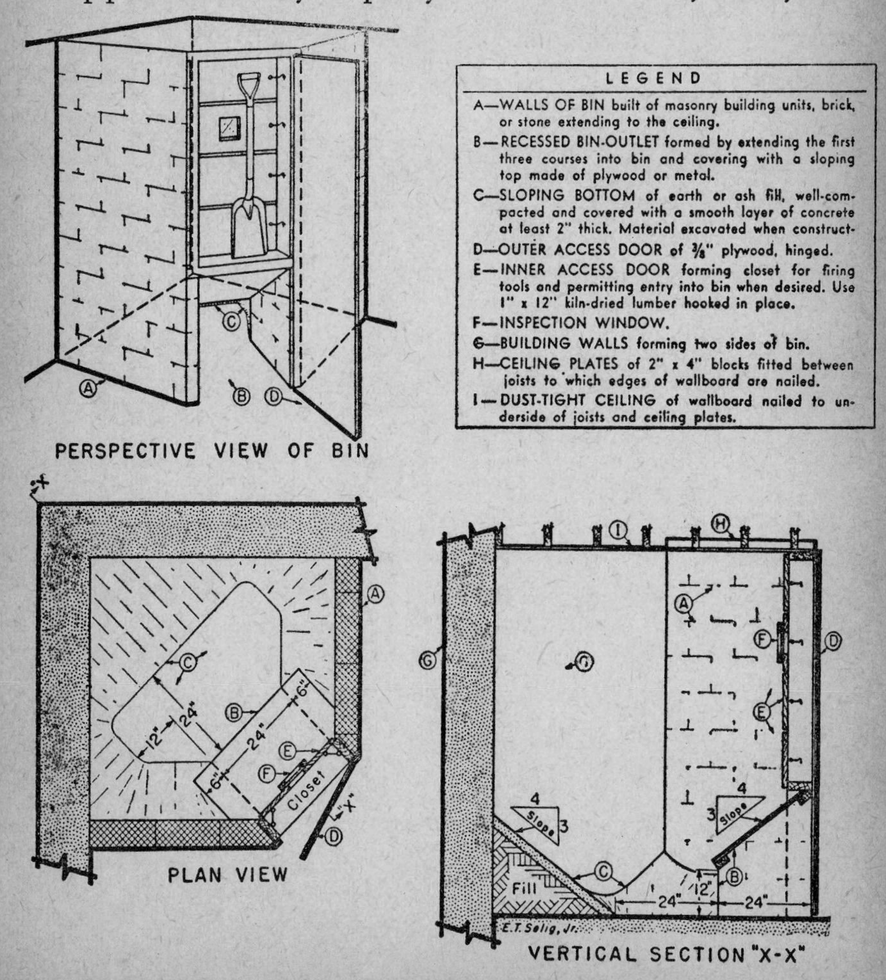

LEGEND
A—WALLS OF BIN built of masonry building units, brick, or stone extending to the ceiling.
B—RECESSED BIN-OUTLET formed by extending the first three courses into bin and covering with a sloping top made of plywood or metal.
C—SLOPING BOTTOM of earth or ash fill, well-compacted and covered with a smooth layer of concrete at least 2" thick. Material excavated when construct-
D—OUTER ACCESS DOOR of 3/8" plywood, hinged.
E—INNER ACCESS DOOR forming closet for firing tools and permitting entry into bin when desired. Use 1" x 12" kiln-dried lumber hooked in place.
F—INSPECTION WINDOW.
G—BUILDING WALLS forming two sides of bin.
H—CEILING PLATES of 2" x 4" blocks fitted between joists to which edges of wallboard are nailed.
I—DUST-TIGHT CEILING of wallboard nailed to underside of joists and ceiling plates.
PERSPECTIVE VIEW OF BIN
PLAN VIEW
Closet
VERTICAL SECTION "X-X"
Slope
Fill
E.T. Selig, Jr.

Fig. 91. Sloping-bottom bin for hand firing, with masonry walls and earth fill.

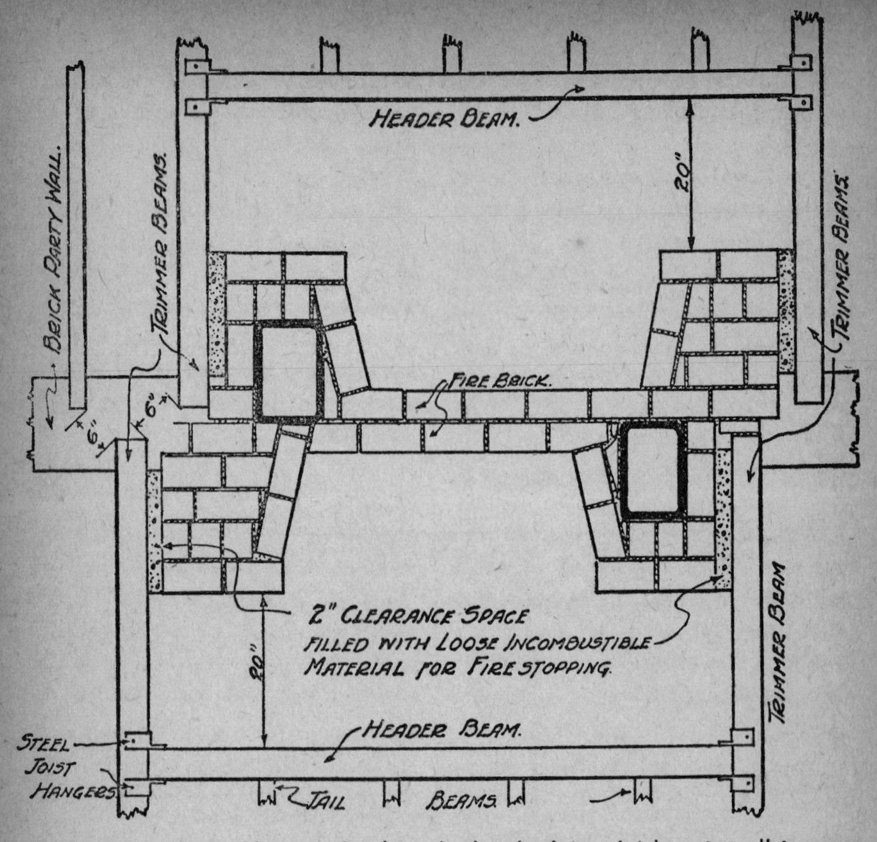

Fig. 92. Method for building two fireplaces back-to-back in a brick party wall to secure proper spacing between ends of floor joists.

pert service man. Ask him to check all possible air leaks into the furnace and heater. Study the fire after the adjustments have been made, and also the gases coming from the top of the chimney. From time to time during the heating season look at the fire and the chimney to see if the original adjustments appear to be maintained.

Regular service calls also serve as a check.

To keep the temperature of the gases that carry heat out the chimney reasonably low, all heat-absorbing surfaces of the heater must be kept as clean as possible. One cleaning a season is seldom enough except, possibly, where gas is used as a fuel. High loads on the heater necessarily cause more loss out the chimney. Do not force the burning any more than necessary.

During the off season, the entire heating equipment should be thoroughly repaired, cleaned, and oiled; leaks should be stopped and all parts adjusted.

The following table gives the percentage of heat in the fuel that goes into the house for the usual domestic heating equipment.

Over-all Efficiencies

(Solid fuels listed are hand-fired)

	High	*Low*
Anthracite	70	50
Bituminous / Subbituminous	65	40
Lignite	53	40
Coke	70	50
Oil	75	50
Gas	80	55

The efficiency of the average household boiler and stoker may be estimated at 35 to 65 percent. The wide range for each fuel shows how greatly the heat loss varies with furnace operation and type of equipment. This loss is due largely to unburned fuel and to excess air carrying heat out the chimney. If a coal has 10 percent ash and the refuse from the ashpit is 50 percent unburned fuel, a loss of, roughly, 10 percent of the fuel is indicated. Poorly adjusted oil burners may cause a great loss of heat from excess air; this may average 10 to 15 percent. A poorly operating oil burner may not burn more than 90 percent of the fuel, the remainder being unburned and lost.

Some heat is lost from heating equipment in the basement. Heat is radiated and carried to the surroundings. Heated air in the basement is likely to find its way into the chimney, especially if the check damper is left open. An open check damper will take air from the base-

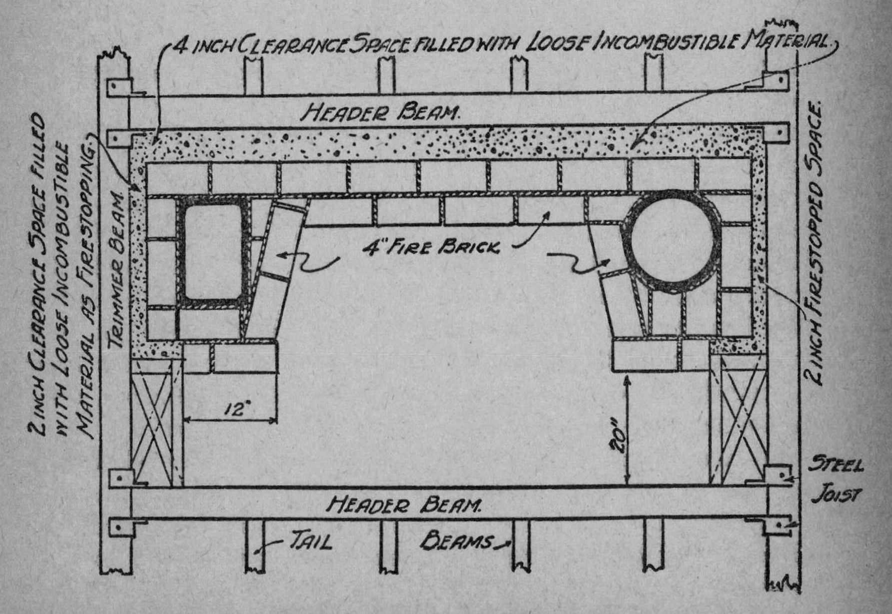

Fig. 93. Floor framing around a single fireplace. Note filling between framing and brickwork, which serves both as insulator and fire-stop.

ment, which must be replaced by other air. This may come from the rooms above, robbing them of their heat. Such air will come to the basement through an open door at the stairs or through the opening usually found between the bottom of the door and the sill. Such loss may be appreciable. Keep the check damper closed except possibly in very mild weather, when it is difficult to maintain a low fire without opening it. Air needed for burning the fuel should come from air leaks or openings into the basement, preferably near the furnace. A small amount of heat in the basement is usually desirable. During war times it can be at a minimum. The amount of heat radiated from the equipment can be controlled by insulation.

A little heat is lost from the house by going into the ground. It usually is a relatively small amount. How much of this can be prevented depends on the individual case. For most houses little saving along these lines can be accomplished. Insulation can be used where possible.

More heat is lost from the house by radiation to surroundings and by being carried away by air. This is a main heat loss. Its amount depends on how much hotter the house is than the outside temperature. If the temperature inside the house is 72° F. and that outside is 32° F., the difference in temperature is 40°. If the house temperature is lowered to 68°, this difference becomes 36°. It may be roughly calculated that the heat loss becomes 36/40 of what it was, or about 10 percent less. When the house is carried at a lower temperature at night, some heat must be used to raise its temperature back to the day normal, but less heat is lost during the night. Tests have shown a saving of about 5 to 10 percent by allowing the house to cool to 60° at night for the warmer outside temperatures. For the colder outside temperatures, a smaller percentage would be saved. A lower house temperature can be carried with comfort if the air is not allowed to become too dry. This may be prevented by various types of humidifiers. Humidifiers are usually provided with hot-air systems; water-pan devices can be used on radiators. The moisture in the air should not be kept high enough to cause appreciable condensation on windows.

Heat loss from the house can also be reduced by means of insulation and storm doors and windows. If the entire house cannot be insulated, insulating beneath the roof is a very effective and usually a very paying scheme. Savings can sometimes be made by studying the pathways of the heat. For example, a reflecting shield against the wall back of a radiator will prevent too much heat from going directly into the wall; pulled down window shades lower the heat loss through the windows.

Heat is not only carried away by air against the sides, windows, and doors of the house, but heat loss also results from cold air from the outside entering the house. To enter, it must drive out the warmer air of the house; it must be heated, so that the desired house temperature is

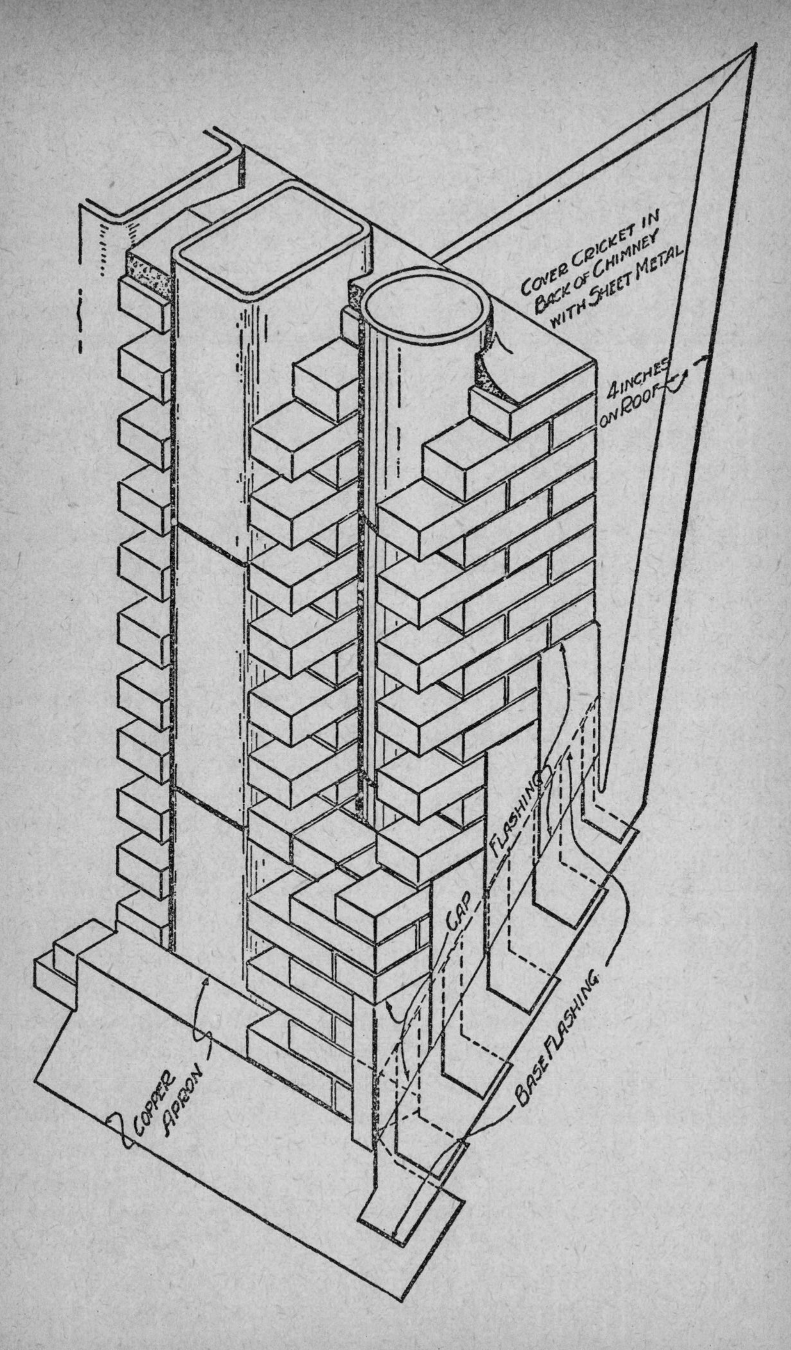

Fig. 94. Details of chimney construction showing method of flashing at roof surface, also a wash course, but no cap surrounding flues at top.

maintained. Such heat loss can be reduced by making the house reasonably airtight; weather-stripping doors and windows and adding storm doors and windows are effective means. The space immediately below the roof should be examined to determine whether there are air leaks at eaves or through ventilators. These should be shut off during the winter.

All outlets to chimneys should be examined for undesirable air leaks. When not in use, fireplaces should be dampered tightly from the chimney; fill in the cracks around the damper if necessary. It is seldom realized how much air can go through a small crack. The inlet air to hot-air systems should come from the inside of the house. As a practical matter, it is doubtful if doing all of these things will result in lack of needed ventilation in the house.

Rooms not absolutely needed should be shut off. If there are water pipes in the walls or water radiators in the room, care must be taken that water in them does not freeze. During the night bedroom doors should be kept closed; in most houses there is a large space beneath the bedroom doors that should be closed with a rug or by other means; the radiators should be shut off; any air registers should be closed tightly, by covering if necessary. The best medical advice appears to be to open bedroom windows only enough for needed ventilation for sleeping.

The total amount of heat saved by weather-stripping, storm doors and windows, and insulation depends on such factors as the type of house, its surroundings, and the severity of the weather. The Bureau of Standards publishes the following table on approximate fuel savings:

APPROXIMATE FUEL SAVINGS IN DWELLING HOUSES

[Expressed in percentage of fuel that would have been required for similar house without insulation or weather-stripping]

	Saving percent
No insulation, weather-stripped	15 to 20
Same, with double (storm) windows	25 to 30
½-inch insulation, not weather-stripped	20 to 30
½-inch insulation, weather-stripped	About 40
½-inch insulation, with double windows	About 50
1-inch insulation, not weather-stripped	30 to 40
1-inch insulation, weather-stripped	About 50
1-inch insulation, with double windows	About 60
[Expressed in percentage of fuel that would have been required for similar house without insulation but with weather-stripping]	
With double windows, no insulation	10 to 15
½-inch insulation only	25 to 35
½-inch insulation, with double windows	40 to 45
1-inch insulation only	35 to 45
1-inch insulation with double windows	50 to 55

HEATING AND FIREPLACES

Fireplaces differ in efficiency and, obviously, more fuel is required to warm a room with a poor fireplace than with a good one.

A poor fireplace from the efficiency standpoint is one built into a chimney on the side or end of a house, with three sides exposed to the weather, with a large throat and flue and without an adjustable damper.

A good fireplace is one built inside the house, so that most of the heat either passing through or stored in its brick or masonry is eventually delivered to the house. It has an adjustable damper so that the warm air lost up the chimney can be limited to that necessary to remove smoke.

Air flow up the chimney can also be limited by closing the windows and doors of the room containing the fireplace. Sometimes, in a tight house, this will make the fireplace smoke. If so, a window near the fireplace may be opened slightly to permit air for combustion to reach the fire place without causing a cold draft across the floor.

Obviously, when the damper is closed, and there is no fire in the fireplace, the fireplace does not affect materially the warmth of the house. Then when the damper is opened, a certain amount of heat supplied by the central heating plant is lost up the chimney and this amount of heat must be replaced by the fire in the fireplace before there is any conservation of furnace fuel.

Considerable heat is delivered to the house from the brick or masonry after the fire in a fireplace has gone out. During this period, the damper can be closed, of course, as soon as the ashes or embers stop smoking.

In general, a fireplace saves oil whenever (a) the room containing it is warmer than the adjacent rooms, whether the radiator in that room is on or off, or (b) the room is as warm with the radiator off as the adjacent rooms. These conclusions are based on the assumption that no room is overheated.

Obviously, a fuel saving can be achieved as described above by means of a stove or space heater and these devices are generally more efficient than fireplaces.

Fuel can be saved by turning off the heat in a closed-off room. A room is considered closed-off when the doors or other communications to other rooms are closed. Obviously, outside windows or doors to such rooms should also be closed. Some heat will enter such rooms from adjacent warm rooms by conduction through the walls and doors.

Some radiator valves have small openings or ports to permit a small flow of water with the valve in the closed position. Such ports are provided to prevent freezing of the radiator, with consequent damage, in very cold weather. The heat loss is small because the flow of water is small and the heat loss can be further reduced by jacketing the radiator with wool, cotton, burlap or some other insulator.

A heating system does not have to supply more heat to a radiator than that radiator dissipates.

METAL CHIMNEYS

A recent addition to the home-heating field has been the development of pre-fabricated metal chimneys (fig. 95). These units are readily installed in new or old work. As they are very light in weight, they do not require any footing or foundation but are supported entirely by the house framework. Chimneys of

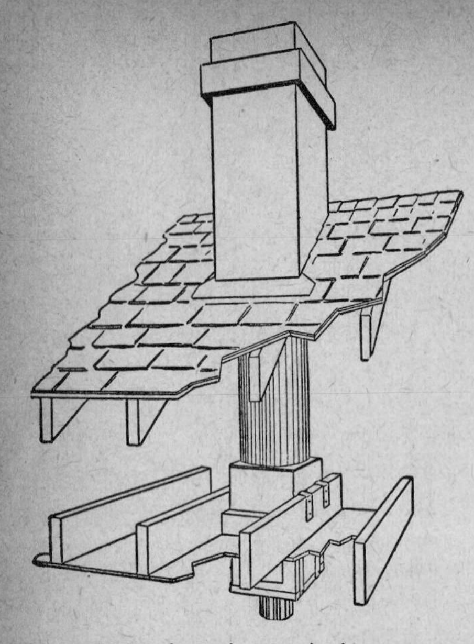

Fig. 95. Ready-made metal chimneys are available for use with all types of heating systems. They are light enough in weight to enable them to be hung from the house framework, thus eliminating the need for chimney footings and foundations.

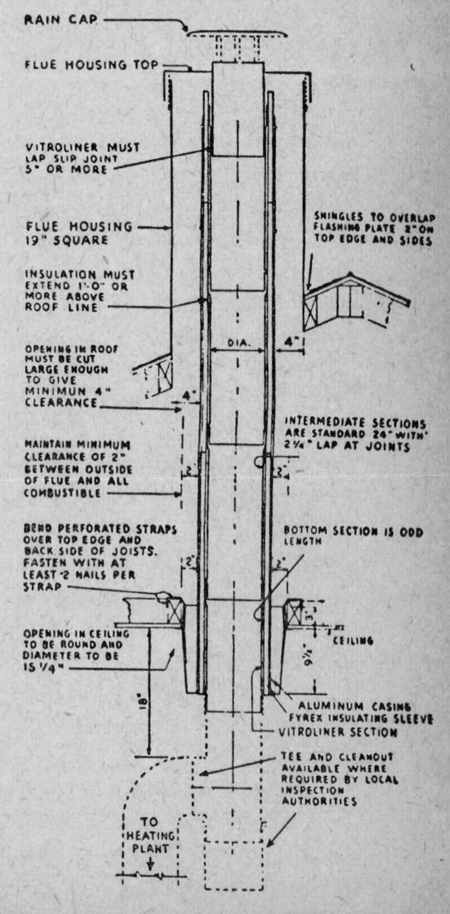

Fig. 96. Detail of metal chimney installations.

A saving in heat is effected if the heat is turned off in sleeping rooms at night, especially when the windows in such rooms are opened.

The saving attainable by wrapping a turned-off radiator with blankets over night is small because the amount of heat stored in the radiator is small. The radiator will cool off during the night, despite the blanket, and the stored heat will be lost anyway. The saving will increase if radiator valve has a port.

A saving of fuel occurs when the thermostat is set down at night. This saving is on the order of 10 percent or less for dwelling houses which is not so great as some people appear to expect but it is worthwhile.

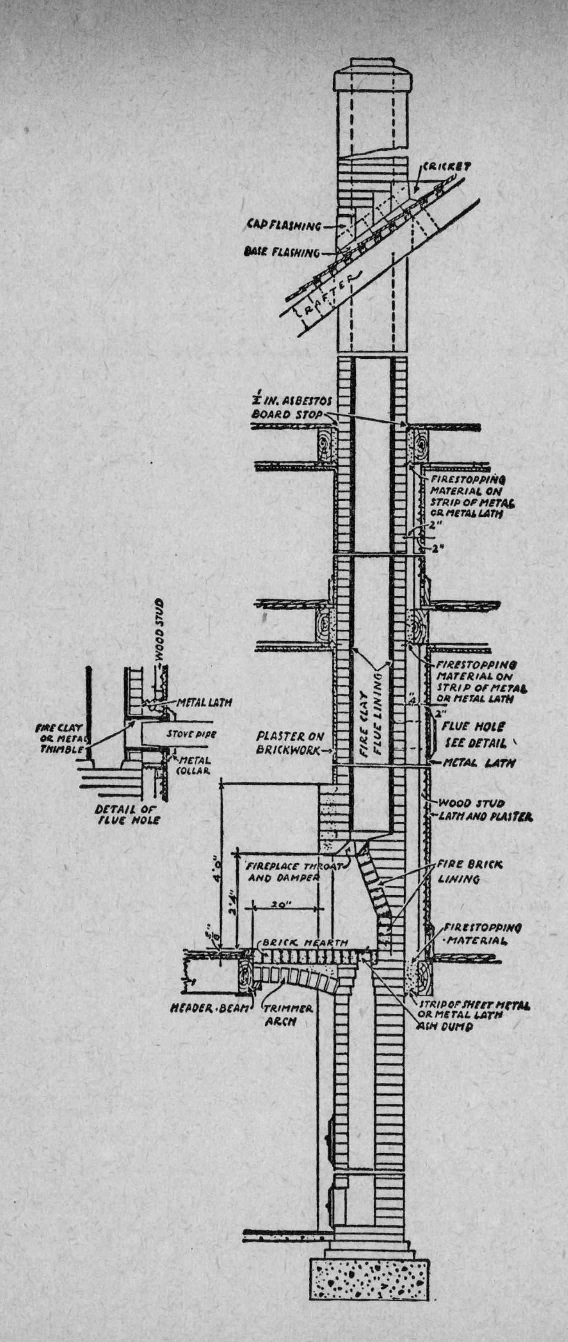

Fig. 97. Standard chimney construction as recommended by the National Board of Fire Underwriters.

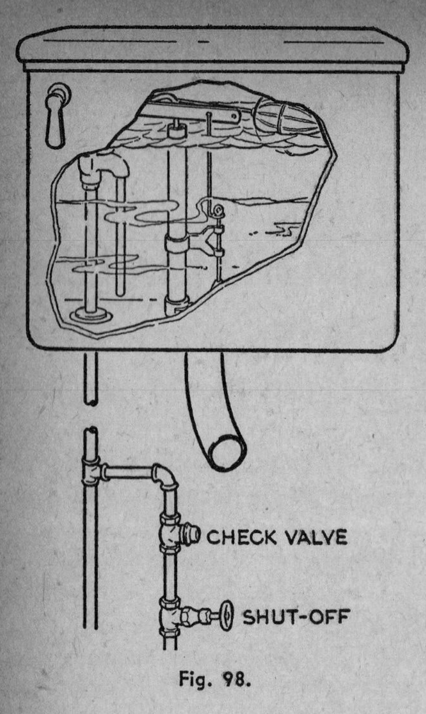

Fig. 98.

this type meet with the approval of the Underwriters' Laboratory.

A special advantage that these metal chimneys have over conventional masonry chimneys is that they can be installed in a matter of hours, while the latter often require days and even weeks to complete.

Figure 96 shows the details of installing one type of this kind of chimney.

AVOIDING CONDENSATION

Water vapor condensing on the sides of flush tanks is a source of annoyance to housekeeping as well as the cause of many rotten bathroom floors. This moisture can be eliminated by connecting a hot water line into the cold water line running to the tank as shown in figure 98. The hot water line should be provided with a shut-off valve and a check-valve to prevent cold water backing up into the hot water line. After the lines have been connected, adjust the shut-off valve on the hot water line so that the temperature of the water in the tank will remain at about 70 degrees F.

SECTION VII

INTERIOR WALL MATERIALS AND FINISHES

Planning the Linoleum Floor Job—Measuring, Cutting, and Packing Linoleum—Installing Linoleum in Single Rooms—Installing 12-foot Linoleum through Doors in Double Rooms—How to Do Pattern Scribing on Linoleum—Linoleum Scribing around Radiators—Linoleum Cove Base—Linoleum on Counter Tops—Turn-Down Sink Rims—Repairing Counter Tops—Stair Treads, Runners, Edgings—Installing Asphalt Tile—Installation Instructions for Resilient Tile—Protection of Asphalt Tile—Dampness Test for Concrete Subfloors—Tile on Wood Floors—Ceramic Tile, Terrazzo, and Marble Subfloors—Metal Subfloors—Fitting Tile to Straight Walls—Installation of Resilient Tile Stair Treads—Plaster—Plaster Proportions—Peeling of Paint—Wrinkling of Paper—Pencil as Expansion Plug—Asbestos Board—Tileboard—Replacing Ceiling Tile—Applying Ceiling Panels—Patching Wallboard—Waterproofing Tileboard—Glass Panels.

SECTION VII

INTERIOR WALL MATERIALS AND FINISHES

PLANNING THE LINOLEUM FLOOR JOB

Before cutting linoleum or lining felt, decide in which direction the strips are to run. For best results, the lining felt and linoleum should be laid so that their seams will run across the floorboards. However, if laying the linoleum in this direction would mean wasteful cutting, it can be laid with the seams running in the direction of the floorboards. In such cases, protect the seams with strips of fabric seam protector.

Linoleum is usually laid with the graining running in the direction of the traffic through the room. This sometimes necessitates the installation of the linoleum with seams running in the same direction as the floorboards.

Where the same pattern of linoleum is to be used in adjoining rooms, it is usually best to run a strip of linoleum through the doorway clear across both rooms. This eliminates a seam at the doorway where the floor gets maximum wear.

If the boards of the floor in one room run in the opposite direction to the floorboards in the other, plan the job so that the seams in the felt and linoleum do not fall directly over the

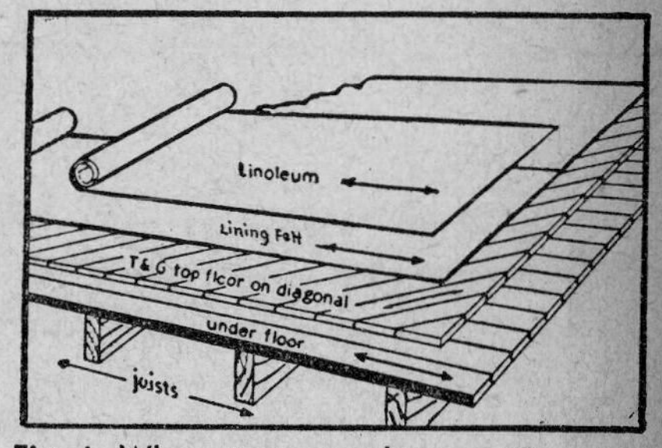

Fig. 1. Where tongue-and-groove floor runs on a diagonal with the underfloor, linoleum and lining felt should be laid at a 45 degree angle with the top floor.

meeting point of the two floors. By eliminating seams at this point, there will be less danger of the expansion and contraction of the wood opening seams or splitting the linoleum.

In a room that is only slightly wider than 6′, 12′, 24′, etc., the use of a border will often make it unnecessary to cut up a full 6′ width of linoleum to cover the last few inches.

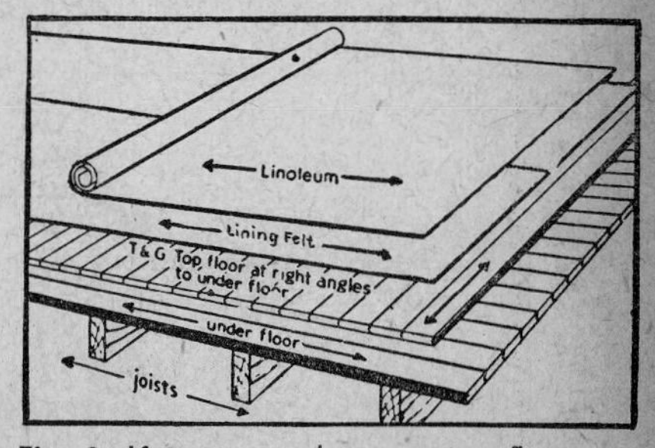

Fig. 2. If tongue-and-groove top floor runs at right angles to underfloor, linoleum and lining felt should be laid across the floorboards for best results.

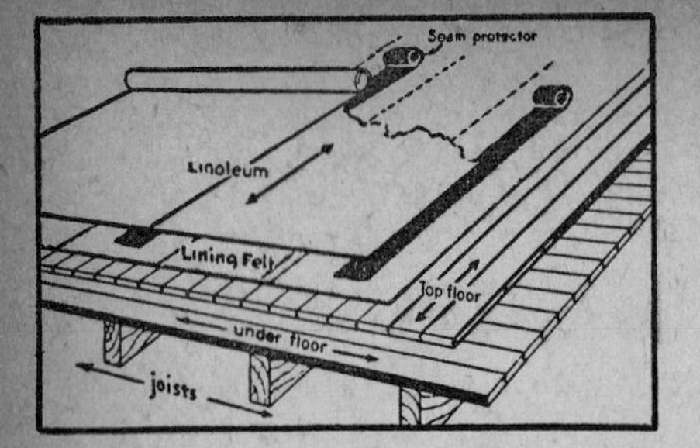

Fig. 3. Where laying linoleum across the floorboards would involve wasteful cutting, follow direction of the boards and use a seam protector.

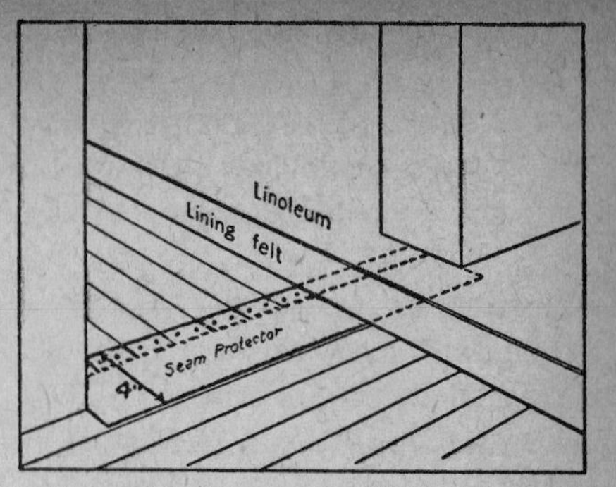

Fig. 5. Where floorboards run in opposite directions, install a strip of seam protector 4" wide. Tack 1 ½" of this on one side of the door line, 2 ½" on the other.

If the most prominent wall of a room is noticeably slanting and has a doorway in it, start laying the linoleum at this slanting wall with a full 6′ width. Continue laying full strips all the way across the room. This will leave a wedge-shaped area to be covered when the opposite wall (which has no doorway) is reached. This piece can be fitted by scribing.

The wedge-shaped piece in such a room should always be laid along the wall that has no doorway. Since the linoleum in front of a door always gets the greatest wear, seams should be as far away as possible.

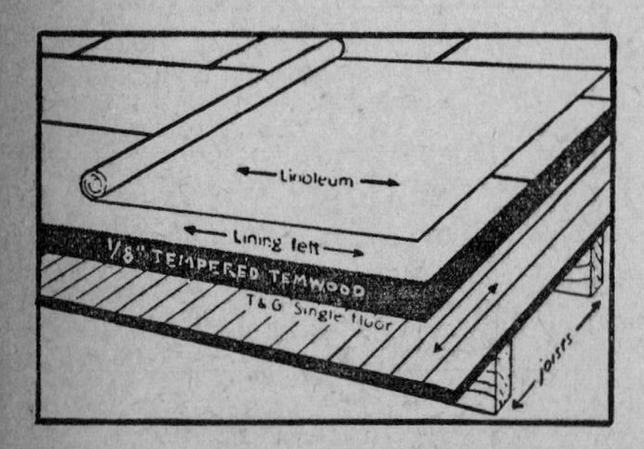

Fig. 4. Single tongue-and-groove floors should be covered with five-ply plywood; and linoleum and lining felt laid across the boards.

When a border is to be installed in a room that is very irregular, lay the border parallel with the walls so that the edges of the field also will be parallel with the walls.

When the floorboards in one room do not run in the same direction as the boards in an adjoining room, the point where the boards meet in the doorway should be covered with a strip of seam protector (fig. 5). Approximately 1½″ of the width of this strip should be tacked firmly to the floor on one side of the line, leaving a 2½″ flap that extends beyond the joint into the other room. This flap is left loose and should not be tacked or pasted down. The lining felt is pasted over this flap to prevent seasonal expansion and contraction of the floorboards from splitting the felt and cracking the linoleum.

If linoleum and a wood floor meet where two rooms join, beveled edging is recommended.

When the subfloor in one room is slightly higher than the subfloor in an adjoining room, it is necessary to make the finished floors equally high where they meet at the doorway. This is done by using a strip of lining felt 6″ wide and long enough to cover the doorway section. The long piece of felt is butted against the boards of the higher floor. A section 4″ wide on the lower floor is spread with paste and the strip of felt is laid in it. This leaves 2″ unpasted.

When the paste has set thoroughly under the 4″ pasted section, grip the unpasted edge of the felt and tear it with a slow movement, pulling slightly toward the paste side. This splits the felt and produces a beveled effect. This method tapers the felt more gradually than sanding or attempting to split it without pasting.

The same tapering method can be used when the gauge of linoleum in one room is thinner than the gauge of linoleum in an adjoining room. Beveled edging or asphalt beveled edging may be installed at the edge to join linoleum to a wood floor.

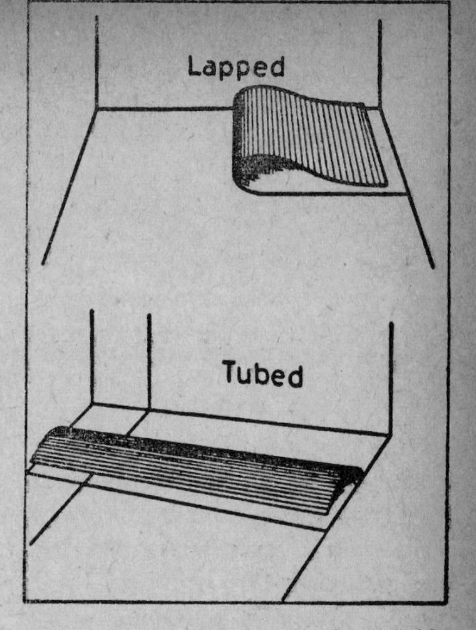

Fig. 6. There are two methods of folding back linoleum, lapping and tubing. Lapping is folding back the short dimension of the goods. Tubing is folding back the long dimension of the material.

MEASURING, CUTTING, AND PACKING LINOLEUM

In the workroom, cut the material 3″ wider than the widest dimension of the room, and 3″ longer than the longest dimension. Cutting in the workroom is important. Remember, there is no room to do it on the job. Cut closely to the 3″ waste allowance. Extra waste complicates the installation problem.

Roll the goods face out, so that the length of the roll equals the shortest dimension of the goods. Make a firm, tight roll.

Tie the roll with heavy twine at the center, placing cardboard or scrap felt under the twine to prevent it from marring the surface of the felt-base material.

At each end of the roll, wrap several turns of heavy wrapping paper. Allow 7″ or 8″ of the paper to extend beyond the ends of the roll. This overhang is then tucked in to protect the ends, and the paper is fastened with twine.

The entire roll is now wrapped in heavy wrapping paper, which is tied at the ends and center.

If the roll may receive very rough handling, place cross-shaped pieces of cardboard at each end of the roll and bend back the flaps. These protectors are often cut from old card-

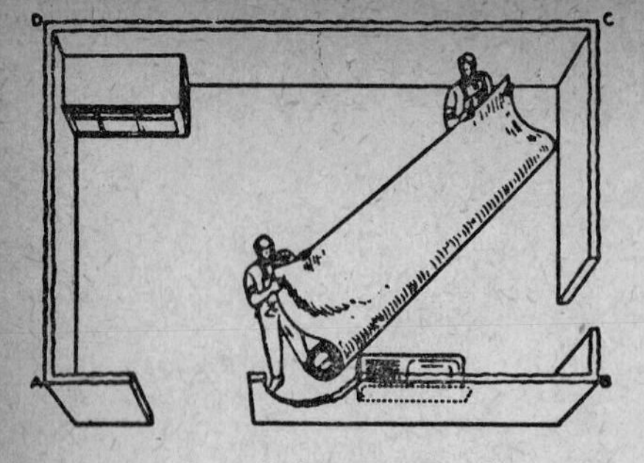

Fig. 7. Lay the roll diagonally in the room, face up. Point it to roll toward the most regular long side—here, **CD.**

board cartons. Ordinarily, however, this extra protection is not necessary.

If the delivery truck is not long enough to take the long roll, tie it firmly to the outside of the truck, resting it on the fenders. Special strap-iron supports can be built on the truck to facilitate this method of handling.

INSTALLING LINOLEUM IN SINGLE ROOMS

When installing the material, it will save considerable time to have a helper, although simpler jobs can be done by one man. The procedure is as follows:

1. Disconnect and remove radiators, refrigerators, stoves, doors, and any other movable furniture or fixtures.

2. With a pinch-bar, raise the quarter-round molding ¼″ from the floor. If parts of the wall extend into the room, remove the quarter-round. Then sweep the floor, check it for loose boards, and hammer in all loose nails.

3. Select the most regular long side of the room as the wall to which the goods will be fitted first. In the kitchen, this is ordinarily the side opposite the sink. The selection of the right starting wall is very important. It should always be a long side of the room.

4. Carry the rolled-up material into the room, after removing the wrappings, and lay it diagonally across the short dimension, so that it will unroll towards the starting wall as in figure 7.

5. The helper and the mechanic unroll about 5′ of the material, face up, as shown in figure 8. Then, each takes one of the free ends of the goods and raises it from the floor, so that it forms a *U,* which can be held by the helper. The mechanic then goes to the opposite end of the roll and lifts one end of it off the floor.

6. The goods is now unrolled back toward wall *BC*. The goods is gradually swung as it is unrolled, so that the edge of the goods becomes parallel to the starting wall. As the mechanic works toward wall *BC,* he

Fig. 8. Unroll about 5' of goods and lift ends to form a **U.** Unroll toward **BC.**

forces the goods against wall *CD*, so that it butts to the wall over the molding. At the same time, the helper—still holding up both ends of the roll in a U-shape—works toward wall *DA*. He holds the goods clear of the cabinet or other projections.

7. When the material is entirely unrolled, the mechanic steps onto it and flashes it up wall *BC*, as in figure 9. The helper, holding the bottom of the *U* off the floor, butts it to *AD* above the quarter-round.

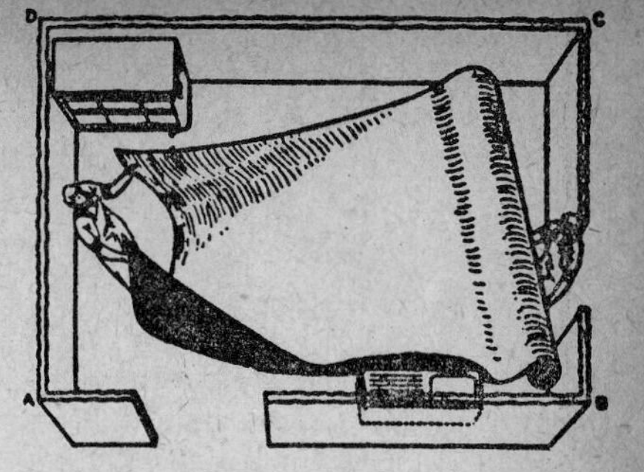

Fig. 9. Butt the edge of the roll toward **CD** and work towards walls **BC** and **AD.** Bring the edge parallel to **CD.**

8. After making sure that the material butts to the wall *CD* at all possible points, the mechanic crosses to the cabinet, as shown by the dotted line in figure 10, and cuts in the side and front of the cabinet at corner *D*. As he does this, the helper holds the goods lightly to take the strain.

9. The mechanic then works around the room, cutting in the sink first and then the doorways. The helper works along with him, holding up the goods to take the strain and prevent tearing.

All during the work, the mechanic should watch for buckling caused by improper fitting. He should immediately find the point of strain and cut in enough clearance to relieve it.

10. At the walls, the material must be cut so that there will be a clearance of from ¼″ to ⅜″ between the edge of the goods and the wall line. This clearance is for "growth" and will greatly reduce the amount of retrimming that will be necessary later.

11. When the quarter-round is replaced, do not force it tight against the goods; this will cause buckling when the material grows. Instead, leave the molding far enough above the goods to allow it to move freely.

12. At doorways or other places where there is no molding, allow at least ⅛″ clearance.

13. Cutting is best done with a notched blade knife, but a linoleum knife can be used. In either case, the blade should be held 45 degrees from the wall—not vertically, as is the usual way.

The 45-degree angle lifts the goods away from the wall and pre-

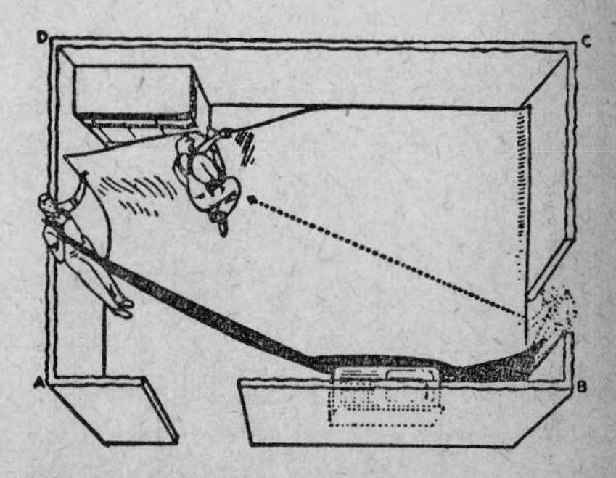

Fig. 10. While helper holds up ends to relieve strain, mechanic flashes goods up **BC** and then crosses over to cut in the side and front of the cabinet at corner **D.**

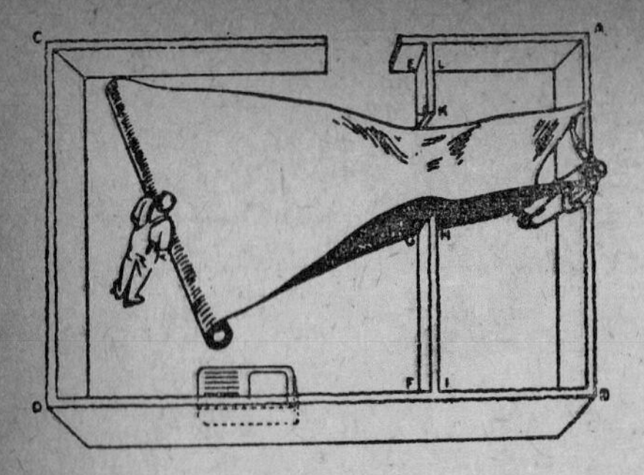

Fig. 11. Where the goods is to be laid through doorway without seams, helper carries goods from larger to smaller room while the mechanic unrolls the material.

vents the knife from marring the woodwork. With a little practice, it is easy to maintain a uniform clearance with the knife at this 45-degree angle.

INSTALLING 12-FOOT LINOLEUM THROUGH DOORS IN DOUBLE ROOMS

It is often desirable to run 12-foot felt-base floor covering from one room through the doorway to a second room, without a seam. The handling of the material is somewhat the same as in single rooms with built-in cabinets or offsets.

1. The material is laid diagonally in the larger room and lifted into a *U*, as in the single room. The helper, holding the *U*, backs through the doorway into the smaller room as the mechanic unrolls toward wall *CD*, as in figure 11.

2. Butting the end of the roll against wall *CE*, the mechanic finishes unrolling and flashes the goods up wall *CD*.

3. The helper butts his end of the goods to wall *AB* above the molding, as is shown in figure 12.

4. While the helper holds up the ends to relieve strain, the mechanic cuts in one side of the door frame, so that the material may be fitted against wall *GF*.

5. The mechanic then cuts across the face of the door frame, *GH*, and makes another cut that permits the goods to fit against walls *HI* and *IB*.

6. The mechanic then cuts in the opposite side of the door frame, so that the goods can be fitted to *CE*, *KA*, *JE*, and *KL*.

7. The mechanic then cuts in the sink, doorways, and wall lines.

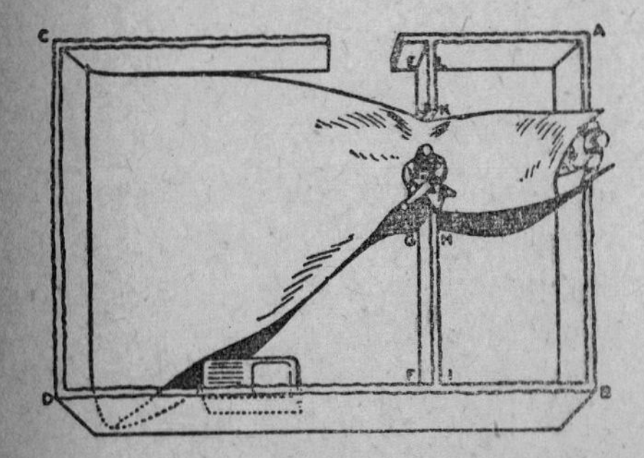

Fig. 12. When mechanic has flashed goods up wall **CD** and helper has butted it to wall **AB**, mechanic cuts in the door frames and fixtures as shown above.

HOW TO DO PATTERN SCRIBING ON LINOLEUM

Pattern scribing consists of two simple operations; (a) scribing the contour of vertical surfaces to a piece of lining felt or heavy wrapping paper; and (b) transferring by

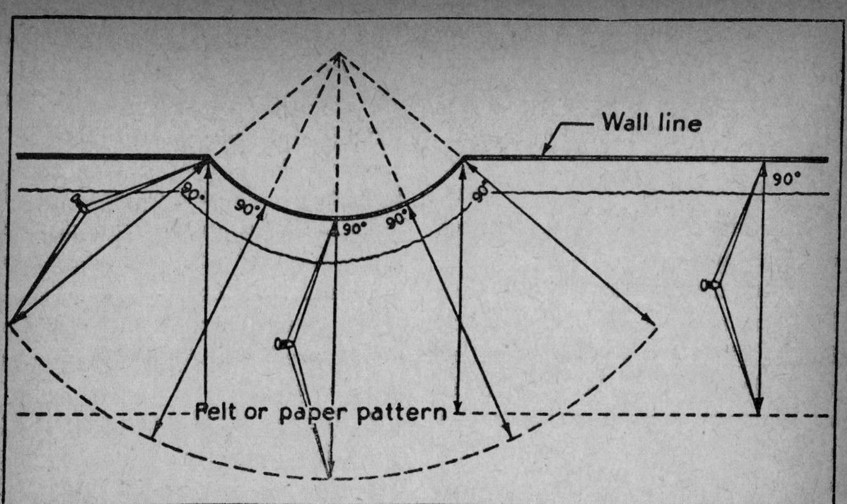

Fig. 13. In pattern scribing, hold the dividers at right angles to the vertical surface and not at right angles to the pattern. With dividers at this angle, draw them along the wall, scribing the exact contour of the wall onto the lining felt or paper pattern.

rescribing the lines on the felt onto the linoleum (fig. 13).

Pattern scribing is an accurate and convenient method of fitting linoleum in a small room or space where it would be difficult to scribe the linoleum itself. Once the pattern is made, the actual cutting of the linoleum can be done in other rooms or in the workroom, so the linoleum can be carried in ready to install.

Pattern scribing can be used to advantage in small bathrooms, closets, etc., and in installing flash type cove base.

Pattern scribing is done in the following manner:

1. Fit all the unpasted strips of lining felt neatly to within ⅛″ (or less) of all vertical surfaces, with the strips butted tightly at the seams —exactly as they will be when pasted down.

2. Across each seam, strike a chalk mark. These lines will indicate whether the felt has slipped during the following operations. Thumbtacks can be used to keep the felt from moving.

3. Set a pair of dividers at ½″. With one point of the dividers pressed against the vertical surface, and with the other point on the lining felt, draw the dividers along the wall and felt, so that the exact contour of the wall is scribed on the felt. In pattern scribing, always hold the dividers at right angles to the vertical surface and not at right angles to the felt, as illustrated in figure 13.

4. The piece of linoleum to be scribed is laid flat on the floor of another room or of the same room. If the same room, first remove the lining felt.

5. Lay the scribed pieces of lining felt on top of the linoleum, so that the chalk lines crossing the seams in the felt are exactly in line. To prevent the felt from slipping, fasten it to the linoleum with small dabs of paste, sandbags, or strips of adhesive tape.

6. With the dividers still set at ½″, place one point on the scribed line of the felt and the other point on the linoleum. Hold the dividers so that they are at right angles to the lines on the lining felt. Then draw the dividers along the scribed line, so the other point scribes the outline of the vertical surface of the field.

7. Remove the lining felt and cut through the scribed lines on the linoleum with a knife.

8. Paste the felt to the floor and roll it in the usual manner.

9. Lay the linoleum unpasted over the lining felt to check its fit with the vertical surfaces. Then, tubing or lapping it back, spread paste on the felt, replace the linoleum, roll it, and smooth the seams in the usual manner.

LINOLEUM SCRIBING AROUND RADIATORS

1. After the felt has been pasted to the subfloor, butt the linoleum against the radiator pipes or legs, parallel to the wall line. In most cases, the four legs of the radiator can be raised off the floor by placing wood blocks under the shoulder of the pipe elbows. Place these blocks behind the vertical pipe, so that the material can be butted to the front end of the pipes. If the legs cannot be raised, fit the material as follows:

2. Set the adjustable point of the scriber at a distance equal to ½ inch more than the greatest distance between the wall and the edge of the linoleum. The extra ½ inch is allowed to take care of discrepancies in the wall line which may have been overlooked.

3. With a straightedge and chalk, draw lines on the linoleum, marking the edges of the radiator pipes and radiator legs; draw these lines at right angles to the edge of the linoleum.

4. Starting at the end of the strip of linoleum, place one end of the scribing tool against the wall. Place the point on the linoleum; draw the tool along the whole length of the linoleum, so that the point marks the linoleum with the exact contour of the wall line. Be sure to repeat this scribing operation beneath the radiator.

5. Place one end of the scribing tool against the front edge of the radiator pipe, so that the point falls between the two parallel lines on the linoleum. Draw the tool across the front edge of the pipe, so that the linoleum will be marked with a line indicating how far into the goods the pipe will eventually extend.

6. Repeat step 5 at each pipe and at each radiator leg. To mark rear legs, first mark the front legs. Then set the dividers the width of the front leg plus the distance between the front and the rear leg. Use this to mark the rear leg.

7. Set a pair of dividers to half the thickness of the radiator legs. Place one point against the line that was scribed from the front edge of the leg. Place the other point midway between the parallel lines. Using this latter point as a center, draw a circle.

8. Repeat step 7 for each of the front and rear legs and each of the pipes. When marking for the pipes, set the dividers to one-half the diameter of the pipes.

a. If the feet of the radiator are not circular, set the dividers to the exact depth of the leg. Then, placing one point against the part of the circle that represents the front edge of the leg, strike an arc between the parallel lines.

9. Trim the linoleum along the scribed line that represents the contour of the wall.

10. After the edge is trimmed, cut openings for the legs. Cut along one of the parallel lines that connect the leg holes so that the linoleum may be slid against the wall. Also cut across the hole for the pipe. In making these various cuts in the material, cut along the lines that separate blocks of different colors, insofar as possible. This will make the seams considerably less conspicuous.

11. Check the linoleum for fit around the pipes and front legs. Do not push the linoleum completely under the radiator for this test, because it will be difficult to remove.

12. If the linoleum checks, tube or lap it back, and spread paste on the felt with a notched steel paste spreader. Then replace the linoleum neatly, rolling it and smoothing seams as previously described.

LINOLEUM COVE BASE

Any linoleum floor becomes more attractive when a neat, colorful cove base forms a sanitary curved joining at the walls.

Flash Type. Flash type cove base is a joining that is virtually an extension of the flooring material. Its installation is not difficult if a few simple rules are observed.

Metal binding strip is nailed to the wall first. Then ⅞″ fillet strip is laid on the underfloor or lining felt to form a coved joining of the floor and wall. Then linoleum is pattern scribed and slipped under the binding strip, curved over the fillet, and pasted flush with the field.

Flash type cove base not only permits the use of any color of linoleum but also eliminates all unsightly and insanitary seams close to the wall.

The strong fabric-covered fillet, which comes in continuous 50′ lengths in coils, is easy to carry and always ready to use. Forming solid backing, its inert core is not affected by moisture.

If desired, metal inside and outside corner pieces can be installed. However, these are not necessary. Metal end stops may be used to close the ends of flash type cove base in modern construction where door frames are omitted.

Preparation of Walls. Concrete: If concrete walls are not equipped with a wood ground of suitable height for nailing the binding strip and optional metal parts, place ⅝″ diameter wood plugs not less than 1″ long in the walls—at the desired height, and at intervals of not more than 12″. The face of the plugs should be flush with the surface of the wall.

The concrete should run all the way down to the floor line. It should be smooth, even, and free from pits or other imperfections that might show through. The concrete should be thoroughly dry.

Plaster: If plaster walls are sound, and if the lath is rigid and not springy, the metal parts of the cove and base may be nailed to the studs and lath. (Otherwise, insert a wood ground not less than 1″ wide and thick enough to be flush with the surface of the plaster.) The top of the ground should be 5⅞″ from the floor level for a 6″ high cove, and 4⅜″ for a 4½″ high cove base.

The plaster below the wood ground should extend all the way to floor level, and its surface should be free from imperfections which might show through later.

If the plaster does not extend to the floor, extend it with patching plaster or with a suitable wallboard furred flush with the face of the plaster. All openings between the wood ground and the wallboard, or between the wood ground and the old plaster, should be filled with patching plaster and finished smooth and level. The plaster and all patches in it should be thoroughly dry.

Preparation of Floors. Metal corner parts, if used, can be nailed direct to wood floors, which should be smooth, solid, and free from cracks and splinters.

If concrete floors do not have a suitable wood ground for nailing the bottom of the metal outside corner pieces, set ⅝″ diameter wood plugs, not less than 1″ long, into the concrete, with their centers 1¼″ from the finished wall line. All holes, expansion score marks, or cracks should be repaired; and the concrete should be thoroughly dry before installing cove base.

End Stops and Corner Pieces. With flash type cove base over wood subfloors, lining felt is installed before the corner pieces and end stops. The flange of the outside corner is cut into the felt so the field is flush with the corner.

End stops and corner pieces should be installed with rosin-coated, flat-headed nails before the binding strip is installed. On plaster walls, the nails should be long enough to reach the studs back of the lath and plaster.

Fitting Binding Strip. Binding strip should be nailed to the wall with flat-headed rosin-coated nails of suitable length, spaced at least every 12″ and driven through the middle of the nail slots.

The top of the binding strip should be flush with the tops of the corner pieces and end stops, if these are used. Otherwise, measure up the wall the height you wish the cove base to reach.

To obtain an accurate measurement, hold one end of the strip firmly in place against one of the corners or end stops. This end should be square and smooth. Where the other end meets the opposite corner or end stop, score the strip with a thin, narrow file.

Never cut the strip with one snip of tin shears, because this will crush the over-hanging bead. Instead, hold the strip so that the over-hanging bead faces you, and score the ridge deeply at the mark with a file. With a gentle backward movement, break the scored beading. Then snip the flange of the strip to the break and dress the edge carefully with the file to remove all protruding burrs.

Installing Fillet Strip. Wax fillet strip (7/8″) is installed before or after the end stops or corner pieces are in place.

On concrete or other floors where lining felt is not used, the fillet is pasted to the floor and wall with suitable paste.

On wood subfloors, where lining felt is used, the fillet is pasted to the wall and to the top of the lining felt. After pasting, the fillet is rolled to shape with a seam roller and fillet forming tool. Then the coved linoleum is installed by pattern scribing.

Pattern Scribing.

1. On the felt, strike chalk lines parallel to the walls. The distance of these lines from the walls should be equal to the width of the border desired.

2. Before spreading paste on the felt for the main area of the floor, square all edges of the field linoleum. Then spread paste over the area bounded by the chalk lines and paste down the field linoleum, matching its edges to the chalk lines accurately.

3. To make a pattern for scribing, square one edge of a piece of lining felt or heavy kraft paper. The width of the pattern should be roughly equal to the width of the border plus the height of the cove. If an outside corner is to be fitted, allow excess paper. This excess paper, when scribed onto the linoleum, provides an overlap in the linoleum so that a mitered joint can be cut at the outside corner.

4. Butt the squared edge of this paper pattern against the squared edge of the field linoleum, and curve the rest of it over the fillet strip and to within 1/4″ of the top of the binding strip.

5. Also fit the pattern roughly to the corner pieces and end stops, if these are used. If the edge of the pattern is brought to within 1/4″ of all metal parts, this will be close enough. Anchor the pattern to the wall with thumbtacks to keep it from slipping during scribing.

6. Set the points of a pair of steel dividers about 1/2″ apart, so that when one leg is placed against the lip of the binding strip, the other leg will extend well over the edge of the pattern paper. With the dividers in this position, scribe a line on the paper pattern, using the binding strip as a guide. Scribe around corner pieces and end stops, if used, in the same way.

7. Remove the scribed paper pattern and match its squared edge to a straight, true edge of a piece of linoleum of ample size and correct color to form the cove base. With the dividers unchanged and using the scribed lines on the paper pattern as a guide, transfer the scribed lines outlining the corners (or corner pieces) onto the linoleum.

8. To allow for the overlap of the binding strip (or end stops, if the latter are used), open the dividers an additional ⅛″. With the dividers set at ⅝″, scribe the lines for these parts.

9. Cut the linoleum carefully along the scribed lines to the required shape. At points where the linoleum will form an outside corner, allow the extra flap for cutting a mitered joint.

10. When the linoleum has been cut, apply paste to the lining felt, fillet strip, and wall.

11. Pre-form the linoleum to approximately the contour of the cove by curving it and shaping with the hand, so that it will be easier to install.

12. Line the ends at the proper height. Force the piece against the wall and fillet with the inside corner forming tool so that the free edge is butted against, and flush with, the field linoleum. Then slide the top under the binding strip. It is highly important that a tight bond between the fillet and linoleum should be obtained.

13. Use a square in cutting the mitered corner. With a linoleum knife, cut through the top piece just enough to score the piece it overlaps. Then cut the under piece.

14. With a linoleum roller, roll that part of the cove and base which is to form the border of the floor. Use hand roller for wall section. In rolling, take care that the edge of the roller is not allowed to ride the curve, as this may damage both the linoleum and the fillet.

15. In small rooms, the entire cove and base can be fitted before the paste is applied to the walls. In large rooms, the sections should be pasted into place as soon as they are cut.

Corners without Metal Pieces. When metal pieces are not used at inside corners, it is necessary that the pieces of linoleum overlap. This can be done by pattern scribing or straight scribing. In the former method, place a scrap of linoleum against the corner. Set the dividers at ½″ and place one leg against the scrap. Place the other leg on the side flap of the pattern and scribe the flap down to the top of the fillet strip. Make a small radius cut where the two cuts meet at corners. This results in the necessary overlap.

Inside corners can also be straight scribed. Scribe one piece of linoleum to fit one side of the corner, and then scribe the other side piece to it, allowing the radius cut described above. Scribe only to the fillet strip.

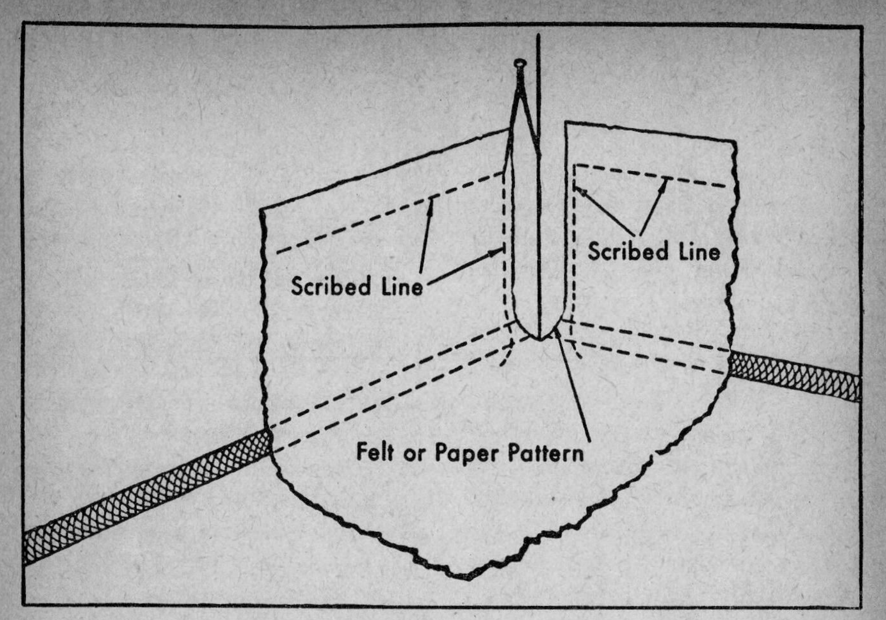

Fig. 14. In making a pattern for a counter-top installation, fit the felt or paper ¼" short of the juncture of the walls. Set dividers at ½" and scribe corner lines on the pattern. With one divider leg in corner, scribe the flap that flashes up the side wall.

LINOLEUM ON COUNTER TOPS

When installing linoleum on counter tops, it is highly important that all joinings be made absolutely watertight, so that moisture cannot work its way under the linoleum and loosen the paste or cement.

Good construction at the basin requires:

a. The right type of metal pan and metal edgings; *b.* Extremely careful fitting of the linoleum; *c.* The use of waterproof linoleum sink-rim cement, and lining felt; *d.* The use of rustproof metal edgings that will not readily spring or bend out of position when bumped.

Many types of edgings and basins are on the market. The manufacturers of most of these items recommend a particular type of construction for use with linoleum.

TURN-DOWN SINK RIMS

A new type of metal sink rim eliminates recess scribing problems. Figure 15 shows the standard type sink rim. The linoleum fits tight against the edge of the rim and must be accurately underscribed for a tight fit.

Figure 15 also shows the turn-down type in place, with the lino-

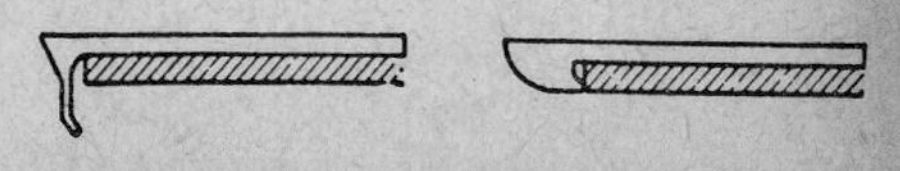

Fig. 15. **Left,** standard sink rim in place; **Right,** turn-down sink rim up.

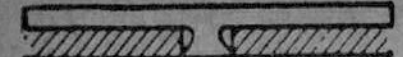

Fig. 16. **Left**, turn-down sink rim down. **Right**, sink top repair strip.

leum knifed to fit against the open edge. Notice the way the edge stands up, higher than the linoleum. After the linoleum is in place, with the adhesive properly spread, the edge is turned down. This is done with a radius block of wood supplied by the metal trim manufacturers. The metal then grips the linoleum, covering its edge (fig. 16).

REPAIRING COUNTER TOPS

A special type of edging is available for making repairs in counter tops. One type (fig. 16) is put in at the time of original installation, anticipating the need for replacing the linoleum around the sink rim at some future date. Flanges extend from the face of the molding in both directions. When the linoleum around the sink rim is to be replaced, it is removed and another piece put in. The edging protects and makes more attractive the place where the old and new linoleum meet.

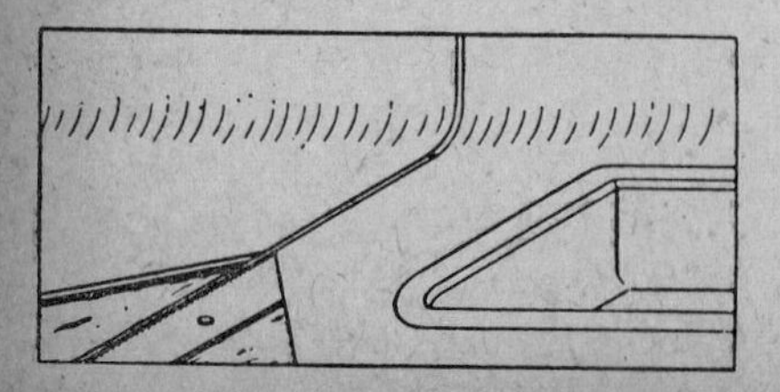

Fig. 17. Repair strip flashed up wall.

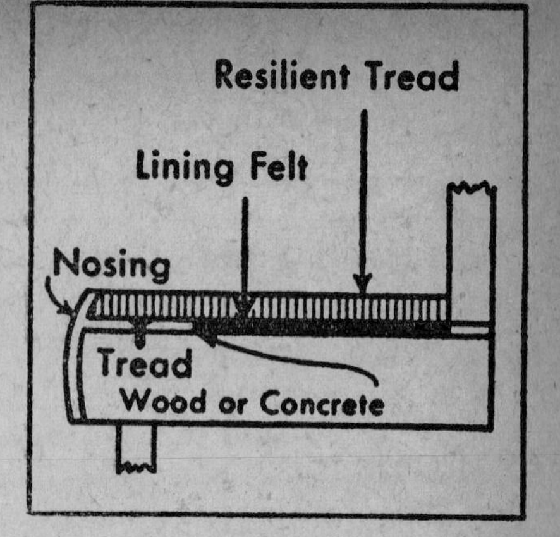

Fig. 18. To install a stair tread, fasten the nosing to the edge of the step. Paste felt from the flange to the riser. Then cut a strip of linoleum 1" longer than the tread and ½" wider. Flash up ends.

Another type of edging (fig. 17) is installed when the repair job is made. The worn linoleum is removed, and the edging, with a flange toward the sink linoleum only, is installed. The new linoleum is then butted against it.

Fig. 19. Cements used for linoleum and other wall and flooring material are easily spread over the surface with a grooved metal spreader.

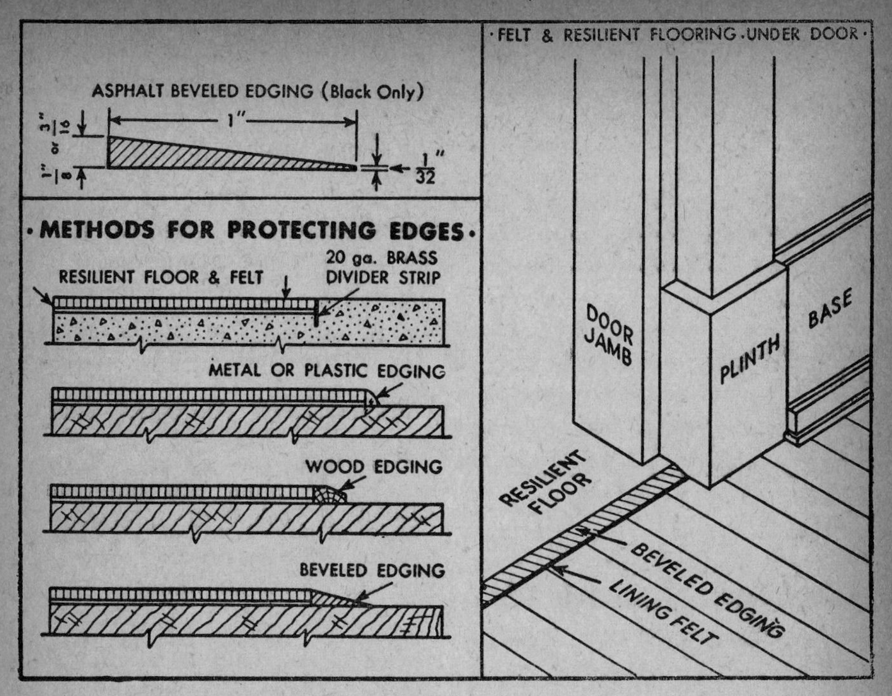

Fig. 20. Adequate protection for the edges of resilient flooring at doors and other areas where edges are exposed is most important to insure that the flooring gives good service. Several methods can be employed to take care of the edges.

Figure 17 also shows the cove finish of this type installation. The edging runs to the base of the cove, where it joins an end stop which runs up the wall. This use of an end stop is necessary because some provision must be made for the meeting point of the two pieces of linoleum on the cove.

STAIR TREADS, RUNNERS, EDGINGS

Installations of linoleum on stairs fall into three types: (a) linoleum treads without risers; (b) separate linoleum treads and risers; and (c) linoleum treads flashed up to cover the riser in a one-piece construction.

Treads. Figure 18 illustrates how to install linoleum treads without risers. It is assumed in this case that the mechanic must install nosing, although in many new buildings the nosing may already have been installed with the flange recessed into the step. If so, the use of felt is not essential except where it is necessary to compensate for a difference in thickness.

Two-Piece Tread and Riser. Where separate pieces of linoleum will be used on the tread and on the riser, cut and fit the tread as in the case of

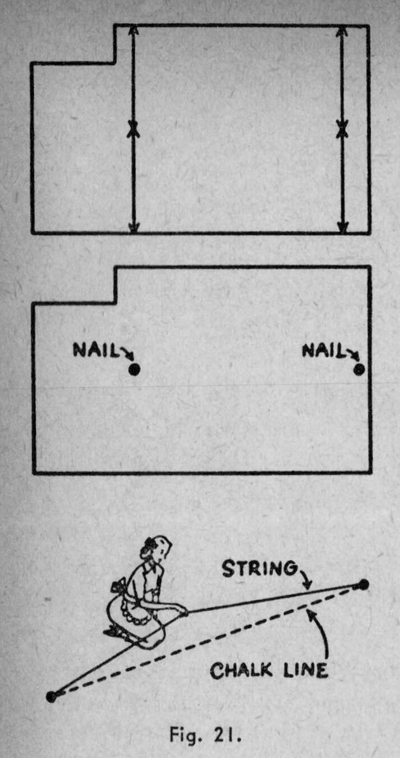

Fig. 21.

a simple tread. The height of the riser strip should be the distance between the top of the linoleum tread and the underside of the tread on the next step. The piece can be cut to this dimension along a straightedge. The ends should be cut long and fitted in exactly as the tread was fitted to the sides. No lining felt is necessary behind the linoleum riser.

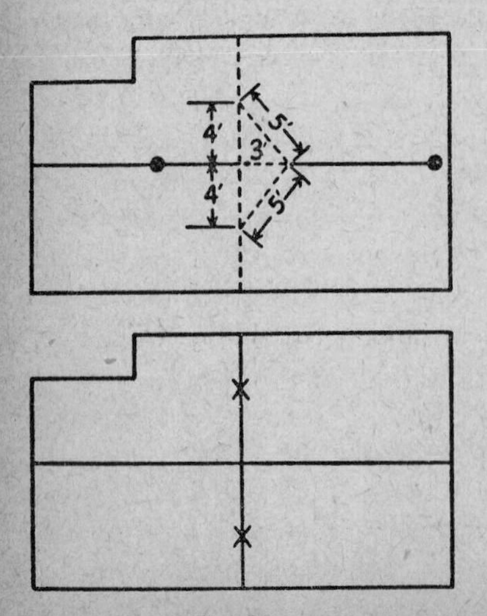

Fig. 22.

INSTALLING ASPHALT TILE

Requisites. a. a tape measure or a ruler. *b.* chalk and chalk line (string). *c.* asphalt tile adhesive. *d.* notched trowel spreader. *e.* awl or icepick. *f.* linoleum knife.

Measure Your Room. Find the center of your room like this: *1.* Measure from wall to wall along each end of room (fig. 21, upper). 2. Drive a nail into center of floor at each end (fig. 21, middle). 3. Rub a string with chalk. Stretch it from nail to nail tightly. Pull the string up and let it snap back on floor, to mark a chalk line (fig. 22, lower). 4. Find the center of this chalk line and at this center start making another chalk line at right angles to the first, in this way:

a. Measure 4 feet toward both side walls. *b.* Then measure 3 feet from center point on longer line. *c.* Then measure exactly 5 feet from 3 foot mark on center line to both 4 foot marks (fig. 22, upper). *d.* A line through these two points will be at right angles to the first center line. (Use 6′, 8′, and 10′ measurements in larger rooms.) (Fig. 22, lower.)

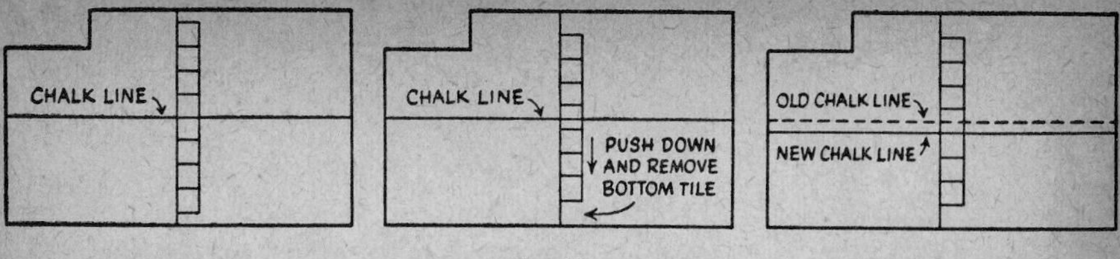

Fig. 23.

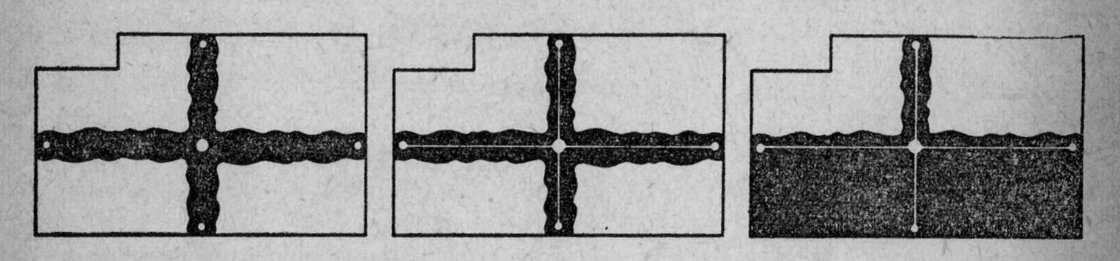

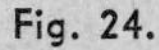

Fig. 24.

Plan for the Border. The border should be at least half a tile wide (4½″) and may be as wide as 9″.

Before laying tile determine the border width in this way (fig. 23):

a. Working out from the intersection of your chalk lines, lay a row of uncemented tiles along the chalk line across the room to each wall. *b.* If the space left for the border along the side wall is less than half a tile in width, move the entire row of tile over a half tile and take one tile from the other end. *c.* Now one of the tile is covering the chalk line. To correct this move your line by moving the nails over a half a tile (4½″) and resnapping your chalk line. *d.* Repeat the above procedure for the other width.

Spread the Adhesive (fig. 24). *a.* Spread adhesive over both chalk lines—leaving ends and center point uncovered. *b.* After adhesive has become "tacky" resnap the chalk lines. *c.* Then spread adhesive over just one half of the room. *d.* Before laying tile wait for the adhesive to dry out and become "tacky." This may take ½ hour to 4 hours, depending on atmospheric conditions. Test adhesive by pressing it with your finger. If it does not stick to your finger it has dried enough to start laying the asphalt tile. *Don't rush!* Adhesive can be left on overnight or 2-3 days if necessary before you lay tile.

If adhesive gets on the face of the tile, remove with wet cloth dipped in scouring powder and rinse with clear water.

Lay the Tile. Follow these rules for laying tile (fig. 25): Starting from the center, work both ways along the guide lines, being careful to keep the tile on the line and making the corners meet exactly. Pyramid the following rows of tile, always working from the center out to the walls like this (fig. 26): *1.* Place tile firmly against tile already

Fig. 25.

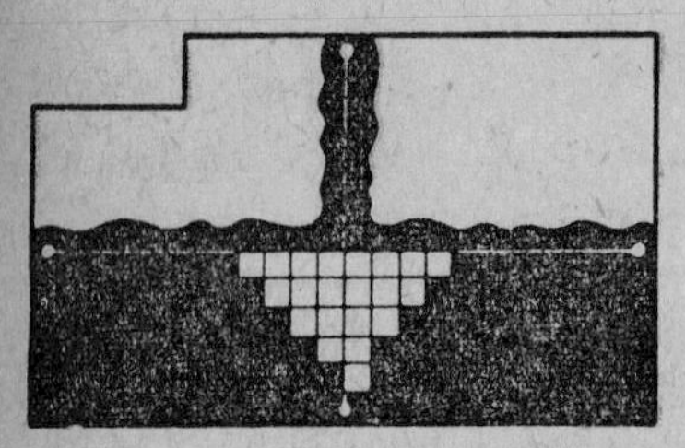

Fig. 26.

laid. 2. Lower each tile carefully into adhesive. 3. Do not slide tile into position. The adhesive will ooze up between the tile.

Cut in Border. Since no wall is straight, the last row, or border, must be tailored to fit. *a.* Place loose tile over last row of installed tile (fig. 27). *b.* On top of these loose tile place another tile flush to the wall (a thin piece of wood laid on the adhesive will keep the tile clean while you are measuring). *c.* Using the topmost tile as a guide, score a deep line with a sharp awl or ice-pick on the underneath tile all the way across (fig. 28). *d.* Snap off on line, starting at one end, never in the center. *e.* Trim off uneven edge with sandpaper. *f.* How to fit tile to door jambs, irregular shapes, etc. Using the same method as in fitting the border, move the top tile along so that you mark with pencil each irregularity of the jamb on the tile below. In this way you will actually draw a pattern of the door jamb on the tile to be cut (fig. 29). *g.* For cutting curves or irregular shapes, heat tile until pliable, with blowtorch, electric heater, or gas oven. Cut with linoleum knife or shears. *h.* How to fit tile to pipes, radiators, etc. Do not install tile under legs of a radiator. Cut a hole where leg will go through, cut the tile from the hole to the edge and, while warm and pliable, press the tile into position (fig. 30).

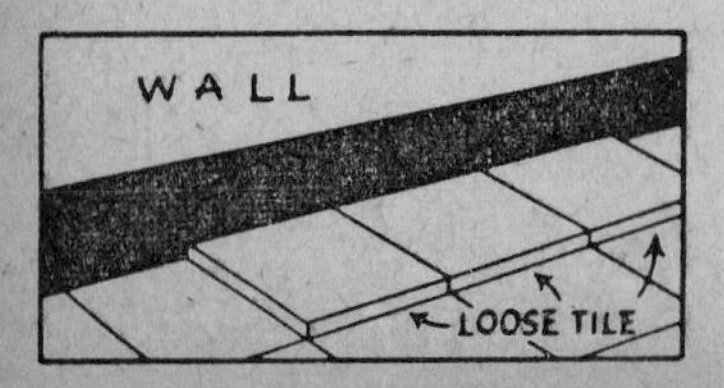

Fig. 27.

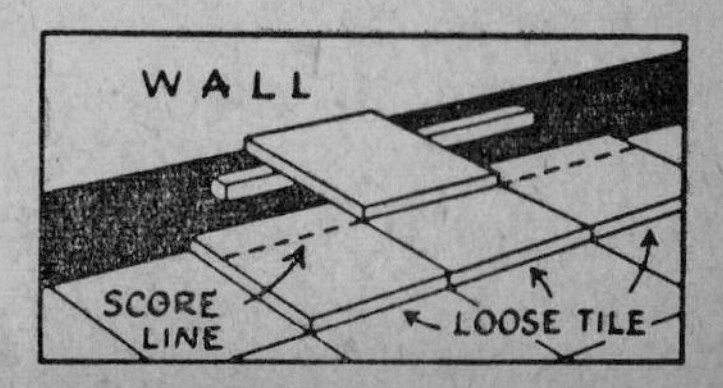

Fig. 28.

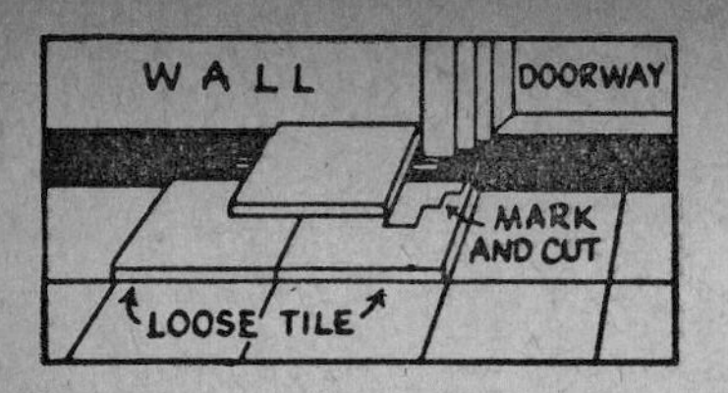

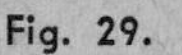
Fig. 29.

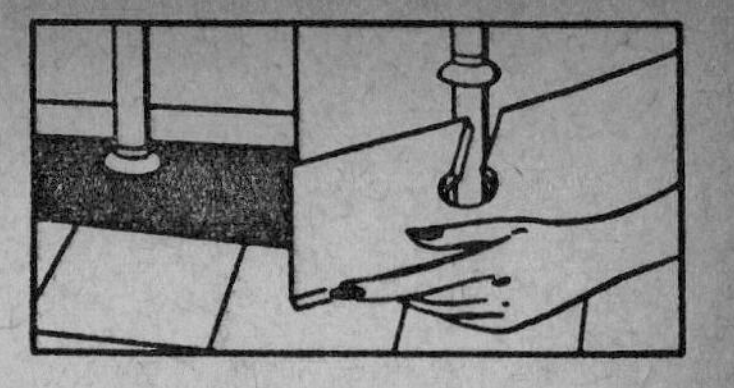

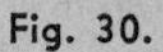
Fig. 30.

INSTALLATION INSTRUCTIONS FOR RESILIENT TILE

A. *Preparation of Subfloors.*

1. Cleaning of Subfloors

a. Oil and Grease—remove by: *1* Scraping, *2* Machine sanding, *3* Scrubbing with strong solution of tri-sodium phosphate, *4* Machine scrubbing with soapy water and clean, sharp sand. (After scrubbing always rinse thoroughly with clean water and leave floor smooth and even.)

b. Paint or Varnish—remove by: *1* Machine sanding, *2* Paint or varnish remover followed by thorough scrubbing with soapy water to remove the paraffine in the varnish remover, then rinsing with clean water.

c. Paint (Concrete Floors)—remove by: *1* Scrubbing with a strong solution of tri-sodium phosphate or, in the case of rubber base paints, which are not removed by alkaline materials, use toluol or xylol. These solvents are highly inflammable and should be used accordingly. Rinse floors thoroughly. *2* Acetylene torch or blowtorch will remove paint from concrete.

d. Wax—Remove by scraping and/or machine sanding or by scrubbing with tri-sodium phosphate. Rinse floors thoroughly.

2. Repairing Old Subfloors

a. Concrete Subfloors. *1* Cracks or Expansion Score Marks—Finish with mastic floor fill. *2* Dusty Concrete—Sweep clean and prime with floor and wall size. *3* Uneven or Badly Spalled Concrete—Level with mastic type floor fill.

b. Wood Subfloors. *1* Loose Boards—Renail. *2* Defective or Badly Worn Boards—Replace with new material. *3* Cracks and Holes—Fill cracks wider than ⅛″ and holes greater than ¼″ with plastic wood or snugly fitted pieces of wood. *4* Warped or Uneven Floors—Machine sand. *5* Sanded Floors—Prime with floor and wall size. *6* Floors Too Uneven to Be Sanded Smoothly—Cover with either

(a) Floor fill, or

(b) A hardboard or 5-ply ⅝″ plywood.

(*b-1*) Apply in 4′ x 4′ pieces with 2d or 3d rosin-coated or cement-coated nails spaced 6″ on centers both ways and at all edges.

(*b-2*) Leave 1/16″ between pieces for expansion.

(*b-3*)Install hardwood wire side up.

7 Single Wood Floors—If tongue-and-groove, same as 2b(6). If square edge, same as new subfloors 3b(3).

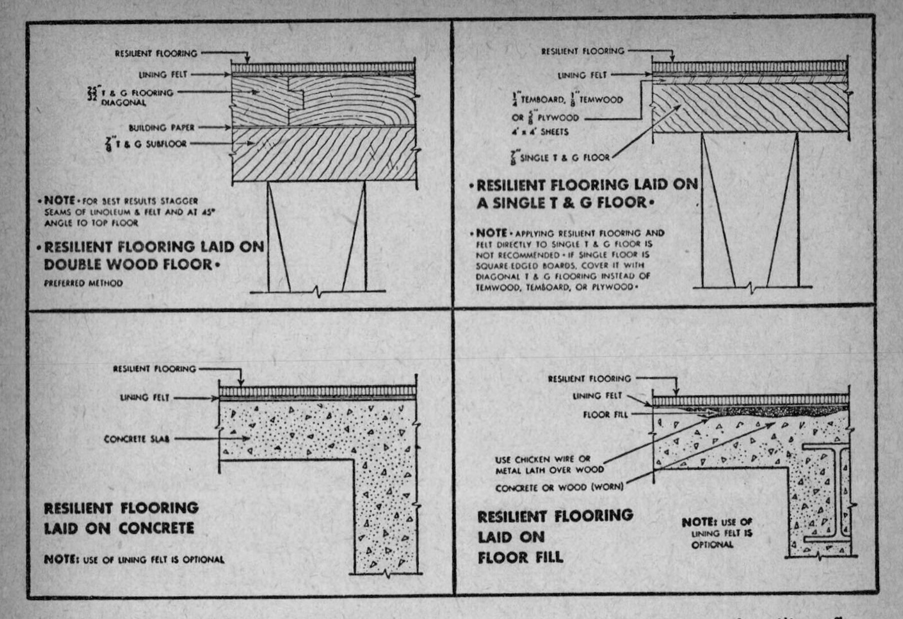

Fig. 31. Proper preparation of the subfloor is most important if any type of resilient flooring is going to last very long. A good rule to follow is to never apply resilient floor coverings to any base unless it is solid, smooth, clean and dry. This figure shows a few of the recommended types of bases suitable for resilient flooring.

3. New Subfloors

a. New Concrete Subfloors—Always test for dampness as described below.

b. New Wood Subfloors. *1.* Single Wood Floors—Cover with hardboard or 5-ply ⅝″ plywood. If not tongue-and-groove, cover with 25/32″ flooring. *2.* Sanded Floors—Prime with one brush coat of floor and wall size to minimize absorption of moisture. *3.* Double Wood Floors—Construct as follows: (a) Under layer—⅞″ boards not over 8″ wide, facenailed at right angles to joists. (b) Upper layer—25/32″ tongue-and-groove flooring not over 3″ face, laid at an angle of 45° to the under layer and blindnailed with 8d cut flooring nails.

B. *Installation Methods.*

1. Lining Felt

a. Always use over wood subfloors and over hardboard or plywood underlayments.

b. Optional on suspended concrete, ceramic tile, marble, terrazzo, or floor fill.

c. Use semi-saturated lining felt.

d. Installing lining felt: *1.* Never install parallel to floor boards. *2.* Butt seams and make tight. *3.* Stagger cross seams. *4.* Cut accurately with a minimum of seams. *5.* Cement with paste. *6.* Roll with a 100-pound roller from the center out to remove air bubbles. *7.* Reroll all seams and edges.

Fig. 32.

2. Adhesives

a. Linoleum Paste. *1.* Always use linoleum paste with linoleum tile to insure satisfactory results. *2.* Spread with a fine-notched steel trowel with notches 1/16″ deep, 1/16″ wide, and ⅛″ apart to cover about 110 sq. ft. per gallon (fig. 32). *3.* Do not spread paste over more than about 36 sq. ft. at one time, because linoleum tile will not bond correctly in paste that has started to set.

b. Waterproof Cement. Use waterproof cement in areas subject to surface moisture and to install top-set rubber cove base.

c. Cove base cement. Use cove base cement for the installation of top-set asphalt cove base.

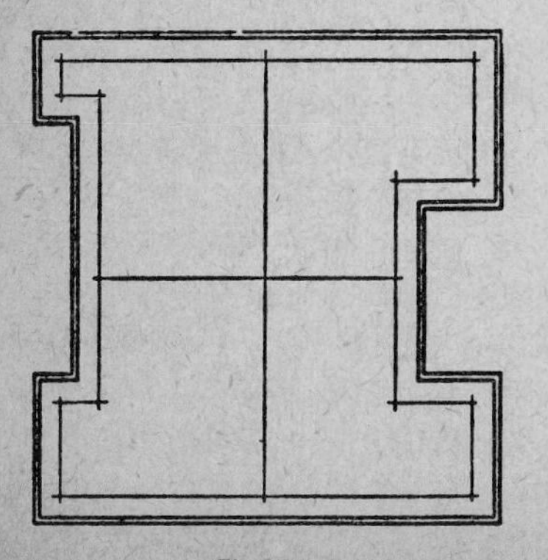

Fig. 33.

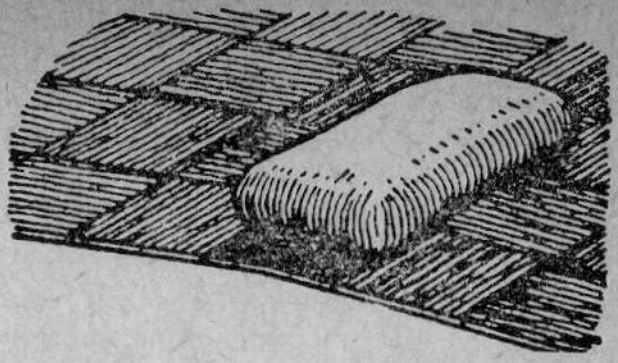

Fig. 34.

3. Layout and Fitting

a. Field area of room should be laid first and should be divided into quarters with chalk lines. Lay quarters one at a time so that tile lines and joints will be kept square and even. Work from center lines to borders (fig. 33).

b. Borders should be carefully determined and laid out with chalk lines at the same time as the field. *1.* Vary width of borders to allow for variance in room dimension and for design selected. *2.* Follow the lines of permanent fixtures or equipment.

c. Roll thoroughly with 100-pound roller immediately after linoleum tile is laid.

d. Sandbag high points until all danger of loosening has passed (fig. 34).

e. Wipe up surplus adhesive. *Do not scrub for 4 or 5 days after installation.*

f. Fit unprotected edges with linoleum tile beveled edging or other

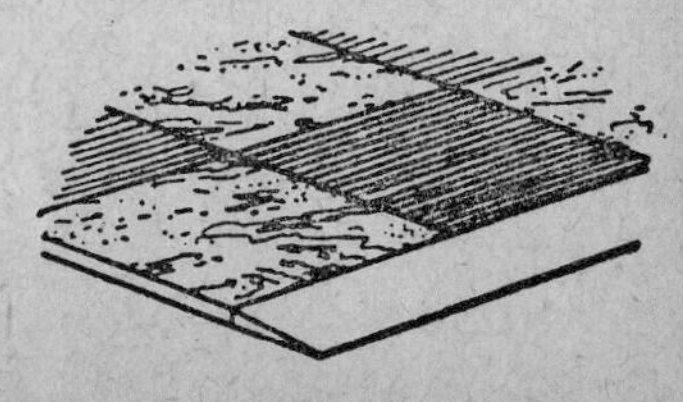

Fig. 35.

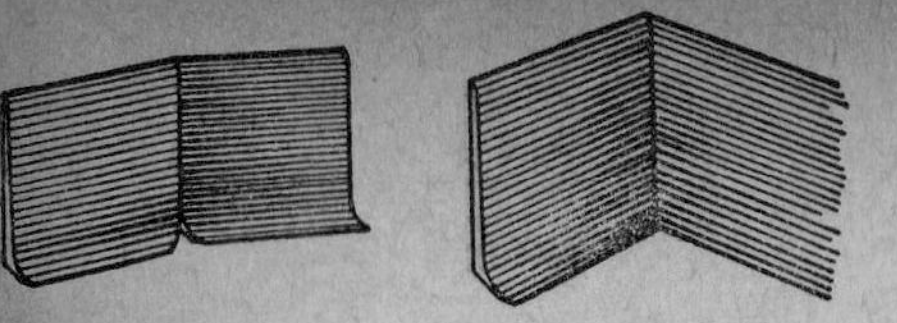

Fig. 36. Inside corners.

suitable metal or wood edge strip (fig. 35).

4. Top-Set Asphalt Cove Base

a. Apply top-set cove base cement to base and then press firmly into place.

b. Form inside corners by cutting a triangular notch in the toe of cove of a 3-foot section (fig. 36), then: *1.* Heat back of base with blowtorch at the point where the corner is to be formed until it can be bent easily. *2.* To insure a good fit, the base should be molded into the corner while still warm. *3.* Base can then be cemented. *4.* Slight irregularities can be smoothed out with the back of a hot knife.

c. Form outside corners on the job from 3-foot sections of base (fig. 37). *1.* Cut a V-shaped groove out of the back of the heated base with a knife. *2.* While the base is still warm, bend and form around corner, or *3.* Base can also be formed around corner by heating the base without notching the back and slowly bent to fit corner. *4.* After base is formed into corner it can be cemented into place.

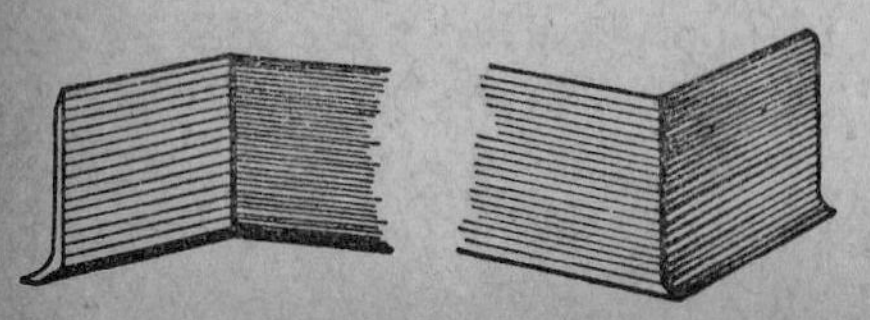

Fig. 37. Outside corners.

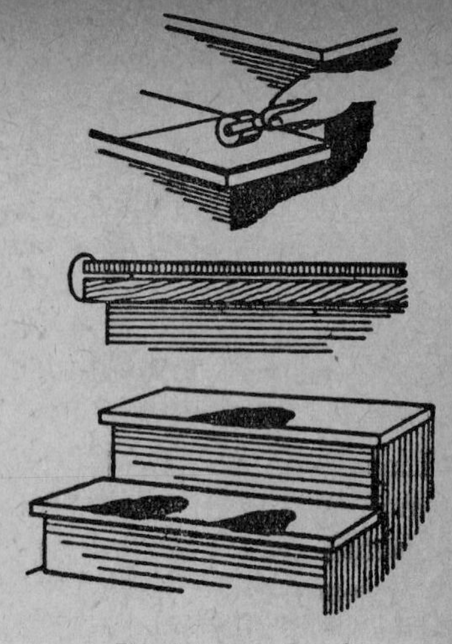

Fig. 38. Stair treads.

5. Stair Treads

a. Cut linoleum tile carefully to fit tread accurately.

b. Cement to tread with linoleum paste. (Use waterproof cement if stairs are near main entrance ways.)

c. Roll in place with a hand roller.

d. Nosings with flange should have the area behind the flange built up with lining felt.

e. Badly worn stair treads can be made smooth and even with floor fill (fig. 38).

Provisions for a Good Job

A constant temperature of at least 70° F. 24 hours prior to installation, during installation, and for 24 hours after the job is completed.

Proper ventilation and lighting.

Hoisting service.

Power for scrubbing and waxing.

After the installation is complete, the owner should cover the linoleum tile with building paper to protect it.

Maintenance Recommendations

Cleaning. Do not wash linoleum tile floors for at least 4 to 5 days after installation. For cleaning, use ½ cupful of liquid cleaner in 10 quarts of warm water. Follow by a thorough rinsing with clear cold water. To remove wax, use a 50% solution.

Waxing. Linoleum gloss wax is a water-emulsion product containing no injurious solvents. It can be applied easily with a cotton-cloth mop or a linoleum gloss applicator. The wax should be applied according to directions on can. Linoleum gloss wax dries to a hard, durable, lustrous finish. A high glossy finish can be produced by buffing with a weighted brush or a polishing machine.

The daily care of a floor which has been waxed consists of brushing with a soft hair brush to remove the dust and dirt.

The Use of Furniture Rests. The concentrated weight of furniture and other equipment often causes indentations in resilient floor installations. Furniture rests and cups help prevent indentation by distributing the weight over a greater floor area. Where furniture rests cannot be used, small blocks of smooth wood should be placed under the corners.

PROTECTION OF ASPHALT TILE

Use of Proper Bearings on Furniture. Resiliency and comfort are advantages of asphalt tile flooring which hard floors do not have. Like any resilient floor, however, it must

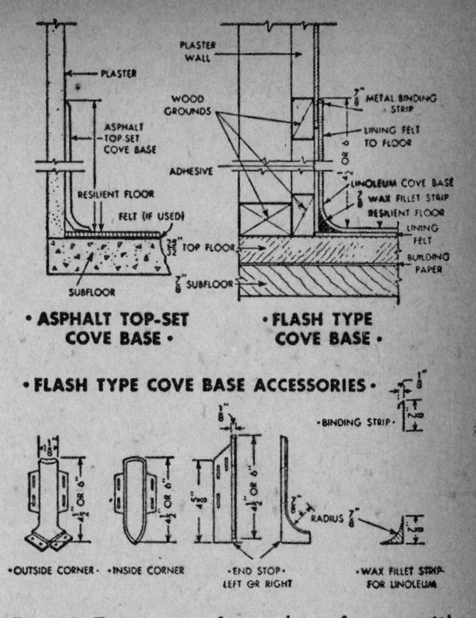

Fig. 39. Two types of cove base for use with resilient floor coverings.

be protected against surface indentation caused by concentrated, sharp-point loads of the furniture or equipment placed on the asphalt tile. Proper types of bearing or contact areas, such as glides, cups or rubber-wheel casters, must be installed. The importance of proper bearing surfaces cannot be over-emphasized. It is recommended that the instructions in the accompanying illustration be carefully followed (fig. 40).

DAMPNESS TEST FOR CONCRETE SUBFLOORS

Before installing resilient tile over a concrete subfloor, the subfloor should be tested for dampness. Concrete subfloors in direct contact with the ground, as well as suspended concrete floors without a well ventilated air space underneath, are al-

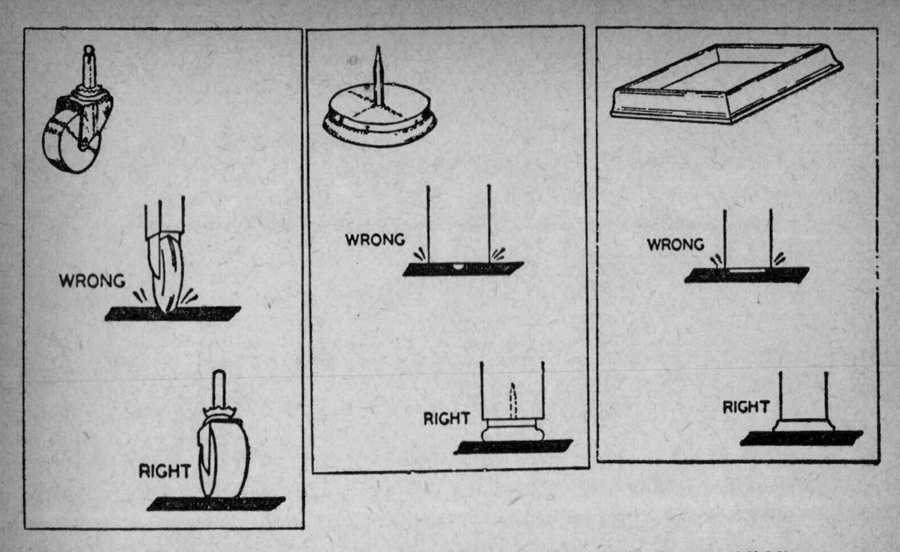

Fig. 40. **Left**, proper bearings for movable furniture on asphalt tile flooring. **Middle**, proper bearings for portable furniture. **Right**, proper bearings for heavy furniture not frequently moved.

ways damp to some degree. Asphalt tile is the only type of resilient tile suitable for installation over such subfloors.

Any type of resilient tile can be installed over suspended concrete subfloors that have proper ventilation under them. Asphalt tile can be installed even over new concrete as soon as the surface is dry enough to apply the primer and adhesive. However, other types of resilient tile should not be installed over new suspended concrete until it is thoroughly dry. It may take as long as two or three months, depending upon the weather, for a new concrete subfloor to dry out to this degree. Therefore, the following test should be made to determine the amount of dampness in the concrete.

1. Form and securely bond a ring of putty, 6″ in diameter and ½″ high on the concrete at each corner of the room and at the center of the room. Inside each ring, drill a small hole in the concrete about 1″ deep with a ¼″ or ½″ star drill. This will allow any moisture present to escape (see the illustration in figure 41 on the next page.)

2. Place a level teaspoon of granulated anhydrous calcium chloride in a watch crystal or on a small piece of glass within each ring and cover each ring with a clock crystal or a piece of glass. Press this glass down on the putty to keep out all outside air. (Granulated anhydrous calcium chloride can be obtained at drug or hardware stores.)

3. If the floor is damp, beads of moisture will appear on the cover glass in 24 to 48 hours and the calcium chloride will be all or partially dissolved.

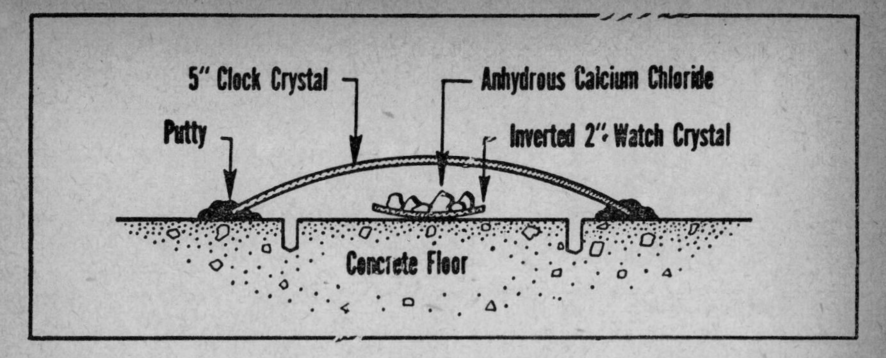

Fig. 41. Make this test before installing any resilient tile over new suspended concrete. Moisture, if present, will appear on clock crystal.

This test indicates only excessive moisture in suspended concrete subfloors. If excessive moisture is found, allow at least 6 to 8 weeks for the concrete to dry out completely before laying resilient tile, except asphalt tile. To dry the concrete completely, the building should be thoroughly ventilated. If the concrete is poured in winter, heat should be provided.

Concrete with a hard glazed finish, or concrete that has been excessively troweled, may require a longer time to dry because such a finish retards the evaporation of moisture. Concrete treated with a hardener also dries slowly.

Concrete of cinder-fill construction also requires a long drying period because it retains a considerable amount of moisture.

All these types of concrete subfloors should be given a test for moisture with anhydrous calcium chloride, as described above.

TILE ON WOOD FLOORS

Resilient tile should not be laid over single wood floors. If a single wood floor consists of tongue and groove boards with a face width of not over three inches, it may be covered with an underlayment of hardboard; 5-ply or greater plywood may also be used. If the single floor consists of straight-edge boards, it should be covered with ⅞″ tongue and groove boards that are not over 3″ in face width.

In double floors, the bottom layer may be of square-edge boards, but the top layer should be of tongue and groove boards laid at an angle of 45° or 90° to the under layer as shown in figure 42.

Cracks wider than ⅛″ and holes larger than ¼″ in diameter should be completely filled with snugly fitting pieces of wood or plastic wood. Defective boards should be replaced with new, sound material. Loose boards should be renailed to make them rigid and secure. All nails should be countersunk and all uneven joints should be planed or sanded smooth.

If a wood subfloor is extremely uneven and cannot be planed and repaired satisfactorily, it can be leveled

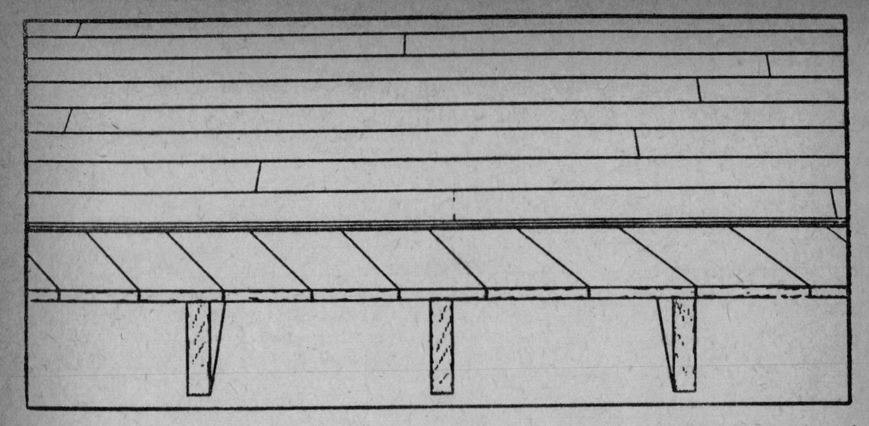

Fig. 42. The top layer of a double wood subfloor should be of tongue and groove boards angled 45° to the bottom layer. The bottom layer may be of straight-edged boards.

with a floor fill. Or if it is a tongue and groove floor, it can be covered with a layer of 5-ply or greater plywood.

If the wood subfloor is in good condition and does not require an underlayment, a thorough cleaning is all that is required. If the surface has been sanded, however, the floor should be primed with an application of floor and wall size. This will prevent the boards from becoming

Fig. 43.

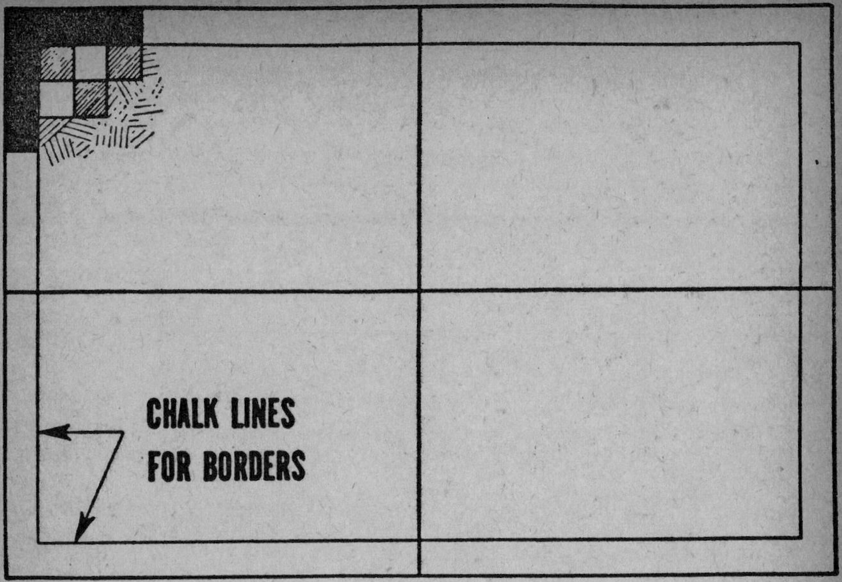

CHALK LINES
FOR BORDERS

Fig. 44.

warped through the excessive absorption of moisture from the adhesive.

For asphalt tile, half of the floor area can be covered with adhesive at one time. To avoid losing the center line, leave ends uncovered and use them as a guide in striking a new line on top of the adhesive. Where the center line is extremely long, it may be helpful to leave several spots uncovered as a further guide in restriking the new line. Or, the adhesive may be spread up to the line without covering it (fig. 43).

Some types of resilient tile are apt to slide out of place while being installed and before the adhesive has

LATTICE STRIPS
BRADDED TO FLOOR

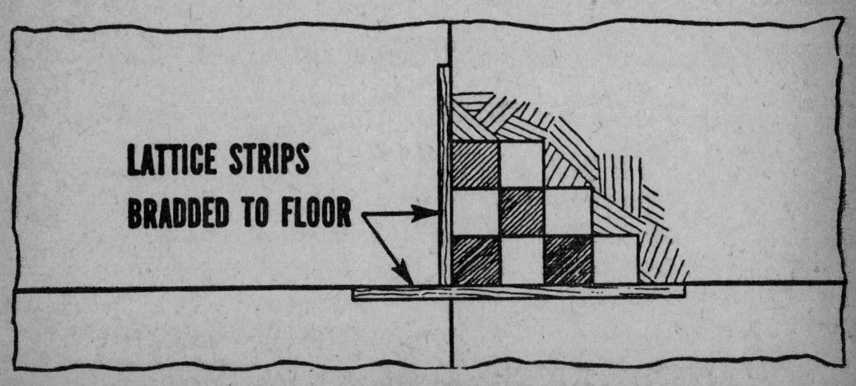

Fig. 45.

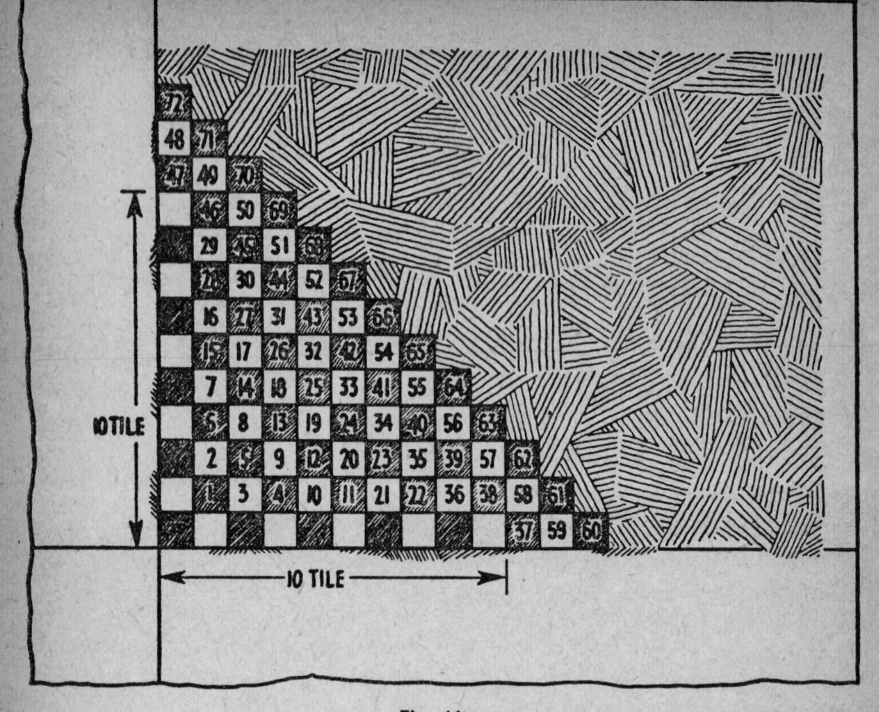

Fig. 46.

set up. Since the tile must be fitted firmly against each other, it is often desirable to start laying the tile in a corner of the room. The walls serve as a base and keep the tile from sliding out of position. If a border is used with any of these materials, it should be fitted into position against the wall before field tile are installed. Then the field tile are fitted against it (fig. 44).

When no border is used, or as an alternate method for starting the installation of rubber tile, linoleum tile, or cork tile, the design can be started in the center of the room by nailing down lattice strips to form a temporary "corner" to serve as a guide for the first few tile. After the center tile are firmly seated in adhesive, the strips can then be removed and the rest of the tile fitted to the seated tile (fig. 45).

Checkerboard designs "on the square" can be laid faster when all of one color tile are laid in diagonal rows. Lay guide tile (about 20); then follow the numerical order (fig. 46).

When two or more marbleized colors of rubber tile or linoleum tile are used in diagonal designs, the graining of the half tile at the borders should run in the same direction as the corresponding color in full tile. To meet this condition, two types of half tile are required—right and left half tile as indicated in figure 47. With the grain of the full tile run-

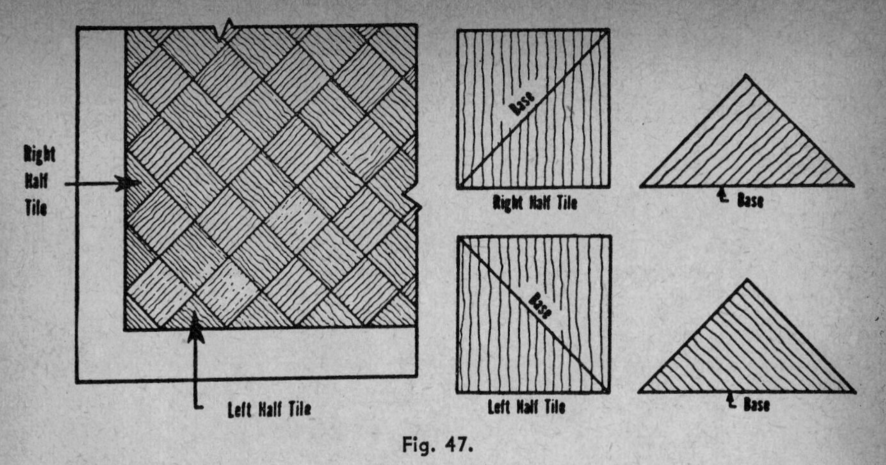

Fig. 47.

ning from top to bottom, right half tile are cut on a diagonal from the lower left corner to the upper right. With full tile in the same position, left half tile are cut on a diagonal from the upper left corner to the lower right corner. The diagonal side, in both cases, becomes the base of the half tile.

CERAMIC TILE, TERRAZZO, AND MARBLE SUBFLOORS

Asphalt tile is the only resilient flooring that should be installed over ceramic tile, terrazzo, or marble subfloors below grade. Other resilient floorings can be laid over these subfloors, if they are above grade.

The floors should be cleaned of all paint, varnish, wax, or oil, and should then be scrubbed with a scrubbing machine using soapy water and clean sharp sand. Badly fitted joints or cracks should be repaired with crack filler finished flush with the surface. If the floors are badly worn or have low places, they should be leveled with a floor fill.

When installing asphalt tile over one of these subfloors in direct contact with the ground, the subfloor should be tested for dampness and primed.

METAL SUBFLOORS

Metal subfloors should be true and even. They should be thoroughly cleaned of all dirt, grease, paint, rust, etc. If there are protruding rivets, welds, or lap joints, the floor should be levelled with underlayment.

FITTING TILE TO STRAIGHT WALLS

Fitting to a straight wall is easy if you follow these steps. As shown in figure 48, butt the final tile, *B*, against *A*, which is the last tile cemented in place.

1. If *B* does not extend all the way to the wall, butt another tile, *C*, to

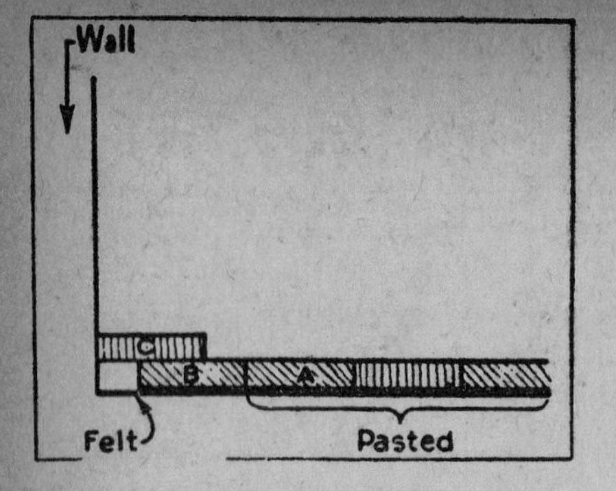

Fig. 48. Butt tile **B** against **A.** Then butt tile **C** to the wall so that it overlaps **B.**

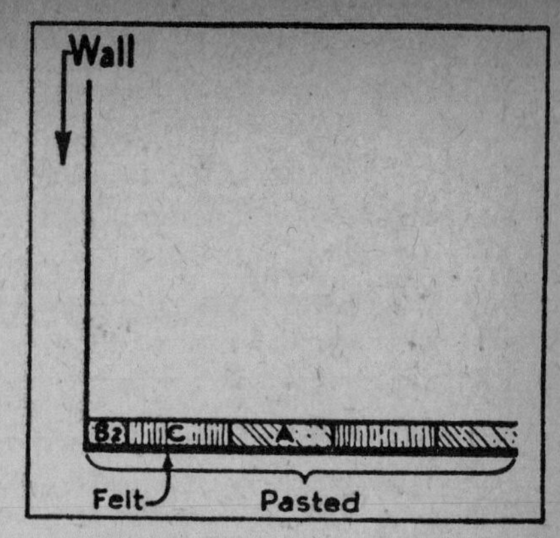

Fig. 50. Butt **B**2 to the wall and move **C** into position formerly occupied by tile **B.**

the wall so that one edge of it laps over *B*, as shown in figure 48.

2. Using the edge of *C* as a guide, score *B* and cut it along the scored line, as in figure 49.

3. Discard the part of *B* that is covered by *C*. This part is referred to as *B1* in figure 49. The part not covered by *C* is referred to as *B2* in figures 49 and 50.

4. Butt *C* against *A*, and move *B2* into position against the wall, as shown in figure 50.

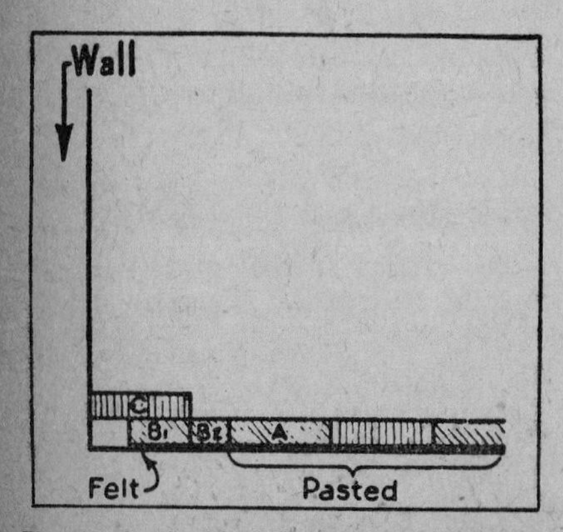

Fig. 49. Scribe block **B** along edge of **C** and cut into two parts shown as B1 and B2.

5. Repeat this operation along all four walls, check the fit, and then remove the pieces and cement them in position. As a final step, remove all excess adhesive.

To fit tile along a straight wall for a diagonal design without a border, use a template cut to the diagonal width of the tile being installed. The last tile for the wall line is measured the same as tile *B* in figure 48, with the template laid over tile *B* in place of tile *C*. Scribe and cut tile *B* as shown in figures 49 and 50. The template can be made of tile or metal. It is usually desirable to keep a set of templates on hand, one for the diagonal width of each of the most commonly used tile sizes.

To avoid joints near corners, install the corners first. Be sure the wall is sound, and free of all paint, dust, dirt, or scale before installing rubber cove base.

Rubber cove base should always be carefully cut cold with a linoleum knife.

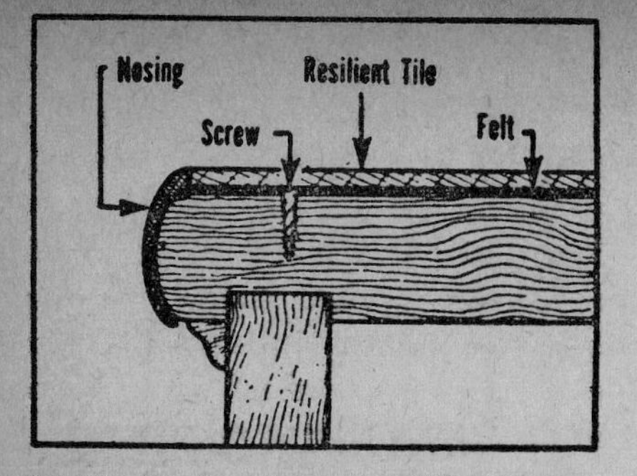

Fig. 51. This is a flange type metal nosing suitable for use when installing treads of resilient tile except asphalt.

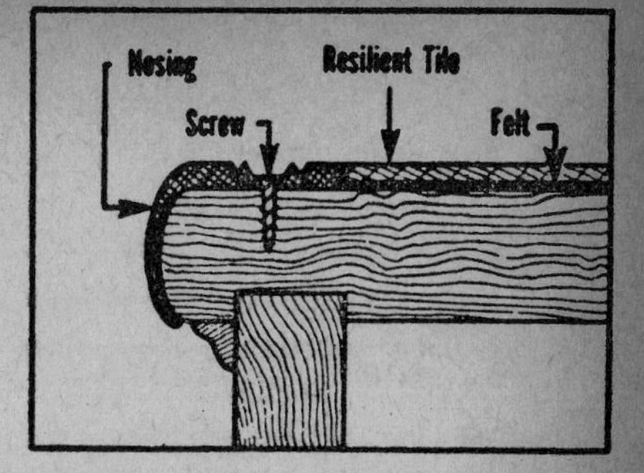

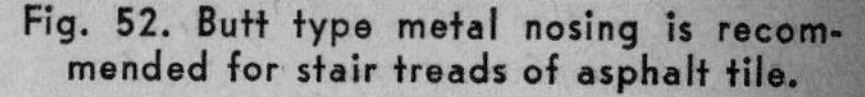
Fig. 52. Butt type metal nosing is recommended for stair treads of asphalt tile.

INSTALLATION OF RESILIENT TILE STAIR TREADS

Stair treads usually are of the same type of material installed on the adjoining floors. The design usually matches or complements either the floor design or border material.

Resilient tile stair treads should be protected by installing metal nosing along the front edge of each step. (Figs. 51 and 52.) If stairs are badly worn or corrugated, they should be leveled with floor fill before installing the treads.

When the step is level and the nosing has been attached, paste down a layer of lining felt. With the factory-cut edge of the felt held against the riser, cut the other three edges to fit at the sides of the step and in back of the metal nosing.

Mark the back edge of the tile with a scriber so that the tile can be cut to fit accurately against the contour of the riser. Hold one point of the scriber at the base of the riser and draw the scriber along the base with the other leg marking the tile.

PLASTER

Gypsum neat plaster may be produced by adding to calcined gypsum materials to improve its plasticity and retarder to control its time of set. This is the chief gypsum product used by the plastering trade. It may be had either fibered or plain and is sold in bags containing one hundred pounds each. Gypsum ready-sanded plasters contain all the necessary ingredients, except water, for either scratch-coat or brown-coat work. Sometimes a shredded wood fiber is used instead of sand, the product being designated gypsum wood-fibered plaster.

Portland Cement. Portland cement is made by heating a natural or artificial mixture of limestone and clay to above 1,200° C, or until it begins to melt. The partially vitrified material is then ground to a fine powder and mixed with a small amount of gypsum to retard its set. It is shipped in cloth or paper bags, containing a standard or customary ninety-four pounds each.

Portland cement requires water in its hardening process, and for complete hydration a sufficient supply of water must be maintained for many days. The conditions to which wall plaster is ordinarily subjected are not those best adapted to developing the full strength of portland cement. On the other hand, portland cement is peculiarly adapted for use as a plaster under continuously and excessively damp conditions.

Since one of the products of the hydration of portland cement is hydrated lime, the hardened material will have an alkaline nature.

Keene's Cement. Keene's cement is made from gypsum heated to such a temperature that its water content is driven off. This product, when mixed with water, will re-crystallize, developing hardness. The reaction takes place so slowly, however, that a small amount of some chemical, such as alum, is used to accelerate its hardening. Keene's cement is used for plasters requiring a hard surface.

Sand. Care should be exercised in the selection of sand, the principal aggregate in plaster. Both the angular and globular types are satisfactory and may be either natural sand or ground rock. Sand should be composed of clean, hard, durable stone particles, free from objectionable matter, with an allowance of not more than 5 percent of loam, silt, and clay. Sand for plaster should be graded to pass a No. 3 or No. 4 sieve, and at least 85 percent should be retained on a No. 100 sieve.

Fiber. The only function of fiber is to enable the plaster to be spread in place without losing too much of it through dropping. The fiber may be of animal or vegetable origin and should be long enough to serve its purpose (one-half inch), but not so long that it will tangle (2 inches). It should be flexible enough to stay buried in the plaster and should be clean, for dust in the fiber is as objectionable as dust is in the sand. It should be evenly distributed throughout the plaster.

Water. Sea water, or water known as brackish, sulphur, chalybeate, or carbonated, should not be used for plastering. With the above exceptions, ordinary drinking water should prove satisfactory.

PLASTER PROPORTIONS

Practically all plaster consists of a mixture of at least two materials besides water. The proportions in which these dry materials are mixed is, of course, important in determining the properties of the plaster. Some attempt is usually made to measure the quantities of the different ingredients, and the importance of this operation is sufficient to warrant conducting it with considerable care and accuracy. The degree of accuracy used is, of course, governed by the cost, but it never pays to guess at the quantities.

One of the great hindrances to the establishment of definite methods of proportioning is the conflict of opinion as to whether the measurements should be made by weight or by volume. Contractors find volume measurements much more convenient.

The ingredients used, however, vary considerably in the weight per unit of volume, even as between different lots of the same brand of the same material. Consequently, a specification calling for a definite volume of material, even if rigidly followed, would not insure the presence of a definite weight of that material in the finished plaster, particularly when the volume is measured "loose." On the other side, the arguments are that the cost of weighing the materials is so great as to be impractical; that the error introduced by proportioning by volume instead of weight, while admittedly large, is still small enough to be negligible; and that it is more important that the finished plaster shall contain a given volume of cementitious material rather than a given weight. The facts are, therefore, that the volume system is in universal use; that there are good reasons why a change should be made to the weight system, but there are also reasons why this change should not be made. It is therefore recommended that all proportions be expressed by volume, with the insistence that the contractor use reasonable care in making the measurements.

The proportion of water has the same effect on plaster as it has on cementitious materials used in other forms—the more water the weaker the hardened product. Fortunately, however, this factor is not of great importance in the plastering industry. The proportion of water is very narrowly limited by the conditions of use. Too little water will make the plaster difficult to spread; too much water will make it slide off the trowel or wall. The proper consistency is, therefore, so closely defined that no further precautions are necessary.

The following proportions, by volume, are recommended for the different kinds of plaster. One volume of lime means one volume of either lime putty or hydrated lime. Gypsum means neat gypsum plaster. The proportions given are for straight lime, gypsum, or portland cement plasters. Lime may be mixed with portland or keene's cement in any desired proportions. Portland cement shall not be mixed with keene's cement or gypsum.

Nothing except water shall be added at the work to ready-mixed mortar, ready-mixed plaster, or gypsum wood fibered, finishing or bond plasters.

For scratch coat on lath, use 1 volume of lime to 1½ of sand, 1 of gypsum to 2 of sand, or 1 of portland cement to 3 of sand. In all cases, hair or fiber may be added in amounts not to exceed 3 bushels per cubic yard of sand.

For scratch coat on masonry, use 1 volume of lime to 3 of sand, 1 of gypsum to 3 of sand, or 1 of portland cement to 3 of sand. If a finish coat is to be used, hair or fiber may be added to the scratch coat in amounts not to exceed 1½ bushels per cubic yard of sand.

For brown coat use 1 volume of lime to 3 of sand, 1 of gypsum to 3 of sand, or 1 of portland cement to 3 of sand. If a finish coat is to be used, fiber may be added to the brown coat

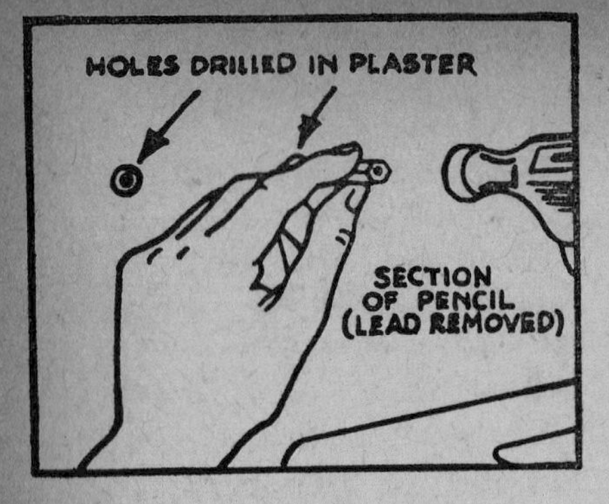

Fig. 53.

in amounts not to exceed 1½ bushels per cubic yard of sand.

For finish coat, the proportions of lime putty and gypsum shall be left to the discretion of the plasterer. He must add enough gypsum so that the material will set at the desired moment, and the proportion to be used will, therefore, depend upon the area of the surface to be plastered, and the weather. Plastic gypsum, which is now on the market, can be used without lime for the finish coat. It is expected that quick-hardening lime, which can be used without gypsum, will soon be available.

PEELING OF PAINT

The peeling or blistering of paint is almost always due to the presence of water in the plaster. It is quite unusual to paint plaster before it is sufficiently dry, so that this phenomenon may be taken to mean that water from some source is getting into the plaster. Look for leaks in the plumbing or flashings, or for the possibility of water seeping through from the

TREATMENTS FOR SUGGESTED JOINTS OF INTERIOR PLYWOOD WALLS

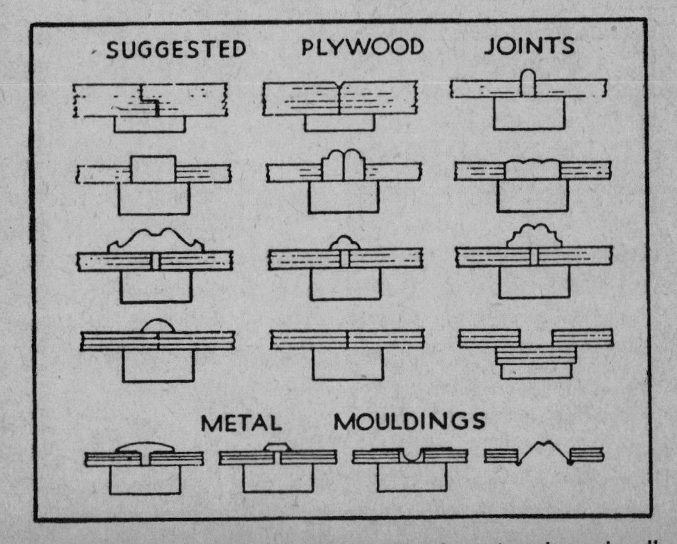

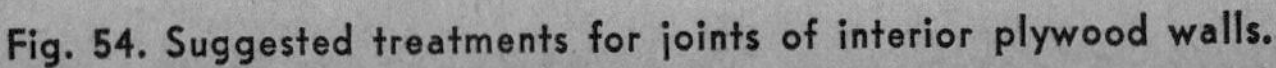
Fig. 54. Suggested treatments for joints of interior plywood walls.

other side of the wall. (This is another reason why furring is recommended.) If the floor is frequently mopped with water, an impervious baseboard is necessary to prevent the water from being absorbed by the capillary action of the plaster.

The action of free lime in the plaster may be identified by what looks like shrinkage cracks in the paint. The areas inclosed by the cracks are very small. The paint film in each area is brittle and lacking in lustre. This should have been prevented by the use of a priming coat.

WRINKLING OF PAPER

Paper expands when it gets wet. The wrinkling of wall paper may, therefore, be taken to indicate that water is condensing out of the air on to the surface of the paper. This is not serious, for the paper usually shrinks back to its original size when it dries out.

Of course, the water may come from a leak, but this can be distinguished by the fact that the wrinkling is localized.

PENCIL AS EXPANSION PLUG

Ordinary hexagonal lead pencils can be used in a pinch as expansion plugs when you have to locate wood screws in a plaster wall. Cut a pencil into ¾″ sections and push the lead out. Drill the wall a snug fit for the pencil lengths. Then drive in the screws, which will split and expand the wood (fig. 53).

A FEW JOINT SUGGESTIONS FOR EXTERIOR PLYWOOD

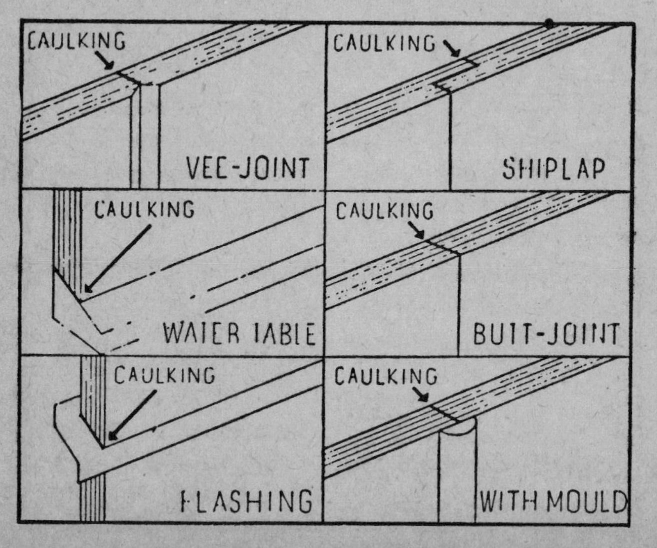

Fig. 55. Suggested joints for exterior plywood.

ASBESTOS BOARD

How To Apply It. Plan all work in advance to avoid waste. Erect the asbestos board so the mottling on all sheets runs in the same direction. (On scored sheets the word TOP appears on the reverse side.)

Do not apply over damp surfaces. If unavoidable, back prime the sheets with shellac. Also prime with clear shellac the portions of sheets which will come in contact with putty (to retard absorption of oil).

For residing over existing walls, replace or repair all rotten or damaged members and nail down loose siding. Provide a reasonably smooth base for the asbestos board.

How To Fasten It. Nailing—Nails should penetrate 1″ into solid wood and may be driven close to the edge (⅜″ minimum) without chipping. Drilling or punching is unnecessary.

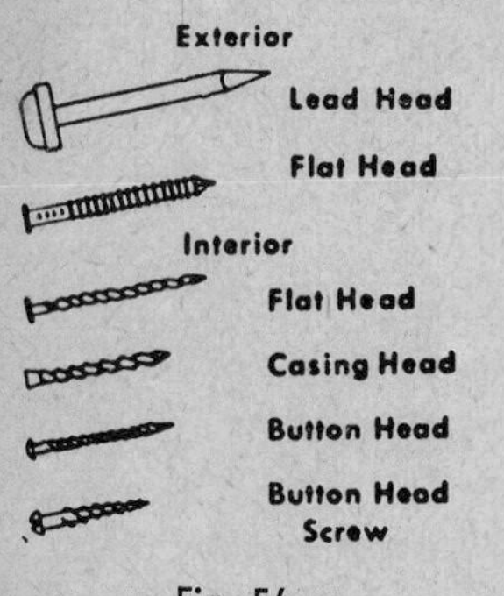

Fig. 56.

Types of Nails—Use non-corrodible nails. Stainless steel drive screw nails with either casing or button heads can be purchased (fig. 56).

Location of Nails—From the starting edge work toward the opposite edge to "wipe" the sheet smooth. Figure 57 shows approved location and spacing for nails. If nails must be pulled use a wood block between the hammer and the asbestos board.

Fig. 57.

Adhesives—Apply with toothed trowel in 3″ spots, ⅛″ thick, staggered on 12″ centers approx., and kept 1″ from sheet edge (fig. 58). Hold with temporary bracing for 24 hours or until set. Supplemental nailing or fastening should always be used (fig. 59).

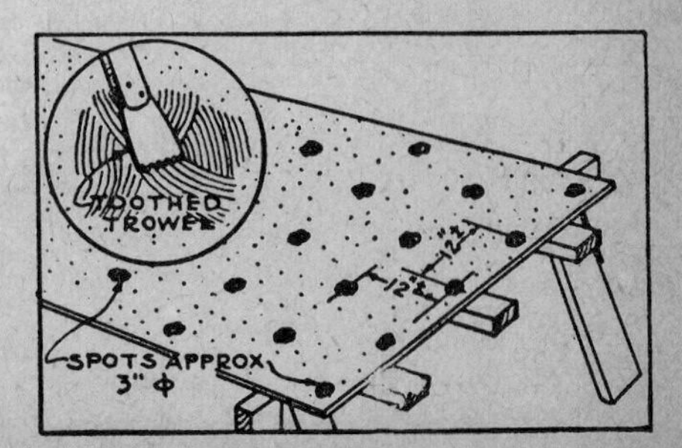

Fig. 58.

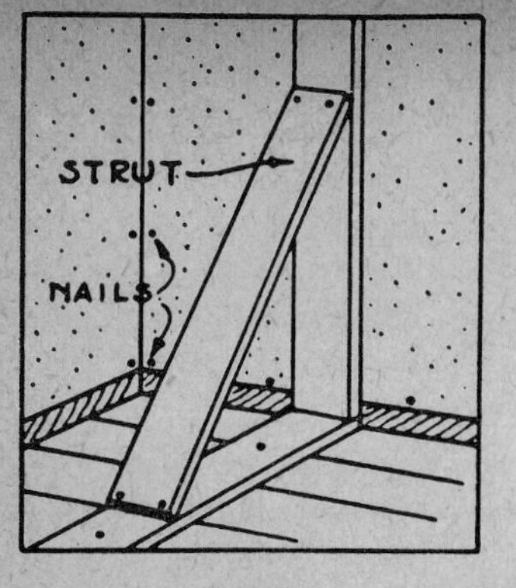

Fig. 59.

How To Work Asbestos Board. Always cut asbestos board with the finished face up so any roughness from cutting will be largely on the underside of the sheet. For smoothing or shaping the cut edge, use a horseshoe or wood rasp or a block and #1 sandpaper.

Sawing—For sawing by hand use a 10 point saw with little or no set. An expensive one is not necessary. Wet the saw with water for faster cutting (fig. 60).

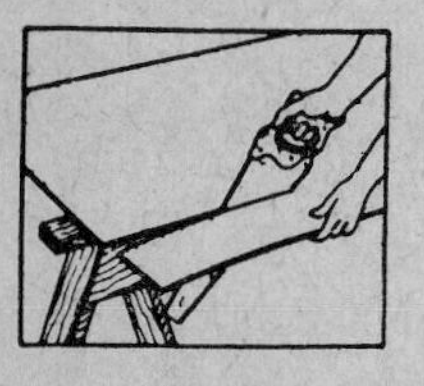

Fig. 60.

"Score and Snap"—Place a straight edge, such as a 2 x 4, along the cutting line. Score several times with a sharp, hard pointed ice pick or awl using the straight edge as a guide. Then, with the scored line along the

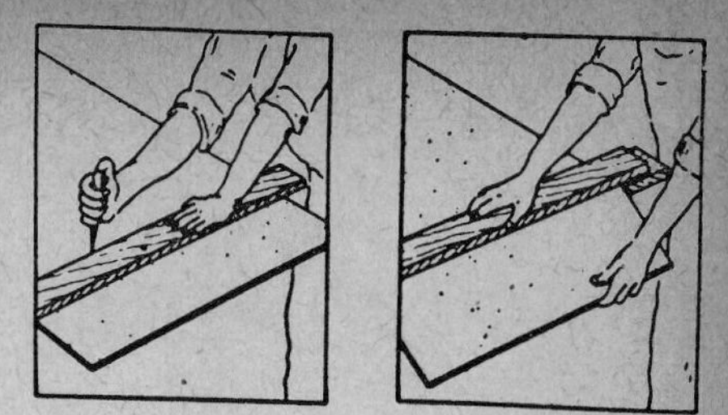

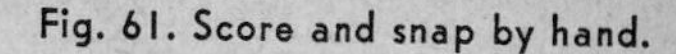

Fig. 61. Score and snap by hand.

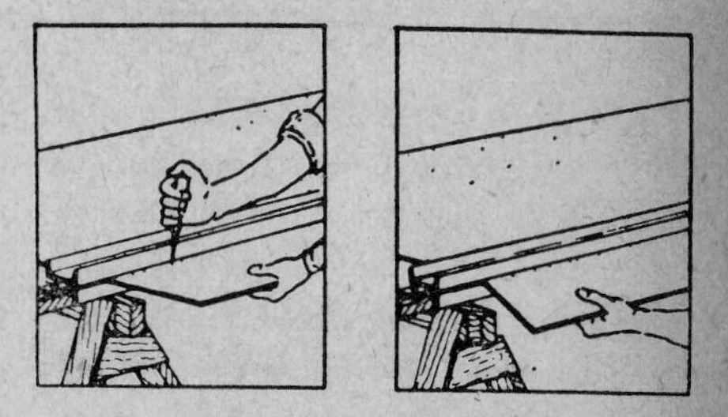

Fig. 62. Score cutting jig.

edge of the bench, hold the straight edge firmly on the line and "snap" off the projecting strip intact (fig. 61).

To save time when many similar pieces such as battens are to be cut, a "score cutting jig" is easy to build. This consists of two metal channels

Fig. 63.

placed back to back to form a clamp. The upper channel acts as a cutting guide (fig. 62).

Circular cuts—Lay out the circle to be cut. For small holes, punch a series of holes about ⅛″ apart using

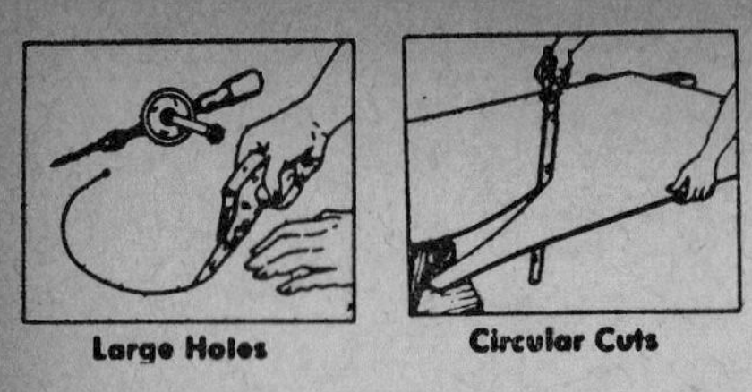

Fig. 64.

a sharpened nail-set. Then, tap with a hammer to knock out the circular piece (fig. 63).

For large holes, first drill a hole on the circumference line as a starting point, then use a keyhole saw (fig. 64).

For curves, a 9″ radius (minimum) can be cut using the point of an ordinary carpenters saw, a 22″ radius (minimum) using about half of the saw blade (fig. 64).

INSIDE CORNER (exterior of building)—Butt the asbestos board. Under the joint white top roofing may be used over the felt. Sketch shows 3/16″ or ¼″ asbestos board applied directly to the studs (fig. 65).

OUTSIDE CORNER—Butted—Butt the asbestos board. Under the joint a strip of white top roofing may be used over the felt. Sketch shows 3/16″ or ¼″ asbestos board applied directly to the studs (fig. 66).

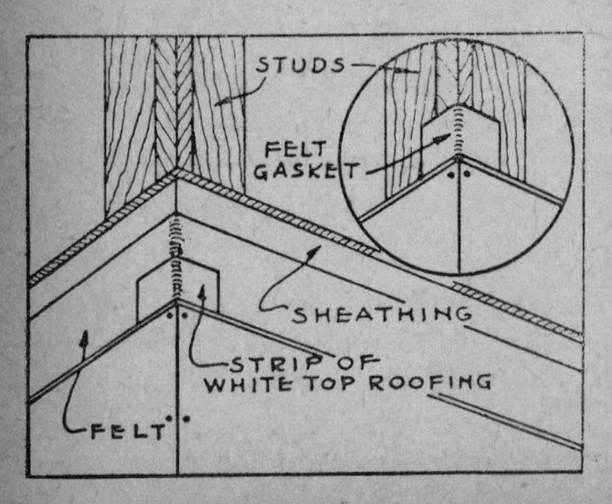

Fig. 65

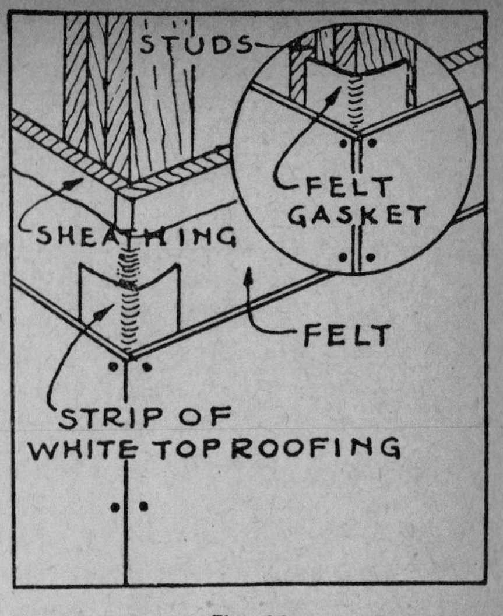

Fig. 66.

OUTSIDE CORNER—Battened—Cover the joint between sheets with corner asbestos board or with wood boards (fig. 67).

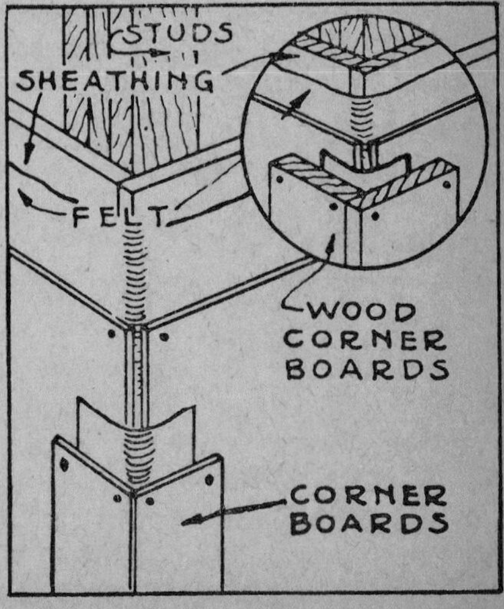

Fig. 67.

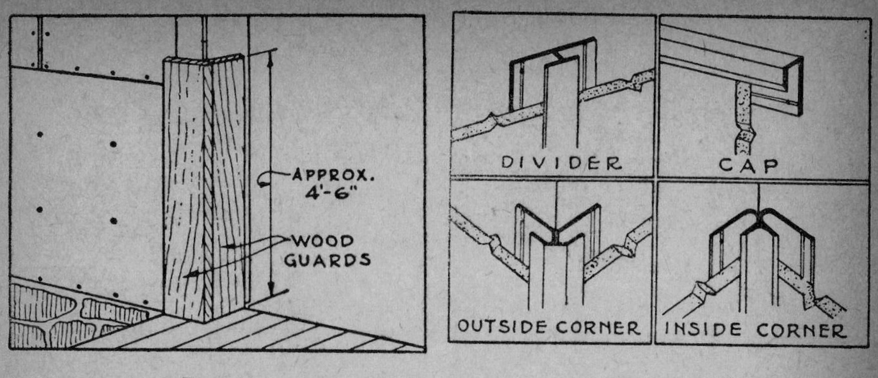

Fig. 68.

Fig. 70.

GUARDS—When an opening is used for heavy traffic a substantial guard of wood should be provided. Carry it high enough to protect the asbestos board trim against passing trucks or machinery (fig. 68).

HEAD AND SILL DETAILS—A flashing of non-corrodible metal is recommended for the head. The sill treatment will be similar for either asbestos board or wood trim. In remodeling, the trim is removed before applying the asbestos board, then the old trim may be replaced or, for a more uniform appearance and elimination of upkeep, use asbestos board trim (fig. 69).

MOULDINGS—Metal or plastic mouldings, applied according to the manufacturer's directions, may be used. With this form of attachment, either face nailing or adhesives should be added to prevent "drumming" (fig. 70).

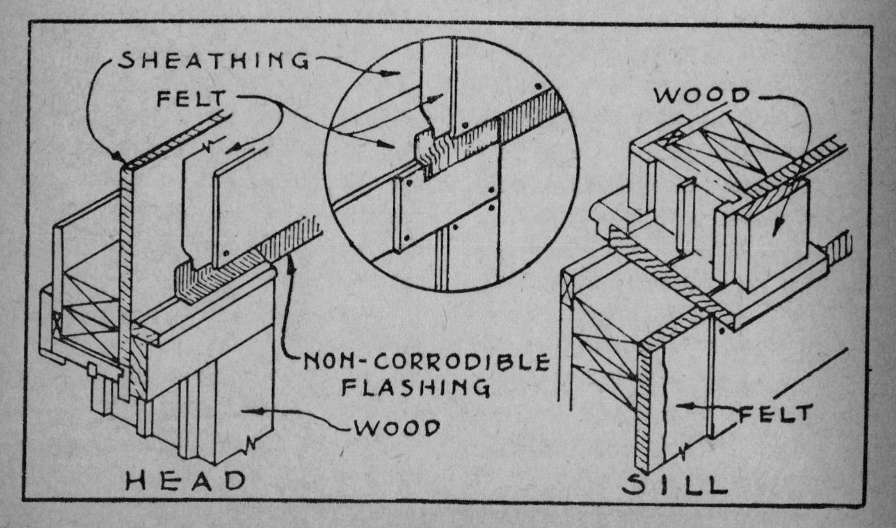

Fig. 69.

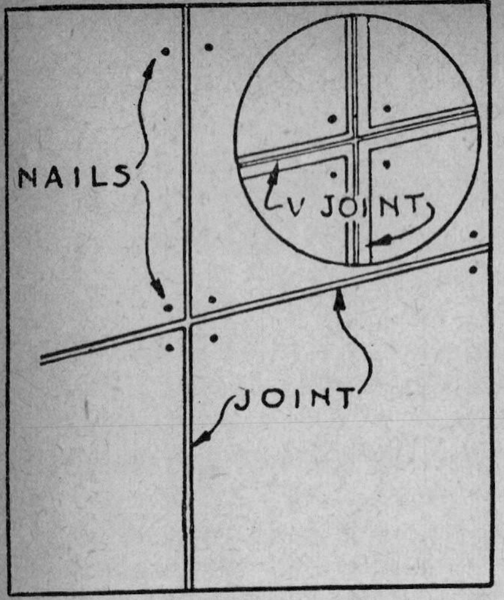

Fig. 71.

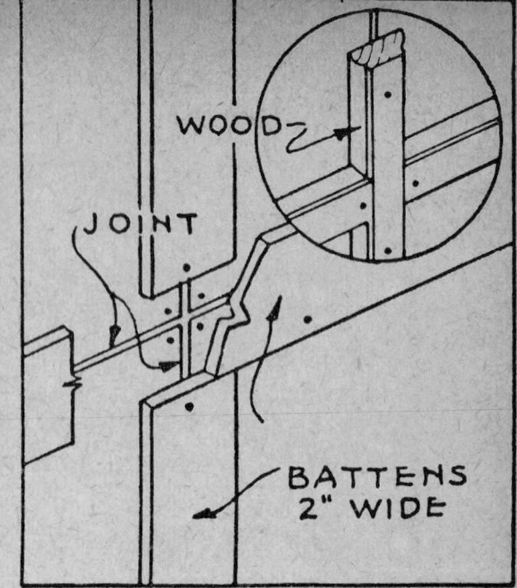

Fig. 72.

BUTT JOINTS—When joints are to be uncovered the edges of the asbestos board sheets should be fitted neatly. Sketch shows a V-joint (preferred) made by beveling the edges of the sheets with a rasp (fig. 71).

BATTENED JOINTS—Use asbestos board (2″ minimum) or wood battens (fig. 72).

DIRECTLY TO STUDS—Use 3/16″ or ¼″ asbestos board only. Maximum stud spacing for this method is indicated and cats must be installed so that all joints are formed over framing members (fig. 73).

OVER BACKING—If the backing is plywood (minimum thickness ⅜″), either ⅛″ or 3/16″ asbestos board may be used as shown in figure 74. When the application is over plaster, furring strips must be installed and only 3/16″ asbestos board is recommended. As shown in figure 75, the furring 1″ by 2″ (minimum) must come under all joints.

TILEBOARD

Tileboard, the modern material for walls and ceilings of bathrooms, kitchens, and other places where a smooth, easily cleaned surface is desired, can be erected by any one who is handy with tools. The average room can be completed in a single day and can be used at once.

Preparation Of Base Surface. You will get a much better job, use less cement, and save time if the base surface for tileboard is made reasonably smooth. This means furring out depressions, knocking off projections, and inserting solid wood or gypsum lath in place of badly broken or loose plaster.

Loose plaster areas may be prepared by chipping away bad plaster and furring out to original wall surface with boards not larger than 1″ x 3″ and spaced not over 2″ apart. Gypsum lath fitted flush with the

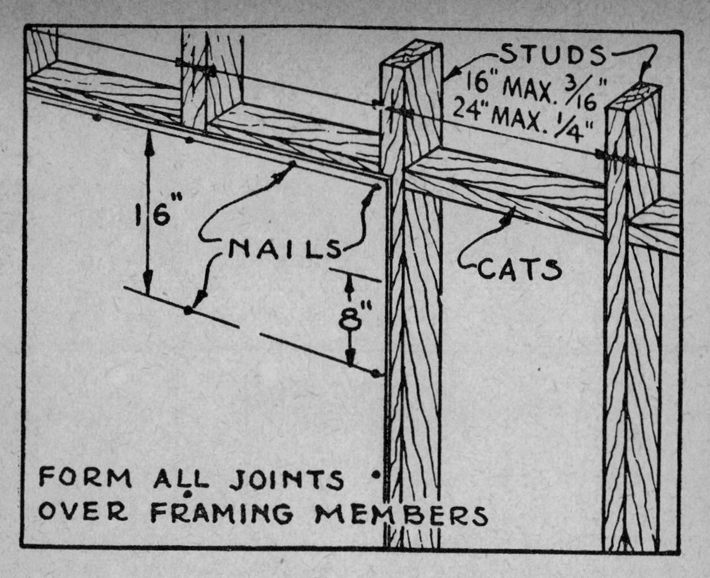

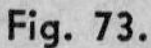
Fig. 73.

original wall surface is an excellent way to repair such areas. The panel is then cemented directly to the repaired surface (fig. 76).

Tileboard should not be applied directly over studding. A continuous surface, free from high spots and hollows, is required for an efficient installation and lasting service. If studs are bare, nail gypsum lath to form a base to which tileboard can be cemented.

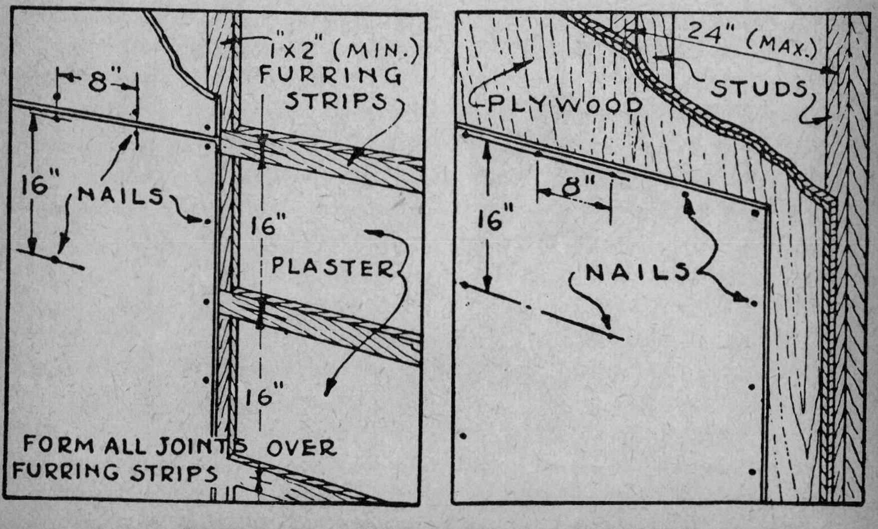

Fig. 74.

Fig. 75.

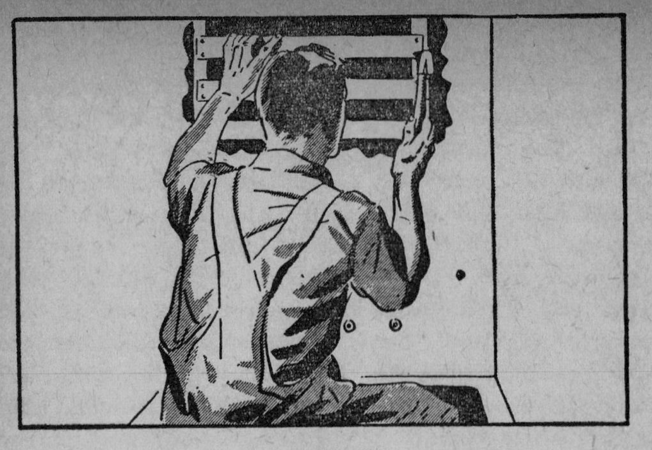

Fig. 76.

Wallpaper, scrim cloth, or similar wall covering should be cleaned off to provide a good bond. By using panelboard cement, tileboard can be installed over painted surfaces if the paint is of good quality and well bonded. If not, it should be removed.

Tileboard should not be applied against any surface likely to become wet, such as a porous wall below grade and in basements.

On-set (or surface mounted) fixtures are recommended for tileboard rather than recessed fixtures. Determine fixture locations in advance, and either be sure there is a solid stud for their supporting nails or screws, or tear out the plaster and

Fig. 77. Before panels are cut, level line is struck around room 50½" above low point on the floor. (Extra 2½" allows for base molding.) If panel behind tub is to be "stepped up" as shown, level line should be struck 48" above the lowest point of the tub since the 2½" allowance for base molding is not required.

substitute a solid piece of wood. This is often necessary on the "spigot" wall over a tub, where studs have been cut to set in the tub.

Cutting and Fitting Panels and Moldings. If tileboard is to be used for walls and ceiling, do the ceiling first, then the walls.

To install tileboard on walls, first find low point of room. Strike a level line around the room 50½″ above this point (fig. 77). Top of tileboard panels should be placed on this line. Base molding will then cover bottom of tileboard panels at least 1″ when job is completed, and, if the panels are set horizontally, they will come up to normal wainscot height. Always work with face of tileboard toward you, except when applying cement. Use reasonable care to protect the smooth high gloss of the tileboard finish.

In applying bathroom walls, it is wise to start on the walls over the tub. And the first of these to be fitted with tileboard should be the wall on which the shower and faucets are located. Take off handles, faucets, and escutcheons of plumbing fixtures projecting from wall. Rough cut your piece of tileboard ¼″ to ½″ oversize to allow shaping to fit uneven walls and tub surface. Set the piece of tileboard against the spigot wall and level it with a spirit level. Hold it there, and with a scriber mark the vertical edge to fit loosely against the adjoining wall. Set scriber about ⅜″ wider than wall variation requires to allow for the channel molding which will go into the inside corner (fig. 78). Always allow approximately ⅛″ end clearance within each channel for expansion. Saw along this line. Use fine-tooth (12-point) saw with little set and bevel the cut slightly to avoid binding.

Set piece up against wall again and scribe as before along bottom to conform to top edge of tub, which may be out of level, and allow about ⅜″ for tub channel molding which will

Fig. 78. To secure proper alignment of material, top edge of panel should be held on or parallel to level line while scribing. Tileboard is then cut from finish side.

fit on bottom of this panel. The tub channel molding, however, will be only as long as the horizontal part of the tub edge. Therefore, the down-curve on the adjoining piece must be scribed without the ⅜″ allowance for the molding.

To locate projecting pipes or fixtures, daub the ends of them with chalk or paint and set the piece of tileboard against them, being careful to allow for the ⅜″ at bottom and side which will be occupied by channels.

Press to leave marks on back. Drive nails through centers of marks, from back to front. Drill holes from front to back, centered on nail holes, making holes slightly larger than pipes so tileboard won't bind. Allow room so bonnets of shower valves can be removed, if necessary. Never force tileboard into place—it should fit freely without binding.

Take piece of tub channel molding slightly longer than distance from inner wall to mark on tub. Set closed end at mark. At inner end, scribe to get exact length needed. Cut with 32-point hack saw. Snip back all inside flanges at joints (fig. 79).

Be sure tileboard for the spigot wall fits properly and sits easily in the tub channel molding. Fit inside corner molding. This sits on top of the tub channel molding and runs up to ½″ from top of the tileboard. Space at top is left so cap molding will sit square against wall.

On back wall over tub, fit tileboard as before. Few tubs sit really level, and tileboard must always be completely level, so allow plenty of width for exact conformity with line of tub top. Adjustment for a slanting tub is made at the bottom of the piece of tileboard. Level the piece and scribe, at bottom first, then end, being careful to line up score lines exactly with those in the piece on the spigot wall. (Always line up score lines at every

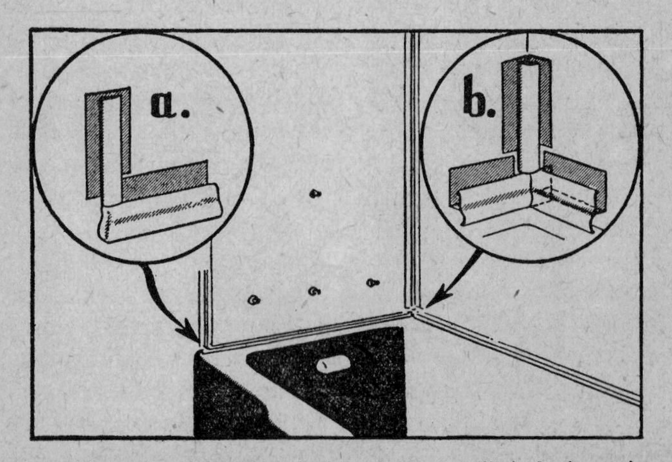

Fig. 79. Before tileboard is cemented, all channels are installed; **A** above shows how connector channel is cut to end of tub channel molding; **B** shows how inside corner and tub channel are cut.

joint of tile-design and streamline tileboard to give neat appearance.)

The tub channel molding running long way of the tub is then coped over corresponding piece of spigot wall. Cut slightly large on your scribed line and file to perfect fit (fig. 79*B*).

The next piece of tileboard, beyond the end of the tub, must be scribed and cut to fit perfectly against the rounded contour of the tub. There is a vertical channel molding between the two pieces (fig. 79*A*), which must be allowed for, but the molding does not follow the curve. Use regular filler, in color to match the tileboard, to smooth out junction of this piece with the tub. Wipe off filler, especially on mortar lines, with clean dry rag. When dry, filler can be smoothed with a cleanser.

Waterproofing. It's important that all joints, edges, and channels where water splashes or stands be thoroughly waterproofed.

Use tube of filler. Lay a continuous string of this in the angle between tub and original wall, thick enough so that when tileboard is applied it will press against it, and tub molding will sit on it for its full length. Next, fill the grooves in the tub moldings and inner corner moldings with this same filler.

When tileboard is set into these channels, the filler should ooze out of every mortar line. Wipe off any excess filler from face of the tileboard and tub and moldings with a rag and kerosene or turpentine.

Cementing. When you have corrected major projections and hollows in walls, the surface is still likely not to be entirely true. The more irregular the surface, the more cement you need.

On fairly smooth walls, panelboard cement can be spread with a small light board (or waste piece of tileboard) in which you have cut notches in one edge, at about ½″ intervals. Notches should be ¼″ deep, 5/16″ wide, with ⅜″ lands between them. These notches leave ridges of cement on the back of the tileboard panel. Apply cement to all parts of panel back, within 2″ of edges. Keep edges clean so board can be handled without smearing the work.

On very rough walls, cement can best be applied in spots. Daub small spots (about 1″ in diameter and ⅜″ thick) on 4″ centers both ways.

All surfaces to receive tileboard should be primed by applying a skim coat of panelboard cement. This provides a cement-to-cement contact and insures a secure bond.

Channels are not nailed to walls, but allowed to "float." The only exceptions are cap moldings and baseboards and outside corner moldings. These latter may be held in place with one nail at the top, one at the bottom, and one in the middle—driven through flange at the back of the channel.

Entrapment of air behind panels can be avoided by applying panel to wall first at the center and gradually pressing the surface toward each end, or first at one end, then gradually toward the other.

Before finishing the job, tap all over each panel to make sure it is solidly fastened. If not, press it firmly into place.

Fixtures and Finishing. On-set fixtures are recommended for use with tileboard. If a recessed fixture is already in place and must remain, such as a soapbox back of a tub, fit tileboard around it as for tub itself, and use tub return molding all around, observing the same waterproofing instructions. When you use on-set fixtures, nail or screw them through to firm studs or pieces of solid wood which have been set flush with the plaster before tileboard is applied.

Replace handles, faucets, and escutcheons removed when tileboard was applied.

CAP MOLDINGS AND BASES. These wooden finishing materials are nailed in place. Use a 1¼″ 17-gauge flat-head needle-point nail every 18″ for the cap, and two every 18″, driven at angles, for the base. Cap moldings can be nailed level by scribing a line above the top of the tileboard to serve as a top guide for the molding. Miter corners. Countersink nailheads; fill with putty and color with touch-up to match molding (fig. 80).

When linoleum cove base is being used, tileboard connector channel will make a satisfactory joint. The connector strip should be substituted for the metal cap strip of the cove base and firmly nailed to the wall. Tileboard is then installed as usual, with the bottom edge of the wall panels resting on the channel groove.

Frequently, pipe fittings on the spigot wall will be found to be too short after the thickness of tileboard

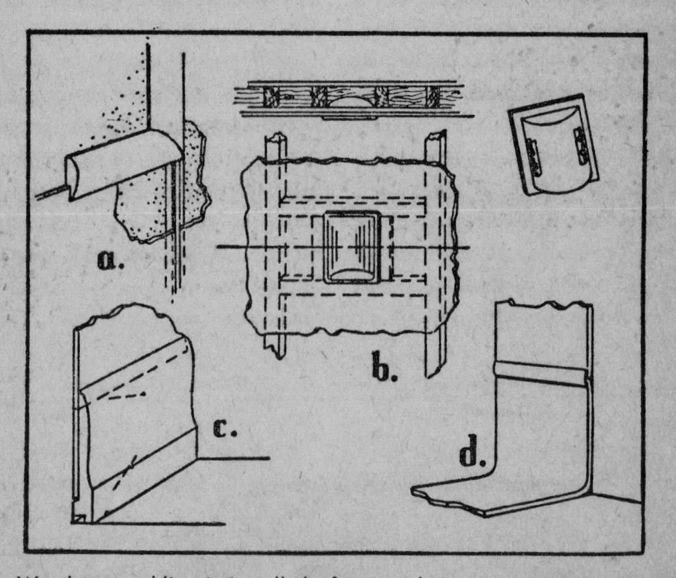

Fig. 80. **a.** Wood top molding is installed after panels are cemented in place. **b.** On-set type of fixtures is most suitable for tileboard job. Fixtures are installed after tileboard is in place. **c.** Base molding is nailed in place for bottom trim. Nails are driven at angles, two every 18". **d.** Where linoleum cove base is used, connector channel is used to link tileboard to linoleum.

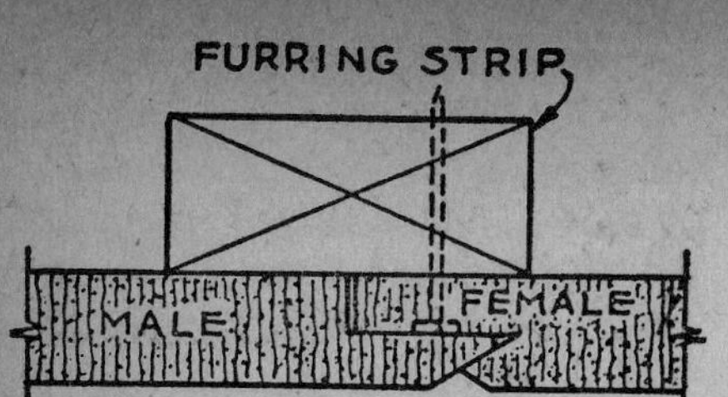

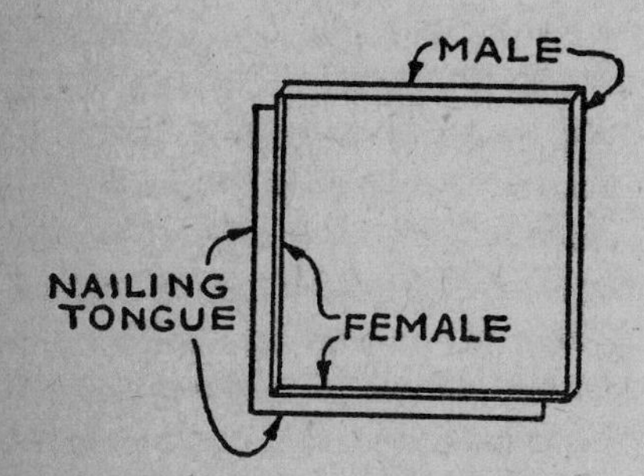

Fig. 81. Insulating board ceiling tile makes a satisfactory finish for new or old work. Each tile has two male edges and two female edges, which allows for concealed nailing and ease in installation.

is added. In these cases, longer fittings should be obtained to replace the short ones. Collars and handles should not be forced on where the fit is too tight.

MAINTENANCE. Mild soap and water will get tileboard clean, quickly and easily. Never use alcohol, strong chemicals, or coarse, abrasive cleaners. A mild cleanser may be used occasionally if necessary, and a paste wax can be used occasionally to maintain the brilliant surface of tileboard.

REPLACING CEILING TILE

Removing damaged ceiling tile and replacing with a new tile is a relatively simple job. First remove the damaged tile, leaving the tongue in place. The tongue can be removed from the tile with a knife or saw. Remove the nailing tongues from the new tile and slip it into position. In most cases it is possible to face nail the new tile into existing furring strips, but if this is impossible, nail a strip of wood to the sides of the furring strips to serve as a nailing base for the tile (figs. 82 and 83).

APPLYING CEILING PANELS

Do not apply direct to framing; always apply to furring strips. Place fasteners not more than 8″ apart along furring strip for all sizes of panels. "Back corner" fasteners must always be applied. Suspended ceiling construction should be held in align-

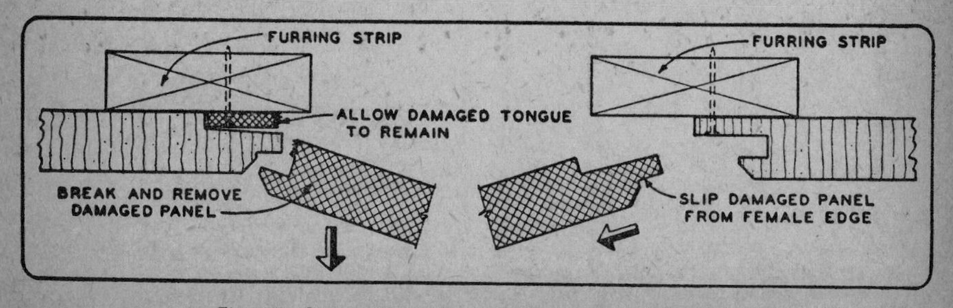

Fig. 82. Step one, replacing damaged ceiling tile.

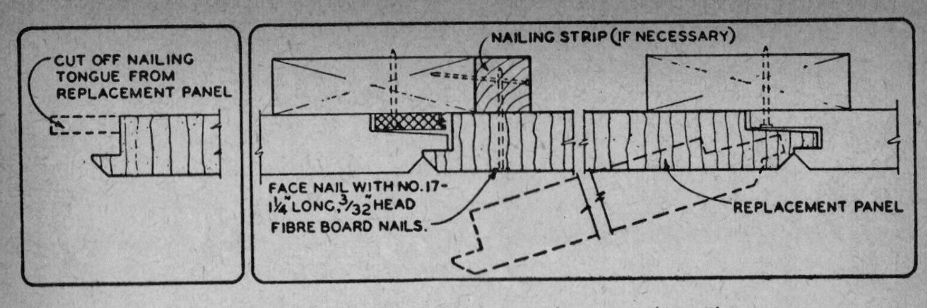

Fig. 83. Steps two and three, replacing ceiling tile.

ment by cross bracing of adequate size and spacing.

If used, batt-type insulation should be supported by wood lath, spaced 6″ on centers, laid across furring strips. Blown-type insulation must be supported by wire screen. Under no circumstances should insulation be supported by the ceiling panels.

Furring strips should be preferably of soft wood to facilitate nailing or stapling. If hard wood is used, care must be taken to replace fasteners that are bent, or in other ways provide unsatisfactory securement.

Open carton 24 hours prior to application to acclimate panels to temperature and moisture conditions. Figure 84 shows the general characteristics of a panel. Figures 85 and 86 show the preparation before installation begins.

Panels may be stapled, as in figure 87, or nailed, as in figure 88. Staples should be placed parallel to the nailing tongue. For concealed nailing, use 1⅛″ No. 13 blued plaster board nails with 5/16″ head driven flush with the surface of the nailing tongue. For exposed nailing, use 1¼″

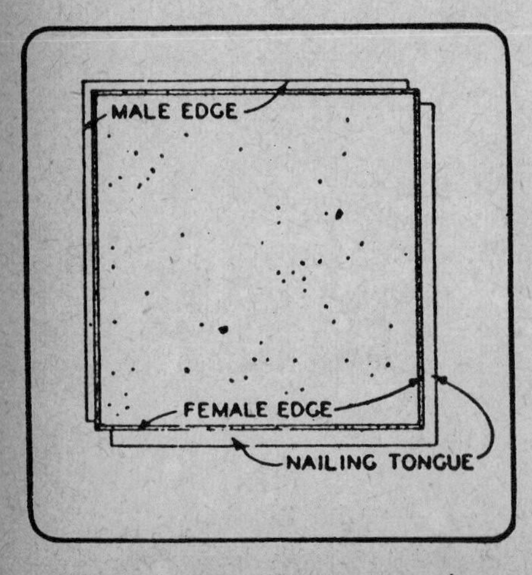

Fig. 84. Characteristics of panel.

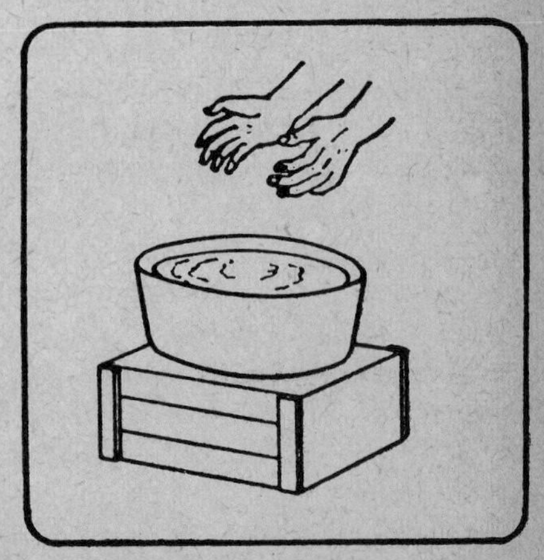

Fig. 85. Scrub hands thoroughly with soap and water.

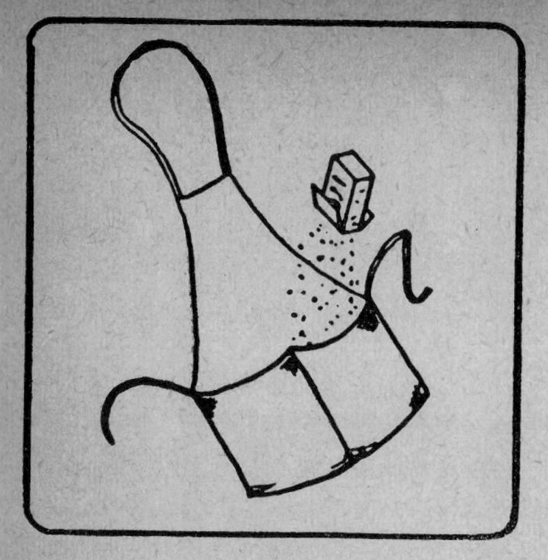

Fig. 86. Mix talc, whiting or corn starch with nails in apron to absorb moisture from hands.

Fig. 87.

No. 17 fibreboard nails with 3/32″ head, driven flush with the surface of the panel.

Panels may be cut with the razor-blade type of cutter, or sawed. Use a fine tooth saw and smooth the exposed cut edges with No. 0 sandpaper. Panels may also be readily grooved and beveled.

Figure 89 shows the method of laying out a ceiling. For example, if the width of the room is 8′6″ or 102″, divide 102″ by 12″ (assumed panel width). The result is 8 panels with 6″ over. Use 7 panels with 18″ over and divide 18″ in half. The result will be a 9″ border. If the length of the room is 10′8″ or 128″, divide 128″ by 12″ (assumed panel length). The result is 10 panels with 8″ over. Use 9 panels with 20″ over. Divide 20″ in half for a 10″ border.

Figures 90 to 92 show the application of furring strips. When applying over old work (fig. 90), sound for the joists; secure 1″x3″ furring at right angles to the joists, and use two nails at each joist. Shim where necessary to make level. Over new work (fig. 91), the procedure is the same, except that it is not necessary to sound for the joists. Figure 92 shows the proper spacing of furring with relation to the border or starting panel.

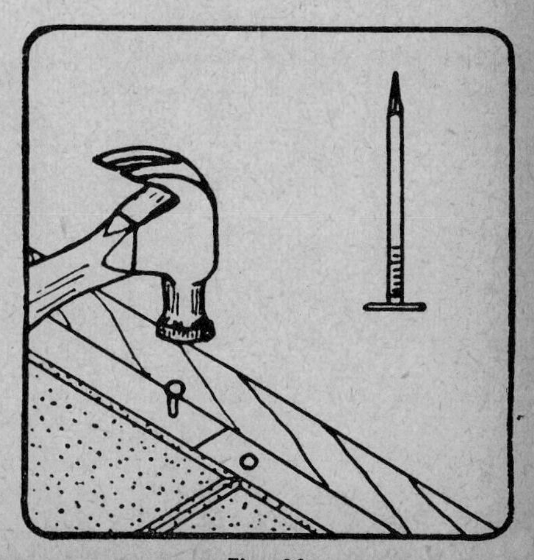

Fig. 88.

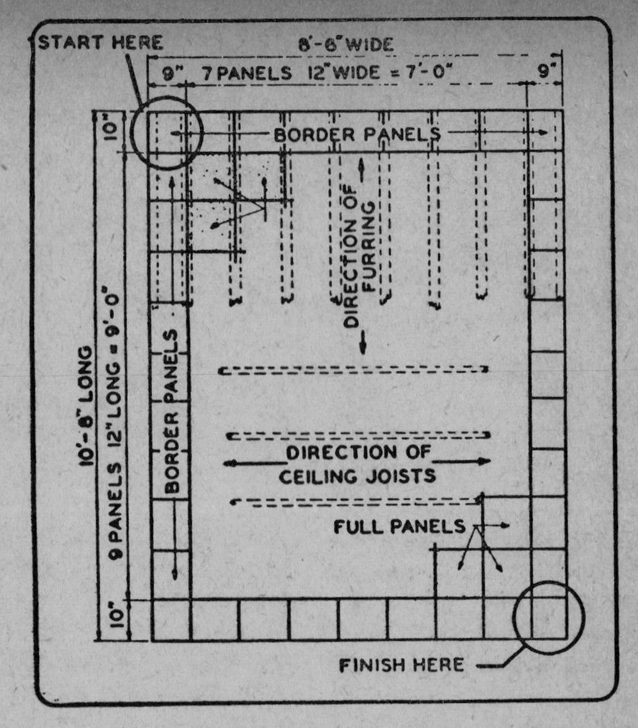

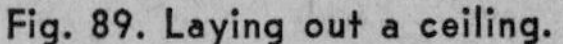
Fig. 89. Laying out a ceiling.

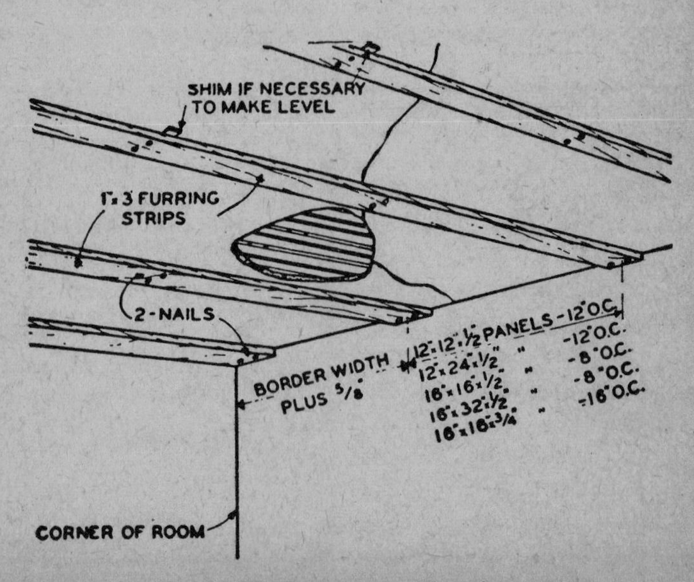

Fig. 90. Furring over old work.

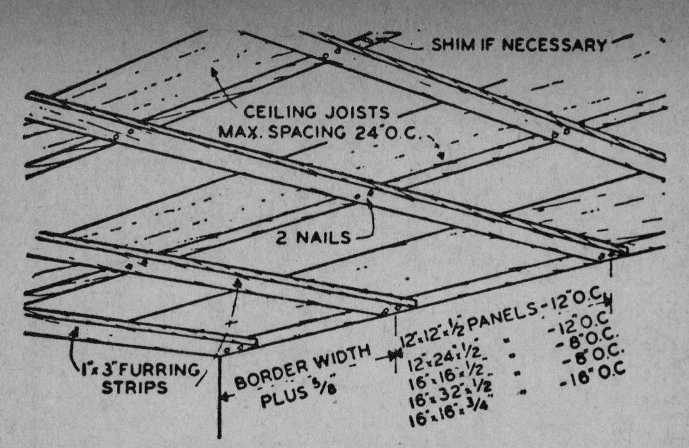

Fig. 91. Furring over new work.

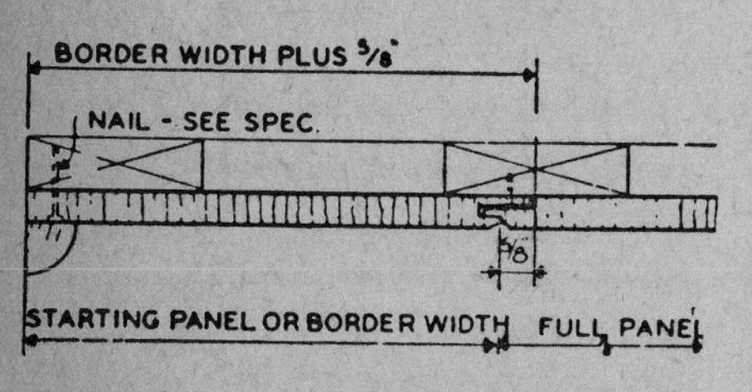

Fig. 92. Spacing of furring related to border.

In applying the panels themselves, fasteners of any kind should not be more than 8″ apart along the furring strip. In figure 93 is shown the application of the starting or border panel. With the nailing tongue facing the center of the area, apply this panel at the corner. Center the edge of the nailing tongue on the center line of furring.

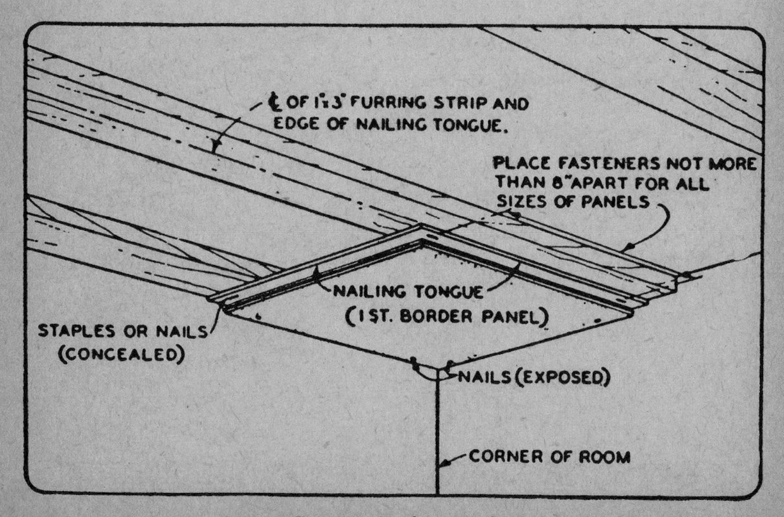

Fig. 93. Border panel.

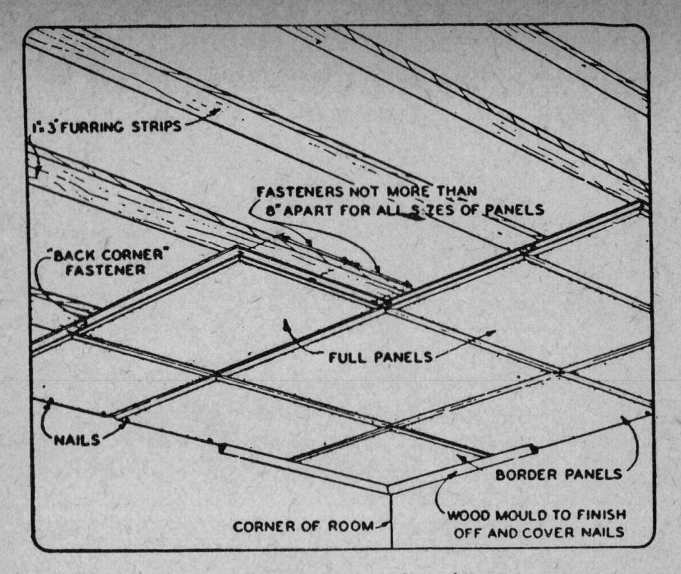

Fig. 94. Joints aligned.

Figure 94 shows the alignment of joints for panels ½″x12″x12″, ½″x12″x24″, and ¾″x16″x16″. Figure 95 shows the same for panels ½″x16″x16″ and ½″x16″x32″. Note the additional furring and fasteners for large size panels. To obtain a broken joint effect, apply panels as in figures 94

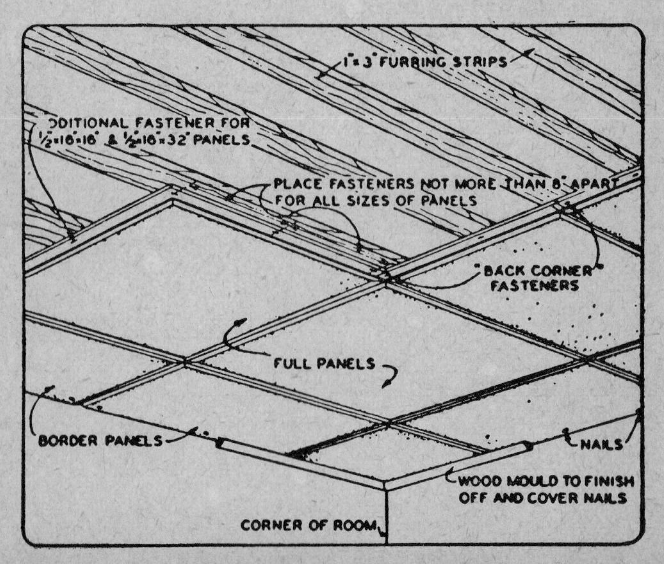

Fig. 95. Joints aligned, larger panels.

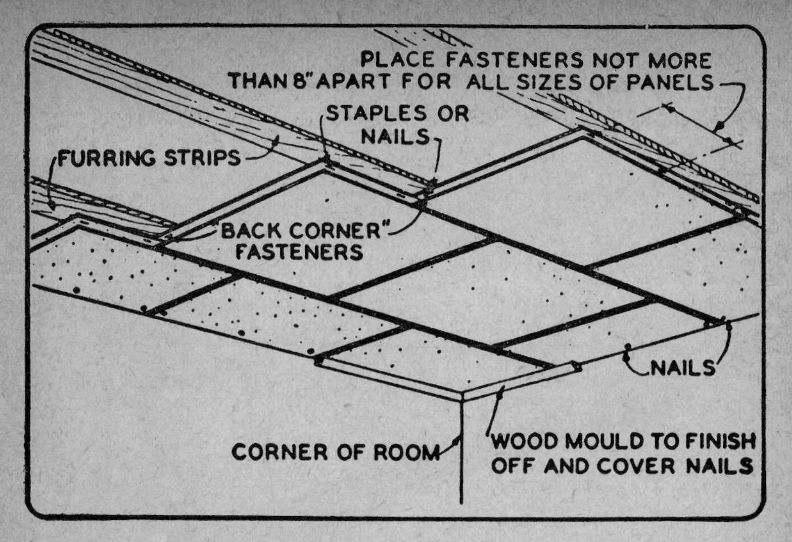

Fig. 96. Broken joints.

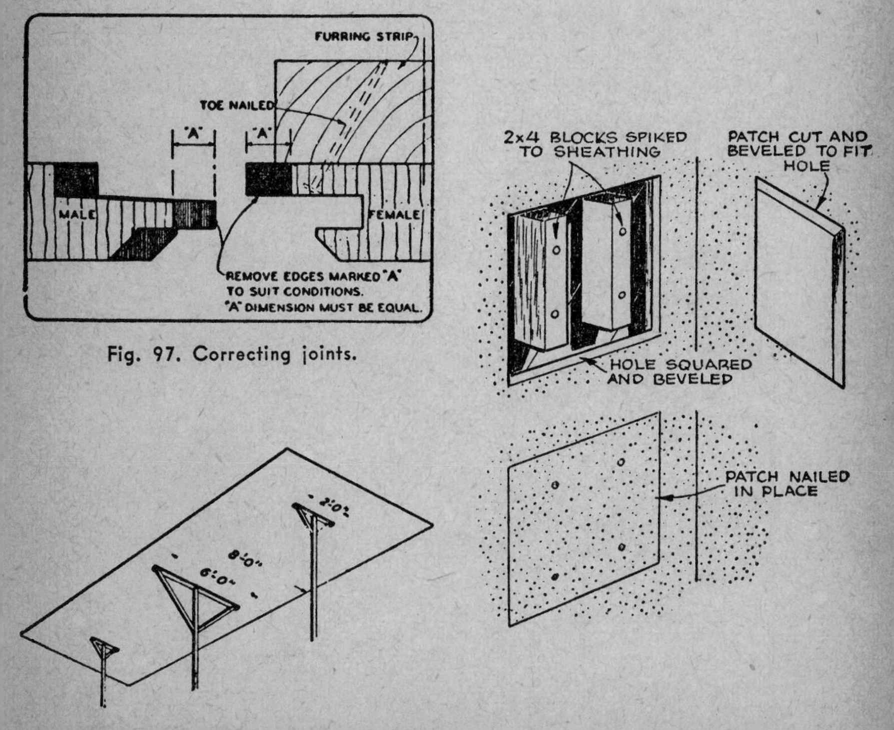

Fig. 97. Correcting joints.

Fig. 98. Use of three Tees for lifting 8' x 18' fiberboard panel to ceiling.

Fig. 99.

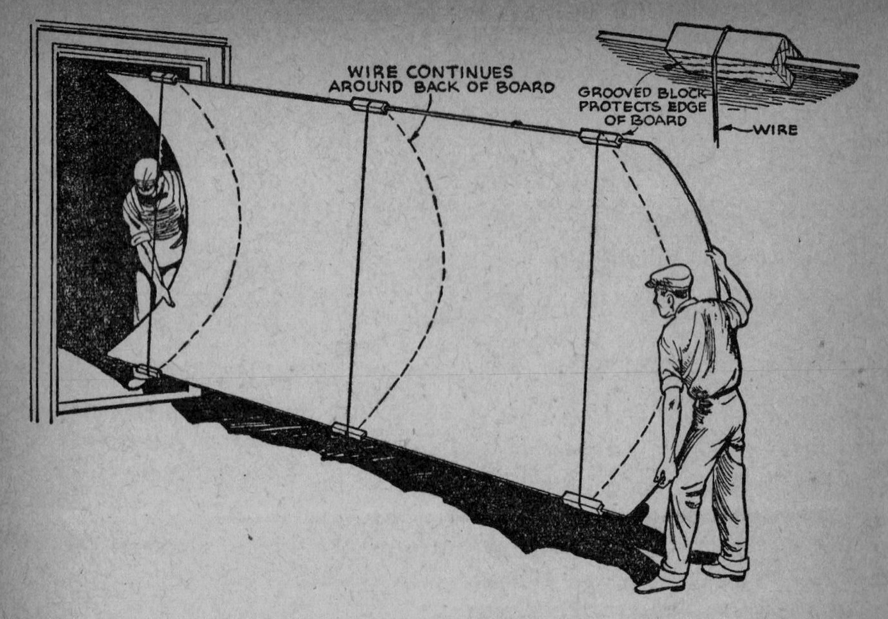

Fig. 100. Large sheets of hardboard can be handled easily by using blocks and wires to bend the sheets until they can be moved through doors and other openings. This procedure will also prevent the sheets from buckling easily.

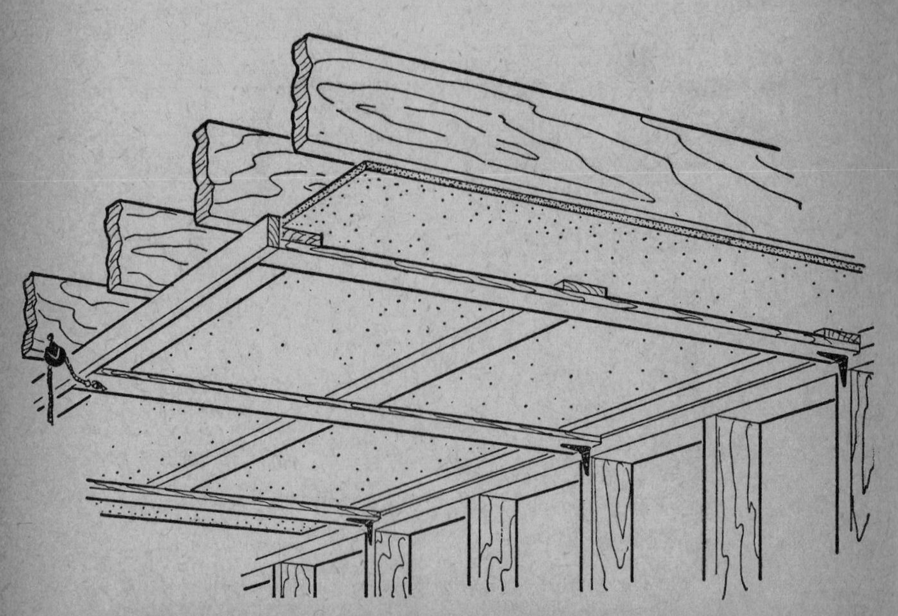

Fig. 101. A jig made out of 1" x 3" and hinged to the wall top plate is a great help when one man working alone is trying to cover a ceiling with large sheets of building board.

or 95, but start alternate courses with half panels.

If joints run off the furring strip, they may be corrected by removing equal amounts from the nailing tongue and the male edges. Correction should not exceed ⅛″ (fig. 97).

PATCHING WALLBOARD

It is often necessary to patch a section of wallboard. This can be accomplished so that the final result when papered or painted will not be conspicuous (fig. 99). The first step is to cut out the damaged area. The edges are given a slight bevel. The patch is then cut to size and its edges are also beveled. Next, two blocks of 2″x4″ are nailed to the sheathing to serve as a nailing base for the patch. When these are secure, the patch is faced nailed.

WATERPROOFING TILEBOARD

Many of the failures of wall tile and tileboard in the bathroom are due to moisture from the tub that gets up in back of the tile or tileboard and softens the cement holding the material to the plaster or plasterboard wall. Figure 102 shows one method of making a waterproof joint at this point.

GLASS PANELS

Glass panels, mounted to a plasterboard base for installation, make an ideal wall material for the bath, in back of the kitchen range, and at similar spots about the house. Fig-

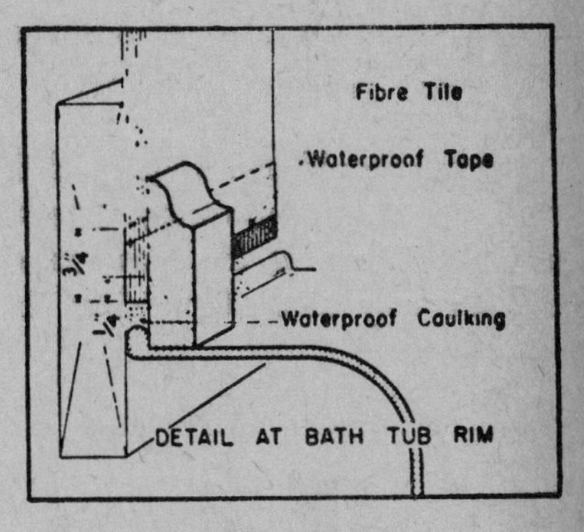

Fig. 102.

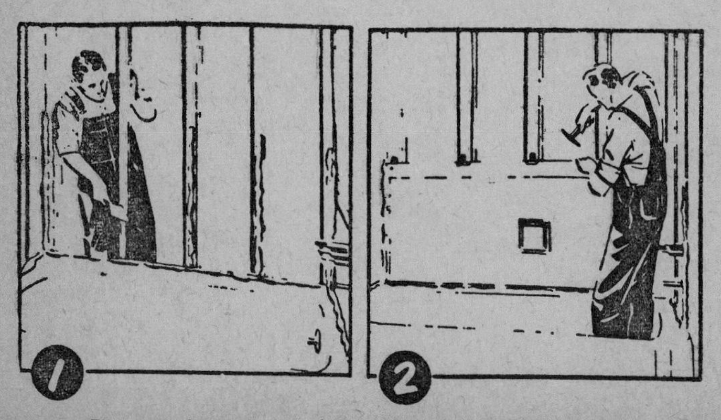

Fig. 103. Steps one and two in applying glass panels.

Fig. 104. Steps three and four in applying glass panels.

ures 103 and 104 show the method of installing this type of glass around a recessed bathtub. The same general instructions apply to other types of installation.

The tub should be levelled and the studs exposed, if necessary. The actual installation of the glass panels requires only four steps. The first step is to place a roll of mastic around the rim for waterproofing. Also, butter the studs with mastic before setting in the panels. The second step is to set in the plate at the back of the tub. Then, fasten plasterboard flanges to the studs, using the special clips obtainable with the panels. The third step is to do the same thing

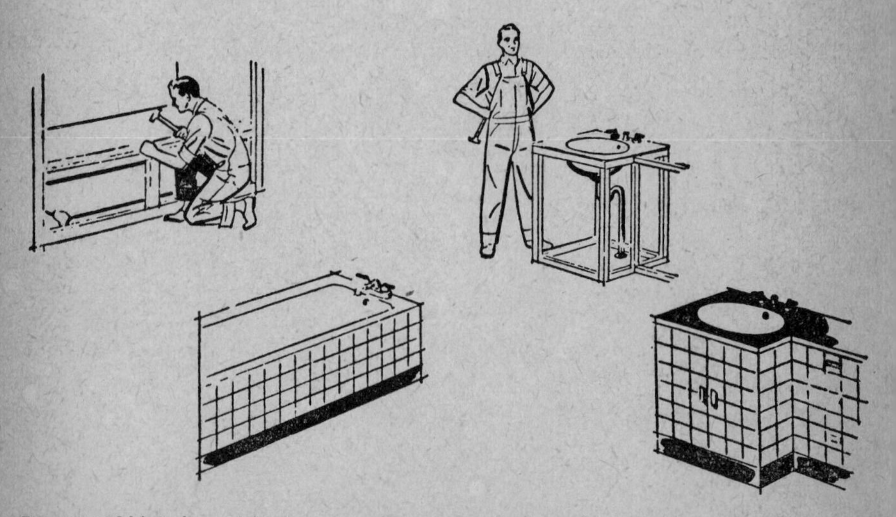

Fig. 105. Old fashioned bathroom equipment can be brought up to date by enclosing the fixture with sheets of tileboard. The frame to support the tileboard is made out of 2" x 2" stock. The tileboard is nailed to this with metal molding around joints and seams between the top of the tileboard and fixture.

with the end panels. Let the plasterboard extend beyond the tub to the next stud. If the wainscot is high enough, follow the same sequence in setting a second course. Then the final step is to clean the glass carefully and fill the joints with a pointing compound.

SIZES, THICKNESSES AND USES OF INSULATING BOARD PRODUCTS

Product	*Sizes*	*Thicknesses*	*Type of Edge*	*Major Uses*
Building Board (b)	4 x 6 ft., 4 x 7 ft. 4 x 8 ft., 4 x 9 ft. 4 x 10 ft., 4 x 12 ft.	½″, ¾″, 1″	Square	General purpose structural insulating board; interior finish, base for plastic paints, wall coverings and other interior decorative finishes.
Sheathing	4 x 8 ft., 4 x 8½ ft. 4 x 9 ft., 4 x 9½ ft. 4 x 10 ft., 4 x 12 ft.	½″, 25/32″	Square	Wall sheathing under siding, brick veneer, shingles or stucco, also as roof sheathing on pitched roofs under various types of roofing. Also to insulate floors of basementless houses.
	2 x 8 ft.	25/32″	Long edges fabricated (a), short edges square	
Lath	16″ x 48″ 18″ x 48″ 24″ x 48″	½″, 1″	Long edges fabricated (a)	Insulating plaster base for walls, partitions and ceilings.
Roof Insulation	23″ x 47″ Note (c)	½″, 1″ 1½″, 2″	Square edges on ½″ thickness. Square edges and/or offset on 1″, 1½″ and 2″ thickness.	For roof insulation under built-up roofing on flat roofs and under certain types of roofing on pitched roofs. Floor insulation for masonry floors.
Tileboard (Panels)	8″ x 8″ 12″ x 12″ 12″ x 24″ 16″ x 16″ 16″ x 32″	½″, ¾″, 1″	Fabricated edges (a)	Decorative, insulating wall and ceiling panels. Frequently used in conjunction with building board and plank.
Plank	Widths: 8″, 10″, 12″ and 16″, Lengths: 6′, 8′, 10′, 12′	½″	Fabricated long edges (a)	Decorative, insulating wall and ceiling finish. Frequently used in conjunction with building board and tileboard (panels).

(a) Fabricated edges means any type of edge treatment other than square edges without reinforcement.
(b) Standard colors and finishes of Building Board are (1) natural finish on both surfaces and (2) one surface natural and the other with light colored finish such as white, ivory, cream or buff.
(c) Also available in a 22″ x 47″ size.

SECTION VIII

PAINTS, PAINTING, FINISHES

Brushes—Keep Brush Clean—Used Brushes—Reclaiming Brushes—Deep-Dipping Spoils Brush—Power Paint Equipment—Spraying Machines—Paint Preparation—Color Blending—Painting Masonry—Home-Mixed Cement Paint—Paint Precautions—Paint Dipping—Clean Before Painting—Smooth the Surface—Dust First—Putty Practices—Spray Painting—Tinting Paints—Painting Interior Wood—Transparent Finishes for Wood—Painting Screens and Frames—Painting near Seashore—Estimating Painting Needs.

SECTION VIII

PAINTS, PAINTING, FINISHES

BRUSHES

Figure 1 shows various kinds of standard paint brushes for various uses. The types and uses are identified as follows:

1, 2, and *3.* Standard 2-, 3-, and 4-inch black china-bristle wall brushes for paint.

4 and *5.* Standard 1- and 2½-inch fitch brushes for shellac, lacquers, and varnishes. Bristles are skunk and black china, single-thick.

6 and *7.* Standard 1- and 4-inch pure badger brushes for varnish-flowing; triple-thick; full chisel.

8. Standard 1½-inch white Russian bristles for varnish-flowing and enameling; double-thick; full chisel.

9 and *10.* Standard 1- and 3-inch camel's-hair bristles, used only for color coats on undercoatings for a varnish schedule on automobile.

11. Standard 3-inch bear bristles for shellac, lacquer, varnish, and enamel; double-thick; full chisel.

12 and *13.* Standard 2-inch Siberian ox-hair bristles for shellac, lacquer, varnish, and enamel: single- and double-thick respectively; full chisel.

14, 15, and *16.* Standard 2/0, 6/0 and 8/0 black china oval, painter's general-purpose paint and varnish brushes; brush (*15*) has tin bridle.

17 and *18.* Standard ½- and 1-inch molding, scrubbing, or rubbing brushes for pumice and oil rubbing or for cleaning work.

19, 20, and *21.* Standard 1-, 2-, and 3-inch black china-bristle, full-chisel, varnish-flowing household general-purpose brush.

22. Standard 2½-inch round painter's duster.

23. Standard 4-inch flat painter's brush.

24, 25, 26, and *27.* Standard ½-, ¾-, 1-, and 1½-inch oval sash tools for painting window sash; black china bristles.

KEEP BRUSH CLEAN

A thoroughly clean paint brush is absolutely essential to good workmanship. Any bristle brush can be readily cleaned, while it is still soft, with the proper thinner for the product in which it has been used. Use turpentine, followed by naphtha or mineral spirits, for a brush which has been in an oil base finish (paint, enamel or varnish). Alcohol should be used for a brush that has been in shellac or alcohol stain. A brush which has been in lacquer should be cleaned with a lacquer thinner—preferably one made by the same

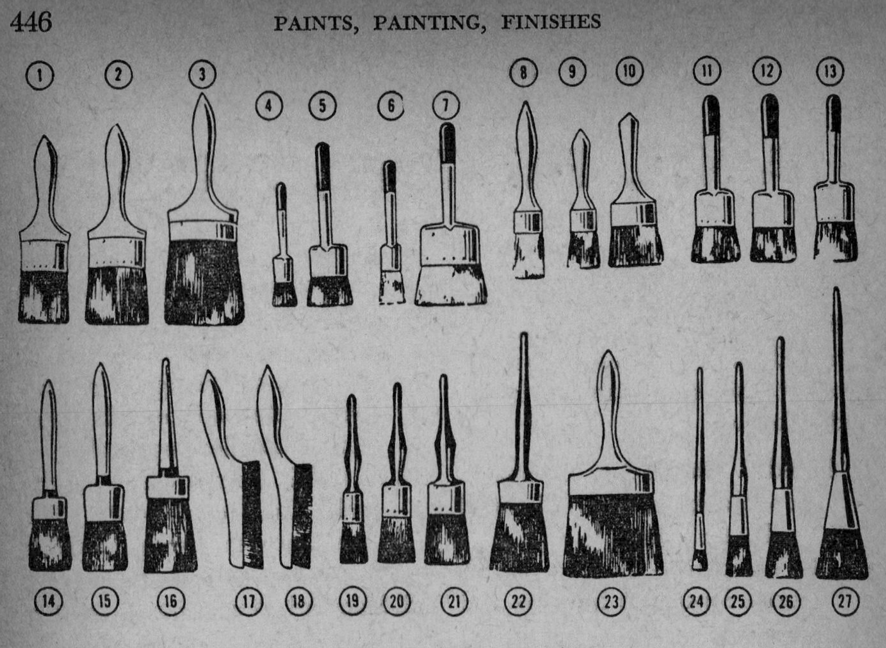

Fig. 1. Various kinds of brushes.

manufacturer who made the lacquer in which the brush was used. Brushes which have been in calcimine, emulsions and other water-thinned paints should be cleaned in water.

Brushes made of pure hog bristles are almost worth their weight in gold these days. Due to the continuing chaos in China, they are exceedingly hard to obtain.

Any new paint or varnish brush may have a few loose bristles. These can be easily removed by tapping the brush gently against the hand and twirling it rapidly between the palms. Any loose bristles which appear in the process can then be pulled out. Finally, the bristles should be combed straight.

Before using a new brush, rinse it in mineral spirits, benzol, or alcohol, and dry by spinning the handle.

USED BRUSHES

Quick-drying paints require prompt cleaning of brushes. To remove oil paints, suspend brush in linseed oil or mineral spirits with bristles submerged but not resting on the bottom of the container; or rinse brush in mineral spirits, wash with soap and warm water, and rinse in warm water. Dry by spinning; then wrap the bristles in strong paper and lay the brush flat. Remove varnishes and enamels with turpentine, mineral spirits, or acetone. Remove shellac with alcohol. Use benzol to wash out both synthetic- and natural-rubber paint.

You can readily remove casein paint with the application of cold water. However, never leave any brush standing in water.

RECLAIMING BRUSHES

To reclaim a worn brush, soak it in a commercial cleaner or in paint remover. Leave it until the bristles are soft and pliable. A mixture of equal quantities of alcohol, acetone, and benzol is also useful in softening bristles. If bristles are badly bent, soak the brush in machine oil and lay it on a heated piece of metal until the oil in the bristles sizzles. While the brush is still hot, reshape and bind the bristles with metal strips or wire. After the brush has cooled, wash it in mineral spirits and rinse with benzol or acetone. Keep the brush wrapped in paper.

DEEP-DIPPING SPOILS BRUSH

Brushes should not be dipped too deeply into paint—just far enough so that, after tapping or wiping lightly against the inner side of the container, they will carry the paint to the job without dripping. Dipping too deep not only wastes paint, but soon spoils a brush by causing a collection of hardened paint to accumulate at the heel of the brush. The heel is the part nearest the ferrule.

POWER PAINT EQUIPMENT

Power equipment normally available includes spray guns, paint mixers, sanders, wire brushes, and floor-buffing machines.

Shaking type paint mixer. Shaking type mixers are used for paint containing highly volatile thinners. These mixers handle as little as ½ pint of paint to as much as four 1-gallon cans. They are electrically operated, blending paint materials together by shaking them in tightly closed containers. Motors must be explosion-proof.

Propeller type paint mixer. The propeller type mixer is used to stir large quantities of paint in open containers. Paint is agitated by propellers or paddles attached to an electrically rotated shaft. For safety, the motor must be explosion-proof.

Spray guns. Spray paint guns are now furnished in a variety of types and sizes. With their use, paint can be applied 5 to 10 times faster than by brush. They are very useful for painting rough surfaces that would wear a brush to pieces. A small gun is used for stenciling, touch-up work, and small jobs.

SPRAYING MACHINES

Special spraying devices are used extensively for applying paints to large interior surfaces and in factories for finishing automobiles, furniture, hardware, and machinery. The results first obtained with exterior spray painting did not compare very favorably with those obtained with brush painting, but as the machines have been improved and more experience gained spray painting has become more satisfactory. A good operator can cover a surface adapted to spray painting as well by using a good machine as by hand brushing and in much less time. This method is particularly good for large surfaces with few openings and little or no trimming. As spray painting outfits are expensive and experience and practice are necessary for their successful operation, this method will be used almost entirely by painting contractors and others who have a great deal of painting to do. With an air brush or paint gun the space is covered so quickly that it must be done right the first time. Any attempt at improvements by going over the same surface a number of times results in too much paint.

The only kind of spray painting that does not require the service of an expert is whitewashing. When properly thinned and strained whitewash can be applied with a bucket or barrel-spraying outfit, such as is used for spraying fruit trees. The nozzle for Bordeaux mixture is suitable for whitewash. Application of white-wash with a high-pressure spray pump is better than brushing because it insures penetration of cracks and crevices.

PAINT PREPARATION

If possible, mix paint materials in the paint shop or mixing room, using a strong, smooth, wood paddle or a mechanical agitator. When using a paddle, work pigment up from bottom of container, stirring until pigment is blended with the liquid.

If pigment has settled in a hard cake, use a mechanical mixer if possible. If hand stirring is necessary, pour the liquid into another container and break up the pigment with a paddle. Pour the liquid back little by little until the mixture is homogeneous, and *box* it by pouring from one container to another, until pigment and liquid form a smooth mixture. Paint purchased under Federal specifications may be rejected if it cannot be stirred to a smooth mixture fairly easily.

To keep unused portions of white lead or colors in oil soft and free from skins, scrape lead or color from sides of the container, sealing the contents from air.

Mixing procedures vary with each paint material. Varnishes and shellac contain no pigment and do not require stirring.

Paste in oil. After opening container, mix in any free oil on top of paste and break up the paste until mixture is smooth. Put the specified amount of paste into mixing can and measure linseed oil, thinner, and drier as required by formula. Add oil in small quantities, followed by the thinner and the drier. Strain this preparation through cheesecloth or a wire mesh to remove lumps and any foreign matter. This improves brushing qualities.

Ready-mixed paint. To prepare or reduce ready-mixed paint, place unopened cans holding 1 gallon or less in a vibrator type mixer for 3 to 10 minutes. Stir paint in large containers with a propeller type mixer. Make any required additions of oil, thinner, or colors after the paint has been mechanically mixed.

Enamel. Use small propeller agitators or hand stirring when mixing enamel. Mechanical shakers cause enamel to bubble or froth, requiring a settling period of from 6 to 8 hours.

COLOR BLENDING

In blending colors, it should be remembered that different samples of the same color vary considerably in strength and tone. The same quantity will not always produce the same result. The names used by different manufacturers for their pigments vary so much that directions given to produce a certain tint may give entirely different results with different brands.

Subduing bright and glaring colors. Colors in paste form that are too bright and glaring may be corrected by adding small amounts of their complementary colors. Yellow is made less intense by adding a little blue and red; blue, by adding a little red and yellow; and red, by adding a little yellow and blue.

Except in rare instances, the addition of black to dull a bright color causes a muddy appearance.

Production of tints. The following illustrations are given as a guide to the production of tints by mixing pastes of different colors:

1. Gray. White lead mixed with lampblack will produce gray from the lightest shade to the darkest, depending upon the proportions of each pigment used. One percent of lampblack will produce a strong "cold, steel-gray" tint. A strong warm gray tint may be obtained by adding a little yellow ocher or sienna to the cold gray tint. If burnt umber is used instead of the ocher or sienna, a series of gray drabs will be obtained.

2. Buff. White lead tinted with yellow ocher will give buff. Cream color results from adding a touch of Venetian red to light buff. Ivory, a tint closely related to cream, is produced by adding a very little medium chrome yellow to white lead. Drab "stone" color is obtained by mixing together about five parts white lead paste, two parts yellow ocher or chrome yellow in oil, and one part burnt umber in oil. Yellow drab will result if the proportions for producing the drab "stone" color are varied.

3. Brown Shades. To produce these shades, mix in varying proportions about three parts Indian red or Venetian red in oil, two parts lampblack in oil, and one part yellow ocher in oil. Umber may replace the lampblack and ocher. Brown drabs may be obtained by adding white lead in oil to the brown shades.

4. Pink. To produce pink, tint zinc oxide with madder lake, carmine, or crimson shades of English vermilion. Purple or lilac is made by tinting white lead with dark Indian red. A small amount of light Indian red may improve the purple effect.

5. Brick Reds. To obtain brick reds, mix about two parts yellow ocher, one part Venetian red, and one part white lead, the exact color depending upon the proportions used.

6. Sapphire Blue. Tint zinc white with ultramarine blue to produce sapphire blue. Sky blue of various depths is produced by adding Prussian blue to white lead.

7. Chrome Green. This green may be obtained by mixing Prussian blue and chrome yellow, which may be further modified by the addition of white, black, or some other color.

Pea green is white lead tinted with medium chrome green (1 part to 100). Apple green is pea green tinted with a little chrome yellow. Bronze green is obtained by adding lampblack to a dark chrome green. A richer effect may be obtained by using a medium chrome green as a base and adding ivory, black, and a small amount of raw umber. Quaker green, a dull green, is produced by darkening white lead and yellow ocher with lampblack and burnt sienna.

Matching Colors. With practice a very good match of a given paint can be obtained, although exact matching requires much skill. Therefore, sufficient paint to cover all surfaces for final-coat painting should be made up at one time.

PAINTING MASONRY

Masonry wall types for best paint results can be rated as follows: (1) New cement-asbestos shingle-faced wall, (2) stone-concrete block, (3) cinder-concrete block, (4) new common brick, (5) lightweight-aggregate-concrete block, (6) cast concrete, and (7) used common brick wall.

Cement-water paints are a decorative and durable coating on exterior walls. The method of applying and curing cement-water paints and the conditions under which painting is done are more important than the composition of the paints, but the portland cement content should not be less than 65 percent by weight of the total paint.

The use of sharp sand in cement-water paint or a priming coat of grout improves the durability of subsequent organic coatings on open-textured walls or those having cracks or other defects.

Ordinary white portland cement or admixtures of cement and lime also give good results. For improved decorative value, the cement coating can be painted with an exterior masonry oil-base, resin-emulsion, or rubber-solution paint.

Cement-water paints should be used for the initial painting of new masonry with the possible exception of cast concrete poured against oiled forms. Further coatings are not necessary, but can be used if desired. A synthetic rubber paint can be applied immediately after the cement-water paint dries, but it is recommended that the cement-water paint age for at least 2 weeks before application of resin-emulsion paints and 3 months before the application of oil-base paints.

Resin-emulsion paints have good decorative qualities and are durable on exterior masonry walls. For open-textured surfaces and brick walls having cracks around the mortar joints, the surface should be treated with a base coat of grout or cement-water paint containing sharp sand before resin-emulsion paint is applied. Resin-emulsion paints have good hiding power and are easy to apply by brush or spray to damp or dry walls. New masonry walls should be allowed to age for at least 3 weeks before painting.

Oil-base paints can be used on open-textured masonry surfaces that have been treated to prevent infiltration of moisture or on close-textured masonry. Both should be allowed to age for a period of from 6 to 12 months before painting. It is essential that walls be dry at the time of painting and be so constructed or so treated as to remain dry after painting. If these coatings are applied to a wet wall or one that becomes wet through structural defects, early failure by scaling and flaking may occur.

Oil-base paints have good serviceability and weather by chalking. This property tends to make them self-cleaning and lessens their tendency to be discolored by dirt and stain.

A grout composed of portland cement and sharp sand is recommended as a base coat on open-textured surfaces such as stone- and cinder-concrete block, lightweight-aggregate-concrete block, and new and used common brick with joints which have not been tooled. The grout should be allowed to age at least 90 days. It may be applied immediately upon erection of the wall or at any time during the aging period of from 6 to 12 months.

If there is a possibility that the wall is damp or contains soluble salts, a protective primer, such as rubber-solution paint, should be used as a first coat over the grout. In this case, one coat of the oil-base paint should be sufficient to give a good finish. Two coats, however, will give greater durability.

Synthetic-rubber paints may be applied to either dry or slightly damp wall surfaces but should not be used on wet surfaces as excessive moisture may prevent adequate bond. These paints are of two types, rubber-emulsion and rubber-solution.

The rubber-solution type is similar in composition to an oil paint except that a rubber resin is used in the vehicle in place of synthetic or natural resin. It may be brushed or sprayed and can be used either as a protective primer under oil-base or resin-emulsion paint or as a complete paint system. Two coats give adequate hiding and good durability. On open-textured surfaces, cement-sand grout should be used and allowed to dry from 3 to 6 days. Rubber-solution paint is particularly suitable for application on cement-asbestos shingles or siding, but will give good service on other masonry surfaces.

HOME-MIXED CEMENT PAINT

Mix thoroughly 15 to 25 pounds of hydrated lime with each bag (96 lbs.) of cement. White portland cement is most commonly used but ordinary cement can be used if a gray color is satisfactory. Twenty-five to 65 lbs. of fine sand (passing No. 100 to No. 20 sieve) to every bag of cement may be mixed in for the first coat. The sand improves the effectiveness of the paint especially on open-texture surfaces such as on cinder blocks.

Tinted paint may be obtained by adding high grade mineral coloring. Two lbs. of calcium chloride dissolved in a quart of water may be added for each 100 lbs. of cement and lime used. The calcium chloride is not absolutely necessary but speeds up hardening of the paint and aids in proper curing. When the above ingredients are thoroughly mixed pour in enough water to make a stiff paste and stir until all particles are wetted. Add more water until a rich cream consistency is obtained. Make only the quantity of paint which can be applied in 3 to 4 hours in cool weather and in less time during hot weather.

PAINT PRECAUTIONS

Do not use white-lead paints in places where they will come in contact with drinking water, silage, or food products.

Do not inhale the dust when scraping or sandpapering surfaces coated with lead paints. If dust cannot be avoided, cover the mouth and nose with loose cotton inclosed in several thicknesses of cheesecloth or with a respirator or mask. Keep the skin as free as possible from paint and thoroughly clean the hands before eating, using oil or grease to remove most of the paint, followed by soap and water.

Handling food with hands that are covered with lead paint is a dangerous practice.

When painting or varnishing indoors keep the windows opened enough to permit free circulation of air.

Keep paints, varnishes, oils, and thinners away from heat and flames; they are inflammable.

Dispose of all rags or waste containing paint, varnish, or oil in such a way as to avoid the possibility of a fire resulting from spontaneous combustion.

PAINT DIPPING

Dipping is another labor-saving method of paint application confined chiefly to factory practice. Articles varying in size from toys to parts of large machines are coated in this way. When the paint is especially well adapted to the purpose and the drying conditions are properly controlled, the coating is continuous, uniform, and durable.

The only other common use of the dipping method is in painting or staining shingles. Shingles should be dipped to cover about two-thirds their length and should be kept in the material long enough to thoroughly color the surface. They should then be set in a trough, tipped to permit the excess of liquid to drain back into the dipping vessel. Shingles that have been dipped in paint should be brushed lightly on both sides to remove the excess.

CLEAN BEFORE PAINTING

Painting should never be done on any type of surface which is not completely free from dirt, grease, rust, or loose particles of old paint.

Before painting, new galvanized-metal surfaces need to be brushed with a special solution. This can be a fairly strong vinegar solution, a solution made up of eight ounces of copper acetate, of copper chloride or copper sulphate in a gallon of water. There are also solutions manufactured especially for the purpose which are readily available at paint stores.

SMOOTH THE SURFACE

Spackling compound may be looked upon as a kind of plaster which is used to fill surface irregularities and cracks in plaster. Hardly an interior paint job exists that will not be better if nail holes, screw holes, dents made by hammers or areas where paint has scaled off, have been carefully leveled with a spackling or surfacing compound. Some of these compositions are made with wood flour and lacquer. They are especially useful on wood. Spackling compound, when mixed with paste paint, is known as Swedish putty. Also used for filling such cracks—especially large ones—is patching plaster.

DUST FIRST

Before painting is started in a room, careful dusting is highly important. It should be done immediately before painting starts. Work should be done from the top of the room downward.

PUTTY PRACTICES

Putty is generally associated in the layman's mind with the glazing of window sash, but to the painter it means a very handy material for a variety of jobs—filling nail holes, filling cracks in upright wood surfaces, filling floor cracks, filling rough spots on sawed-off board ends, etc.

The principal use of glazier's putty is for fastening window glass in sash. If it is made properly and of suitable ingredients, it will give practically a lifetime of service. The ideal glazing putty is one which does not adhere to the hand or putty knife, but which does adhere indefinitely to glass and wood. It also spreads readily, does not sag after it is applied, and remains soft enough to be easily removed in case the glass needs replacement. When inserting glass into new window frames, it is important to see that new wood is carefully primed before the putty is applied and that the putty when it has set, is given a protective coating.

SPRAY PAINTING

Make certain that the surface to be sprayed is correctly prepared, that paint material is of proper consistency, and that spraying equipment is properly adjusted and operated. Preparation of various surfaces is treated in later sections. Enamels and lacquers containing high proportions of volatile thinners must usually be thinner for spraying than for brushing.

Operating spray gun. Operators of paint-spraying equipment should be thoroughly familiar with the equipment and its maintenance. Keep manufacturer's data available for ready reference.

When hoses have been attached to air and material connections, the spray gun is ready for operation. Practice on a piece of material similar to that being sprayed to check adjustment and operation of the gun. There is no set rule for spray-gun pressure because it varies considerably with the nozzle combination,

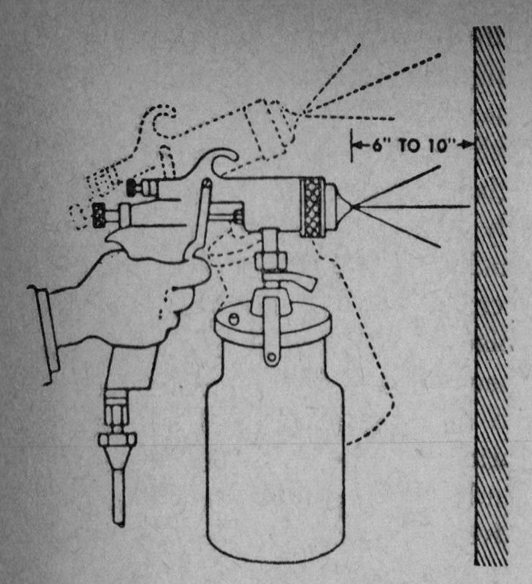

Fig. 2. Spray gun held perpendicular to surface to prevent uneven deposit of paint.

the paint used, and the surface to be coated. On most guns, turn the air-control screw clockwise for a round spray, and counterclockwise for a fan spray. Turn the material-control screw clockwise to decrease the flow and counterclockwise to increase it. As the width of the spray is increased, increase the flow of paint to get the same coverage on the wider area.

Spray-gun stroke. Always keep the spray as nearly perpendicular as possible to the surface being painted. This prevents dusting, a condition in which paint spray evaporates and hits the surface in nearly dry particles (fig. 2). Tilting the gun as shown by dotted lines in figure 2 causes paint to be sprayed on one side from a shorter distance, applying more paint at this point.

Use a free arm motion and feather-cut each end of the stroke. This is done by pulling the gun trigger after beginning the stroke and releasing it before the stroke is completed. Do not arc the gun; this causes an uneven deposit of paint and excessive overspray at the ends of the stroke (fig. 3).

The consistency of the paint and the thickness of coating desired usually determine the speed of spraying. Make a few trial sprays and adjust the gun for a speed consistent

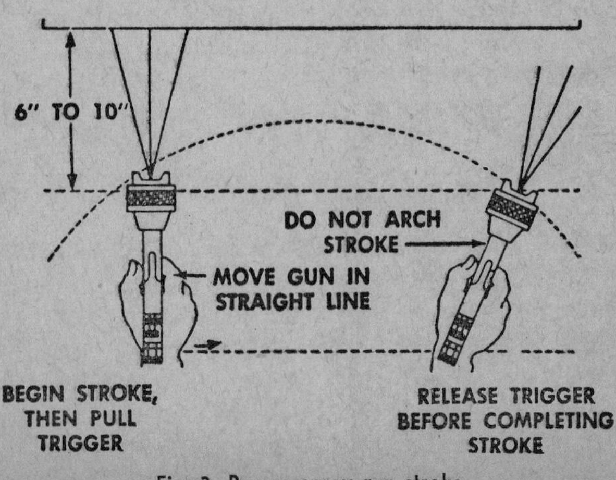

Fig. 3. Proper spray-gun stroke.

with the ability of the operator and the desired finish.

Spraying corners. When approaching a corner, stop 1 or 2 inches short of the corner. Holding the gun in the position shown in figure 4, spray the entire corner in one operation. When the corner is sprayed as indicated in figure 5, paint is wasted and in addition the adjacent surface is oversprayed which results in sags in the finish.

Spray patterns. Normal spray patterns are shown in figure 6. Distorted patterns are caused by improper technique or mechanical difficulties.

Paint clogging. Clogging of the side ports by dried paint restricts the passage of air, so that the full air pressure from the clean side port forces the fan pattern in the direction of the clogged side (*1*, fig. 7). Dissolve the dried material with thinner. Do not use a metal instrument on

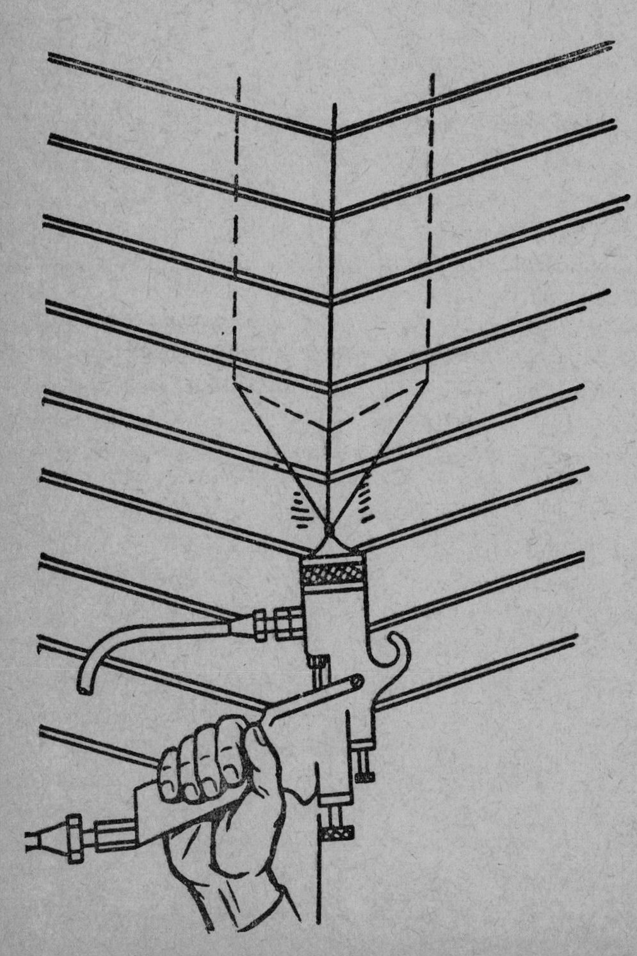

Fig. 4. Correct method of spraying corners.

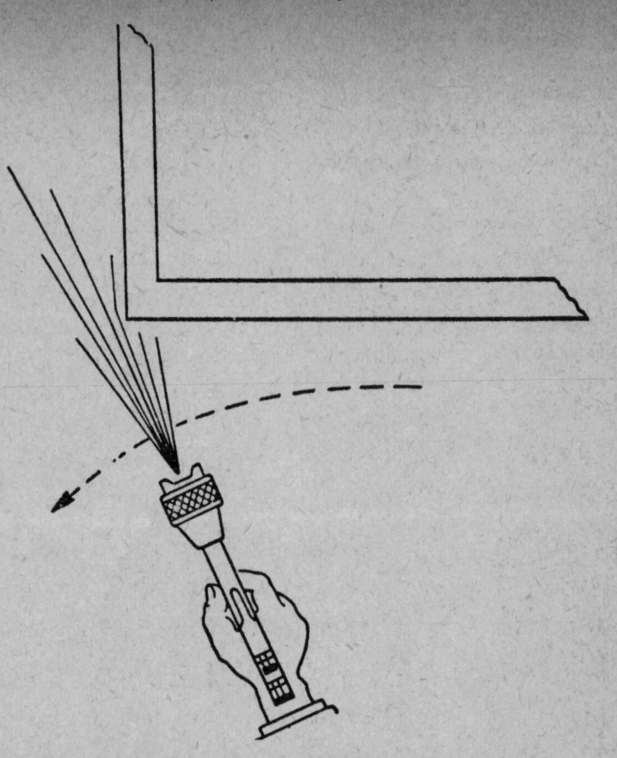

Fig. 5. Incorrect method of spraying corners.

openings, because this may enlarge or mutilate them. If reaming is necessary, use a match stick, broomstraw, or any other soft implement. The pattern shown in *2,* figure 7, results when dried material around the outside of the material-nozzle tip restricts the passage of air through the center opening of the air nozzle. Remove the air nozzle and wipe off the paint-nozzle tip with thinner. This pattern may also be caused by a loose air nozzle.

Atomizing pressure. Too high an atomizing pressure causes a split spray (*3,* fig. 7), while a fan spray that is heavy in the middle or has a salt-and-pepper appearance is a result of low pressure (*4,* fig. 7). If the air pressure is correct, a split pattern may be caused by attempting to get too wide a spray with thin material. To correct this fault, open the material-control needle valve to full position by turning the regulating screw to the left. At the same time, turn the spray-width adjustment screw to the right. This reduces width of the spray, but corrects split patterns.

Spitting. Spitting is the alternate discharge of paint and air or paint and water. The four principal causes of spitting and best corrective measures are hereon discussed:

1. If packing around the material-control needle valve is dried, back up the knurled nut and place two drops of machine oil on the packing. It is sometimes necessary to replace packing.

2. If material nozzle is loose or there is dirt between the material-nozzle seat and the body, clean the back of the nozzle and nozzle seat with thinner and put them back tightly against the body.

3. If swivel nuts fit poorly on the siphon cup or material hose, replace the defective nuts.

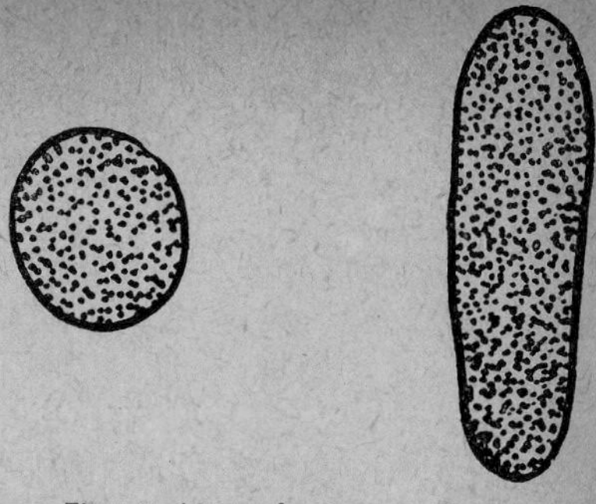

Fig. 6. Normal spray patterns.

4. If lubricating oil and water accumulate in the gun, use petcock on valve to remove water. Do this fre-

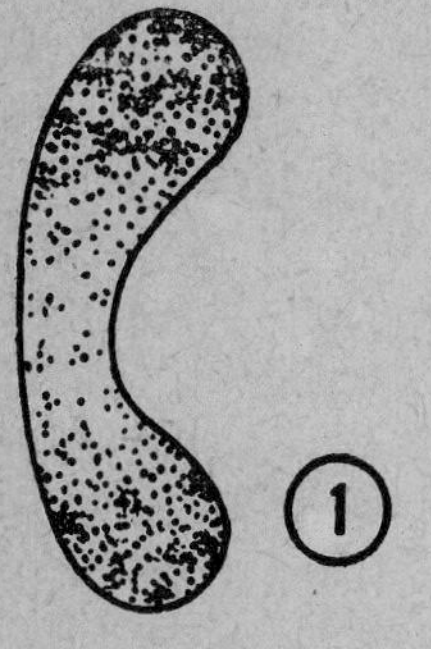

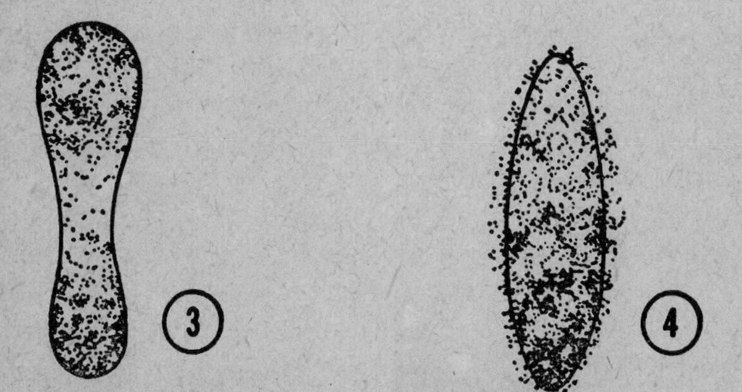

Fig. 7. Defective spray patterns. **1.** Fan pattern resulting from clogging of side ports. **2.** Pattern caused by clogging of nozzle. **3.** Split spray caused by high atomizing pressure. **4.** Salt-and-pepper spray caused by low atomizing pressure.

quently. Water sometimes enters the gun by condensation in the air-reducing valve between the air compressor and the spray gun.

Air leakage. Air leakage from the front of the gun indicates that the air valve is improperly seated. This is caused by foreign matter on the valve or seat and by wear or damage to these parts. Air also leaks from the front of the gun when the air-valve spring is broken or when the valve stem is bent or sticks from lack of lubrication.

Paint leakage. Paint leakage from the front of the gun indicates that the fluid needle is not seated properly. Look for damaged fluid tip or needle, or foreign matter on the tip. Also check for wrong size of needle, broken fluid needle spring, or a packing nut which is too tight.

Adjusting air pressure. Many defects in spray painting, such as blushing or blooming, are the result of faulty control of air pressure. Proper adjustment of pressure prevents excessive offspray and minimizes fogging of adjacent painted surfaces.

TINTING PAINTS

Colors in oil are used for tinting or giving color to oil paint or enamel. These are concentrated color pigments made from natural earth or chemical compounds and are mixed with oil to form a paste. Pigmented oil stains for wood are sometimes made by thinning colors in oil.

Paste in oil. To mix colors in oil with white pigment pastes: reduce heavy paste to semipaste consistency with an oil thinner; thin colors in oil with turpentine or mineral spirits to consistency of canned milk, unless they are already a soft paste; add color gradually to paste, stirring constantly with wooden paddle or propeller agitator until desired tint is obtained; pour in remainder of oil, thinner, and drier.

Ready-mixed paint. If necessary, reduce colors in oil with turpentine or mineral spirits to the consistency of heavy cream. Mix the paint thoroughly by boxing, or with a mechanical mixer. Add color in small amounts, stirring after each addition until the desired tint is obtained.

Enamels. Use colors in oil for all tints. Mix enamel well by hand-stirring or with a small propeller agitator, and add color gradually.

Casein and synthetic resin-emulsion paint. Colors in water, manufactured especially for tinting these paints, are slightly thinned with water and stirred thoroughly into paste paint. Mix casein powder paint with water to form a paste before adding thinned tinting material. Colors in oil thinned with turpentine or mineral spirits may be used for pastel shades, but tinting color must be added in such small amounts and mixed so thoroughly with each addition that no separation of the water-oil mixture occurs.

Cement-water paint. Procure the desired tint of cement-water paint direct from the paint supply source. Cement-water paints tinted on the job are seldom satisfactory, presenting a mottled or streaked appearance after application.

PAINTING INTERIOR WOOD

Paints. Use priming paint or a mixture of self-priming flat wall paint and gloss enamel for priming. For finish coats apply flat wall paint, gloss enamel, or semi-gloss enamel.

Painting new surfaces. Prepare a new surface by removing with sandpaper such imperfections as planer marks, hammer marks, and raised grain. Wipe off dust and dirt with turpentine or mineral spirits. If wood frames, trim, and wood base have been installed against damp plaster, do no painting until plaster has dried.

Apply one primer coat and one finish coat. Two coats of finish paint may be applied if the primer and first finish are applied thinly. Allow at least 18 hours between coats. After priming, fill all nail holes, cracks, and other defects with white-lead whiting putty. After the putty has dried, sand the surface. Coat knots or sappy places with shellac (not over 2-pound cut).

Repainting. Wipe off painted or varnished woodwork (flat or low gloss) with mineral spirits. Remove glaze by sandpapering, and then wipe the surface clean with mineral spirits. Remove cracking, checking, or scaling coatings with paint-and-varnish remover. Use turpentine to clean off wax deposited by paint remover, and refinish the surface as new work. If paint has been applied over a stain that bleeds through, coat affected area with a seal coat of aluminum varnish composed of 2 pounds paste to 1 gallon of varnish.

For old work, one coat may be sufficient if applied over paint of the same or a similar color. Otherwise, two coats may be necessary.

TRANSPARENT FINISHES FOR WOOD

It is often desirable to stain woodwork and finish it with transparent coatings such as varnish or sealer and wax instead of paint. Varnish or sealer and wax also may be used without first staining the wood.

Preparing surfaces. To prepare surfaces for transparent finishing, sand

Fig. 8. Protect siding on the ends as well as surface. Paint butt joints when siding is being put in place. Paint the surface as soon as it is in position.

woodwork to remove all marks and blemishes. Remove grease with mineral spirits, benzene, or turpentine, and be sure that the surface is free of dust.

Preparing pigment oil stains. Prepare stains according to the following formula:

For natural wood finish:

½ gallon boiled linseed oil
½ gallon turpentine or mineral spirits

To this, add desired high-strength colors in oil in approximately these proportions:

Cherry: 11½ pints burnt sienna
Mahogany: 1 part vandyke brown; ½ part rose
Light oak: 1 part raw sienna; ¼ part raw umber
Dark oak: 1 part raw sienna; ½ part burnt umber; touch of burnt sienna
Old maple: ½ part each of raw sienna, burnt sienna, and raw umber
Walnut: 1½ parts vandyke brown or 1 part burnt sienna, ¼ part drop black

Staining. Stains for softwoods are pigment oil stains usually mixed by the painter on the job. They may be applied directly to the bare wood or the wood may first be sealed with one coat of wood sealer or one coat of thin shellac varnish (about 1-pound cut), depending on the effect desired. Apply pigment oil stain with rags or spread it by brush. Wipe off the excess before the stain dries.

The hardwoods are divided into those with pores smaller than those in birch and those with pores at least as large as those in birch. To stain hardwoods that have pores smaller than those in birch, use pigment oil stains in the same manner as on softwoods, or apply penetrating oil stains made with dyes, or water stains. It is seldom desirable to apply sealer or shellac to hardwoods before staining. When penetrating oil stain is used, apply a thin coat of shellac varnish (2-pound cut) after stain has dried. When water stain raises the grain of hardwoods, apply a wash coat of thin shellac varnish (½-pound cut) and smooth the surface lightly with No. 000 sandpaper.

Hardwoods with larger pores may be finished in a similar manner, except that pores may be filled with either natural or colored wood filler. Fillers are usually darker than the wood or stain, but for unusual effects they may be a light color. Apply filler before an oil stain but after a water stain, or use a colored filler when no stain is applied. Brush filler vigorously across the grain. Allow it to stand 10 to 30 minutes for volatile portion to evaporate, and remove excess filler by wiping with rags, first across the grain, then lightly along the grain.

Varnishing. Interior varnish is best for interior wood trim. Apply varnish with a clean brush, either flat or oval in shape. Take a full load of varnish on the brush but not enough to drip off. Brush the varnish out well, but brush no longer than is necessary, since a thin coat is better than a thick one which may run, sag, or wrinkle. Subsequent coats are usually a little thicker. Spread them out vigorously. Allow at least 24 hours for drying between coats. After one coat has dried hard, rub the surface lightly with steel wool before applying the next coat. The number of coats needed depends on the absorptive qualities of the wood and the desired fullness of finish.

Although interior woodwork is usually left in the natural varnish gloss, furniture of good quality may be rubbed to the desired luster. Varnish must be thoroughly dry and hard before it is rubbed. Use a felt pad, pumice stone, and either water or a mineral oil such as kerosene as lubricant. Coarse pumice produces a dull finish; fine pumice a higher luster. Water as the lubricant works faster than oil but requires more skill to avoid rubbing through the coating at edges of the work. After rubbing to the desired luster, wipe surface clean and apply furniture polish or wax.

Sealer-and-wax finish. Instead of varnish, a sealer-and-wax finish may be used. Shellac varnish is a suitable sealer if woodwork is not likely to be subjected to moisture. Apply one or two coats of shellac varnish (3- to 4-pound cut). Shellac varnish dries rapidly, and therefore must be spread quickly and evenly. Rub the surface with fine steel wool or fine sandpaper after each coat of shellac has dried. The surface is finally polished with wax. Apply wax uniformly with a soft cloth. Allow it to set for 30 minutes; then polish by rubbing briskly with a soft cloth or felt pad, stroking along the grain of the wood.

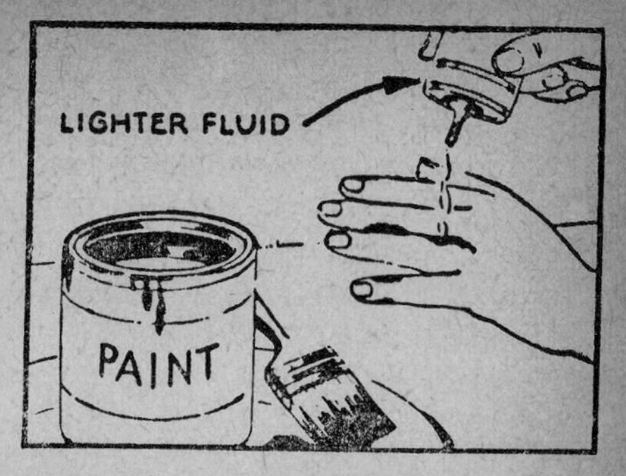

Fig. 9. After completing a painting job you may discover that you've run out of turpentine or other thinner with which to remove paint from your hands. A few drops of cleaning or lighter fluid will quickly remove the spots and save you a trip to the store.

Instead of shellac varnish, floor sealer may be used, particularly if woodwork is to be subjected to moisture. Brush or mop sealer on the surface, allow it to stand about 30 minutes, and rub with No. 2 steel wool, stroking along the grain. Wax after allowing the sealer to dry for 24 hours.

Refinishing. It is possible to apply natural or stained color in refinishing old natural-finished hardwood or softwood trim if the old coating is completely removed by sandpapering. If woodwork is not to be stained, light sanding is sufficient. For complete refinishing of old stained wood, remove existing varnish with paint-and-varnish remover. Wash the wood with turpentine to dissolve wax left by the remover. Sandpaper or rub the surface with steel wool and remove any remaining dust. If a lighter stain is desired, or if existing color is dark and uneven, sandpapering must be thorough enough to uncover clean wood.

Another method of lightening old stain is to apply a bleaching solution of about 8 ounces of oxalic acid added to 2 quarts of hot water. More than one application is often necessary. After the surface has dried, smooth down raised grain with fine sandpaper. Brush off dust and refinish as new wood. If the old stained surface is in good condition and no change in color is desired, light sandpapering and revarnishing, or light papering and revarnishing, or resealing, are sufficient.

PAINTING SCREENS AND FRAMES

Before painting screen windows and doors, remove accumulated dirt and rust, and make necessary repairs. Paint varies with the type of screen cloth.

Galvanized screen. Apply one coat of black enamel, both to frame and galvanized screening on buildings which have wood siding. Enamel is best applied by spraying. Thin the enamel with 1 pint of mineral spirits to 1 gallon of enamel. Where spray equipment is not available, paint screen cloth with a wood block, approximtaely 2 by 4 by 6 inches, covered with piled carpet. Dip the carpeted surface of the block into a pan containing the enamel and apply it to the screen.

Copper or bronze screen. Use cream paint for frames of screens having copper or bronze cloth. Paint frames which have been exposed less than two years with one coat of finishing paint and those exposed more than two years with one primer coat and one finish coat. Apply a coat of spar varnish to the screen cloth.

PAINTING NEAR SEASHORE

It is sometimes advisable, particularly at the seashore, to add a small amount of good exterior varnish to the topcoat of paint. The amount of varnish added should be quite small —about a pint to a gallon of paint. However, care should be taken to select a varnish that mixes properly with the paint, because some good spar varnishes thicken some paints. The varnish should be tried in the paint on a small scale to see that it mixes properly. It is not advisable to add varnish to the undercoats.

ESTIMATING PAINTING NEEDS

Estimate the amount of paint gallonage required for the walls of a room by multplying the length of the room by the height . . . and doubling the total (for the two walls.) Then learn the area of the other two walls by multplying the width of the room by the height, then doubling this total. The two totals, added together, give the number of square feet in all four walls. This figure, divided by the number of square feet covered by a gallon, will give the quantity needed for one coat. A gallon of flat oil paint will cover approximately 630 square feet; casein and emulsion paints, about 540. A window or door area is not deducted unless it is greater than 100 square feet in size.

An average small room will take one gallon of paint per coat for smooth finish walls. One pint of enamel covers about 65 square feet.

SECTION IX

TOOLS, NAILS, SCREWS AND HARDWARE

Finding Angles with a Framing Square—Saw Blade Used for Draw Knife—Bench Planes—Holder Aids in Sawing Curves—Broken Blade Makes Small Saw—Nail Head Used as Nail Set—Filing to a Line—Wedge Screwdriver Grips Screw—Lag Screws Driven with Brace–Don't Fall for These–Hold Tight–Portable Electric Tools–What Nail?–Know Your Hinges–Screw Sizes–Special Plywood Fastenings–Rescreening Tip–Another Screening Tip.

SECTION IX

TOOLS, NAILS, SCREWS AND HARDWARE

FINDING ANGLES WITH A FRAMING SQUARE

Knowing an angle and being able to copy that angle in wood are two different things. Most protractors are too small to permit angles to be copied off reliably, and a good protractor head may not always be available. A framing square, however, will usually serve the purpose nicely (fig. 1). The following table shows how to use one for obtaining degree settings. In all cases the reading on the blade is 12″. If an angle of, say, 32° is wanted, lay a straightedge from 12″ on the blade to 7½″ on the tongue. The smaller angle formed by one arm and the straightedge is the desired one. To obtain an angle of 58° (the complement of 32°) use the same setting but read the larger angle. Once the angle is found on the framing square a taper jig or bevel square can be set to fit.

The table can also be used in reverse, as when the lean of a hopper side is given in inches. If the slope

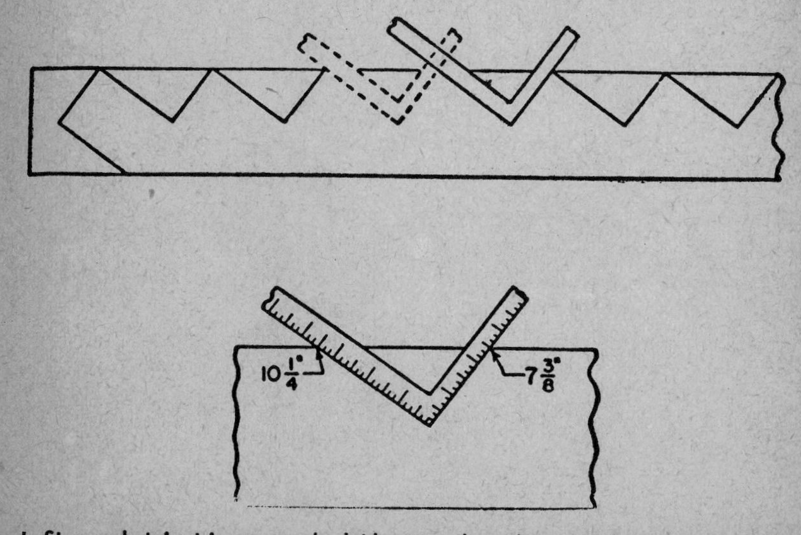

Fig. 1. Step and stair stringers can be laid out easily with a steel framing square. Here a stringer is being laid out to have 10¼ inch treads and 7⅜ inch risers.

is known to be, for example, 2½″ in 12″, the angle is just slightly under 12°. Intermediate values can be estimated fairly closely.

Fig. 2. Use of square for squaring wide timber.

TABLE OF DEGREES FOUND BY MEASUREMENTS ON FRAMING SQUARE

(Read 12″ on blade of square in all cases)

Degrees	*Tongue Reading*
2	$\frac{7}{16}$+
4	$\frac{25}{32}$+
6	1$\frac{9}{32}$−
8	1$\frac{11}{16}$−
10	2$\frac{3}{16}$+
12	2$\frac{9}{16}$
14	2$\frac{31}{32}$−
16	3 7/12−
18	3$\frac{15}{16}$−
20	4$\frac{7}{16}$
22	4¾
24	5$\frac{11}{32}$
26	5⅞
28	6⅜
30	6$\frac{15}{16}$−
32	7½
34	8$\frac{3}{32}$+
36	8$\frac{23}{32}$+
38	9⅜
40	10$\frac{1}{16}$+
42	10$\frac{13}{16}$−
44	11 7/12
45	12

SAW BLADE USED FOR DRAW KNIFE

One of the handiest woodworking tools, the draw knife, is also one of the hardest to find in the smaller sizes. Two bolts and a broken power-hacksaw blade however can solve that problem. Remove the bolt heads and saw slots in the threaded ends. Grind a cutting edge on the back of the blade and secure the ends in the slots with washers and nuts.

Fig. 3. Use of square for squaring narrow timber.

BENCH PLANES

Bench planes, as shown in figure 6, are used on the bench, primarily for shaving and smoothing with the grain of the wood. They vary in length from 24 inches for a jointer or fore plane to as little as 5½ inches for a small smoothing plane.

Adjustment. To adjust the plane, hold it bottom side up in the left hand and sight down along the smooth, bottom surface. Turn the adjusting nut until the cutting edge just projects. If the blade does not project evenly, straighten it by moving the adjusting lever to the right or to the left.

For certain kinds of work (such as making heavy cuts), it may be necessary to adjust the frog. In this case,

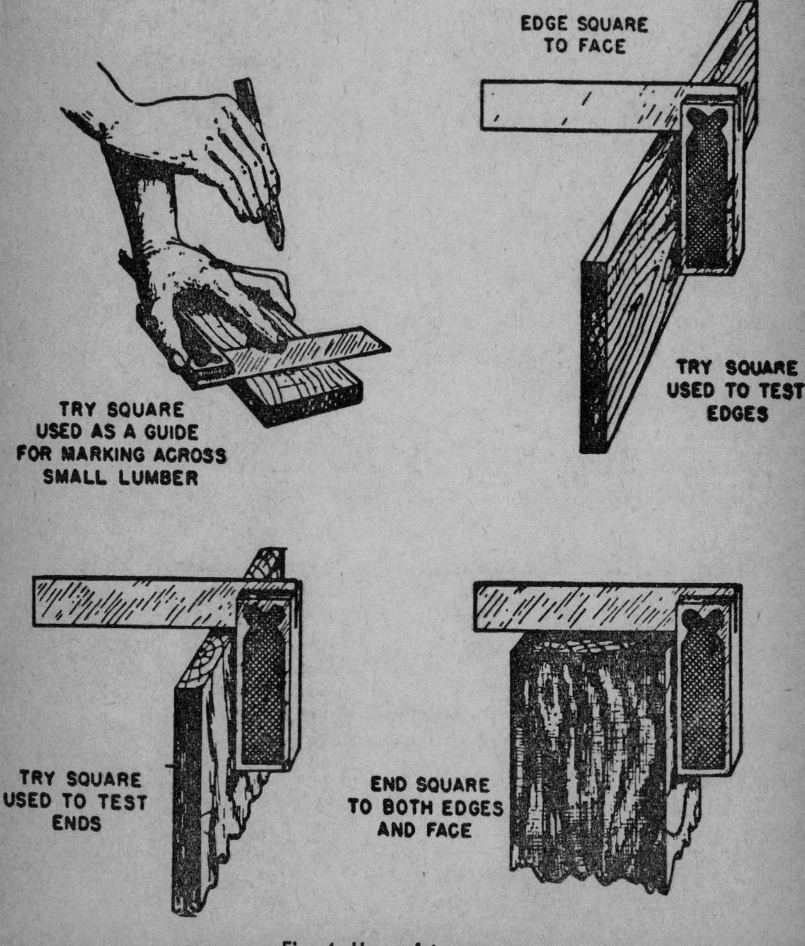

Fig. 4. Uses of try square.

loosen the frog screws and turn the frog adjusting screw until the frog is moved backward far enough, then tighten the frog screws. This procedure opens the mouth of the plane and permits larger chips to be cut.

Operation. Hold the plane firmly with the right hand on the handle and the left hand on the knob (fig. 7). Place the plane on the edge or surface of the wood at a slight lateral angle, push forward and down with both hands, taking long, even strokes. On the return stroke, either tilt the plane to the side or raise the plane completely.

The length of the projecting cutting edge depends upon the kind of

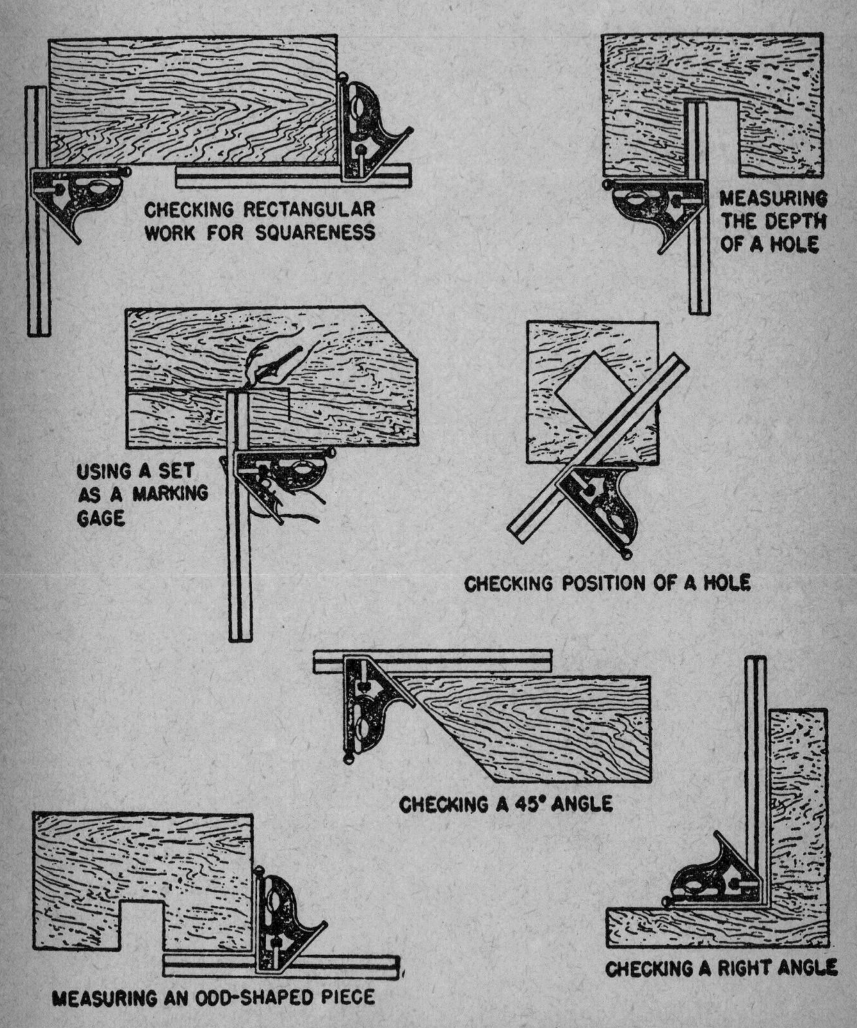

Fig. 5. Combination try square and its uses.

HOLDER AIDS IN SAWING CURVES

en sawing compound curves bandsaw or jigsaw, it's com- practice to tack the waste back get a flat surface on the table ubsequent cuts. The extra ef- this involves as well as the risk lamaging a saw blade on the s or brads that hold the waste be avoided if you make yourself olding jig like that in figure 17. disadvantage is that the work t be reclamped when you saw up to the jig, but this can be done quickly. Drill holes near the edges of two hardwood blocks, open them out into slots, and assemble with bolts, washers, and wing nuts.

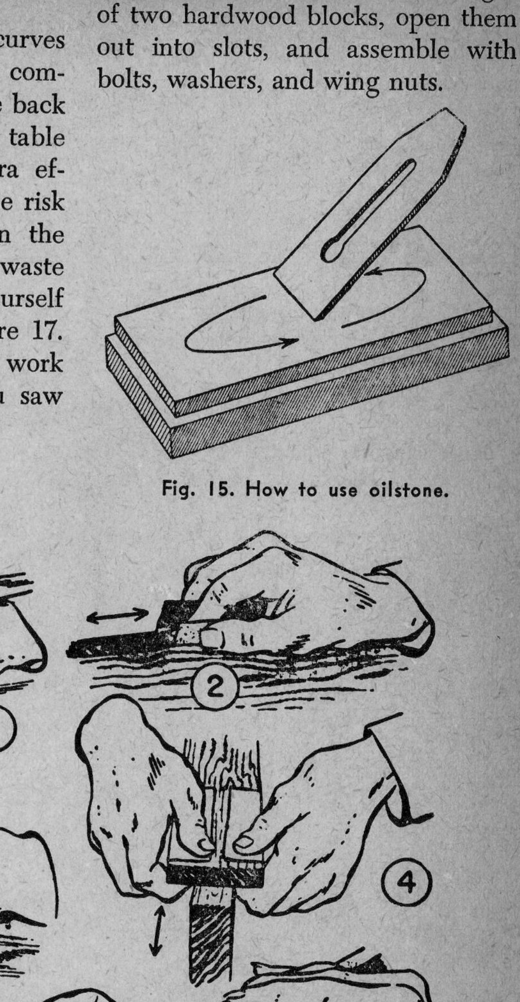

Fig. 15. How to use oilstone.

Fig. 16. How to use sandpaper.

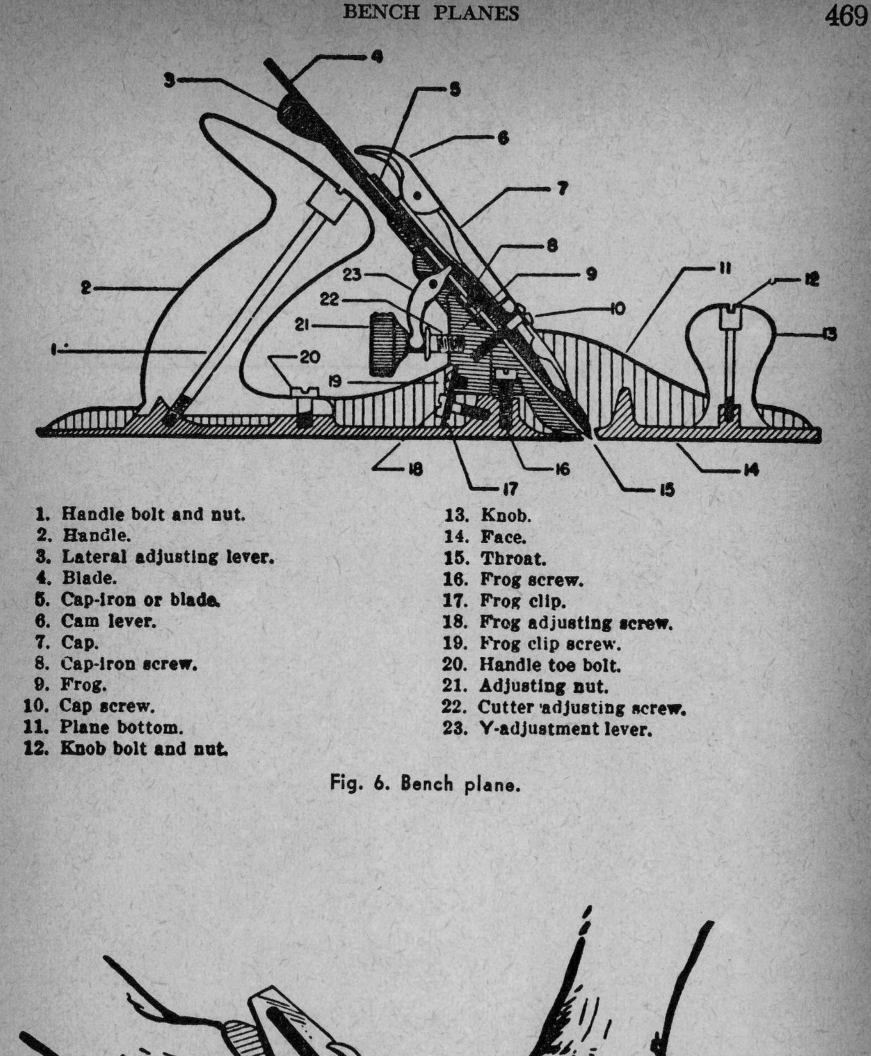

1. Handle bolt and nut.
2. Handle.
3. Lateral adjusting lever.
4. Blade.
5. Cap-iron or blade.
6. Cam lever.
7. Cap.
8. Cap-iron screw.
9. Frog.
10. Cap screw.
11. Plane bottom.
12. Knob bolt and nut.
13. Knob.
14. Face.
15. Throat.
16. Frog screw.
17. Frog clip.
18. Frog adjusting screw.
19. Frog clip screw.
20. Handle toe bolt.
21. Adjusting nut.
22. Cutter adjusting screw.
23. Y-adjustment lever.

Fig. 6. Bench plane.

Fig. 7. How to use a plane.

Fig. 8. How to use marking gauge.

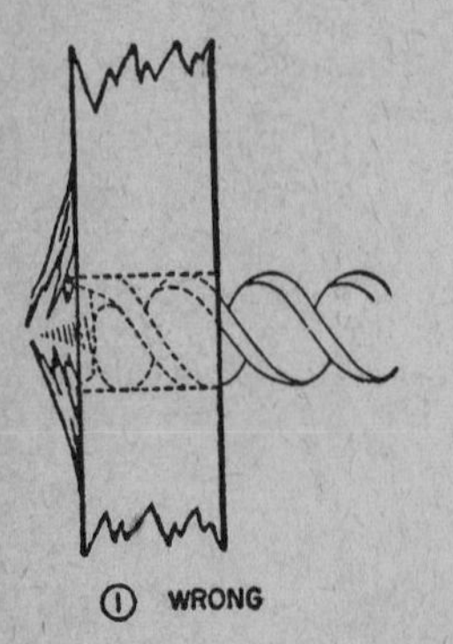

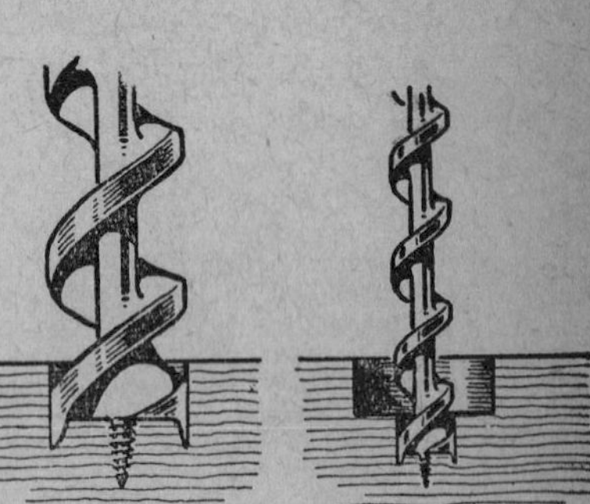

Fig. 10. It is perfectly practical to use an ordinary bit to countersink. The countersink should be bored first as this will allow the smaller bit to be centered.

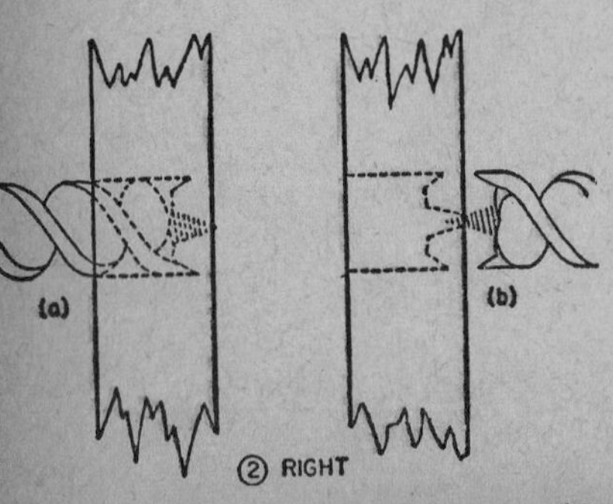

Fig. 9. Right and wrong way to use auger bit.

wood being cut and upon the amount of wood to be removed. Always have the grain of the wood slope upward in the direction of the planing stroke.

Care and sharpening. Never lay the plane face down. It should always be laid on its edge, otherwise the blade may be nicked or dulled by contact with hard surfaces. Make certain that wood to be planed is entirely free of nails, dirt, or other foreign matter. When the plane is not being used, it should be covered with a thin coat of oil. When the plane is put into the tool box, the blade should be withdrawn slightly so that it does not project beyond the face.

The blade is sharpened with an oilstone or with a tool grinder with a fine abrasive wheel. The angle of the bevel should be between 20° and 30°. Care should be taken to keep the cutting edge straight and exactly perpendicular to the length of the blade.

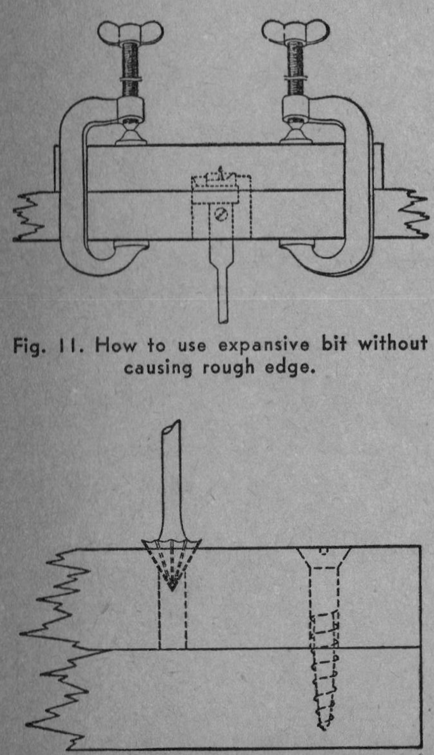

Fig. 11. How to use expansive bit without causing rough edge.

Fig. 12. Use of countersink bit.

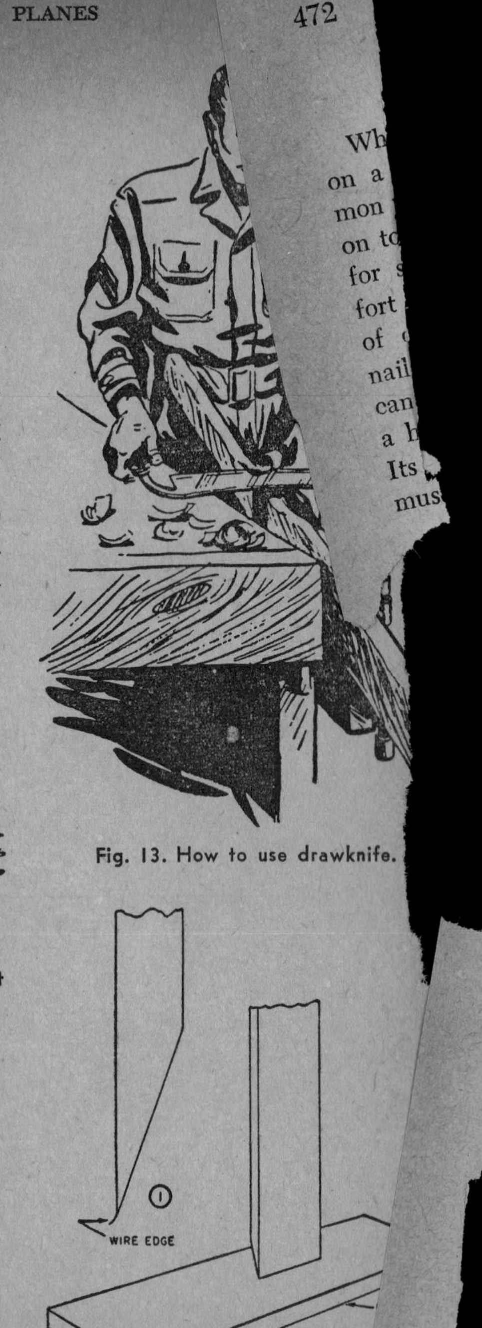

Wh
on a
mon
on t
for
fort
of
nail
can
a h
Its
mus

Fig. 13. How to use drawknife.

Fig. 14. Wire edge and method of

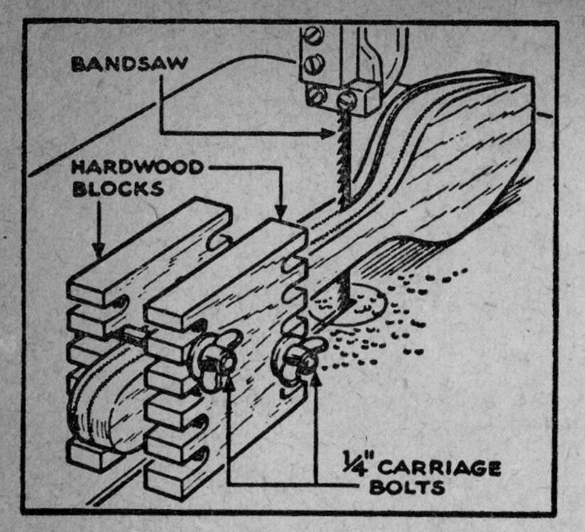

Fig. 17.

BROKEN BLADE MAKES SMALL SAW

Fitted with a handle, a 6″ length of broken ¼″ bandsaw blade will make a useful keyhole saw. The detachable file handle shown has a thumbscrew that clamps the blade. An ordinary file handle could be used with a screw put through it and a hole punched in the blade to hold it firmly while sawing (fig. 18).

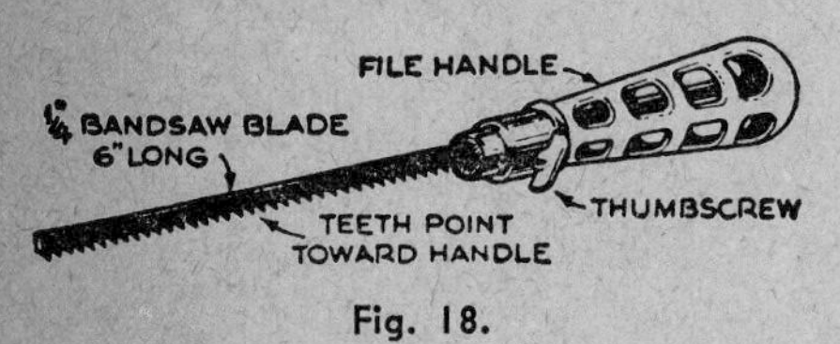

Fig. 18.

NAIL HEAD USED AS NAIL SET

When you are doing rough carpentry work, one of the nails that you are using will serve as a nail set. Simply place the edge of the head against the head of the driven nail and hammer it down (fig. 20).

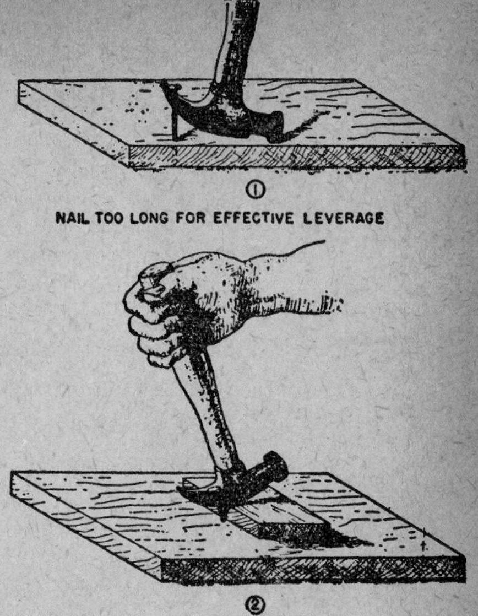

Fig. 19. How to pull nails with hammer.

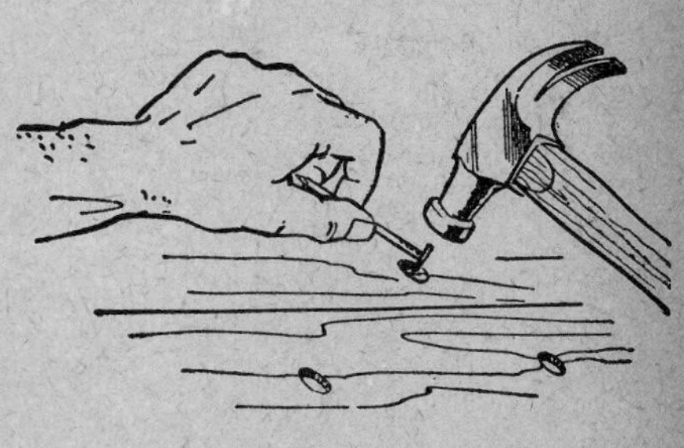

Fig. 20.

Fig. 21. A method of starting a nail when only one hand is free.

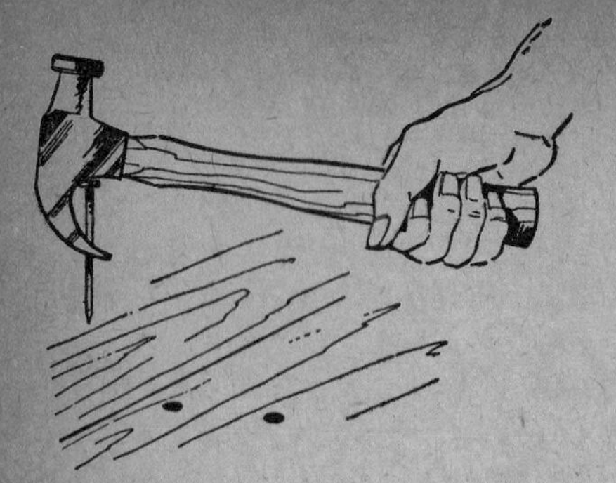

Fig. 22. A simple way to start a nail with one hand.

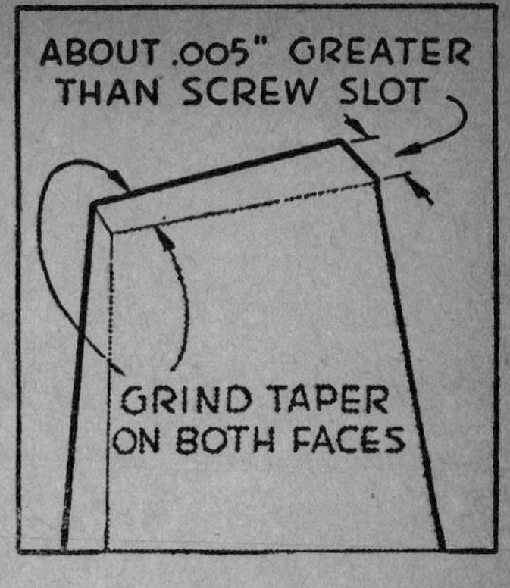

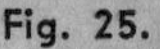

Fig. 25.

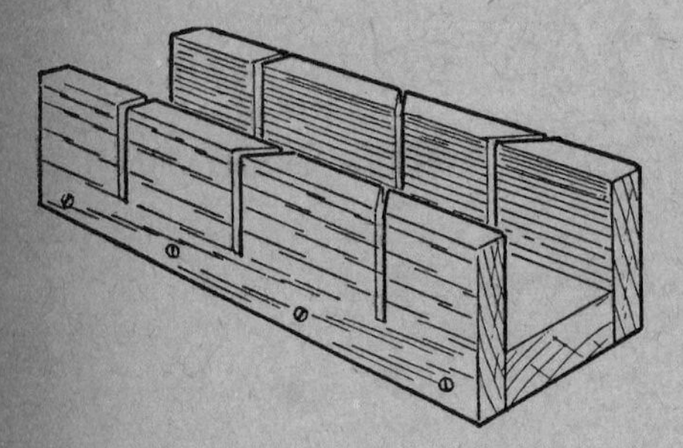

Fig. 23. A simple home made miter box constructed out of 1" by 3" stock.

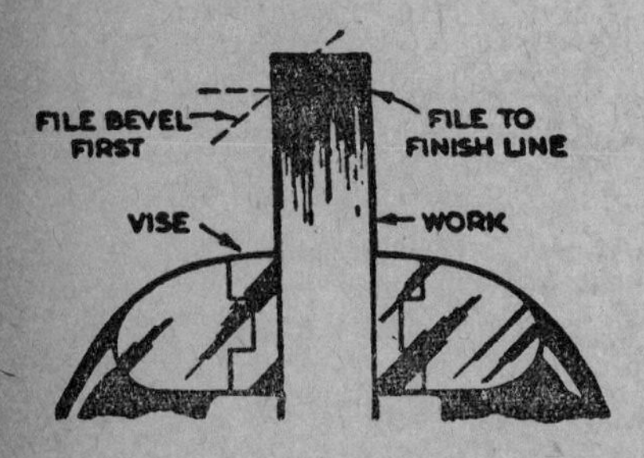

Fig. 24.

FILING TO A LINE

When you have to shorten a piece to a scribed finish line, first file a bevel on the marked side to the finish line, and then file down squarely to the base of the bevel. In this way the amount of material to be removed can be accurately controlled, and there will be less danger of taking off too much stock. On fairly thick pieces, it may be advantageous to file bevels on both sides before starting to file through the middle (fig. 24).

WEDGE SCREWDRIVER GRIPS SCREW

When a screw must be threaded into a tapped hole that can't be reached by hand, time will be saved if it is fastened to the screwdriver. This can be done by grinding down the blade of a long-handled screwdriver until it is about .005″ thicker than the width of the screw slot, and then grinding a slight taper to form a wedge. Jam the blade in from the end of the slot so it will get a firm grip (fig. 25).

LAG SCREWS DRIVEN WITH BRACE

If you have to drive a number of lag screws with an open-end wrench,

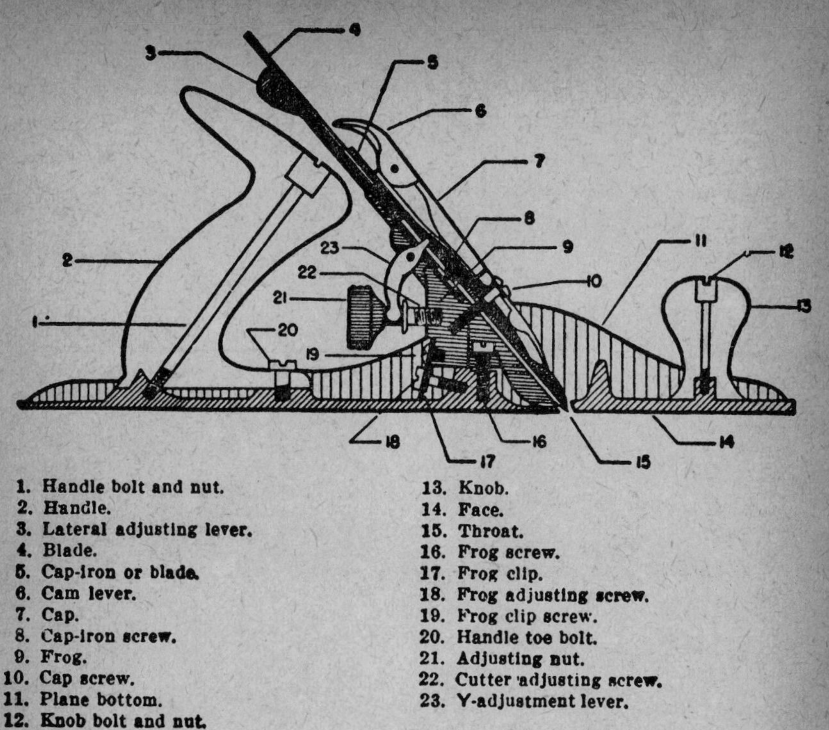

1. Handle bolt and nut.
2. Handle.
3. Lateral adjusting lever.
4. Blade.
5. Cap-iron or blade.
6. Cam lever.
7. Cap.
8. Cap-iron screw.
9. Frog.
10. Cap screw.
11. Plane bottom.
12. Knob bolt and nut.
13. Knob.
14. Face.
15. Throat.
16. Frog screw.
17. Frog clip.
18. Frog adjusting screw.
19. Frog clip screw.
20. Handle toe bolt.
21. Adjusting nut.
22. Cutter adjusting screw.
23. Y-adjustment lever.

Fig. 6. Bench plane.

Fig. 7. How to use a plane.

Fig. 8. How to use marking gauge.

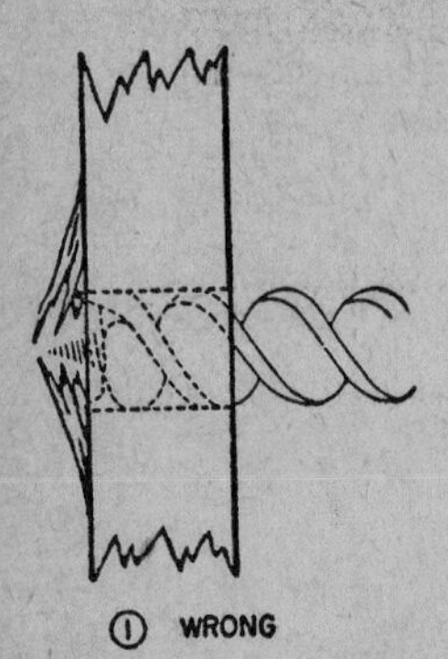

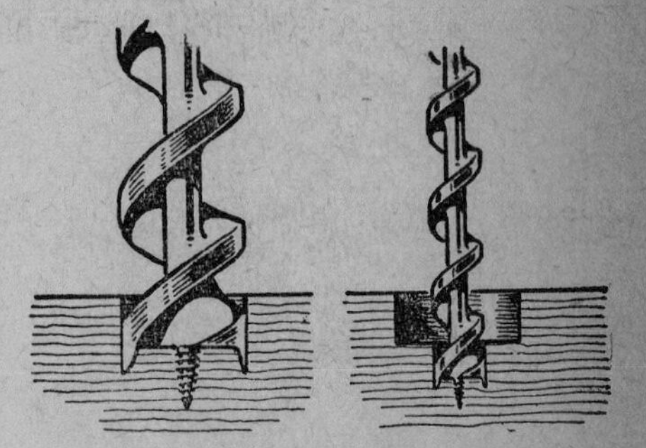

Fig. 10. It is perfectly practical to use an ordinary bit to countersink. The countersink should be bored first as this will allow the smaller bit to be centered.

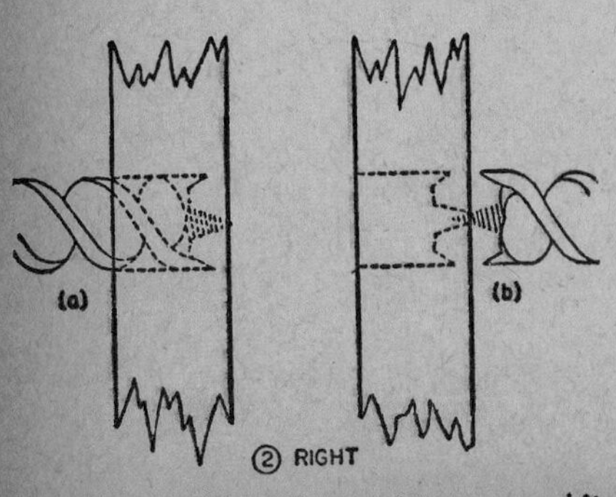

Fig. 9. Right and wrong way to use auger bit.

wood being cut and upon the amount of wood to be removed. Always have the grain of the wood slope upward in the direction of the planing stroke.

Care and sharpening. Never lay the plane face down. It should always be laid on its edge, otherwise the blade may be nicked or dulled by contact with hard surfaces. Make certain that wood to be planed is entirely free of nails, dirt, or other foreign matter. When the plane is not being used, it should be covered with a thin coat of oil. When the plane is put into the tool box, the blade should be withdrawn slightly so that it does not project beyond the face.

The blade is sharpened with an oilstone or with a tool grinder with a fine abrasive wheel. The angle of the bevel should be between 20° and 30°. Care should be taken to keep the cutting edge straight and exactly perpendicular to the length of the blade.

Fig. 13. How to use drawknife.

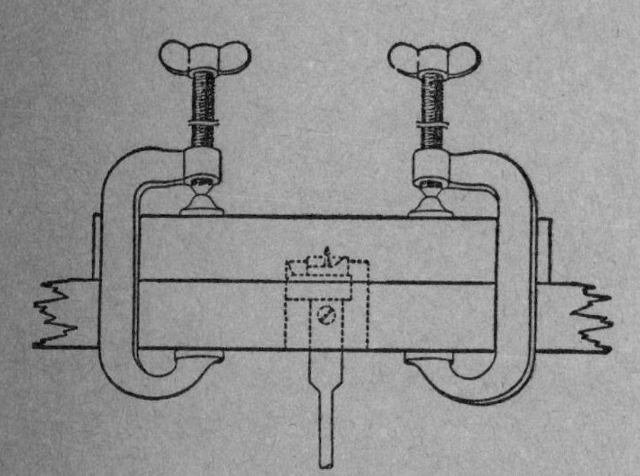

Fig. 11. How to use expansive bit without causing rough edge.

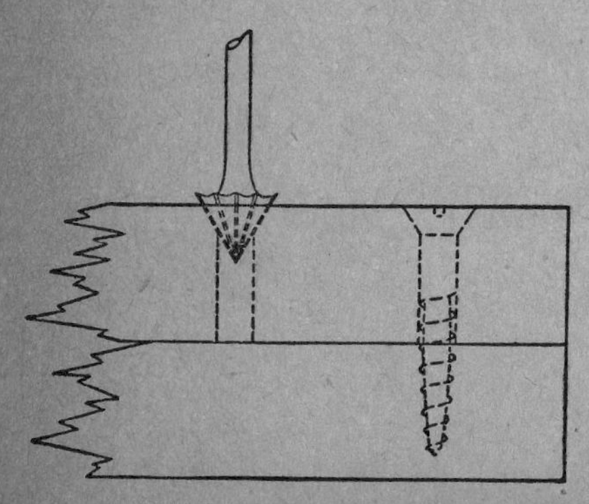

Fig. 12. Use of countersink bit.

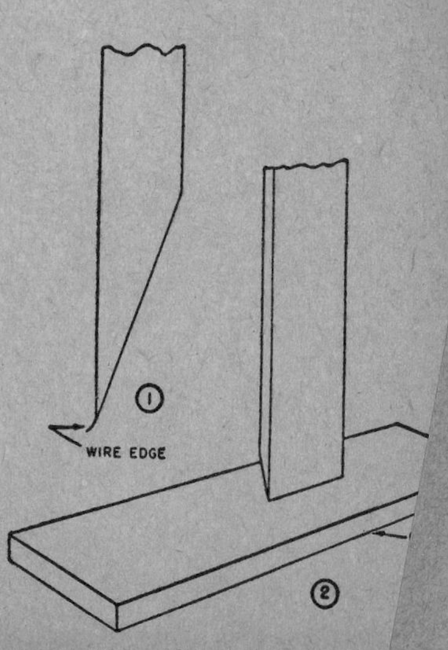

Fig. 14. Wire edge and method of

HOLDER AIDS IN SAWING CURVES

When sawing compound curves on a bandsaw or jigsaw, it's common practice to tack the waste back on to get a flat surface on the table for subsequent cuts. The extra effort this involves as well as the risk of damaging a saw blade on the nails or brads that hold the waste can be avoided if you make yourself a holding jig like that in figure 17. Its disadvantage is that the work must be reclamped when you saw up to the jig, but this can be done quickly. Drill holes near the edges of two hardwood blocks, open them out into slots, and assemble with bolts, washers, and wing nuts.

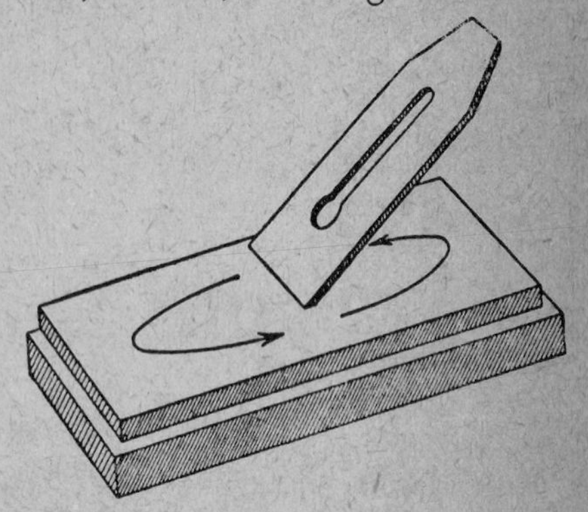

Fig. 15. How to use oilstone.

Fig. 16. How to use sandpaper.

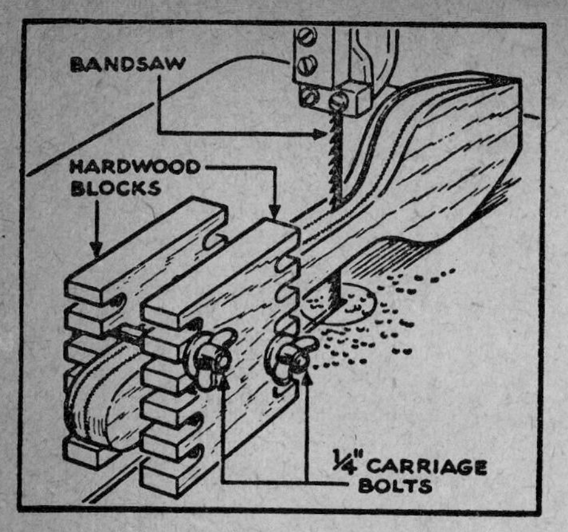

Fig. 17.

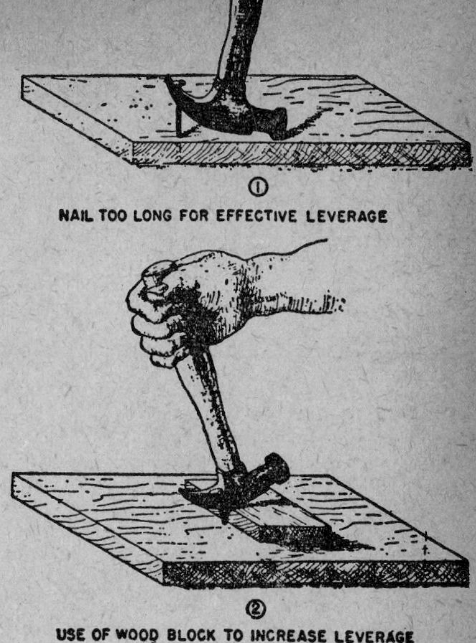

①
NAIL TOO LONG FOR EFFECTIVE LEVERAGE
②
USE OF WOOD BLOCK TO INCREASE LEVERAGE

Fig. 19. How to pull nails with hammer.

BROKEN BLADE MAKES SMALL SAW

Fitted with a handle, a 6″ length of broken ¼″ bandsaw blade will make a useful keyhole saw. The detachable file handle shown has a thumbscrew that clamps the blade. An ordinary file handle could be used with a screw put through it and a hole punched in the blade to hold it firmly while sawing (fig. 18).

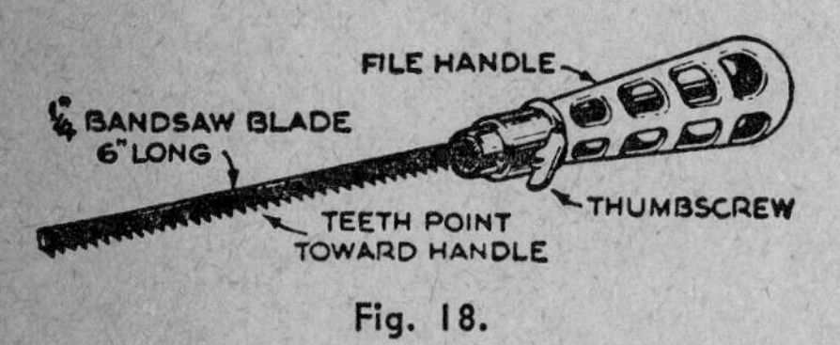

Fig. 18.

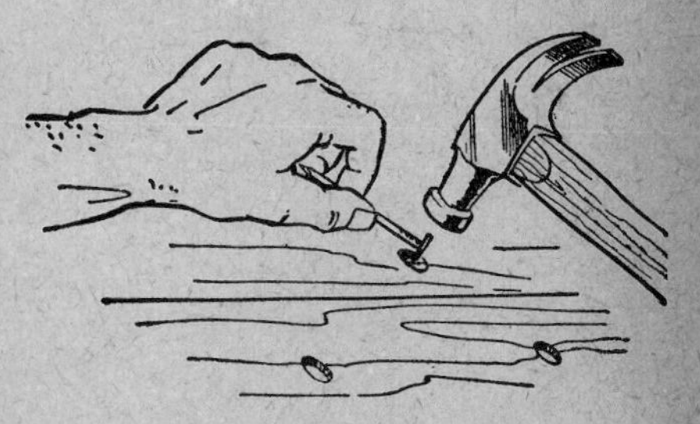

Fig. 20.

NAIL HEAD USED AS NAIL SET

When you are doing rough carpentry work, one of the nails that you are using will serve as a nail set. Simply place the edge of the head against the head of the driven nail and hammer it down (fig. 20).

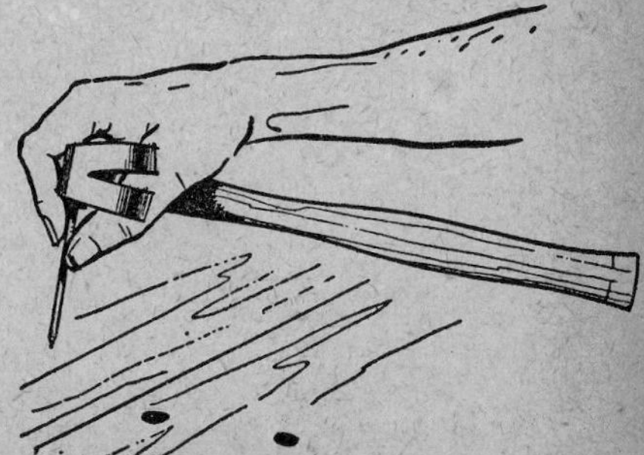

Fig. 21. A method of starting a nail when only one hand is free.

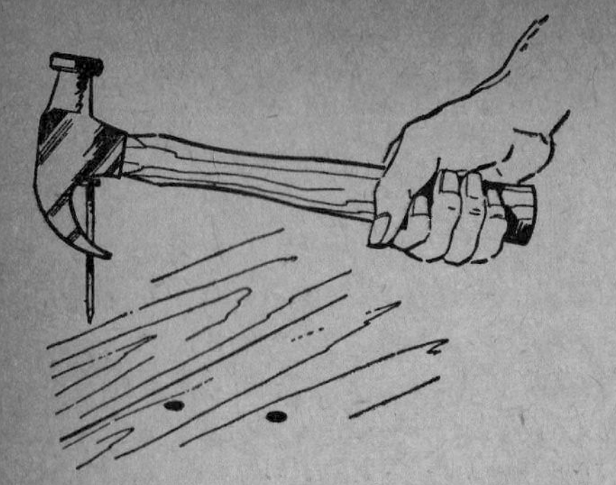

Fig. 22. A simple way to start a nail with one hand.

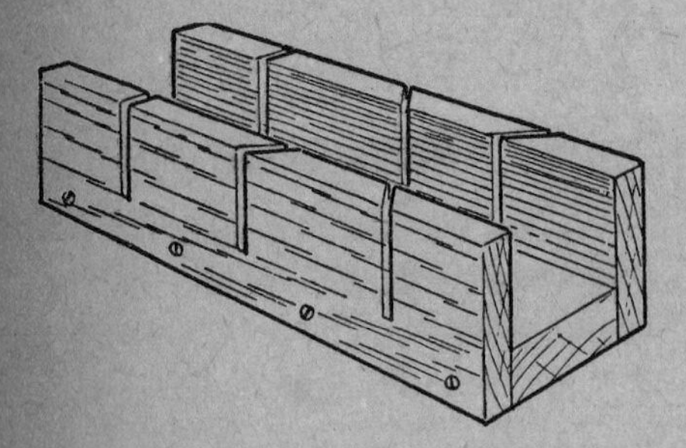

Fig. 23. A simple home made miter box constructed out of 1" by 3" stock.

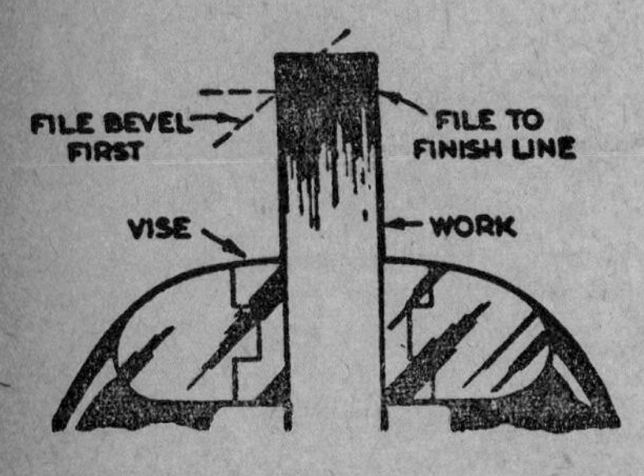

Fig. 24.

FILING TO A LINE

When you have to shorten a piece to a scribed finish line, first file a bevel on the marked side to the finish line, and then file down squarely to the base of the bevel. In this way the amount of material

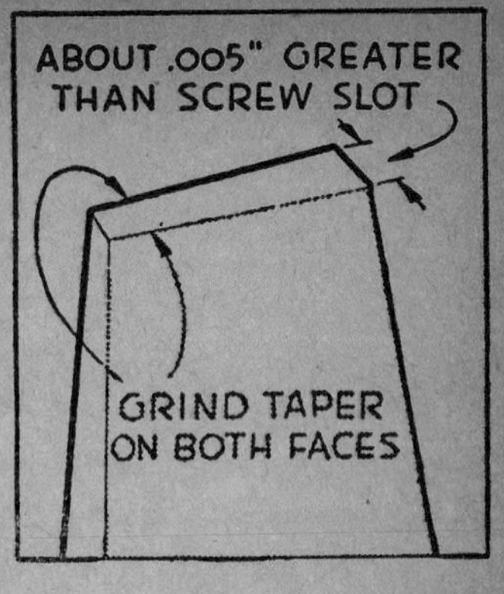

Fig. 25.

to be removed can be accurately controlled, and there will be less danger of taking off too much stock. On fairly thick pieces, it may be advantageous to file bevels on both sides before starting to file through the middle (fig. 24).

WEDGE SCREWDRIVER GRIPS SCREW

When a screw must be threaded into a tapped hole that can't be reached by hand, time will be saved if it is fastened to the screwdriver. This can be done by grinding down the blade of a long-handled screwdriver until it is about .005″ thicker than the width of the screw slot, and then grinding a slight taper to form a wedge. Jam the blade in from the end of the slot so it will get a firm grip (fig. 25).

LAG SCREWS DRIVEN WITH BRACE

If you have to drive a number of lag screws with an open-end wrench, after a while it gets to be quite a task. Switch to a brace and quickly drive the screws to within an inch, finishing up with the wrench. Of course, the proper pilot holes must be drilled first.

DON'T FALL FOR THESE

Seven roofing errors are shown in figure 26, two each in Nos. *1*, *3*, and *4*. One in No. *3* is a little tricky, but you will get it if you look carefully.

Answers.

1. The starting shingle course should project about 1¼″ beyond the sheathing, and it should be a double course with covered joints. Either error allows rain to soak into the sheathing.

2. A straightedge used to align the shingle course being laid should be narrow enough to expose the butts of the course beneath so joints can be seen.

3. Roofers prefer to cut off the tips of shingles with the corner of a hatchet. Note also that the joints of alternate shingle courses come over each other. Joints should be offset about 1½″ to avoid three in a line if the shingle between splits at the joint.

4. At least 1″ space should be left between shingles and the vent-flashing sleeve to permit dirt to wash away. Rip-rap shingles should overlap alternately from both sides of the ridge.

HOLD TIGHT

Clamps are indispensable tools in any woodworking shop, but they are often misused. How many errors can you spot in figure 27?

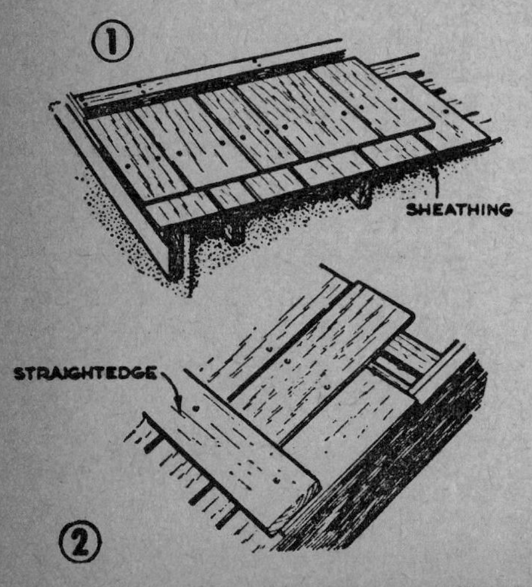

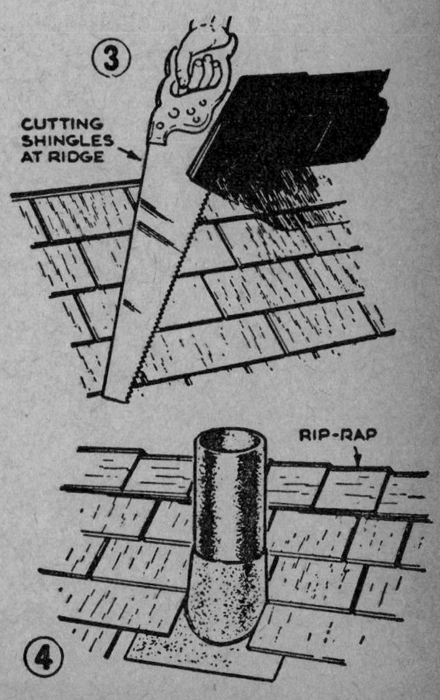

Fig. 26.

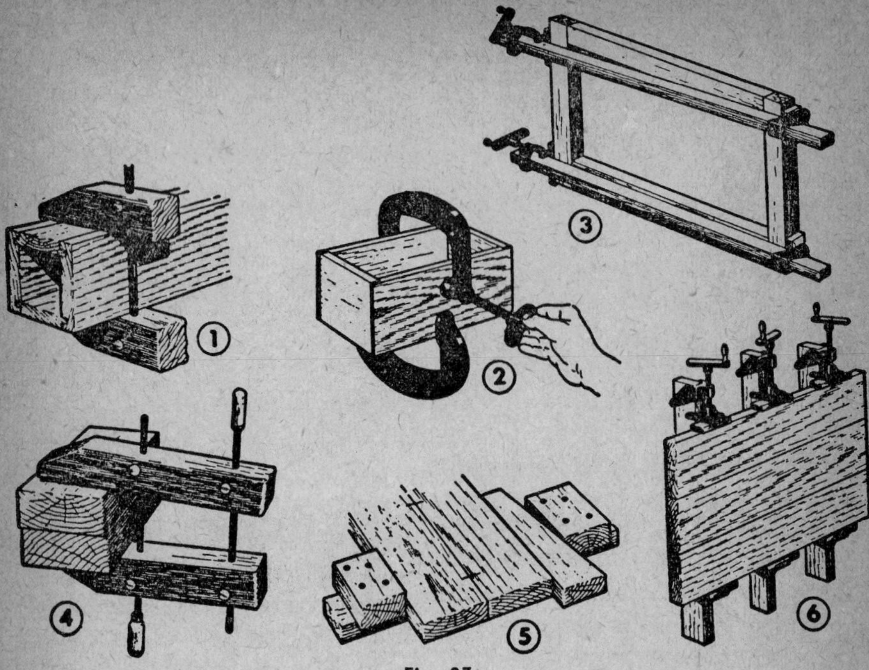

Fig. 27.

Answers.

1. The clamps should be applied to the other sides of the column. In this position, you would merely squeeze the vertical sides—and the pressure would have no effect on the joints.

2. There are two errors. Blocks should be used between jaws and work, for bare clamps will mar the wood. Also, pressure at the center of the box sides will spring them in, opening the joints. Either apply clamps at both ends or use heavy wood pads to distribute pressure along the sides.

3. Ordinarily the clamps should be parallel to the rails of the frame since any inclination tends to pull the frame out of square. Clamps may be used as seen here, however, to draw the frame true if it tends to be out of square upon assembly.

4. The jaws of the hand screw should be parallel, distributing the pressure evenly across the width of the pieces being glued.

5. One wedge used like this will not deliver full pressure. You should either use two opposing wedges or position the clamp block at an angle equaling the taper of the single wedge.

6. Since all the clamps are on one side, the boards may buckle outward. This can be avoided by placing the center clamp opposite the outer two.

PORTABLE ELECTRIC TOOLS

A great variety of portable, electrically powered tools have been developed that make it possible for you to do many household jobs much faster and more efficiently than by hand power. Frequently these tools will quickly pay for their cost in time saved and improved quality of workmanship. Drills, sander-polishers, and saws are probably the most popular and all-around convenient of the many tools available.

Most portable electric tools are powered by universal motors, which can be connected to direct current or to alternating current from 25 to 60 cycles. It is most important, however, that the voltage of the power source does not vary more than 10% either way from the voltage specified on the indicator-plate of the tool; otherwise, loss of power and serious overheating will result. It is also important that all electric tools be grounded while in use, and most especially where dampness is present. The tool should be equipped with a 3-conductor cable, of which the third or green wire is the grounding wire. One end of this wire is attached to the frame of the tool. The other end projects from the end of the attachment plug and should always be fixed to a suitable ground *before* plugging in the tool. It may be attached to a grounded outlet box or water pipe or conduit. A spike or rod driven at least 2½ feet into the ground will also serve.

The electric cable is the "life line" of the tool and should be carefully protected from damage. When not in use, hang up the cable loosely coiled —no sharp bends or kinks. Keep it clean. Keep it away from oils and greases, which ruin the rubber. And avoid handling it roughly.

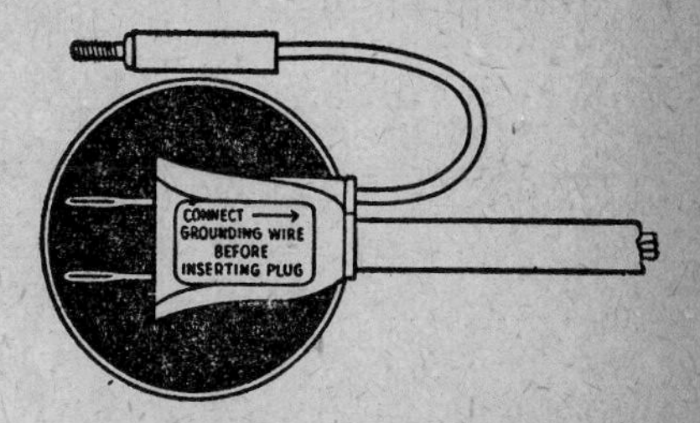

Fig. 28. Plug with projecting ground wire.

You must always be careful to use the correct size of extension cord with any electric tool. One determinant of the correct size is the distance the cable runs. The farther it runs the heavier it must be to avoid serious loss of power. Ordinary lighting cord is not heavy enough.

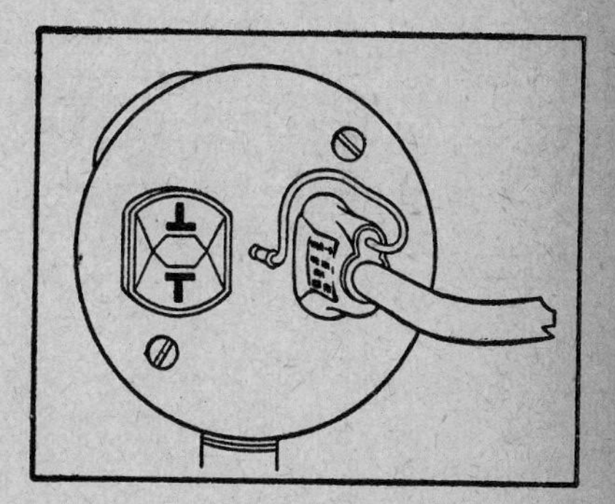

Fig. 29. Ground wire in grounded box.

The life of any tool is considerably lengthened by proper maintenance, but this is particularly true of electric tools. A good general rule is to relubricate regularly every sixty days to six months, depending on use. Remove the gear case, flush out old grease with kerosene, and, with gears in place, refill the housing (but not

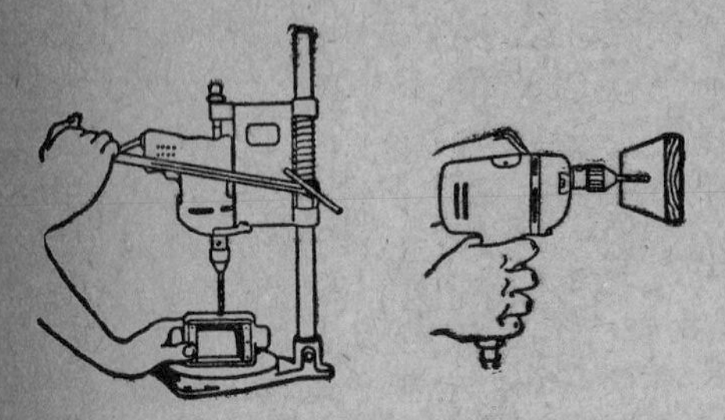

Figs. 30 and 31. Left: Bench stand converts portable drill into drill press. Right: Aim the drill like a pistol.

too much) with fresh grease. The armature bearing at the commutator end can be lubricated after extensive use with a drop or two of oil. Tools out of service for a long time should be completely relubricated before use. The carbon brushes should be inspected frequently and replaced when badly worn. Replace weak brush springs, too. Keep brushes clean and sliding freely in their guides. Keep the commutator clean and smooth. Rub it very lightly with fine sandpaper (not emery cloth) while turning on a lathe. If badly grooved, turn it down on a lathe or send armature to be repaired. Keep all soldered lead connections tight; resolder if loose.

ELECTRIC DRILL

Electric Drill. There is a variety of sizes of electric drills available. Either the ¼-inch or ½-inch size will be handy for general work around the home. There is no limit to the uses to which you can put it, whether you are working on a major construction job or are making casual improvements here and there about the house. You can get some idea of a drill's versatility from the following, incomplete list of available attachments: abrasive kit; buffing and polishing kit, including cotton buffing wheel, wire wheel brush, general purpose grinding wheel; all kinds of sanding discs, lamb's wool bonnets for high-lustre polishing; pile-fabric pads; wire cup brushes for cleaning, buffing, burnishing; adjustable bench stand, to turn the drill into a drill press and provide greater pressure and accuracy; sanding table, to help you achieve extremely fine control; honing attachment.

Although an electric drill has so many possibilities that it would be impossible to present all the instructions, tricks, and "kinks" that have been used at one time or another, it is hoped that the following "do's and dont's" will help you do a better job and solve some of your problems.

Electric drills are most frequently used with twist-drill bits for drilling holes. The drill supplies the power to turn the bit, the operator exerts forward pressure to feed the bit into the work. In general, high speed and light feed are recommended. Do not constantly overload the drill. Always grasp the control handles firmly. Aim the drill as you would a pistol. For straight holes, the drill must be kept at right angles to the work.

Clean the bit before placing it in the chuck. Be sure that the chuck jaws are tightened securely after inserting drill bits, arbors, etc.

Before starting any drilling, establish the exact location and diameter

Fig. 32. Normal bit for general work.

of the hole. Lay out the work carefully and mark the exact center of the hole with a centerpunch or nail. This makes a start in the metal or wood for the point of the drill. Be sure the work is firmly anchored or clamped. And back up thin metal with a substantial wooden block.

The twist drill normally used for general purpose work has cutting lips ground to a 59° angle. These lips must be kept sharp and of equal length with the point on dead center. Otherwise, the drill will cut a rough, uneven hole. A dull bit wastes your time and energy and does slow work.

In drilling particularly deep holes in wood, the drill bit should be partially removed from the hole while in motion. This clears the chips, speeds up drilling, and prevents damage to the bit or drill.

In drilling metal, use cutting oil to keep the drill bit cool and permit easy disposal of chips. (No lubricant is necessary in drilling cast iron.) Relieve pressure on the drill when the bit is about to break through in order to prevent damage to the bit and tool.

One of the most important uses for your electric drill is drilling pilot holes for wood screws. It is all too common practice to force screws into wood without using a pilot hole. The accompanying illustrations show the dangers of this practice and the advantages gained from the correct size of pilot and shank-clearance holes.

Figure 33 shows how, in end-grain driving, the grain tends to force the screw off its perpendicular path. Figure 34 shows the tendency in side-grain driving to split the wood. The wood screw does not remove material but merely compresses it. This compression takes place along lines of least resistance and the wood easily splits, minimizing the holding power of the screw and spoiling appearance. Figure 35 shows a correct pilot hole (indicated by the inner circle), which gives the screw holding power in a

Fig. 33. End-grain driving.

Fig. 34. Side-grain driving.

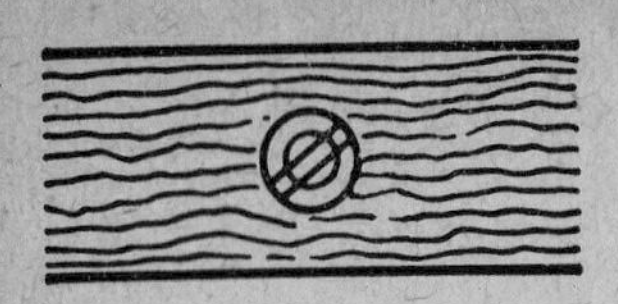

Fig. 35. Inner circle shows pilot hole.

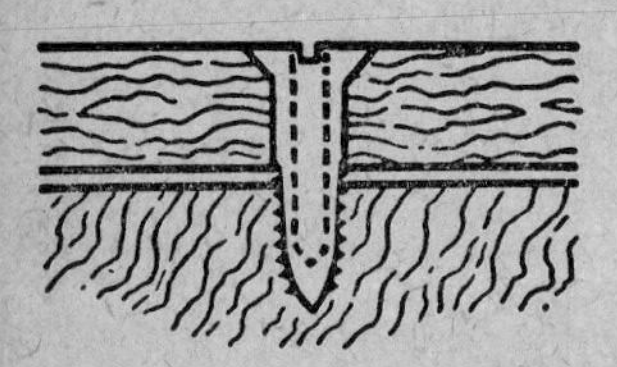

Fig. 36. Screw-root pilot hole, shown by broken lines.

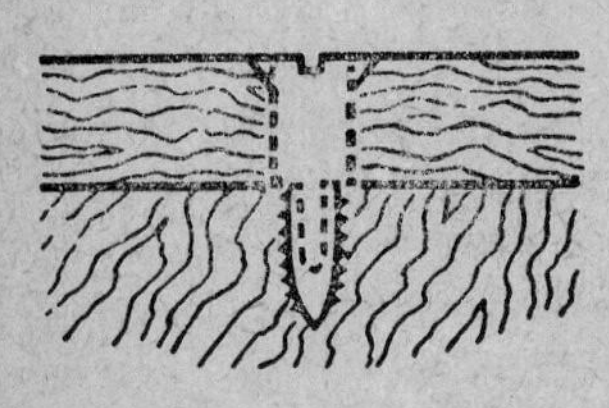

Fig. 37. Correct root-and-shank pilot hole, shown by broken lines.

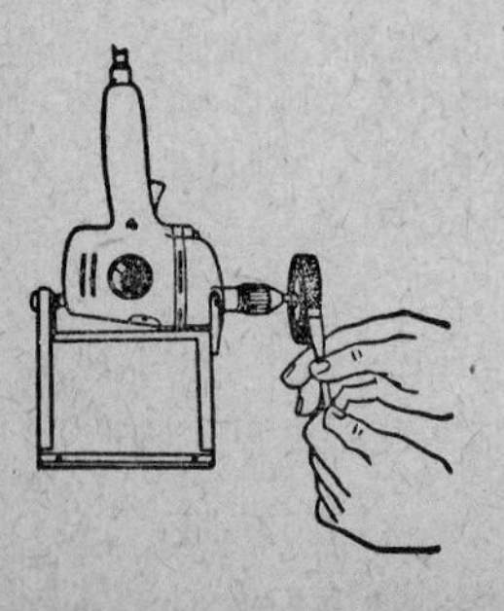

Fig. 38. A sander can act as a grinder.

full 360° circumference and prevents splitting.

Figure 36 shows the disadvantage of drilling only a pilot hole the size of the screw-root diameter. This condition increases the load on the driver and has a tendency to separate the two pieces rather than to pull them together. Figure 37 shows the correct way to drill the pilot and shank-clearance holes.

ELECTRIC SANDER-POLISHER

Electric Sander-Polisher. The 5-inch size of sander-polisher is a convenient and handy one for home work. It will do many jobs that an electric drill does, but the no-load speed of a sander-polisher rates higher than that of the drill and you should therefore be careful when using it for other jobs than those for which it is designed.

As is the case with the drill, many attachments are available to give this tool a wide range of adaptability. You can mount it on a horizontal stand and have both hands free for small or fine work. A sanding table can be attached to make things even easier. The sander-polisher can also be used as a sharpening and grinding tool for light work.

When sanding, remember that there is a proper grade and grit of sanding paper for every job. Controlling factors in selecting the right one are: the material you are going to work with, the state of the material, and how fine the finish is to be. In most cases, you will find it best to use a series of papers, each one finer than the last, to achieve the desired results. For an extremely fine surface, it is usually better to do the final operation by hand, using a fine-grit sandpaper or a pad of fine steel wool.

The usual method of using the electric sander as a portable tool is to attach a rubber backing pad by hand (do not thread it on by running the motor) and then to attach a sanding disc by means of a screw and washer. Make sure that the screw is tight and that the disc is free to revolve before turning the sander on.

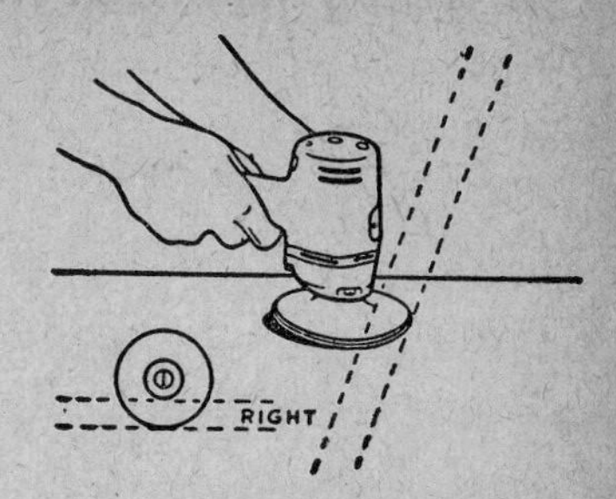

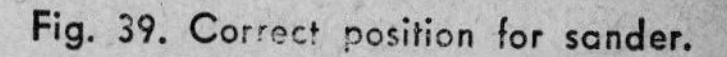
Fig. 39. Correct position for sander.

Grasp the control handles firmly and operate the tool freely, without forced effort or unnecessary pressure. Heavy pressure will slow the cutting action and reduce the life of the abrasive. The weight of the tool by itself will supply enough pressure in most cases.

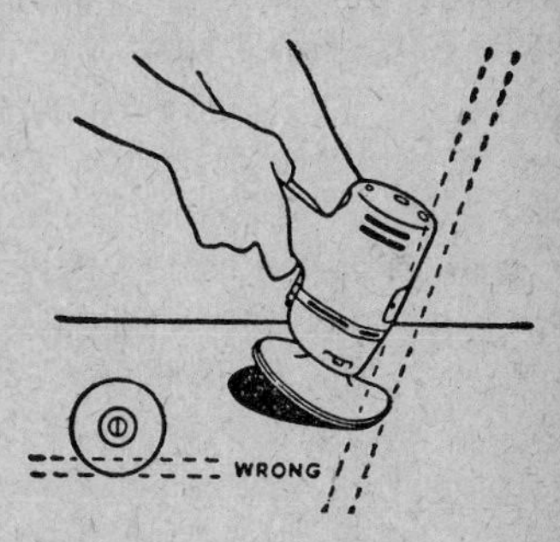

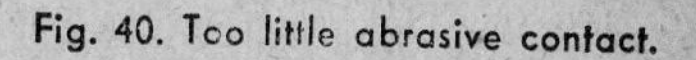
Fig. 40. Too little abrasive contact.

To obtain maximum efficiency, the sanding disc should be held as flat against the surface being sanded as possible without affecting the smoothness of the tool's operation. The accompanying illustrations show the correct procedure. The two positions marked "wrong" result in either too little or too much abrasive contact. Where only the outer edge of the disc is used, a rough-cut surface is obtained. If, on the other hand, the disc is placed flat against the work, the cutting action is irregular and bumpy and the tool is hard to control. For best results tip the tool slightly with just enough pressure to bend the disc as shown in the illustration marked "right."

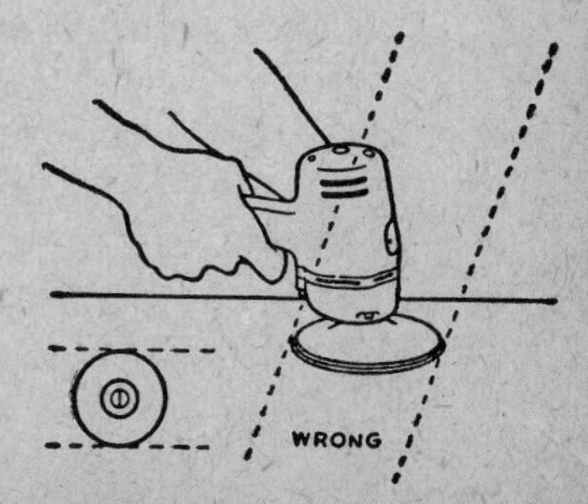

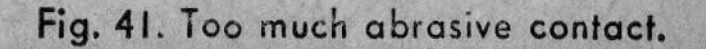
Fig. 41. Too much abrasive contact.

Keep the tool moving back and forth with a long, sweeping motion,

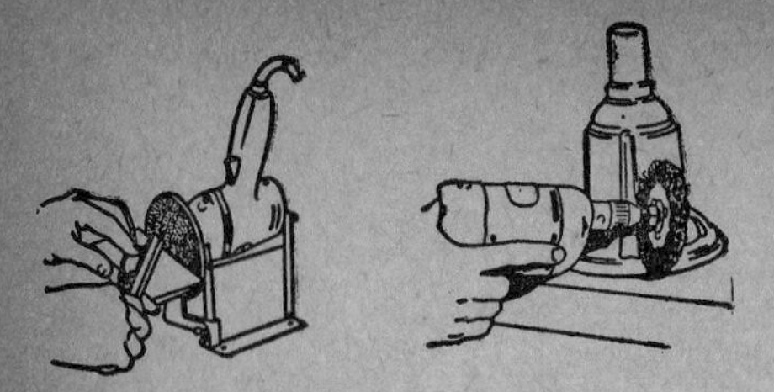

Figs. 42 and 43. Left: A sanding table can be attached to the sander. Right: A wire brush saves many sanding discs.

advancing along the surface to produce smooth, continuous coverage. Preferably do not hold the sander in one spot or use circular or spiral motion. The proper procedure will enable you to maintain a flat surface and keep the amount of swirls to a minimum.

The electric sander-polisher can be mounted on a horizontal stand and, if desired, a sanding table may also be attached. Under these circumstances, a metal sanding plate is generally employed as a backing and the proper abrasive paper or emery cloth is glued or cemented to it. Used in this way, the sander makes it easy for you to form plastic, wood, and metal. In addition, it can be used to sharpen edged tools such as chisels, plane bits, and so on.

The sanding plate is attached to the sander by means of an arbor. It should be tightened by hand. After it is secure, plug in and turn on the sander. Apply cement to the revolving plate until a thin film of the adhesive is spread on in uniform thickness. Then turn off the tool and press onto the plate the abrasive paper or cloth selected, making sure that it is attached smoothly and is centered.

To change sanding discs, first pull off the old disc. Then turn on the tool and remove the old cement by means of a putty knife held against the metal sanding plate as it revolves.

The material to be sanded should be placed to the left of center of the revolving disc, so that the disc will come down into the work and the material can be fed in evenly. Feed the work into the revolving disc without undue pressure and keep it moving back and forth so as not to load up the disc in one particular spot.

For polishing and waxing, a lamb's wool bonnet is most popular, although some craftsmen prefer pile-fabric pads, which are generally used to rub down surfaces. The bonnet is attached by tieing it over the rubber backing pad with a drawstring. Tie the drawstring tightly and tuck the loose ends under the inside of the pad to prevent fouling with the spindle.

The first thing in polishing is to be sure that the surface to be polished is absolutely clean. All dirt, grit, and other foreign substances and all previous polishes and waxes must be removed. The new wax or polish should be applied sparingly with a damp

Fig. 44. Cleaning the sanding plate.

cloth. A thin coat will last longer and look better than a heavy coat.

Make sure the bonnet or pad is free to revolve before you turn the tool on. The method of polishing is the same as for sanding. Tilt slightly for the most efficient operation. Use a long sweeping motion back and forth to produce the smoothest finish and highest lustre and to avoid burning the surface.

A wire brush can be attached to the sander-polisher, and it is excellent for removing loose, scaly paint from wood or metal or rust from metals. It will save you the cost of many sanding discs. Where a fine finish is desired, use a sanding disc of the proper grit after wire brushing. Wire brushes will lose their cutting edge after considerable use. They can be resharpened easily, however, by holding the revolving wire brush against a revolving grinding wheel. This will grind square the ends of the wire bristles, thus setting up sharp points as good as new. Be sure to use a heavy rag to protect your hands when attaching or removing wire brushes from the sander-polisher.

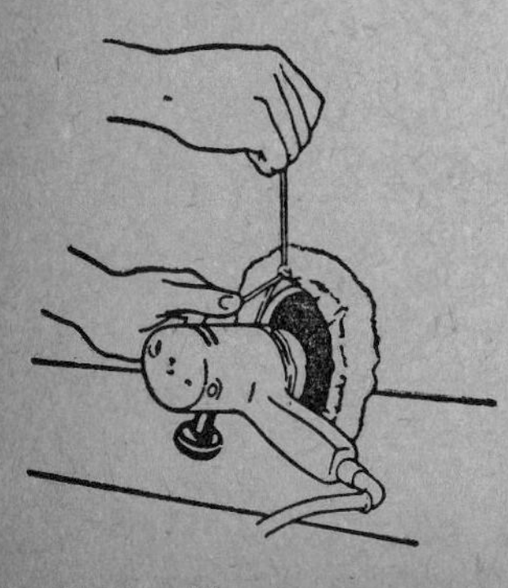

Fig. 45. Attaching bonnet to sander.

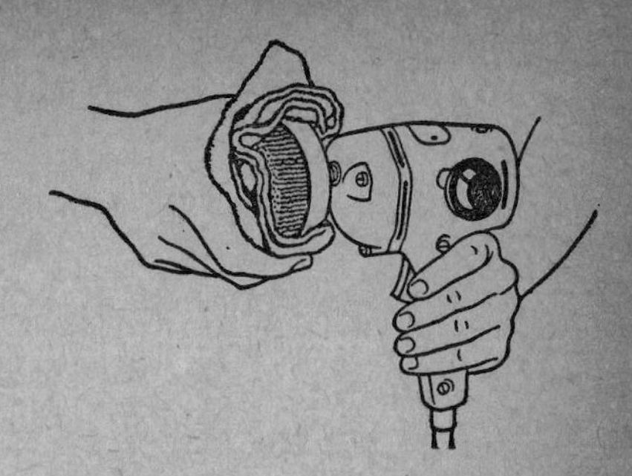

Fig. 46. Use rag to handle wire brush.

ELECTRIC SAW

Electric Saw. A good portable electric saw is a powerful and versatile tool. Besides handling ripping, crosscutting, and other sawing operations, it can be used with abrasive discs to cut such materials as tile and marble. A good 6-inch electric saw will cut 2-inch lumber with ease. You may prefer or need the 8-inch size if you are planning to do a lot of heavy work, but one of these two sizes should answer your needs.

All electric tools should be handled with care, but an electric saw demands the maximum of safety precautions. Always use the grounding wire and always attach it before plugging into the power source! This is especially important on a construction site where the ground may be damp. Always disconnect the saw before changing blades or making any adjustments or inspections! Always disconnect the saw when it is not in active use! Never tie back or use any other means to prevent the free protective action of the blade guard! If your feet or hands slip, release the trigger switch immediately!

If you are using an electric saw at a considerable distance from the power source, you must use an extension cable of the proper size to prevent loss of power. The farther the distance, the larger must be the size.

You should always take the time to select the proper blade for the type of cut you want. The few minutes required for changing over is nothing to the results obtained by using the correct blade. For instance, if you are sawing reclaimed lumber and cannot remove all the nails, be sure to use a nail-cutting blade and thus prevent costly damage. Always keep the blade sharp and properly set. More poor sawing results from a dull blade than from any other cause. A dull blade will make the saw creep, swerve, or stall. It puts a strain not only on the motor but on the operator also. Furthermore, dullness will draw part of the temper from the blade. You may not feel competent to sharpen your own blades, but one thing you can do that will help a lot is to keep the gullets clean.

To change blades, first disconnect the cable plug as a safety measure. Then hold the lower blade guard completely open and insert a nail through the hole near the rim of the blade. The nail will rest against the bottom of the saw shoe and prevent the blade from turning. Then turn the holding screw counter-clockwise with a wrench and remove the screw and outer washer. Lift off the blade. Put on the new blade with the teeth pointing toward the front of the saw. Clean the blade, the washers and the threads of the holding screws to prevent uneven seating. Reassemble and tighten securely.

A good electric saw will have various adjustments and attachments to give you close control over your work. You should be able to adjust the depth of the cut so that only a minimum of the blade projects below the material. This keeps blade friction at a minimum and results in cooler, faster sawing. There should also be a bevel adjustment for cutting at desired angles and a rip-fence attachmen to guide the saw in cutting at predetermined distances from the edge of a board.

When you are ready to use the saw, after the ground wire has been connected and the cable plugged into the power source, rest the front of the saw shoe on the work and line up the blade with the cutting line. Be sure that the blade teeth are not yet in contact with the work and that the lower blade guard is free. Then press the trigger and guide the saw through its cut with firm pressure but without forcing. Undue force actually slows down the cutting and produces a rougher cut. The rule is: Hold the saw firmly against the material and move it forward at a sufficient speed to permit free cutting by the blade.

If the saw stalls, do not release the trigger switch. Back the saw until blade momentum has been regained. *Then,* either shut off the motor or start to cut again. This procedure will greatly increase the life of your switch.

As a cut is completed, release the switch and allow the blade to stop before lifting the saw from the work.

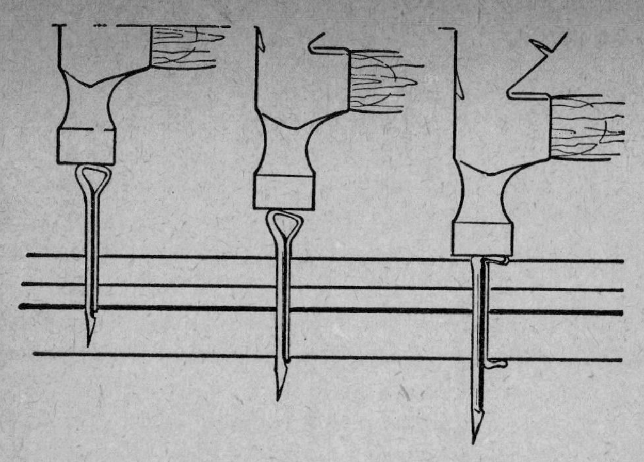

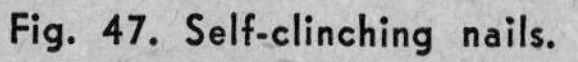

Fig. 47. Self-clinching nails.

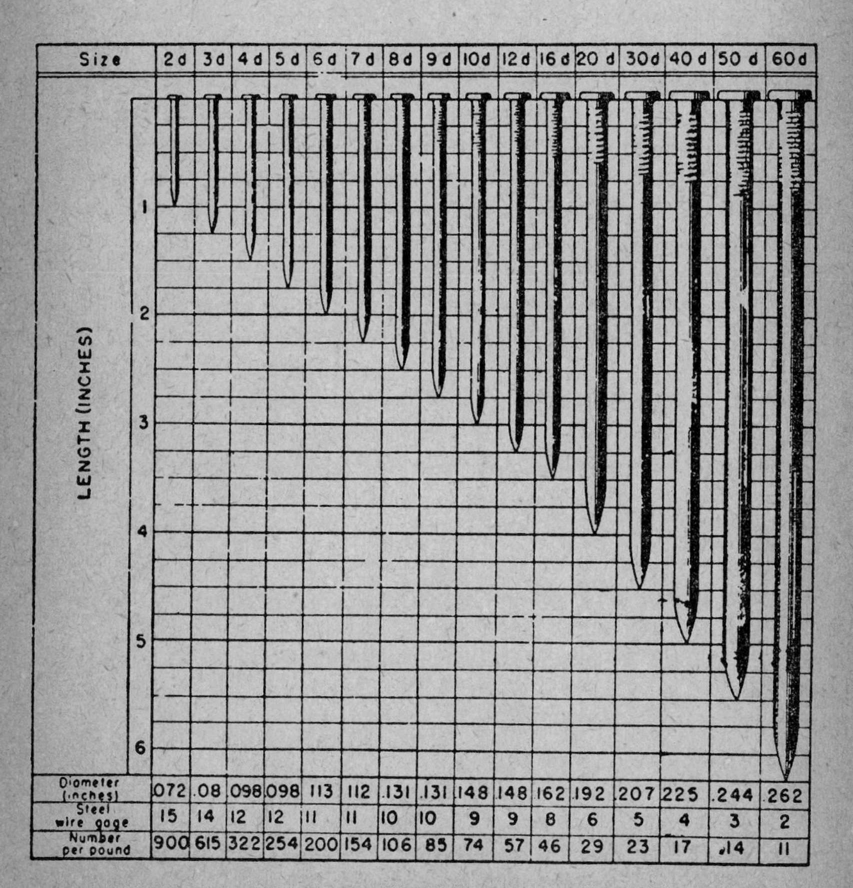

Size	2d	3d	4d	5d	6d	7d	8d	9d	10d	12d	16d	20d	30d	40d	50d	60d
Diameter (inches)	072	.08	.098	098	113	112	.131	.131	.148	.148	.162	.192	.207	225	.244	.262
Steel wire gage	15	14	12	12	11	11	10	10	9	9	8	6	5	4	3	2
Number per pound	900	615	322	254	200	154	106	85	74	57	46	29	23	17	14	11

Fig. 48. Nail sizes.

WHAT NAIL?

APPROXIMATE WEIGHT OF 3D HOT-DIPPED, ZINC-COATED NAILS PER SQUARE OF RANDOM-WIDTH SHINGLES, FOR WEATHER EXPOSURES GIVEN.

	Weight Lbs.	Oz.	Weight Lbs.	Oz.	Weight Lbs.	Oz.	Weight Lbs.	Oz.
16-inch shingle	3½-inch exposure		4-inch exposure		4½-inch exposure		5-inch exposure	
Grade 1	2	14	2	8	2	3½	2	0
Grade 2	3	10	3	3	2	13½	2	9
Grade 3	4	2	3	12	3	5	3	0
18-inch shingle	4-inch exposure		4½-inch exposure		5-inch exposure		5½-inch exposure	
Grade 1	2	8	2	3½	2	0	1	13
Grade 2	3	3	2	13½	2	9	2	5
Grade 3	3	12	3	5	3	0	2	11
24-inch shingle	6-inch exposure		6½-inch exposure		7-inch exposure		7½-inch exposure	
Grade 1	2	4	2	1	2	0	1	14
Grade 2	2	12	2	9	2	7½	2	5
Grade 3	3	0	2	12	2	10½	2	8

Note: The above figures are for new roofs. For overroofing, as larger nails are used, increase weights of nails needed two-thirds for 16″ and 18″ shingles and three-fourths for 24″ shingles.

APPROXIMATE WEIGHT OF 5D HOT-DIPPED, ZINC-COATED NAILS PER SQUARE OF RANDOM-WIDTH SHINGLES WHEN APPLIED TO SIDE WALLS, FOR WEATHER EXPOSURE GIVEN. (Read note below before using table.)

	Weight Lbs.	Oz.	Weight Lbs.	Oz.	Weight Lbs.	Oz.	Weight Lbs.	Oz.	Weight Lbs.	Oz.
16-inch shingle	5½-inch exposure		6-inch exposure		6½-inch exposure		7-inch exposure		7½-inch exposure	
Grade 1	3	0	2	12	2	8	2	6	2	3
Grade 2	3	12	3	7	3	2	2	15	2	12
Grade 3	4	5	4	0	3	11	3	6	3	1
18-inch shingle	6-inch exposure		6½-inch exposure		7-inch exposure		7½-inch exposure		8-inch exposure	
Grade 1	2	12	2	8	2	6	2	3	2	0
Grade 2	3	7	3	2	2	15	2	12	2	8
Grade 3	4	0	3	11	3	6	3	1	2	11
24-inch shingle	8-inch exposure		9-inch exposure		10-inch exposure		11-inch exposure		12-inch exposure	
Grade 1	2	0	1	13	1	10	1	8	1	5
Grade 2	2	6	2	4	2	0	1	12	1	10
Grade 3	2	9	2	6	2	3	1	15	1	12

Note: The above figures are for new single-coursed side walls. For over-walling, as 6d nails are needed for 24-inch shingles, increase the corresponding weights one-half. For double-coursing with butt-nailing, small-headed 5d nails are required, and therefore 10 per cent may be deducted from weights as listed. A 12-inch exposure will require half as many nails as a 6-inch exposure, a 14-inch half as many as a 7-inch, etc.

SIZE, TYPE, AND USE OF NAILS[1]

Size	Length (inches)	Diameter (inches)	Remarks	Where used
2d	1	0.072	Small head	Finish work, shop work.
2d	1	.072	Large flat head	Small timber, wood shingles, lath.
3d	1¼	.08	Small head	Finish work, shop work.
3d	1¼	.08	Large flat head	Small timber, wood shingles, lath.
4d	1½	.098	Small head	Finish work, shop work.
4d	1½	.098	Large flat head	Small timber, lath, shop work.
5d	1¾	.098	Small head	Finish work, shop work.
5d	1¾	.098	Large flat head	Small timber, lath, shop work.
6d	2	.113	Small head	Finish work, casing, stops, etc., shop work.
6d	2	.113	Large flat head	Small timber, siding, sheathing, etc., shop work.
7d	2¼	.113	Small head	Casing, base, ceiling, stops, etc.
7d	2¼	.113	Large flat head	Sheathing, siding, subflooring, light framing.
8d	2½	.131	Small head	Casing, base, ceiling, wainscot, etc., shop work.
8d	2½	.131	Large flat head	Sheathing, siding, subflooring, light framing, shop work.
8d	1¼	.131	Extra-large flat head.	Roll roofing, composition shingles.
8d	1½	.131	Extra-large flat head.	Roll roofing, composition shingles.
9d	2¾	.131	Small head	Casing, base, ceiling, etc.
9d	2¾	.131	Large flat head	Sheathing, siding, subflooring, light framing
10d	3	.148	Small head	Casing, base, ceiling, etc., shop work.
10d	3	.148	Large flat head	Sheathing, siding, subflooring, framing, shop work.
12d	3¼	.148	Large flat head	Sheathing, subflooring, framing.
16d	3½	.162	Large flat head	Framing, bridges, etc.
20d	4	.192	Large flat head	Framing, bridges, etc.
30d	4½	.207	Large flat head	Heavy framing, bridges, etc.
40d	5	.225	Large flat head	Heavy framing, bridges, etc.
50d	5½	.244	Large flat head	Extra-heavy framing, bridges, etc.
60d	6¼	.262	Large flat head	Extra-heavy framing, bridges, etc.

[1] This chart applies to wire nails, although it may be used to determine the length of cut nails.

KNOW YOUR HINGES

When you step into a hardware store, do you say,

"Give me a couple of hinges," or, "A pair of 3″ by 3″ loose-pin butts?"

It may make the difference between a project to be proud of and one that doesn't quite come off. Essentially, a hinge is just a gadget that lets you bend wood around a corner without breaking it. But there's always the right one for the right spot.

Butt hinges, as shown in figures 49 and 50, used more than any other type, come either swaged or flat. The leaves of a swaged hinge are mortised into the wood members. Consequently, the leaves are de-

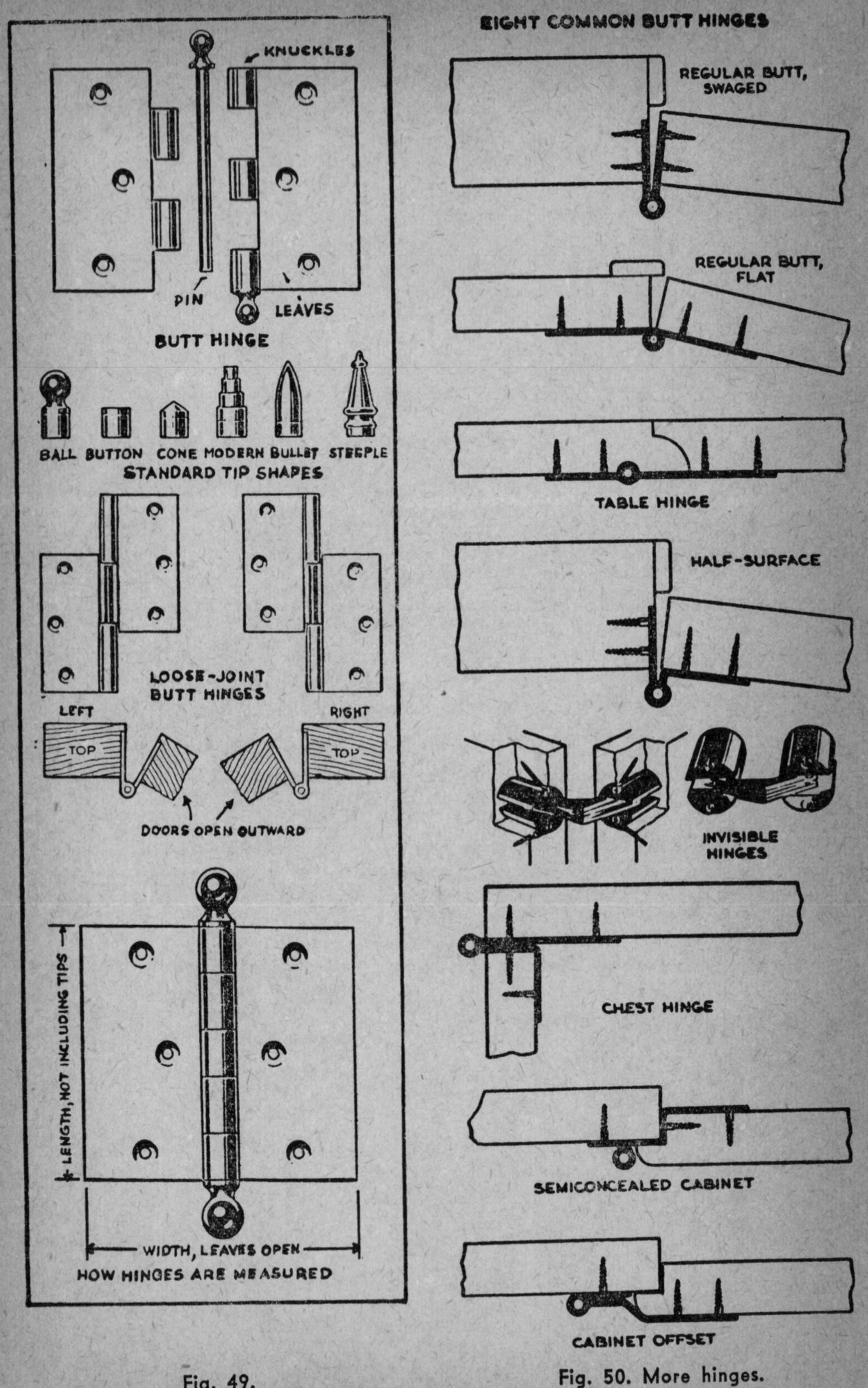
KNUCKLES
PIN
LEAVES
BUTT HINGE
BALL
BUTTON
CONE
MODERN
BULLET
STEEPLE
STANDARD TIP SHAPES
LOOSE-JOINT BUTT HINGES
LEFT
RIGHT
TOP
TOP
DOORS OPEN OUTWARD
LENGTH, NOT INCLUDING TIPS
WIDTH, LEAVES OPEN
HOW HINGES ARE MEASURED
EIGHT COMMON BUTT HINGES
REGULAR BUTT, SWAGED
REGULAR BUTT, FLAT
TABLE HINGE
HALF-SURFACE
INVISIBLE HINGES
CHEST HINGE
SEMICONCEALED CABINET
CABINET OFFSET

Fig. 49.

Fig. 50. More hinges.

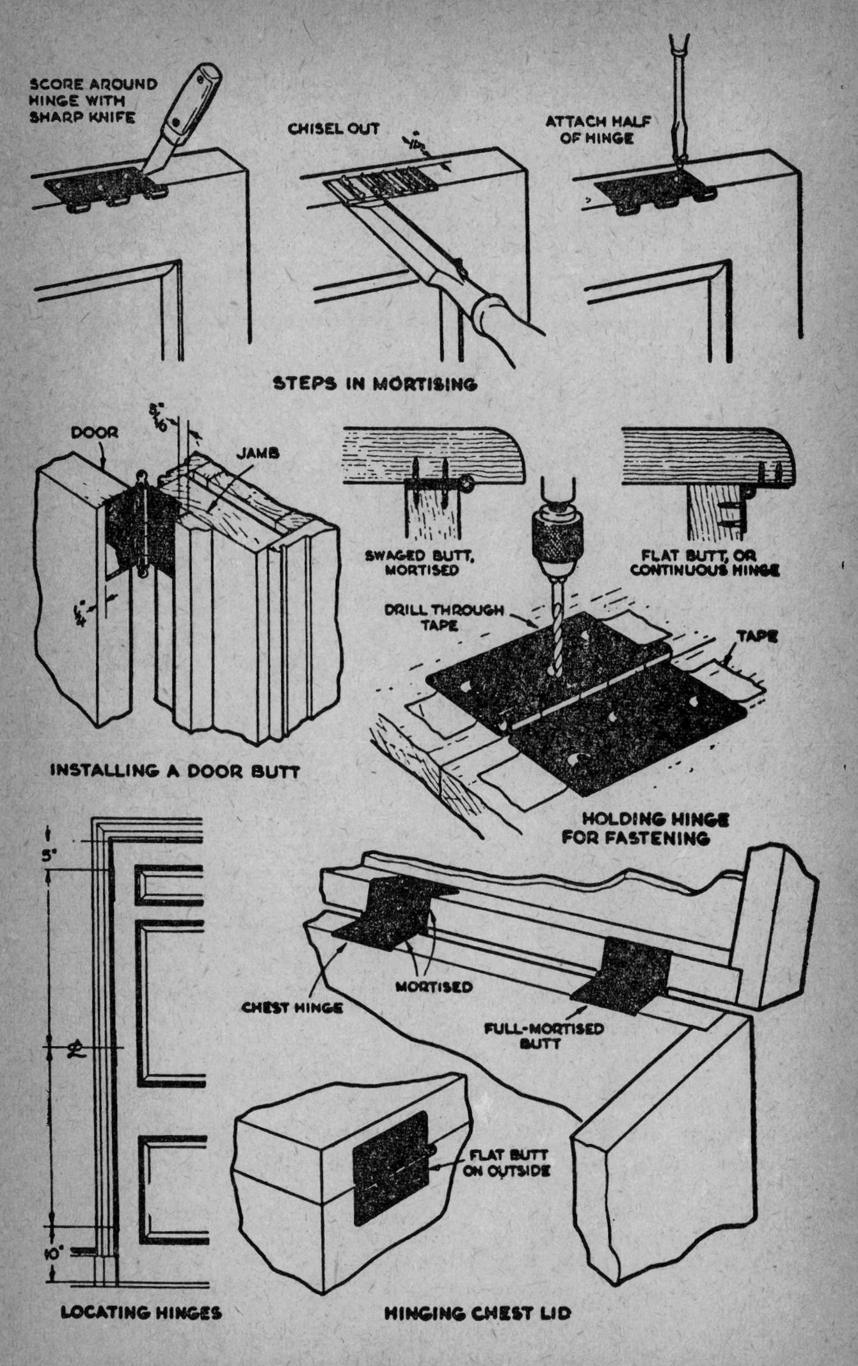
SCORE AROUND HINGE WITH SHARP KNIFE
CHISEL OUT
ATTACH HALF OF HINGE
STEPS IN MORTISING
DOOR
JAMB
INSTALLING A DOOR BUTT
SWAGED BUTT, MORTISED
FLAT BUTT, OR CONTINUOUS HINGE
DRILL THROUGH TAPE
TAPE
HOLDING HINGE FOR FASTENING
5"
10"
LOCATING HINGES
MORTISED
CHEST HINGE
FULL-MORTISED BUTT
FLAT BUTT ON OUTSIDE
HINGING CHEST LID

Fig. 51.

pressed slightly from the kunckles so they come together when the hinge is closed. The leaves of a flat hinge form a straight line when open, the knuckles all projecting on one side. A flat hinge is used for full-surface application (fig. 51).

Besides the ordinary rectangular butt hinge, here are some variations:

Loose-joint butts. These have only one kunckle on each leaf. There's a fixed pin in the bottom one so they may be separated by lifting off the top section. They're available in right- and left-hand assemblies for such uses as casement windows and cabinet doors.

Half-surface butts. Used when you want one leaf mortised into the jamb and the other flush on the door surface.

Semiconcealed cabinet hinges. These are made for both flush and lipped doors. The swinging leaf is bent to fasten to both the edge and inside surface of the door.

Offset cabinet hinges. Made for lipped doors. Each leaf is attached on the outside.

Double-acting butts. This is a complex hinge engineered to operate in both directions. You'll find them on folding screens, for example.

Continuous or piano butts. A long strip hinge that may be cut to the desired length.

The U.S. Bureau of Standards estimates that the entrance door of the average home opens and closes 15,000 times a year. So the importance of adequate hinging is obvious. This table gives recommended hinge sizes for various doors.

Door Thickness	*Door Width*	*Hinge Height*
¾″ to 1⅛″	up to 24″	2½″
⅞″ to 1⅛″	up to 36″	3″
1⅜″	up to 32″	3″
1⅜″	32″ to 37″	4″
1¾″	up to 37″	5″
2″ to 2½″	up to 43″	6″

Doors larger than 2½″ thick and 43″ wide take heavy-duty, ball-bearing butts.

All hinge dimensions above refer to the length of the joint, not to the spread of the leaves. To figure the proper width of butt hinges, double the thickness of the door, add the thickness of the trim, and deduct ½″ for doors up to 2¼″ thick. Deduct ¾″ for doors up to 3″ thick. For example, a 2″ door with no trim would require a butt with a leaf spread of 3½″.

Pivot hinges have a much more restricted use than butts. You'll find them on heavy gates, the doors of farm buildings, and sometimes on garage doors. The strap part of these hinges has a loop at the end that swings on the pivot. Shutter hinges are similar, except the straps are offset to let the shutter swing flush with the casing.

SCREW SIZES

Lag or Coach Screws

	Diameters (inches)			
Lengths (inches)	¼	⅜, $\frac{7}{16}$, ½	⅝, ¾	⅞, 1
1	x	x		
1½	x	x	x	
2, 2½, 3, 3½, etc., 7½, 8 to 10	x	x	x	x
11 to 12		x	x	x
13 to 16			x	x

Wood Screw Sizes and Dimensions

Length (inches)	Size numbers																	
	0	1	2	3	4	5	6	7	8	9	10	11	12	14	16	18	20	24
1/4	x	x	x	x	x													
3/8	x	x	x	x	x	x	x	x	x	x								
1/2		x	x	x	x	x	x	x	x	x	x	x	x					
5/8		x	x	x	x	x	x	x	x	x	x	x	x	x				
3/4			x	x	x	x	x	x	x	x	x	x	x	x	x			
7/8			x	x	x	x	x	x	x	x	x	x	x	x	x			
1				x	x	x	x	x	x	x	x	x	x	x	x	x	x	
1 1/4					x	x	x	x	x	x	x	x	x	x	x	x	x	x
1 1/2					x	x	x	x	x	x	x	x	x	x	x	x	x	x
1 3/4						x	x	x	x	x	x	x	x	x	x	x	x	x
2						x	x	x	x	x	x	x	x	x	x	x	x	x
2 1/4						x	x	x	x	x	x	x	x	x	x	x	x	x
2 1/2						x	x	x	x	x	x	x	x	x	x	x	x	x
2 3/4							x	x	x	x	x	x	x	x	x	x	x	x
3							x	x	x	x	x	x	x	x	x	x	x	x
3 1/2									x	x	x	x	x	x	x	x	x	x
4									x	x	x	x	x	x	x	x	x	x
4 1/2													x	x	x	x	x	x
5													x	x	x	x	x	x
6														x	x	x	x	x

Gage and diameter																									
Steel wire gage	17	15	14	13	12	11	10	9	8	7	6½	6	5	4½	4	3	2½	2	1	0½	0	00	00½	000	0000
Diameter (inches)	.054	.072	.080	.091	.105	.120	.135	.148	.162	.177	.184	.192	.207	.216	.225	.243	.253	.262	.283	...	.306	.331	...	.362	.393

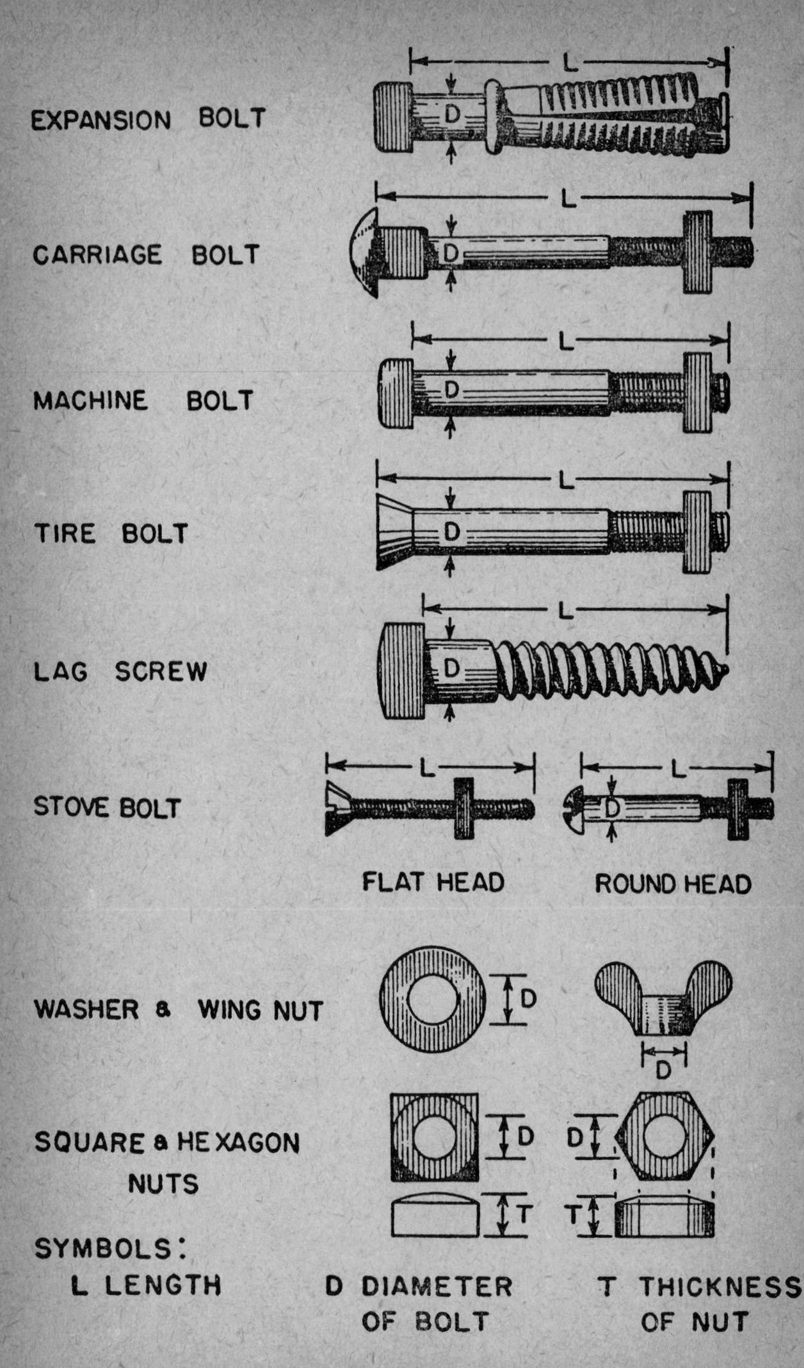

Fig. 52. Types of bolts (size designated by dimensions indicated).

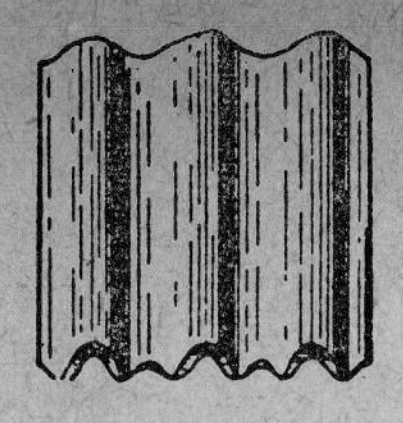

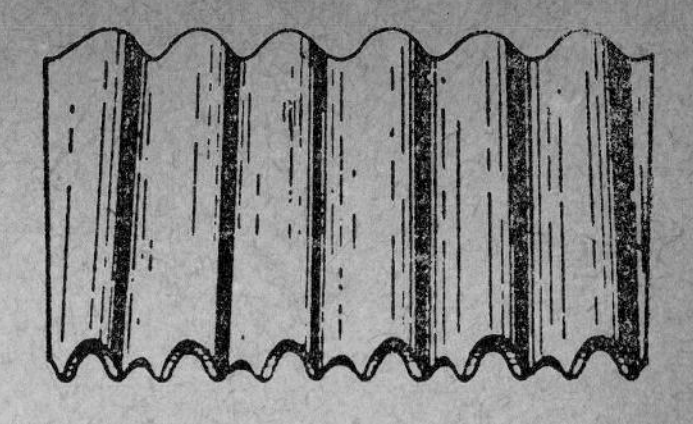

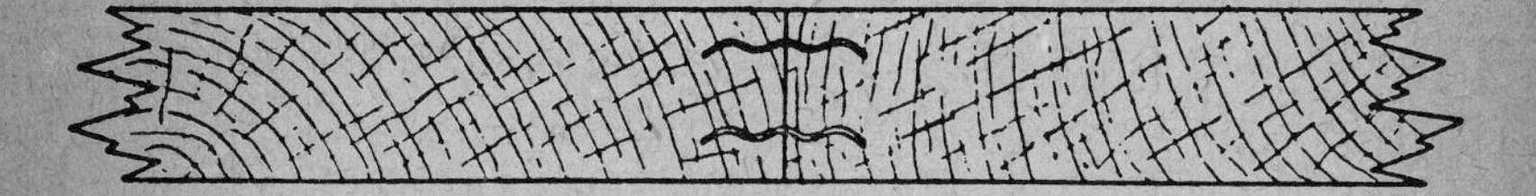

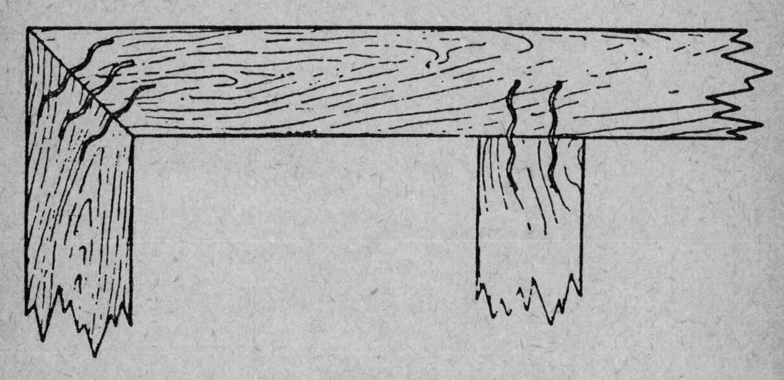

Fig. 53. Corrugated fasteners and their uses.

SPECIAL PLYWOOD FASTENINGS

Reference to figure 55 shows that while the common carriage bolt (*1*) is often useful with plywood, special fastenings are now available. *2* shows a flush-head bolt having a stepped flare that fits into the countersunk hole. Head fins prevent turning. In *3*, a special roundhead screw meshes with a self-locking nut stamped from sheet steel. The clips, bent upward to fit the thread, are drawn down when the screw is tightened, locking it against vibration, while the claws anchor the nut.

A bolt with a reduced threaded section screwing into a sleeve is shown in *4*. It is locked by a washer and nut. The finned cone of the flush-head bolt in *5* prevents turning and makes a weathertight and nondistorting fastening.

6 shows two inserts that prevent damage to holes in plywood parts

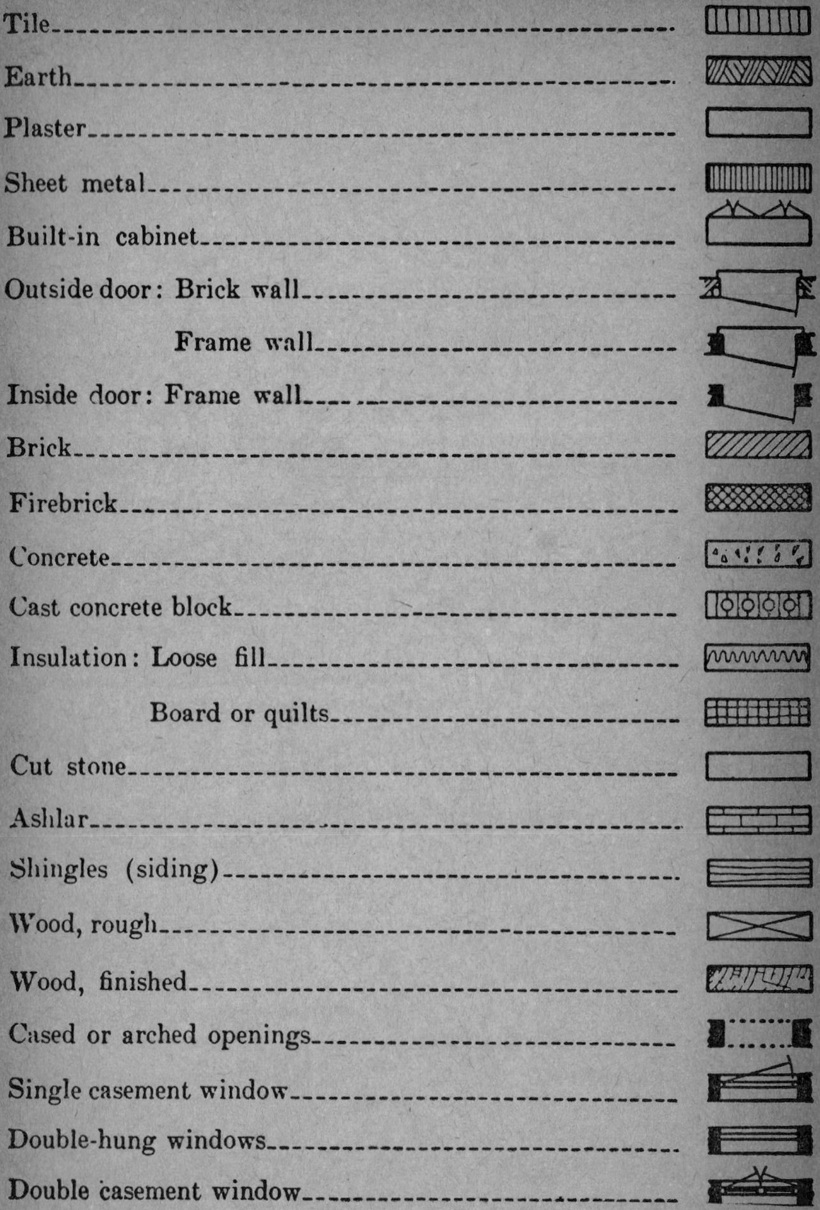

Tile

Earth

Plaster

Sheet metal

Built-in cabinet

Outside door: Brick wall

Frame wall

Inside door: Frame wall

Brick

Firebrick

Concrete

Cast concrete block

Insulation: Loose fill

Board or quilts

Cut stone

Ashlar

Shingles (siding)

Wood, rough

Wood, finished

Cased or arched openings

Single casement window

Double-hung windows

Double casement window

Fig. 54. Architectural symbols.

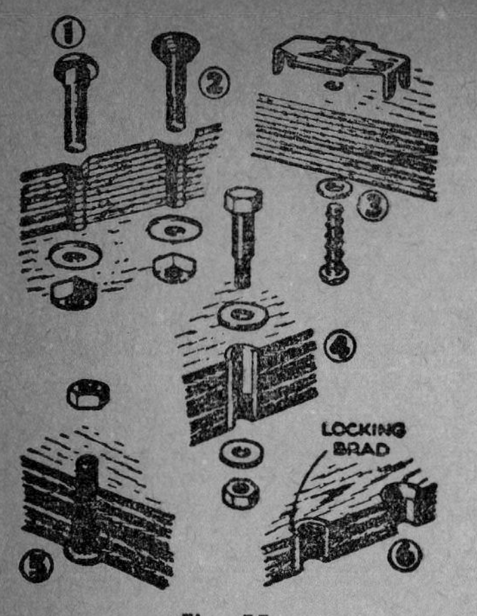

Fig. 55.

Fig. 56.

that are often disassembled. One is a threaded sleeve having two semi-circular slots for locking with brads, and the other is a grommet fitting into a countersunk hole and crimped on the underside to form a socket for a flush-head screw.

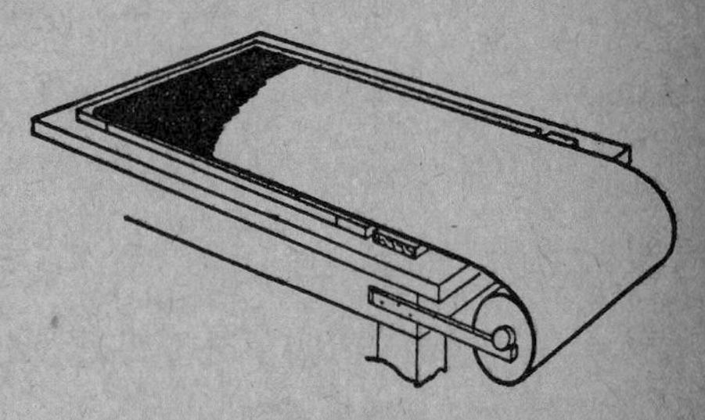

RESCREENING TIP

Here, in figure 56, is an assembly for installing wire screening onto wood frames that can be made on any workbench, pair of saw horses or strong kitchen table. It is a great convenience as well as a time saver when there are several frames to be covered with wire screening. The end of the wire screening is first attached to one end of the frame securely.

Then, with the ends raised, the frame is sprung downward at the middle and held with pins, cleats or clamps attached to the center uprights, while the screening is pulled

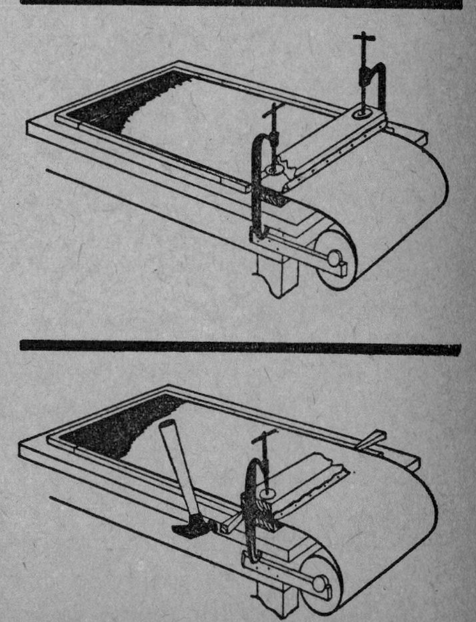

Fig. 57.

straight, hand-tight, and attached at the other end. Release the frame to its normal position and secure the screening to both sides. Be careful not to spring the frame too much or it will be damaged, and also the screening will be pulled too taut when the frame is released. Use staples, tacks or short nails to attach screening to the frame.

ANOTHER SCREENING TIP

When there are a number of frames to be covered with wire screening, it will save time in the long run to construct a special jig for this purpose. Figure 57 illustrates a simple screening jig which can be made with two large metal clamps and a solid table. The surfaces of the clamping bar are covered with strips cut out of an old inner tube so that there will be no chance of the screening slipping out of position. Nail the far end of the screening to the frame and then pull the screening down over the frame so that it is even on both sides. Pull the screening hand tight and then fasten it in this position by turning down the clamps. When the clamping bar is tight against the screening, drive wood wedges between the bottom clamping block and the frame. This will tighten the screening and hold it in this position so that the bottom and sides can be nailed secure. CAUTION: Take care when driving in the wedges not to run them in too far because they exert great pressure and may even tear the screening loose from the far end.

INDEX

A

Aggregate
  concrete, 5
  equipment for screening, 4
  in cold weather, 6
  testing, 3
  washed by hand, 5
Agricultural drain tile, 55
Air, exchanging, 275
Architectural symbols, 494
Asbestos board
  application, 420–424
  over insulating board, 132
  over solid wood backing, 132
  to studs, 131
Asphalt
  furnace for melting, 55
  tile
    installing, 400
    protection, 407
Attic
  insulation, 262
  ventilation, 268
Awnings for casement windows, 179

B

Balloon frame construction, 104
Barbecue pit, 37
Basements, damp, 51
Bathrooms
  eye-catching, 355
  fixtures, 356
  plans, 353
Batt and blanket insulation, 264–267
  studs, between, 83
Battens for roll roofing, 233
Bay, dining room, framing, 97
Bedroom closets, 180–181
Bench planes, 467
Bin, flour, 201
Board
  asbestos, 420–424
  ironing, 201
  plaster, 83
  tile, 424, 439
  wall, 83, 439
Boilers, connecting, 343
Bolts, 492
Braced frame construction, 103
Brick
  bonding to masonry, 32
  cavity wall, 33
  corners in pattern bonds, 42
  facing
    bonded to header blocks, 33
    4-inch, 32
  fireplace, outdoor, 45

Brick—*Continued*
  incinerator, 46
  pattern bonds, 41
  reinforced masonry wall, 42
Bridging, wall, 121
Brushes, paint, 445
Building interior walls, 33
Butt-joints, 146

C

Cabinets
  kitchen, 184, 188
  serving, 185
  storage, 189–192
  utility and food, 193–196
  wall, 187
Canvas roofing, 231
Carpet stairs, how to, 204
Ceiling
  panels, applying, 431
  tile, replacing, 431
Cellar, small, 6
Cement
  coloring materials, 6
  keene's, 416
  portland, 415
Ceramic tile, 413
Chimney (*see also* Fireplace)
  construction, 377
  framing, 116–118
  hollow tile construction, 44
  masonry, 37
  metal, 380
  standard, 381
Circuit (electrical) requirements, 293
Closets
  bedroom, 180–181
  business, 183
  shelves and cabinet, 200
Coal bins
  construction details, 364
  tables (of delineation), 366–367
Compression set, flooring, 161
Concrete
  aggregate, 5
  cored floor units, 30
  floors, 10, 13–16
  flower pot, 26
  lawn roller, 26
  masonry units, 27
  posts, 25
  poured stairs, 10
  precast joist floors, 29
  proportions, 3
  subfloors, dampness test, 407
  support for garage wall, 9
  tamper, 16
Condensation, avoiding, 382

Construction
  balloon frame, 104
  braced frame, 103
  fireplace, 43
  flooring, 158
  gable roof, 118
  gambrel roof, 120
  girder, 91
  joints, 146–147
  sill, 92–93
  stair, 95
  subfloor, 162
  western frame, 102
Contents of lumber, 79
Corrosion of pipes, 316
Counter tops
  linoleum on, 397
  repairing, 398
Cove base
  asphalt top-set, 407
  flash type, 407
  linoleum, 393
Cupboard, corner, 183

D

Dado joints, 147
Dampness test for concrete, 407
Dining-room storage, 184
Doors
  and window framing, 107
  combination screen and storm, 177
  garage, 179
  interior, plans, 178
  linoleum, installing through, 390
  quickly built, 177
  stay shut, 178
Dormer
  over stairwell, 96
  typical, 119
Downspouts and gutters, 245
Draft stopping, 113–16
Drain tile, 55
Drainage
  and vent pipes, 315, 335
  for drives, 25
Drip caps, 136
Drip from gables, 212
Drives, 17, 20–25, 60

E

Eaves, troughs and downspouts, 247
Electric tools, portable, 477-484
Electricity
  circuit requirements, 293
  low-voltage, 302
  outlets
    requirements, 283
    summary, 295–297
  service requirements, 293
  space heating by, 291
  special outlets, 292
Electricity—*Continued*
  switch control, 304
  symbols, 284
  wiring tips, 300
Exhaust fan, 271, 274–275
  safety control, 273
Exposure, shingle, 219

F

Fences
  dimensions and spacings, 207
  picket, 206
  stretcher, 207
Figure in wood, 114
Finishing floors, 168–172
Fireplace (*see also* Chimney)
  building back-to-back, 374
  construction, 43
  floor framing, 375
  framing plans, 117
  hollow tile, 44
  outdoor, 45
  stone, 61
Fire stopping, 81, 88–89, 109–112
Fittings (pipes), 315
Fixtures
  bathroom, 356
  light (*see* Light fixtures)
Flashings
  chimney, 261
  closed valley, 256
  doorways, 258
  open valley, 255
  ridges and hips, 253
  roof and wall intersections, 25-
  tips, 259
  vent pipe, 253
Flexible glass, 49
Flooring
  compression set, 161
  cut-away view, 158
  edge grain and flat grain, 160
  finishing, 168–172
  hardwood
    amounts required, 159
    refinishing, 172
  hiding cracks, 160
  laying and nailing, 164–168
  nail schedule, 157
  new strip over old, 157
  parquet, 157
  plank, 157
  softwood, grades of, 156
  subfloor, 159, 162
Floors
  concrete, 13–16
  laying tile, 120
  linoleum job, 385
  nailing, 164–168
  precast joist concrete, 29
  tile on wood, 409
Flour bin, 201
Flower pot, concrete, 26
Food storage room, 199

Foundations
  extending, 7
  temporary buildings, 134
Frames, picture, 206
Frame walls, strength and rigidity of, 80
Framing
  bay in dining room, 97
  chimney
    above fireplace, 116
    at floors, 118
    at roof, 118
  door and window, 107
  openings in walls or partitions, 98
  plans of fireplace, 117
  post and stringer, 206
  reducing height of foundation, 105
  studs at partition corners, 94
Furnaces
  floor, 362
  for melting asphalt, 55
  hand, 369

G

Gables
  preventing drip from, 212
  roof construction, 118
Galvanized sheets, 237
Gambrel roof construction, 120
Garage
  doors, 179
  drain trap, 352
Girder construction, 91, 133
Glass
  blocks
    installation, 43
    lighting stairways, 50
    mortar set panels, 49
    openings for panels, 45
    partitions, 47
    steps for laying, 48
  panels, 439
Glazier's points, 174
Grading, 62
Gravity retaining walls, 59
Gutters and downspouts, 245

H

Hardwood
  flooring
    amounts required, 159
    refinishing, 172
  lumber, grades of, 76
Heating and fireplaces, 379
Hinges, 176–177, 487
Hose, garden, repairing, 350
Hot water
  saving, 352
  tanks, 341

I

Incinerator
  household use, 46
  inexpensive, 81
Insulation
  adds comfort, 12
  attic, 262
Insulation—*Continued*
  batt and blanket, 83, 264–267
  fuel savings, 263, 378
  increased, 35
  pipes, 333
  present house, 264-267
  temperatures (U.S.), 262
  thicknesses, 262
  tools for attic, 264
  vacuum cleaner, 271
  widths, 265
Ironing board, 201

J

Joints
  butt, 146
  dovetail, 145
  miter, 147

K

Kitchen table and counter, 199

L

Laundry tubs, repairing, 350
Lawn roller, concrete, 26
Light fixtures
  additional lighting, 297
  graphical symbols, 284
  measuring, 282
  outlet requirements, 283
  reflection, 283
  summary of required, 281
Lightning, protect against, 242
Linoleum
  counter tops, 397
  cove base, 393
  floor job, planning, 385
  folding back, 387
  installing
    cement spreader, 398
    single rooms, 388
    stairs, 399
  measuring, cutting and packing, 387
  pattern scribing, 390
  scribing around radiators, 392
Lumber (*see also* Wood *and* Yard lumber)
  contents of, 79
  coordinated house design, 81
  piling posts, 86–87
  reducing waste, 84
  standard
    hardwood grades of, 76
    widths and thicknesses, 77
  warp, various kinds, 85

M

Masonry
  bonding brick to, 32
  chimney, concrete blocks, 37
  concrete block patterns, 36
  painting, 450
  shower stall, 38

Masonry—*Continued*
  stone facing to, 31
  stucco on concrete, 39
  units, concrete, 27
Membrane waterproofing, 51, 58
Metal subfloors, 413
Moisture barriers in walls, 270
Mortise
  and tenon, 147
  built up with shims, 145

N

Nailing
  floors, 164–168
  shingles, 217
  studding, 108
Nails
  roofing, 245
  schedule for flooring, 157
  sizes, quantities, uses, 216, 485

O

Oak flooring
  finishing, 168–172
  grades, 152
  laying and nailing, 164–168
Openings, framing around, 98
Outlets (electrical)
  requirements, 283
  special, 292
  summary, 295–297
Overroofing with shingles, 222
Overwalling with shingles, 223

P

Paint
  brushes, 445
  color blending, 449
  home-mixed cement, 451
  masonry, 450
  peeling of, 418
  power equipment, 447
  precautions, 452
  preparation, 448
  spray, 453
  zinc, 240
Paper
  roof, how to, 234
  wrinkling of, 419
Parquet flooring, 157
Pattern scribing on linoleum, 390
Peeling of paint, 418
Pickets, 206–207
Pictures frames, 206
Pipes
  brass
    cutting, threading, installation, 316
    dope, 327
    making up joints, 323
    reaming, 322
  cast iron, 310, 311
  cleaning, 345
  conditions and sizes, 315
  copper and brass, 309
Pipes—*Continued*
  corrosion, 316
  drainage and vent, 315
  fittings, 315
  hangers, 342
  insulating, 333
  joining different kinds, 331
  joints and connections, 332, 344
  one-pipe system, 333
  selecting, 309
  sewer grade, 329
  sizes of house distribution, 314
  stopping leaks, 348
  thawing, 347
  threading nipples, 321
  two-pipe system, 333
  water, 311, 344
  water-closet connections, 332
  wrought, 310
Planes, bench, 467
Plaster
  board, 83
  gypsum neat, 415
  proportions, 416
Plumbing wall, 106
Plywood
  fastenings, 493
  walls, 418
Porch columns, 135
Posts
  basement, 105
  concrete, 25
  good and poor practice, 135
  installing extra, 90
  plumbing, 105
  poor way to pile, 86–87
  seasoning against stump, 85
  stringer framing, 206
  wood, methods of seasoning, 81
Protect against lightning, 242
Puttying, 173, 453

R

Rabbeting and grooving, 148
Rabbets
  end and edge, 149
  plane, 150
Racks, shoe, 182
Radiators
  and convectors, 363
  linoleum, scribing around, 392
Rafter
  laying out, 125
  tables, 130
Reaming brass pipe, 322
Red cedar shingles
  application of, 138
  grades, 220
  overroofing with, 222
  overwalling with, 223
Resilient tile installation, 403
Roof
  eaves, troughs and downspouts, 247

Roof—*Continued*
joining to walls, 125
moss on, 226
new over old, 244
paper, how to, 234
repairing, 249
shed, 215
shingles, covering capacity, 214
slate repair, 248
snow guards, 247
stop leaks in old, 243
trusses, 122
Roofing
canvas, 231
nails, 245
roll
battens, 233
laid with roof slope, 232
new or replacement, 228
sizes and weights, 227
Router, 151

S

Safety control, exhaust fans, 273
Scale from water backs, removing, 350
Screw sizes, 490–491
Sewer grade pipe, 329
Shed roof, 215
Sheets, galvanized, 237
Shingles
corners, 140
estimating requirements, 137, 214
exposure, 219
hatchet, 216
hips and ridges, 221
nails, 216
quantities, 211
roof covering capacity, 214
staining and painting, 224
wood, 219
Shoe racks, 182
Siding
estimating, 108
sizes, 108
Sill construction, 92–93, 133, 137
Silt test, 4
Sink rims, turn-down, 397
Slate, inserting new, 248
Sliding window, hinge locks, 177
Snow guards, 247
Snow loads, 211
Softwood flooring, 156
Space heating by electricity, 291
Spouts, 136
Spray painting, 453
Staining shingles, 224
Stairs
building outdoor, 204
carpet, how to, 204
construction, 95
linoleum, installing, 399
Stair treads
linoleum, installation, 399
resilient tile, installation, 415
Storage
cabinet, 189–192
dining-room, 184
food, 199
utility and food, 193–196
Straightening walls, 107
Stretcher fence, 207
Stucco
bottle caps in, 41
on concrete masonry, 39
overcoating on wood frame, 40
refinishing old jobs, 42
Studding
mark location of, 141
nailing, 108
Studs
asbestos board, applying, 131
framing at partition corners, 94
Subfloor
concrete, dampness test, 407
construction, 159, 162
marble, 413
metal, 413
spaces for expansion, 141

T

Tables
folding, 202
kitchen, 199
Tables (of delineation)
coal bins, 366–367
eaves, troughs and downspouts, 247
electrical
outlets, summary, 295–297
symbols, 284
flooring
hardwood, 159
nail schedule, 157
oak, 152
softwood, 156
frame walls, strength of, 80
insulation, 263, 378, 441
light fixtures, 281
lumber
contents of, 79
hardwood, 76–77
yard, 73–74
moisture barriers in walls, 270
nails, 485–487
outlets, electrical, 295–297
pipes
cast iron, 311
conditions and sizes, 315
copper and brass, 310
galvanized, 312–313
sizes of house distribution, 314
rafter, 130
roll roofings, 227
screw sizes, 490–491
Tamper, concrete, 16
Tanks
hot water, 341
stopping leaks, 348
toilet, adjusting flush valves, 343

Temperatures (U.S.), 262
Terrazzo, 413
Thawing a frozen pipe, 347
Threading nipples and pipe, 321
Tile
  board
    erection, 424
    waterproofing, 439
  ceiling, replacing, 431
  ceramic, 413
  fitting to straight walls, 413
  resilient
    installation, 403
    on wood floors, 409
    stair treads, 415
Tooled joints, 29
Tools, portable electric, 477-484
Troughs, eaves and downspouts, 247
Trusses, roof, 122

U

Utility and food storage cabinet, 193–196

V

Ventilation, attic, 268
Ventilators
  installing in glass block panels, 361
  simple, 238

W

Wallboard
  patching, 439
Walls
  anchoring sills and plates, 30
  asbestos board on, 131
  brick and concrete masonry, 33
  brick facing and concrete blocks, 32
  bridging, 121
  cabinet, 187
  door and window frames, 35
  frame, strength of, 80
  framing concrete floor units, 30
  gravity retaining, 59
  interior, building, 33
  joining interior and exterior, 30
  joining roofs to, 125
  moisture barriers, 270
  openings for door and window frames, 34
  plumbing and straightening, 106
  plywood, 418
  precast concrete sills and lintels, 34
  retaining, 60
  straight, fitting tile to, 413
  strength and rigidity, 80
  switch and outlet boxes, 35
  ventilating and heating ducts, 35
Warped boards, fitting, 142
Warp, lumber, various kinds, 85
Waste
  cutting down, 80
  materials in multiples of 4 inches, 82
  reducing to minimum, 84
Water-closet connections, 332
Waterproofing, membrane, 51, 58
Western frame construction, 102
Widths and thicknesses of lumber, 73–77
Windows
  awnings for casement, 179
  hinge locks sliding, 177
  puttying panes, 173
  sash and frame, 175
Wiring
  electrical, tips on, 300
  light fixtures, 282
  low-voltage, 302
Wood (*see also* Lumber)
  figure in, 114
  floors, tile on, 409
  on concrete or masonry, 134
  posts, methods of seasoning, 81
  shingles, 219
  suitability for various uses, 65–73
Wrinkling of paper, 419

Y

Yard lumber (*see also* Lumber)
  rough and surfaced, 73
  softwood, 74

Z

Zinc paint, 240